How this Text Can Help You Succeed

Your Sullivan/Struve text helps you *Do the Math* with innovative features designed to provide help when you need it most—when you are away from the classroom and your instructor.

Sullivan/Struve Examples

Our Examples place the annotations to the left of the algebra, rather than to the right, as is the practice in other math texts.

Placing the annotations on the left makes more sense because you are used to reading from left-to-right.

The left-to-right annotations explain what you are about to do in solving the problem. Think of these annotations as your "teacher in the book."

EXAMPLE 3 Solving a Linear Equation by Combining Like Terms

Solve the linear equation: $3y - 2 + 5y = 2y + 5 + 4y + 3$

Solution

$$3y - 2 + 5y = 2y + 5 + 4y + 3$$

Combine like terms: $\quad 8y - 2 = 6y + 8$

Subtract $6y$ from both sides: $\quad 8y - 2 - 6y = 6y + 8 - 6y$

$$2y - 2 = 8$$

Add 2 to both sides: $\quad 2y - 2 + 2 = 8 + 2$

$$2y = 10$$

Divide both sides by 2: $\quad \dfrac{2y}{2} = \dfrac{10}{2}$

$$y = 5$$

Check $\qquad 3y - 2 + 5y = 2y + 5 + 4y + 3$

Let $y = 5$ in the original equation: $\quad 3(5) - 2 + 5(5) \overset{?}{=} 2(5) + 5 + 4(5) + 3$

$$15 - 2 + 25 \overset{?}{=} 10 + 5 + 20 + 3$$

$$38 = 38 \quad \text{True}$$

Because $y = 5$ satisfies the equation, the solution of the equation is 5, or the solution set is $\{5\}$. ∎

Quick ✔ *In Problems 12–14, solve each linear equation. Be sure to verify your solution.*

12. $2x + 3 + 5x + 1 = 4x + 10$
13. $4b + 3 - b - 8 - 5b = 2b - 1 - b - 1$
14. $2w + 8 - 7w + 1 = 3w - 1 + 2w - 5$

Quick Check Exercises

Each group of Quick Check exercises is preceded by an Example that teaches you how to work the problems. Your instructor may assign Quick Check exercises as part of your homework.

The Quick Checks are visually linked to the exercise sets by the tan background so they are easy to find.

Answers to all of the Quick Checks and the odd-numbered exercises are found in the Answer Section at the back of the text.

1.1 EXERCISES

MyMathLab

PRACTICE   WATCH   DOWNLOAD   READ   REVIEW

1–30. *are the* Quick ✔*s that follow each* EXAMPLE

Building Skills

In Problems 31–36, determine which of the numbers are solutions to the given equation. See Objective 1.

31. $8x - 10 = 6; x = -2, x = 1, x = 2$

32. $-4x - 3 = -15; x = -2, x = 1, x = 3$

33. $5m - 3 = -3m + 5; m = -2, m = 1, m = 3$

34. $6x + 1 = -2x + 9; x = -2, x = 1, x = 4$

35. $4(x - 1) = 3x + 1; x = -1, x = 2, x = 5$

36. $3(t + 1) - t = 4t + 9; t = -3, t = -1, t = 2$

In Problems 37–58, solve each linear equation. Be sure to verify your solution. See Objective 2.

37. $3x + 1 = 7$ **38.** $8x - 6 = 18$

39. $5x + 4 = 14$ **40.** $-6x - 5 = 13$

41. $4z + 3 = 2$ **42.** $8y + 3 = 5$

43. $-3w + 2w + 5 = -4$ **44.** $-7t - 3 + 5t = 11$

45. $3m + 4 = 2m - 5$ **46.** $-5z + 3 = -3z + 1$

47. $5x + 2 - 2x + 3 = 7x + 2 - x + 5$

48. $-6x + 2 + 2x + 9 + x = 5x + 10 - 6x + 11$

49. $3(x + 2) = -6$ **50.** $4(z - 2) = 12$

51. $\dfrac{4y}{5} - \dfrac{14}{15} = \dfrac{y}{3}$ **52.** $\dfrac{3x}{2} + \dfrac{x}{6} = -\dfrac{5}{3}$

53. $\dfrac{4x + 3}{9} - \dfrac{2x + 1}{2} = \dfrac{1}{6}$

54. $\dfrac{2x + 1}{3} - \dfrac{6x - 1}{4} = -\dfrac{5}{12}$

STUDY SMARTER

CHAPTER
Test Prep
VIDEO CD

Step-by-step solutions on video for all
chapter test exercises from the text

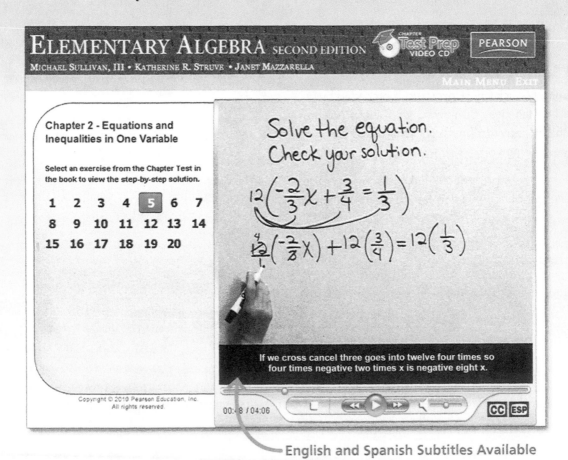

ELEMENTARY ALGEBRA SECOND EDITION   Test Prep VIDEO CD   PEARSON
MICHAEL SULLIVAN, III · KATHERINE R. STRUVE · JANET MAZZARELLA

MAIN MENU EXIT

**Chapter 2 - Equations and
Inequalities in One Variable**

Select an exercise from the Chapter Test in
the book to view the step-by-step solution.

1   2   3   4   **5**   6   7
8   9   10   11   12   13   14
15   16   17   18   19   20

Solve the equation.
Check your solution.

$$12\left(-\frac{2}{3}x + \frac{3}{4} = \frac{1}{3}\right)$$

$$\overset{4}{\cancel{12}}\left(-\frac{2}{8}x\right) + 12\left(\frac{3}{4}\right) = 12\left(\frac{1}{3}\right)$$

If we cross cancel three goes into twelve four times so
four times negative two times x is negative eight x.

00:48 / 04:06   ⏮ ▶ ⏭   CC ESP

English and Spanish Subtitles Available

INCLUDED WITH EVERY NEW COPY OF THIS TEXTBOOK!

Departmental Course Syllabus

TRIDENT TECHNICAL COLLEGE

MAT 101
Beginning Algebra
3 credit hours

3 contact hours (3 lecture hours)

Catalog Description

This course includes the study of rational numbers and their applications, operations with algebraic expressions, linear equations and applications, linear inequalities, graphs of linear equations, operations with exponents, and factoring.

Prerequisite MAT 032 or appropriate placement score

What will I learn? At the end of this course, you should be able to:

1. Perform basic operations of addition, subtraction, multiplication, and division with real numbers.
2. Solve first degree equations and inequalities and graph lines and linear inequalities.
3. Factor algebraic expressions.
4. Solve quadratic equations by factoring.

Textbook and Required Materials

Elementary Algebra by Michael Sullivan, Katherine Struve, and Janet Mazzarella (2nd edition, Prentice Hall 2009)

Grading System and Policy The College-wide grading scale is

91–100 = A, 81–90 = B, 71–80 = C, 65–70 = D, below 65 = F

There will be a comprehensive departmental final exam, which everyone must take (no exemptions), and which counts 25% of the final grade. The remaining 75% will be specified by your instructor's syllabus addendum.

Attendance/Withdrawal Before attending classes, you must meet all prerequisites and officially register for all courses. Prompt and regular attendance is your responsibility. You are responsible for all material covered and all assignments made in class. Any time you are absent from a class, laboratory or other scheduled events, it is your responsibility to make satisfactory arrangements for any make-up work permitted by the instructor.

An absence is defined as nonattendance for any reason, including illness, emergency or official leave. If you arrive late to class, you may not be allowed into the classroom and may be considered absent for that period. If you leave before the instructor dismisses class, you may also be considered absent. All class sessions are important. Any time you miss a class you increase your risk of making a failing grade.

If you quit coming or participating in the course and do not officially withdraw by the withdrawal date for each semester, you will receive a grade of F. Your instructor cannot assign a grade of W. If you receive financial aid or veterans' aid, your aid may be revised as a result of any changes in your course schedule.

Instructor availability Your instructor is available to you outside of class for academic assistance. Full-time faculty members maintain and post regularly scheduled office hours. Part-time faculty members are accessible in a variety of ways, which may include conferences before and after class or by appointment, telephone conferences, and E-mail. The phone number for reaching your instructor is provided on your syllabus addendum.

See your syllabus addendum This is a departmental syllabus for all sections of the course. As such, it tries to address issues common to all sections. There will be issues (grading details, office hours, and the like) that are specific to your section, and these details will be covered in an addendum issued by your instructor.

Activated Electronic Communication Devices

These devices, such as cell phones and pagers are NOT permitted in TTC classrooms. On-call emergency personnel are required to report to their instructors and cannot communicate by electronic means during a testing situation.

For Students Enrolled in Online or Other Distance-Learning Sections To confirm that you are actively involved in this course you need to contact the instructor at least once per week. Forms of contact can include (but are not limited to) posting/receiving emails, participating in online class discussions or chat rooms, and completing and submitting course assignments. Please see the instructor's addendum for any additional instructions.

ADA Statement The College will make reasonable accommodations for persons with documented disabilities. Students with disabilities should notify Services for Students with Disabilities (located in the Student Success Center) and their instructors of any special needs. Instructors should be notified on the first day of classes.

Textbook Portions Covered

The course will cover the book sections listed below. You may want to use the supplementary materials available in The Learning Center (920/ 211C).

Unit 1 Operations on Real Numbers and Algebraic Equations	Chapter 1 & section 8.1
Unit 2 Equations and Inequalities in One Variable	Chapter 2
Unit 3 Introduction to Graphing and Equations of Lines	Chapter 3
Unit 4 Exponents and Polynomials	Chapter 5
Unit 5 Factoring Polynomials	Chapter 6, sections 1–7

College Information TTC uses e-mail as the standard communication system to send information to students and uses TTC Express to post final course grades. To access your accounts go to www.tridenttech.edu.

Access to computers for academic courses The College has computer labs available for student use on all three campuses. Students who experience problems with home computers should plan to accomplish their assignments at the college.

Department Head Elizabeth White at 574-6538

Division Admin. Asst. 574-6015 (emergencies only)

SUGGESTED STUDY HABITS FOR MATH STUDENTS

1. **Attend class <u>regularly</u>** and arrive <u>on time</u>. Students who miss class have great difficulty being successful in a math class.

2. **Take notes in class. Review your notes <u>soon</u>** after class. If there is a concept you do not understand, ask your instructor for help either during office hours or during class if there is time.

3. **Do the assigned homework as <u>soon</u>** after class as possible while the concepts are fresh in your mind.

4. **When you work the homework problems, <u>show every step</u>**. This will make it easier to find a mistake if your answer disagrees with the answer in the back of the book.

5. **Learning math is a <u>step by step</u>** process. <u>Keep up</u> with your assignments. You must understand today's topic in order to learn tomorrow's concept.

6. **You may benefit by studying <u>with</u>** another student or with a small group of students, especially when preparing for a test.

7. **Be sure to allow yourself <u>adequate time</u>** to get to class, especially on test day. Remember to bring your <u>pencil</u> and <u>calculator (if allowed)</u>.

8. **<u>Review</u>** your tests carefully when they are returned and make sure you understand any problems that are incorrect.

9. **Take advantage of the <u>Learning Center</u>** in 920/211 to receive extra help.

10. **See your instructor <u>immediately</u>** whenever help is needed. Do not wait until a lot more material is covered.

11. **<u>Organize</u>** and <u>save</u> all notes, homework, and tests so that they can be used to prepare for the final exam. To study for the final exam begin with the final review. Then go to the unit tests. Finally refer to notes, homework, and the text, particularly in areas that are weak.

12. **Maintain a <u>positive</u>** attitude toward the course. Believe in yourself. You are enrolled in the course because the department determined you have the necessary prerequisites for the course.

MAT 101/152
Beginning Algebra
Unit 1 Review (1.2 – 1.8, 8.1)

TRIDENT TECHNICAL COLLEGE

1. Use the set $\{-6, -3\frac{1}{4}, -2, 0, 1, \sqrt{3}, 7, 8.6\}$ to answer the following. List all elements of the set that are:

   a) natural numbers **b)** integers **c)** rational numbers **d)** real numbers

2. Perform the indicated operations and write your answer in lowest terms.

   a) $-6 + (-3)$ **b)** $7.32 - (-9.41)$ **c)** $(-12)(-3)(-2)$ **d)** $-25 \div 10$

   e) $-\frac{2}{3} - \left(\frac{-1}{4}\right)$ **f)** $\frac{5}{6} - 3$ **g)** $\frac{-3}{4} \cdot \frac{14}{9}$ **h)** $2\frac{1}{5} \div 1\frac{1}{3}$

   i) $16 - (7 - 13) + 5$ **j)** $-15 + (-3) - \frac{1}{2}$ **k)** $(-10)^2$ **l)** -10^2

   m) $\sqrt{-49}$ **n)** $60 \div 0$ **o)** $0 \div -5$ **p)** $\sqrt{121}$

   q) $(-5)^3$ **r)** $\frac{32}{.08}$ **s)** $\frac{5}{8} \div (-2)$ **t)** $(-0.5)(-0.26)$ **u)** $\sqrt{\frac{16}{81}}$

3. Fill in the blanks.

   a) The _____ or the opposite of a number x is the number that is the same distance from 0 on the number line as the number x, but on the opposite side of 0.

   b) The _____ of a real number x, denoted by $|x|$, is the distance between the number x and 0 on the number line, and the distance is always taken to be ___.

4. Replace the ? with the correct symbol: $<, >, =$

   a) $\frac{3}{4}$? $\frac{2}{3}$ **b)** -2 ? -3 **c)** $|-5|$? $-|-5|$ **d)** 3.45 ? 3.5

5. For each expression, identify the number of terms and the requested coefficient.

   a) $2x^3 + x^2 - 4x + 2$; what is the coefficient of the squared term?

   b) $t^3 - \frac{t}{4}$; what is the coefficient of the linear term?

6. Evaluate each expression.

   a) $-16 \div (-4)^2 - 3 - (-2)$ **b)** $\frac{2(-3) - 4^2}{3(-6) - (4 - 11)}$ **c)** $-3^2 + 2[20 \div (7 - 11)]$

   d) $6(-8 + 10)^2 - 5(7 - 10)$ **e)** $2^3 - (-5) + 6 \div 2 + 1$ **f)** $14 \div 7 - 3 \div 1 + 6$

   g) $4 - [3 - (6 - 5)^9 - 2]$ **h)** $8 - 4(2) \div 1 - 7^2$

7. Match the property of real numbers with its example.

   a) Identity Property **b)** Commutative Property **c)** Additive Inverse Property
   d) Associative Property **e)** Multiplicative Inverse **f)** Distributive Property

   1) $x + 2 = 2 + x$ **2)** $5 \cdot \frac{1}{5} = 1$ **3)** $4(x + y) = 4x + 4y$

   4) $a + (-a) = 0$ **5)** $(2)(4 \cdot 7) = (2 \cdot 4)(7)$ **6)** $9 + 0 = 9$

8. Evaluate the following expressions with the given values of the variable.

   a) $5x - 3y$; $x = -2$ and $y = 4$ **b)** $2x^2 - 3xy$; $x = -3$ and $y = -5$

9. Simplify each algebraic expression.

   a) $-3(2x - 1) + (x - 4)$ **b)** $\frac{3}{4}(8x^2 - 4) - (x^2 - 4)$

   c) $4(3x + 1) - 6(x - 2y) + 8$ **d)** $7n^2m^3 - 8n^2 - 3m^3 - 12n^2m^3$

10. A football team lost 2 yards, gained 4 yards, and lost 8 yards on three consecutive plays. What was their total loss or gain of yards? Express the answer as a positive or negative integer.

11. The length of a rectangle is 4 feet more than 3 times its width. The perimeter is represented by the algebraic expression $2(3x + 4) + 2x$. Simplify this expression.

12. John had \$278.51 in his checking account. He deposited \$180.00, wrote a check for \$179.81 and withdrew \$200.00. How much money does John have in his checking account after these transactions?

Answers

1. a) $1, 7$ b) $-6, -2, 0, 1, 7$ c) $-6, -3 \ 1/4, -2, 0, 1, 7, 8.6$ d) all of the numbers are real

2. a) -9 b) 16.73 c) -72 d) -2.5 or $\dfrac{-5}{2}$ e) $\dfrac{-5}{12}$ f) $-\dfrac{13}{6}$ g) $\dfrac{-7}{6}$

h) $\dfrac{33}{20}$ i) 27 j) $-18\dfrac{1}{2}$ or $\dfrac{-37}{2}$ k) 100 l) -100 m) not a real number

n) undefined o) 0 p) 11 q) -125 r) 400 s) $-\dfrac{5}{16}$ t) 0.13 u) $\dfrac{4}{9}$

3. a) additive inverse b) absolute value; positive

4. a) $>$ b) $>$ c) $>$ d) $<$

5. a) 4 terms; coefficient $= 1$ b) 2 terms; coefficient $= -\dfrac{1}{4}$

6. a) -2 b) 2 c) -19 d) 39 e) 17 f) 5 g) 4 h) -49

7. a) 6 b) 1 c) 4 d) 5 e) 2 f) 3

8. a) -22 b) -27

9. a) $-5x - 1$ b) $5x^2 + 1$ c) $6x + 12y + 12$ d) $-5n^2m^3 - 8n^2 - 3m^3$

10. -6 yards **11.** $8x + 8$ **12.** \$78.70

MAT 101/152
Beginning Algebra
Unit 2 Review (2.1–2.8)

TRIDENT TECHNICAL COLLEGE

1. Solve and check each linear equation.

   a) $7x + 2 = -19$

   b) $-2(x-4) = 8 - 2x$

   c) $-3(4x - 1) = 7(3 - 3x)$

   d) $0.03x + 2.1 = 27$

   e) $0.3x - 1 = 0.5(x + 2) - 0.2x$

   f) $\frac{1}{12}x - \frac{1}{36} + \frac{x}{4} = \frac{1}{4} + x$

   g) $\frac{x}{2} = \frac{x-4}{5}$

   h) $\frac{x-6}{4} = 8$

   i) $\frac{x}{4} - 2 = -2x$

   j) $\frac{2}{7}(5x+4) = \frac{1}{2}(3x)$

   k) $3(2x - 3) + 4x = 9$

   l) $3x - (2x + 4) = 2(x + 1) - 2x + 1$

2. Solve each linear inequality. For each problem, write the solution using inequality signs, using interval notation, and then graph on a number line.

   a) $5(2x - 3) \geq x + 3$

   b) $2x - 5 < 10 + 5x$

   c) $-3(x + 2) < 12$

   d) $\frac{1}{2} + x < 4(x + 3) - x$

3. Solve each equation for the specified variable.

   a) $d = rt$; solve for r

   b) $P = 2l + 2w$; solve for w

   c) $3x + 2y = 8$; solve for y

   d) $-2x - 3y = 12$; solve for x

4. Match each phrase to its mathematical expression.

   a) the sum of 10 and a number   **1.** $2x - 10$

   b) 10 less than a number   **2.** $10/y$

   c) 10 less than twice a number   **3.** $10y$

   d) twice the sum of a number and 10   **4.** $x + 10$

   e) the quotient of 10 and a number   **5.** $2(x + 10)$

   f) the product of 10 and a number   **6.** $x - 10$

5. For each of the following, write an equation and solve.

   a) What is 60% of 50?

   b) What number is 12% of 86?

   c) 20% of what number is 120?

   d) What percent of 300 is 240?

   e) The sales tax rate in South Carolina is 6%. If Wes buys a motorcycle for $19,500 what will be total bill including tax?

   f) The sales tax in Georgia is 4%. Vance bought a new DVD player for a total of $130, including tax. What was the price of the DVD player before taxes?

   g) Betty received a 5% increase from last year's salary. If her new salary is $99,750, what was last year's salary?

6. Fill in the blank.

   a) Two angles whose sum is 90° are called ___ angles.

   b) Two angles whose sum is 180° are called ___ angles.

   c) The sum of the measure of the interior angles of every triangle is ___ degrees.

7. For each of the following, write an equation and solve.

   a) A can of soda has twice as many calories as an apple. If you eat both, you consume 360 calories. How many calories are in each?

   b) In a triangle, the second angle is 5 degrees more than the first angle. The third angle is three times the measure of the first angle. Find the angles.

   c) The length of a rectangle is 10 feet more than ½ the width. Given the perimeter of the rectangle is 38 feet, find the length and the width.

   d) Two cars are leaving Dallas, one traveling north and the other south. The car traveling north is going 70 mph and the one traveling south is going 65 mph. How long before the two cars are 540 miles apart?

   e) Find two supplementary angles such that the measure of one angle is 15° less than 2 times the first.

   f) Eight less than the product of four and a number is twenty-four. Find the number.

   g) A rectangular patio has dimensions that are consecutive odd integers. The patio's perimeter is 48 feet. Find the dimensions of the patio.

Answers

1. **a)** x = − 3   **b)** x = all real numbers   **c)** x = 2   **d)** x = 830
   e) no solution   **f)** x = − 5/12   **g)** x = − 8/3   **h)** x = 38
   i) x = 8/9   **j)** x = 16   **k)** x = 9/5 or 1.8   **l)** x = 7

2. **a)** x ≥ 2 ; [2, ∞)   **b)** x > − 5 ; (− 5, ∞]

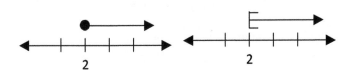

c) x > − 6 ; (− 6, ∞)   **d)** x > − 23/4 ; (− 23/4, ∞)

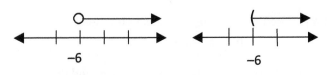 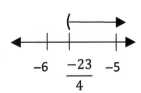 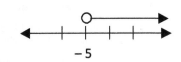 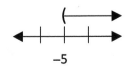 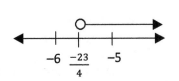

3. **a)** $r = \dfrac{d}{t}$ **b)** $w = \dfrac{p - 2l}{2}$ **c)** $y = \dfrac{-3x + 8}{2}$ **d)** $x = \dfrac{3y + 12}{-2}$

4. **a)** 4   **b)** 6   **c)** 1   **d)** 5   **e)** 2   **f)** 3

5. **a)** x = 0.60(50)   **b)** x = 0.12(86)   **c)** 0.20x = 120   **d)** x(300) = 240
   x = 30   x = 10.32   x = 600   x = 80%
   e) 19,500 + 19,500(0.06) = x   **f)** x + 0.04x = 130   **g)** x + 0.05x = 99,750
   x = $20,670   x = $125   x = $95,000

6. **a)** complementary   **b)** supplementary   **c)** 180 degrees

7. **a)** 2x + x = 360   **b)** x + 3x + x + 5 = 180   **c)** $38 = 2w + 2(\frac{1}{2} w + 10)$
   apple = 120 cal.   Angles = 35, 40, 105 degrees   width = 6 ft.; length = 13 ft
   soda = 240 cal.
   d) 70t + 65t = 540; t = 4 hrs   **e)** x + 2x − 15 = 180; angles = 65, 115 degrees
   f) 4x − 8 = 24   **g)** 2x + 2(x + 2) = 48
   x = 8   dimensions: 11 ft × 13 ft

MAT 101/152
Beginning Algebra
Unit 3 Review
Chapter 3 (Sections 1–6)

TRIDENT TECHNICAL COLLEGE

1. Determine which ordered pair is a solution to $2x - y = 8$
   - **a)** $(2, 4)$
   - **b)** $(-2, -3)$
   - **c)** $(3, 2)$
   - **d)** $(3, -2)$

2. State the coordinates of each point shown.

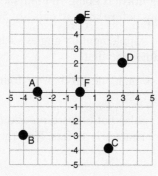

3. Given the equation $2x - 7y = 14$
   - **a)** find the y-value, if $x = -2$
   - **b)** determine the x-intercept
   - **c)** determine the y-intercept

4. Determine the slope and y-intercept for each linear equation.
   - **a)** $3x - 4y = 8$
   - **b)** $y = \dfrac{2}{3}x + 3$

5. Find the slope of the line through each pair of points.
   - **a)** $(-2, 5)$ and $(3, 8)$
   - **b)** $(3, -4)$ and $(-5, -6)$
   - **c)** $(8, 3)$ and $(-2, 3)$
   - **d)** $(-9, 2)$ and $(-9, 4)$

6. Create a table of 3 values of x and y and graph the linear equations.
   - **a)** $2x + y = 4$
   - **b)** $y = \dfrac{2}{3}x - 1$

7. Determine the x- and y-intercepts for each of the linear equations and then graph.
   - **a)** $2x - 3y = 6$
   - **b)** $4x + y = 8$

8. Write the equations in slope-intercept form and graph the linear equations.
   - **a)** $3x + y - 2 = 0$
   - **b)** $-x - 2y = 4$

9. Graph using any method.
   - **a)** $y = -2x + 3$
   - **b)** $y = 3x$
   - **c)** $x = -2$
   - **d)** $y = 3$

10. Determine whether the two lines given are parallel, perpendicular or neither.
    - **a)** $L_1: y = \dfrac{1}{2}x - 2$
      $L_2: y = \dfrac{1}{2}x + 3$
    - **b)** $L_1: 2x + 3y = 6$
      $L_2: 3x + 2y = 12$
    - **c)** $L_1: y = \dfrac{-2}{3}x$
      $L_2: 3x - 2y = 7$

11. Find the equation of the line using the given information. Write your answer in slope-intercept form.

    a) slope = 2; y-intercept $(0, -3)$ **b)** slope = 0; y-intercept $(0, 4)$

    c) m = -4; goes through the point $(-3, -4)$

    d) m = $\dfrac{3}{4}$; goes through the point $(4, -6)$

    e) goes through the points $(0, -2)$ and $(-3, 0)$

    f) goes through the points $(5, 3)$ and $(5, -4)$

    g) goes through the point $(4, 2)$ and is parallel to $2x - 4y = 8$

    h) has a y-intercept of $(0, -8)$ and is perpendicular to $y = \dfrac{3}{2}x + 9$

Answers

1. a) not a solution   **b)** not a solution   **c)** not a solution   **d)** yes, the ordered pair is a solution

2. A $(-3, 0)$ **B** $(-4, -3)$ **C** $(2, -4)$ **D** $(3, 2)$ **E** $(0, 5)$ **F** $(0, 0)$

3. a) $y = \dfrac{-18}{7}$ **b)** x-int: $(7, 0)$ **c)** y-int: $(0, -2)$

4. a) m = 3/4; y-int: $(0, -2)$ **b)** m = 2/3; y-int: $(0, 3)$

5. a) m = $\dfrac{3}{5}$ **b)** m = $\dfrac{1}{4}$ **c)** m = 0   **d)** m = undefined (no slope)

6. a)

x	y
0	4
1	2
−1	6

b)

x	y
0	−1
3	1
−3	−3

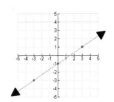

7. a) x-int: $(3, 0)$
     y-int: $(0, -2)$

b) x-int: $(2, 0)$
     y-int: $(0, 8)$

8. a) $y = -3x + 2$

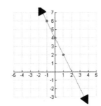

b) $y = \dfrac{-1}{2}x - 2$

9. a)

b)

c)

d)

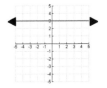

10. a) parallel   **b)** neither   **c)** perpendicular

11. a) $y = 2x - 3$ **b)** $y = 4$ **c)** $y = -4x - 16$ **d)** $y = \dfrac{3}{4}x - 9$

    e) $y = \dfrac{-2}{3}x - 2$ **f)** $x = 5$ **g)** $y = \dfrac{1}{2}x$ **h)** $y = \dfrac{-2}{3}x - 8$

MAT 101/152
Beginning Algebra
Unit 4 Review, Chapter 5

TRIDENT TECHNICAL COLLEGE

1. Determine which of the following is a polynomial. If it is not a polynomial, state the reason.

 a) $x^3 - 4x^2 + 5x - 9$ **b)** $-9x^{-3} + 5x^{-1} + 8$

 c) $\frac{1}{2}x^2 + \frac{3x}{4} - \frac{2}{3}$ **d)** $-4x^2 + \frac{1}{x} - 22$

 e) -10

2. Given the polynomial: $x^6y + 54x^3y^2 + 8x$, answer the following.

 a) Name the polynomial (monomial, binomial, trinomial)

 b) What is the degree of the first term?

 c) What is the degree of the second term?

 d) What is the degree of the third term?

 e) What is the coefficient of the first term?

 f) What is the degree of the polynomial?

3. Perform the indicated operation. Simplify your answer and write with positive exponents.

 a) $2^3 \cdot 2$ **b)** $\frac{3^{15}}{3^{12}}$

 c) $\frac{2^{-3}}{2^{-4}}$ **d)** $(4^{-1})^{-3}$

 e) $(2^3)(2^4)$ **f)** $(x^5)(-x^4)$

 g) $(y^3)(-y)^4$ **h)** $(2xyz^4)(4x^2y^3z^5)$

 i) $(-4x^4y^0)^2 \cdot (3xz)^2$ **j)** $(-3x^2y^{-6})^3$

 k) $\left(\frac{2x^{-2}}{3x^3}\right)^{-4}$ **l)** $\left(\frac{x^2y^7z^3}{xy^4z^3}\right)^8$

 m) $\left(\frac{3x^0y^{-3}z^{-4}}{5x^{-5}y^{-2}z}\right)^2$ **n)** $\left(\frac{x^{-2}y^5z^4}{xy^4z^{-2}}\right)^{-1}$

 o) $(5a^2 - 8ab + 2b^2) + (-6a^2 + 5ab - 7b^2)$ **p)** $(13x^2 - 5xy^2 + 7x - 5)$
 $- (3x^2y + 4xy^2 - 6x + 11)$

 q) subtract $(6x^2 + 2x - 9)$ from $(-5x^2 + 7x + 2)$

4. Multiply

 a) $5x^4(-3x^7)$ **b)** $5x^7(20x^9y^4)$

 c) $4x^2(-5x - 4)$ **d)** $3x^3(-2x^6 + 5)$

 e) $3xy^3(-3x^2y^3 + 6xy - 5x + 4)$ **f)** $-4x^2y^3(-8xy^2 - 5xy + y - 1)$

 g) $(x + 7y)(3x - 5y)$ **h)** $(4x - 3)(9x - 1)$

 i) $(3x - 5)^2$ **j)** $(5x - 7)(5x + 7)$

 k) $(a - b)(a^2 + ab + b^2)$ **l)** $-3x(x - 7)(2x - 5)$

 m) $(x - 2)^3$ **n)** $(2x - 3)(x^2 - 4x + 5)$

5. Divide

   a) $\dfrac{-3x^4 + x^3 - 6x^2 + 15x - 3}{3x}$

   b) $\dfrac{12x^3 - 8x^2 + 6x - 18}{6x}$

   c) $(6x^2 + 12x - 5) \div (3x)$

6. Convert from decimal notation to scientific notation.

   a) 789,000,000

   b) 0.000000127

   c) -8100

   d) -0.005

7. Convert from scientific notation to decimal notation.

   a) 4.59×10^{-4}

   b) -1.39×10^6

   c) The distance from the earth to the sun is 9.29×10^7 miles.

8. Multiply and express the answer in scientific notation.

   a) $(3 \times 10^{-4})(8 \times 10^{-2})$

   b) $(103,000,000)(0.0002)$

9. Divide and express your answer in decimal notation.

   a) $\dfrac{5.6 \times 10^{-4}}{2 \times 10^2}$

   b) $\dfrac{220,000}{0.000011}$

Answers

1. **a)** yes   **b)** no, a polynomial cannot have negative exponents   **c)** yes
    d) no, a polynomial cannot have variables in the denominator   **e)** yes

2. **a)** trinomial   **b)** 7   **c)** 5   **d)** 1   **e)** 1   **f)** 7

3. **a)** 16   **b)** 27   **c)** 2   **d)** 64   **e)** 128
    f) $-x^9$ **g)** y^7 **h)** $8x^3y^4z^9$ **i)** $144x^{10}z^2$ **j)** $\dfrac{-27x^6}{y^{18}}$

    k) $\dfrac{81x^{20}}{16}$ **l)** x^8y^{24} **m)** $\dfrac{9x^{10}}{25y^2z^{10}}$ **n)** $\dfrac{x^3}{yz^6}$ **o)** $-a^2 - 3ab - 5b^2$
    p) $13x^2 - 3x^2y - 9xy^2 + 13x - 16$ **q)** $-11x^2 + 5x + 11$

4. **a)** $-15x^{11}$ **b)** $100x^{16}y^4$ **c)** $-20x^3 - 16x^2$ **d)** $-6x^9 + 15x^3$
    e) $-9x^3y^6 + 18x^2y^4 - 15x^2y^3 + 12xy^3$ **f)** $32x^3y^5 + 20x^3y^4 - 4x^2y^4 + 4x^2y^3$ **g)** $3x^2 + 16xy - 35y^2$
    h) $36x^2 - 31x + 3$ **i)** $9x^2 - 30x + 25$ **j)** $25x^2 - 49$ **k)** $a^3 - b^3$ **l)** $-6x^3 + 57x^2 - 105x$
    m) $x^3 - 6x^2 + 12x - 8$ **n)** $2x^3 - 11x^2 + 22x - 15$

5. **a)** $-x^3 + \dfrac{1}{3}x^2 - 2x + 5 - \dfrac{1}{x}$ **b)** $2x^2 - \dfrac{4}{3}x + 1 - \dfrac{3}{x}$ **c)** $2x + 4 - \dfrac{5}{3x}$

6. **a)** 7.89×10^8 **b)** 1.27×10^{-7} **c)** -8.1×10^3 **d)** -5×10^{-3}

7. **a)** 0.000459   **b)** $-1,390,000$ **c)** 92,900,000

8. **a)** 2.4×10^{-5} **b)** 2.06×10^4

9. **a)** .0000028   **b)** 20,000,000,000

MAT 101/152
Beginning Algebra
Unit 5 Review
Chapter 6

TRIDENT TECHNICAL COLLEGE

1. Factor completely.

   a) $4x + 24$ 　　　　　　**b)** $7x^5 - 9x^4$ 　　　　　　**c)** $3x^2y + 6x^2y^2$

   d) $25x^2yz^3 + 125x^3yz$ 　　**e)** $5x(x-2) - 3(x-2)$ 　　**f)** $x^3 - 5x^2 + 8x - 40$

   g) $a^2 - 2a - ab + 2b$ 　　**h)** $y^3 + 3y^2 - y - 3$ 　　**i)** $x^2 + 9x + 18$

   j) $3x^2 - 30x + 72$ 　　　**k)** $6x^2 + 16x + 10$ 　　**l)** $-8a^2 + 4ab + 4b^2$

   m) $x^2 + 10x + 25$ 　　　**n)** $x^4 - 4x^3 - 21x^2$ 　　**o)** $2z^5 + 14z^4 + 12z^3$

   p) $x^2 - 121$ 　　　　　**q)** $10y^2 - 160$ 　　　　**r)** $x^2 - 3x + 2xy - 6y$

   s) $9x^2 + 100$ 　　　　**t)** $x^4 - 81$ 　　　　　**u)** $2x^5 - 32x$

   v) $-6x^4 - 21x^3 + 90x^2$ 　**w)** $y^2 - 4y + 21$ 　　**x)** $4x^2 - 20x + 25$

2. Simplify the expression in lowest terms.

   a) $\dfrac{3x^2y - 15xy - 42y}{6x - 42}$ 　　**b)** $\dfrac{2y^2 - 12y + 18}{12 - 4y}$ 　　**c)** $\dfrac{x^4 - 16}{x^2 - 4x - 12}$

3. Solve.

   a) $(x + 6)(x - 7) = 0$ 　　**b)** $-2x(x + 9) = 0$ 　　**c)** $a^2 - 4a - 12 = 0$

   d) $x^2 - 8x + 16 = 0$ 　　**e)** $3y^2 - 4 = -4y$ 　　　**f)** $3x^2 + 21x = -18$

   g) $(x - 1)(2x - 5) = 9$ 　**h)** $2x^2 - 5x - 24 = -3x$ 　**i)** $4x^2 = 64$

4. Write an equation and solve.

   a) The rectangle shown has an area of 84 square inches. Determine the length and width.

   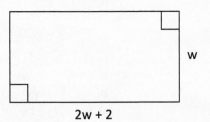

   b) The area of a rectangle is 36 square feet. Determine the length and width of the rectangle if the length is 4 times the width.

   c) The product of two consecutive positive odd integers is 143. Determine the two integers.

5. Write an equation and solve the right triangles for any missing sides.

   a) 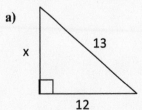　　　　**b)**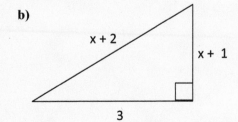

6. If $h = -16t^2 + 80t$ represents the height in feet of a rocket t seconds after it was fired, when will the rocket be 96 feet high? (Hint: when $h = 96$)

Answers

1. **a)** $4(x + 6)$

b) $x^4(7x - 9)$

c) $3x^2y(1 + 2y)$

d) $25x^2y\,z(z^2 + 5x)$

e) $(x - 2)(5x - 3)$

f) $(x - 5)(x^2 + 8)$

g) $(a - 2)(a - b)$

h) $(y + 3)(y + 1)(y - 1)$

i) $(x + 6)(x + 3)$

j) $3(x - 4)(x - 6)$

k) $2(3x + 5)(x + 1)$

l) $-4(2a + b)(a - b)$

m) $(x + 5)^2$

n) $x^2(x - 7)(x + 3)$

o) $2z^3(z + 6)(z + 1)$

p) $(x + 11)(x - 11)$

q) $10(y - 4)(y + 4)$

r) $(x - 3)(x + 2y)$

s) prime

t) $(x + 3)(x - 3)(x^2 + 9)$

u) $2x(x + 2)(x - 2)(x^2 + 4)$

v) $-3x^2(2x - 5)(x + 6)$

w) prime

x) $(2x - 5)^2$

2. $\dfrac{y(x+2)}{2}$

b) $\dfrac{-1}{2}(y - 3)$

c) $\dfrac{(x-2)(x^2+4)}{x-6}$

3. **a)** $x = -6, x = 7$

b) $x = 0, x = -9$

c) $a = 6, a = -2$

d) $x = 4$

e) $y = -2, y = 2/3$

f) $x = -6, x = -1$

g) $x = -\frac{1}{2}, x = 4$

h) $x = -3, x = 4$

i) $x = 4, x = -4$

4. **a)** $84 = w(2w + 2)$
$w = 6\ \text{in}, l = 14\ \text{in}$

b) $36 = w(4w)$
$w = 3\ \text{ft}, l = 12\ \text{ft}$

c) $x(x + 2) = 143$
$x = 11, x = 13$

5. **a)** $x^2 + 12^2 = 13^2$
$x = 5$

b) $(x + 1)^2 + 3^2 = (x + 2)^2$
sides of triangle $= 3, 4, 5$

6. $96 = -16t^2 + 80t$

$t = 2\ \text{sec}$ and $t = 3\ \text{sec}$

Mat 101 Elementary Algebra

Simplify each expression in lowest terms.

1) $\dfrac{x^2 + 5x + 6}{x + 3}$

2) $\dfrac{y^2 - 25}{y + 5}$

3) $\dfrac{2x^2 + 16x + 30}{x + 5}$

4) $\dfrac{b^2 - b - 12}{b + 3}$

5) $\dfrac{m^2 + 4mn - 5n^2}{m - n}$

6) $\dfrac{x^4 - 81}{x + 3}$

7) $\dfrac{2x^2 + 12x}{x + 6}$

8) $\dfrac{2m^2 - 24m + 72}{m - 6}$

9) $\dfrac{x^2 + 100}{x + 10}$

10) $\dfrac{-p^2 - 11p - 30}{p + 6}$

11) $\dfrac{4y^3 + 12y^2 - 40y}{y + 5}$

12) $\dfrac{3x^2 y - 15xy - 42y}{3x + 6}$

13) $\dfrac{6p^4 + 5p^3 - p^2}{p^3 + p^2}$

14) $\dfrac{2x^2 - 3x - 20}{4 - x}$

15) $\dfrac{ax + bx - 4a - 4b}{a + b}$

Solutions

1) $x + 2$

2) $y - 5$

3) $2(x + 3)$

4) $b - 4$

5) $m + 5n$

6) $(x^2 + 9)(x - 3)$

7) $2x$

8) $2(m - 6)$

9) in lowest terms

10) $-(p + 5)$

11) $4y(y - 2)$

12) $y(x - 7)$

13) $6p - 1$

14) $-(2x + 5)$

15) $x - 4$

MAT 101 BEGINNING ALGEBRA FINAL EXAM REVIEW

This review is not designed to give you a list of every possible test question, but will give you some idea of what types of questions might be asked. The final exam is comprehensive, that is, it covers the key objectives of the entire course. You may wish to study your tests as well as the chapter summaries, chapter review exercises, chapter practice tests and the cumulative review test provided in your textbook. No calculators will be used on this exam.

I. Match the property of the real number system with the appropriate example.

1. $-9(1) = -9$ **A.** Additive Inverse property

2. $-3 + 4 = 4 + (-3)$ **B.** Identity Element of addition

3. $6(0) = 0$ **C.** Associative property of addition

4. $(-5)(-6) = (-6)(-5)$ **D.** Commutative property of addition

5. $-4 + 0 = -4$ **E.** Commutative property of multiplication

6. $[7 + (-3)] + (-2) = 7 + [(-3) + (-2)]$ **F.** Distributive property

7. $-5(7 + 8) = -5(7) - 5(8)$ **G.** Identity Element of multiplication

8. $3 + (-3) = 0$ **H.** Multiplication property of zero

II. Simplify each expression.

9. $-17 - (-6)$ 10. $6[2 + 7(5 - 9) - 1]$

11. $-2(-3)^2 - 24$ 12. $-9 \div 0$

13. $-11 - (-3)$ 14. $(-2 + 1)^3 - (5 - 2)^2$

15. $\dfrac{4 + 5^2 \div 5}{6 - (-3 + 2)}$ 16. $-3^2 + 15 \div 3(2)$

17. $3\sqrt{16} - \sqrt{36}$ 18. $|10 - 15| + |3|$

19. $4(2c^3 - 3c^2) - (4c^2 - 6c)$ 20. $-4x^2 - (-8x^2) + (3x)^2$

III. Evaluate.

21. $x^2 - 2yz$ when $x = -2, y = 5$ and $z = 3$ 22. $3x^2 - 2x + 1$ when $x = -2$

IV. Solve these linear equations.

23. $17y + 12 = -5$ 24. $10(x - 3) - x + 2 - 2(x + 1)$
$= 3(3 + x) - 9$

25. $\dfrac{x}{4} + \dfrac{x}{6} = \dfrac{1}{2}(x + 3)$ 26. $.5(w + 1) = 2.5w - 7.5$

27. $3(4n + 5) - 2n = 5(n - 6)$ 28. $\dfrac{2(2x - 4)}{5} = \dfrac{3x + 6}{4} - \dfrac{3}{2}$

29. $\dfrac{x}{3} - 7 = 9$ 30. $\dfrac{4}{5}x - 1 = \dfrac{2}{7}x + 3$

31. $-5(3 - 4x) = -6 + 20x - 9$ 32. $3x - 12x = 24 - 9x$

V. Solve for the indicated letter.

33. $h = 3(p + 2k)$; solve for k

34. $3x - y + 7 = 0$; solve for y

35. $y = mx + b$; solve for x

VI. <u>Write an equation</u> and then <u>solve</u> the following.

36. Given the supplementary angles A and B, if angle A is 8° more than three times angle B, find the measure of each angle.

37. The sum of a number and twice the number is 57. What is the number?

38. For 3 consecutive integers, the sum of the smallest and largest integers, added to four more than the middle integer, equals 97. What are the 3 integers?

39. One angle of a triangle is 20° greater than the first angle. The third angle is twice as large as the first angle. What are the measures of the 3 angles?

40. The width of a rectangle is 8 feet less than the length. If the perimeter of the rectangle is 64 feet, what are the dimensions of the rectangle?

41. James took out a simple interest 2-year loan of $5000. If the interest paid on the loan was $250, find the interest rate. ($I = prt$)

42. What is 40% of 18?

43. You are scheduling parties for a restaurant. One dining room holds four more than twice as many guests as a second room. Together they hold 127 guests. How many can you schedule into the smaller room?

44. At Cloth World a fabric worker has a 106 yard bolt of cloth that has to be cut into three lengths. The second piece is to be 4 yards longer than the first. The third piece is to be three times as long as the second piece. What is the length of each piece?

45. The sum of two consecutive <u>even</u> integers is sixty-two. What are the integers?

46. Dillard's advertised a 25% off sale on their coats. If the sale price was $150 on a particular coat, what was the original price?

VII. Solve and graph the inequality on a number line. State the solution in interval notation.

47. $3y + 9 < 27$

48. $\frac{2}{3}(t+2) \le \frac{1}{4}(2t-6)$

49. $2 - \frac{x}{5} < -3$

VIII. Graph the linear equations on a Cartesian Coordinate System.

50. $5x + 3y = 15$

51. $-2x + y = 3$

52. $y = 4$

53. $y = \frac{3}{2}x + 1$

54. Determine the slope of the line through the given points.

    a) $(9, 3)$ and $(5, -6)$ **b)** $(-2, 3)$ and $(-2, -1)$ **c)**

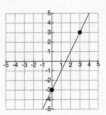

55. Write an equation of a line, in slope-intercept form, given the following information.

    a) through the points $(-1, -2)$ with slope of m $= -2$

    b) through the points $(1, 6)$ and $(3, -2)$

    c) through the point $(-3, 0)$ and perpendicular to $y = 3x + 4$

    d) parallel to $x + 2y = 6$ and contains the point $(2, 4)$

    e) perpendicular to $2x - 4y = 4$ and contains the point $(4, 6)$

IX. Answer the following questions using the polynomial: $-2x^3y^2 + 5x^2 - 7y^2$

56. How many terms are there in this polynomial?

57. What is the special name for this polynomial?

58. What is the coefficient of the term $5x^2$?

59. What is the degree of the term $-2x^3y^2$?

60. What is the degree of the polynomial?

X. Perform the indicated operation and simplify. Write your answer in standard form.

61. $- 8m - 3m$

62. $(8a - 9)(4a + 3)$

63. $(2x)^3(5x)^2$

64. $(a - b) - (a - b) - (a - b)$

65. $(2m - 5)^2$

66. $(-4a^2b^4)^3$

67. $(2x + 1)(2x - 1)$

68. $- 4x(x - y)$

69. Subtract $(-x^2y - 2x + 3y)$ from $(x^2y + 2x - 3y)$

70. $3x - [x - (5x - 1)]$

71. $- 5h - (- 6h)$

72. $2x^2y^3(x^2y - 3x^2y^3)$

73. $\dfrac{2x^5 + 6x^3 - 4x^2}{-2x^2}$

74. $\dfrac{5y^2 + 22y + 8}{25y^2 - 4}$

75. $\dfrac{12x^5y^3}{18x^3y^7}$

76. $-7(y - 2) - 3(4 - 6y)$

77. $(2x - 3)(7x + 5)$

78. $(3x - 1)(2x^2 + 3x - 1)$

XI. Reduce to simplest exponential form. Write all answers with positive exponents.

79. $(2a)^{-1}$

80. $2a^{-1}$

81. $2y^{-3}y^{-5}$

82. $(2a^4)^{-3}$

83. $\dfrac{x^{-2}y^4z^0}{x^5y^{-2}}$

84. $\left(\dfrac{a^3}{b^4}\right)^{-2}$

85. $\left(\dfrac{21x^4y^3}{7y^2}\right)^3$

86. $3c^2(2c^4d^3)^2$

XII. Completely factor the following polynomials or state that it is prime.

87. $x^2 + 12x + 35$ **88.** $6x^2 + 11x + 3$ **89.** $1 - 7x - 18x^2$

90. $3x - 3y + 2x^2 - 2xy$ **91.** $9a^3b - 12a^2b^2 + 3ab^3$ **92.** $25y^2 - 36$

93. $9a^2b - 24ab + 16b$ **94.** $x^2 - 2x - 15$ **95.** $x^2 - 10x + 16$

96. $x^2 - 10x + 9$ **97.** $4x^2 - 36$ **98.** $25x^2 + 81$

99. $x^4 - 16$ **100.** $10x^2 - 23xy - 5y^2$ **101.** $5x^3y - 35x^2y + 50xy$

102. $4x^2 - 4xy + y^2$ **103.** $x^4 - 10x^3 + 21x^2$

XIII. Simplify the following.

104. $\dfrac{6x^4 + 5x^3 - x^2}{x^3 + x^2}$ **105.** $\dfrac{x^2 - 121}{x - 11}$

XIV. Solve the following quadratic equations by factoring.

106. $x^2 - x - 6 = 0$ **107.** $x^2 + x = 2$ **108.** $x^2 - 9 = 0$

109. $2y^2 - y = 0$ **110.** $x^2 = 121$ **111.** $x^2 = -8x - 15$

112. $x^2 = 3x$

XV. Write an equation and then solve the following quadratic equations.

113. The length of a rectangle is 2 centimeters less than twice the width. Its area is 84 square centimeters. Find the dimensions of the rectangle.

114. A hang-glider pilot accidentally drops his compass from the top of a 576 foot cliff. The height h of the compass after t seconds is given by the quadratic equation $h = -16t^2 + 576$. When will the compass hit the ground? (Hint: The compass is on the ground when h = 0)

115. The longer leg of a right triangle is 4 feet longer than the shorter leg. The hypotenuse is 8 feet longer than the shorter leg. Find the length of each side of this triangle.

Answers

1. G   **2.** D   **3.** H   **4.** E   **5.** B   **6.** C   **7.** F   **8.** A

9. -11 **10.** -162 **11.** -42 **12.** undefined

13. -8 **14.** -10 **15.** $\dfrac{9}{7}$ **16.** 1

17. 6   **18.** 8   **19.** $8c^3 - 16c^2 + 6c$ **20.** $13x^2$

21. -26 **22.** 17   **23.** -1 **24.** $\dfrac{15}{2}$

25. -18 **26.** 4   **27.** -9 **28.** 32

29. 48   **30.** $\dfrac{70}{9}$ or 7 7/9   **31.** all real numbers   **32.** No solution

33. $k = \dfrac{h - 3p}{6}$ **34.** $y = 3x + 7$ **35.** $x = \dfrac{y - b}{m}$ **36.** $\angle A = 137°; \angle B = 43°$

37. $x + 2x = 57; x = 19$ **38.** $x + x + 2 + x + 1 + 4 = 97; x = 30; 30, 31, 32$

39. $x + x + 20 + 2x = 180; x = 40;$ angles ... 40°, 60°, 80°

40. $2(L) + 2(L - 8) = 64; L = 20$ ft; W = 12 ft

41. $250 = 5000(r)(2); r = .025$ or 2.5%

42. $.40(18) = 7.2$

43. $x + 2x + 4 = 127; x = 41;$ smaller room .. 41 guests

44. $x + x + 4 + 3(x + 4) = 106$; $x = 18$; 1st piece.. 18 yds; 2nd piece.. 22 yds; 3rd piece.. 66 yds

45. $x + x + 2 = 62$; $x = 30$; 2 numbers . . . 30 & 32   **46.** $x - .25x = 150$; $x = \$200$

47. $y < 6$ $(-\infty, 6)$ **48.** $t \leq -17$ $(-\infty, -17]$ **49.** $x > 25$ $(25, \infty)$

6   −17   25

50. $5x + 3y = 15$ **51.** $-2x + y = 3$ **52.** $y = 4$ **53.** $y = \dfrac{3}{2}x + 1$

54. a) $m = \dfrac{9}{4}$ b) undefined   c) $m = 2$

55. a) $y = -2x - 4$ b) $y = -4x + 10$ c) $y = \dfrac{-1}{3}x - 1$ d) $y = \dfrac{-1}{2}x + 5$
    e) $y = -2x + 14$

56. 3   **57.** trinomial   **58.** 5   **59.** 5   **60.** 5

61. $-11m$ **62.** $32a^2 - 12a - 27$ **63.** $200x^5$ **64.** $-a + b$

65. $4m^2 - 20m + 25$ **66.** $-64a^6b^{12}$ **67.** $4x^2 - 1$ **68.** $-4x^2 + 4xy$

69. $2x^2y + 4x - 6y$ **70.** $7x - 1$ **71.** h   **72.** $2x^4y^4 - 6x^4y^6$

73. $-x^3 - 3x + 2$ **74.** $\dfrac{y + 4}{5y - 2}$ **75.** $\dfrac{2x^2}{3y^4}$ **76.** $11y + 2$

77. $14x^2 - 11x - 15$ **78.** $6x^3 + 7x^2 - 6x + 1$ **79.** $\dfrac{1}{2a}$ **80.** $\dfrac{2}{a}$

81. $\dfrac{2}{y^8}$ **82.** $\dfrac{1}{8a^{12}}$ **83.** $\dfrac{y^6}{x^7}$ **84.** $\dfrac{b^8}{a^6}$

85. $27x^{12}y^3$ **86.** $12c^{10}d^6$

87. $(x + 5)(x + 7)$ **88.** $(2x + 3)(3x + 1)$ **89.** $(1 - 9x)(1 + 2x)$

90. $(x - y)(3 + 2x)$ **91.** $3ab(3a - b)(a - b)$ **92.** $(5y - 6)(5y + 6)$

93. $b(3a - 4)^2$ **94.** $(x - 5)(x + 3)$ **95.** $(x - 8)(x - 2)$

96. $(x - 9)(x - 1)$ **97.** $4(x + 3)(x - 3)$

98. prime   **99.** $(x - 2)(x + 2)(x^2 + 4)$ **100.** $(2x - 5y)(5x + y)$

101. $5xy(x - 5)(x - 2)$ **102.** $(2x - y)^2$ **103.** $x^2(x - 7)(x - 3)$

104. $6x - 1$ **105.** $x + 11$

106. $x = 3$ or $x = -2$ **107.** $x = -2$ or $x = 1$ **108.** $x = \pm 3$

109. $y = 0$ or $y = \dfrac{1}{2}$ **110.** $x = \pm 11$ **111.** $x = -3$ or $x = -5$

112. $x = 0$ or $x = 3$ **113.** $(2w - 2)w = 84$; $w = 7$ cm and $l = 12$ cm

114. $0 = -16t^2 + 576$; $t = 6$ sec

115. $x^2 + (x + 4)^2 = (x + 8)^2$ sides = 12, 16, & 20 ft.

PEARSON   ALWAYS LEARNING

Elementary Algebra

Math 101
Second Custom Edition for Trident Technical College

Michael Sullivan, III

Katherine R. Struve

Janet Mazzarella

Taken from:
Elementary Algebra, Second Edition
by Michael Sullivan, III, Katherine R. Struve, Janet Mazzarella

Cover Art: Courtesy of Photodisc/Getty Images.

Taken from:

Elementary Algebra, Second Edition
by Michael Sullivan, III, Katherine R. Struve, and Janet Mazzarella
Copyright © 2010, 2007 by Pearson Education, Inc.
Published by Prentice Hall
Upper Saddle River, New Jersey 07458

This special edition published in cooperation with Pearson Learning Solutions.

All trademarks, service marks, registered trademarks, and registered service marks are the property of their respective owners and are used herein for identification purposes only.

Pearson Learning Solutions, 501 Boylston Street, Suite 900, Boston, MA 02116
A Pearson Education Company
www.pearsoned.com

Printed in the United States of America

8 9 10 V092 16 15 14 13

000200010270765328

MT

ISBN 10: 1-256-13516-X
ISBN 13: 978-1-256-13516-6

*To my father, Michael Sullivan, an unbelievable mentor,
to the memory of my Mother, who is missed dearly,
and to Stefan and Zofia Wilk, who helped
in so many ways.*

—Michael Sullivan

*To my husband, Dan Struve, for his
encouragement and support.*

—Katherine R. Struve

*To my students, who have inspired me more than
I can say; and to the two of whom I am most proud,
my children, Kellen and Jillian Mazzarella.*

—Janet Mazzarella

About the Authors

With training in mathematics, statistics, and economics, Michael Sullivan, III has a varied teaching background that includes 18 years of instruction in both high school and college-level mathematics. He is currently a full-time professor of mathematics at Joliet Junior College. Michael has numerous textbooks in publication, including an Introductory Statistics series and a Precalculus series, which he writes with his father, Michael Sullivan.

Michael believes that his experiences writing texts for college-level math and statistics courses give him a unique perspective as to where students are headed once they leave the developmental mathematics tract. This experience is reflected in the philosophy and presentation of his developmental text series. When not in the classroom or writing, Michael enjoys spending time with his three children, Michael, Kevin, and Marissa, and playing golf. Now that his two sons are getting older, he has the opportunity to do both at the same time!

Kathy Struve has been a classroom teacher for nearly 30 years, first at the high school level and, for the past 16 years, at Columbus State Community College. Kathy emphasizes classroom diversity: diversity of age, learning styles, and previous learning success. She is aware of the challenges of teaching mathematics at a large, urban community college, where students have varied mathematics backgrounds and may enter college with a high level of mathematics anxiety.

Kathy served as Lead Instructor of the Developmental Algebra sequence at Columbus State where she developed curriculum and provided leadership to adjunct faculty in implementing graphing calculator technology in the classroom. She has authored classroom activities at the Elementary Algebra, Intermediate Algebra, and College Algebra levels and conducted workshops at local, state, and national conferences. In her spare time Kathy enjoys spending time with her two adult daughters and biking, hiking, and traveling with her husband.

Born and raised in San Diego county, Janet Mazzarella spent her career teaching in culturally and economically diverse high schools before taking a position at Southwestern College 18 years ago. Janet has taught a wide range of mathematics courses from arithmetic through calculus for math/science/engineering majors and has training in mathematics, education, engineering, and accounting.

Janet has worked to incorporate technology into the curriculum by participating in the development of Interactive Math and Math Pro. At Southwestern College, she helped develop the self-paced developmental mathematics program and spent two years serving as its director. In addition, she has been the Chair of the Mathematics Department, the faculty union president, and the faculty coordinator for Intermediate Algebra. In the past, free time consisted of racing motorcycles off-road in the Baja 500 and rock climbing, but recently she has given up the adrenaline rush of these activities for the thrill of traveling in Europe.

Contents

Preface

We would like to thank the reviewers, class testers, and users of the first edition of *Elementary Algebra* who helped to make the book an overwhelming success. Their thoughtful comments and suggestions provided strong guidance for improvements to the second edition that we believe will enhance this solid, student-friendly text.

The Elementary Algebra course serves a diverse group of students. Some of them are new to algebra, while others were introduced to the material but have not yet grasped all the concepts. Still other students realized success in the course in the past but need a refresher. Not only do the backgrounds of students vary in respect to their mathematical abilities, but students' motivation, reading, and study skills also range considerably.

This diversity makes teaching Elementary Algebra challenging. It is imperative that texts recognize the diversity of the classroom and address the array of needs of the many students.

Elementary Algebra introduces students to the logic and precision of mathematics. We expect students to leave the course with an appreciation of this precision as well as of the power of mathematics. Our students need to understand that the concepts we teach in this course form the basis for future mathematics courses. Once they have a conceptual understanding of algebra, students recognize that the material is not merely a series of unconnected topics. Instead, they see a story in which each new chapter builds on concepts learned in previous chapters.

To reinforce this idea, we remind our students of a helpful fact—mathematics is about taking a problem and reducing it to another problem that we have already seen. Taking a problem and reducing it to parts that are easier to solve help students to see the forest for the trees (and, to carry the metaphor further, prevent them from feeling that they are lost in the woods).

In short, to address the many needs of today's Elementary Algebra students, we established the following as our goals for this text:

- Provide students with a strong conceptual foundation in mathematics through a clear, distinct, thorough presentation of concepts.
- Offer comprehensive exercise sets that build students' skills, show various intriguing applications of mathematics, begin to build mathematical thinking skills, and reinforce mathematical concepts.
- Provide students with ample opportunity to see the connections among the various topics learned in the course.
- Present a variety of study aids and tips so students quickly come to view the text as a useful and reliable tool that can increase success in the course.

Develop an Effective Text for Use In and Out of the Classroom

Given the hectic lives led by most students, coupled with the anxiety and trepidation with which they approach this course, an outstanding developmental mathematics text must provide pedagogical support that makes the text valuable to students as they study and do assignments. Pedagogy must be presented within a framework that teaches students how to study math; pedagogical devices must also address what students see as the "mystery" of mathematics—and solve that mystery.

To encourage students and to clarify the material, we developed a set of pedagogical features that help students develop good study skills, garner an understanding of the connections between topics, and work smarter in the process. The pedagogy used is based upon the more than 65 years of classroom teaching experience that the authors bring to this text.

Examples are often the determining factor in how valuable a textbook is to a student. Students look to examples to provide them with guidance and instruction when they need it most—the times when they are away from the instructor and the classroom. We have developed two example formats in an attempt to provide superior guidance and instruction for the students.

Innovative Sullivan/Struve Examples

The innovative *Sullivan/Struve Example* has a two-column format in which annotations are provided to the **left** of the algebra, rather than the right, as is the practice in most texts. Because we read from **left to right,** placing the annotation on the left will make more sense to the student. It becomes clear that the annotation describes what we are about to do instead of what was just done. The annotations may be thought of as the teacher's voice offering clarification immediately before writing the next step in the solution on the board. Consider the following:

EXAMPLE 3 **Combining Like Terms to Solve a Linear Equation**

Solve the equation: $2x - 6 + 3x = 14$

Solution

$$2x - 6 + 3x = 14$$

Combine like terms: $\quad 5x - 6 = 14$

Add 6 to each side of the equation: $\quad 5x - 6 + 6 = 14 + 6$

$$5x = 20$$

Divide both sides by 5: $\quad \dfrac{5x}{5} = \dfrac{20}{5}$

$$x = 4$$

Check Verify that $x = 4$ is the solution.

$$2x - 6 + 3x = 14$$

Substitute 4 for x in the original equation: $\quad 2(4) - 6 + 3(4) \overset{?}{=} 14$

$$8 - 6 + 12 \overset{?}{=} 14$$

$$14 = 14$$

Since $x = 4$ results in a true statement, the solution of the equation is 4, or the solution set is $\{4\}$. ∎

Quick ✔ *In Problems 6–9, solve each equation.*

6. $7b - 3b + 3 = 11$ **7.** $-3a + 4 + 4a = 13 - 27$

8. $6c - 2 + 2c = 18$ **9.** $-12 = 5x - 3x + 4$

Showcase Examples

Showcase Examples are used strategically to introduce key topics or important problem-solving techniques. These examples provide "how-to" instruction by offering a guided, step-by-step approach to solving a problem. Students can then immediately see how each of the steps is employed. We remind students that the *Showcase Example* is meant to provide "how-to" instruction by including the words "how to" in the example title. The *Showcase Example* has a three-column format in which the left column describes a step, the middle column provides a brief annotation, as needed, to explain the step, and the right column presents the algebra. With this format, students can see each step in the problem-solving process in context so that the steps make more sense. This approach is more effective than simply stating each step in the text.

EXAMPLE 3 How to Solve an Inequality Using the Addition Property of Inequality

Solve the linear inequality $3y + 5 \leq 2y + 8$ and express the solution set using set-builder notation and interval notation. Graph the solution set.

Step-by-Step Solution

Step 1: Get the expressions containing variables on the left side of the inequality.	Apply the Addition Property of Inequality and subtract 2y from both sides:	$3y + 5 \leq 2y + 8$ $3y + 5 - 2y \leq 2y + 8 - 2y$ $y + 5 \leq 8$
Step 2: Isolate the variable y on the left side.	Apply the Addition Property of Inequality and subtract 5 from both sides:	$y + 5 - 5 \leq 8 - 5$ $y \leq 3$

Figure 16

The solution set using set-builder notation is $\{y \mid y \leq 3\}$. The solution set using interval notation is $(-\infty, 3]$. The solution set is graphed in Figure 16. ∎

Quick ✔

12. To ____ an inequality means to find the set of all replacement values of the variable for which the statement is true.

13. The ____ ____ __ ____ states that the direction, or sense, of each inequality remains the same when the same quantity is added to each side of the inequality.

In Problems 14–17, find the solution of the linear inequality and express the solution set in set-builder notation and interval notation. Graph the solution set.

14. $5n - 3 > 4n$ **15.** $-2x + 3 < 7 - 3x$

16. $5n + 8 \leq 4n + 4$ **17.** $3(4x - 8) + 12 > 11x - 13$

Quick Check Exercises

Placed at the conclusion of most examples, the *Quick Check* exercises provide students with an opportunity for immediate reinforcement. By working the problems that mirror the example just presented, students get instant feedback and gain confidence in their understanding of the concept. All *Quick Check* exercise answers are provided in the back of the text. We believe that the *Quick Check* exercises will make the text more accessible and encourage students to read, consult, and use the text regularly.

Superior Exercise Sets: Paired with Purpose

Students learn algebra by doing algebra. The superior end-of-section exercise sets in this text provide students with ample practice of both procedures and concepts. The exercises are paired and present problem types with every possible derivative. The exercises also present a gradual increase in difficulty level. The early, basic exercises keep the student's focus on as few "levels of understanding" as possible. The later or higher-numbered exercises are "multi-task" (or Mixed Practice) exercises where students are required to utilize multiple skills, concepts, or problem-solving techniques.

Throughout the textbook, the exercise sets are grouped into eight categories—some of which appear only as needed:

1. **Preparing for...** problems are located at the opening of the section. They are problems that deal with prerequisite material for the section along with page references so students may remediate, if necessary. Answers to the Preparing for... problems appear as a footnote on the page.

2. **Quick Check** exercises, which provide the impetus to get students into the text, follow most examples and are numbered sequentially as the first problems in each section exercise set. By doing these problems as homework and the first exercises attempted, the student is directed into the material in the section. If a student gets stuck, he or she will learn that the example immediately preceding the Quick Check exercise illustrates the concepts needed to solve the problem.

3. **Building Skills** exercises are drill problems that develop the student's understanding of the procedures and skills in working with the methods presented in the section. These exercises can be linked back to a single objective in the section. Notice that the Building Skills problems begin the numbering scheme where the Quick Checks leave off. For example, if the last Quick Check exercise is Problem 20, then we begin the Building Skills exercises with Problem 21. This serves as a reminder that Quick Check exercises should be assigned as homework. In addition, the Building Skills exercises are keyed to each learning objective.

4. **Mixed Practice** exercises are also drill problems, but they offer a comprehensive assessment of the skills learned in the section by asking problems that relate to more than one concept or objective. In addition, we may present problems from previous sections so students must first recognize the type of problem and then employ the appropriate technique to solve the problem.

5. **Applying the Concepts** exercises are problems that allow students to see the relevance of the material learned within the section. Problems in this category either are situational problems that use material learned in the section to solve "real-world" problems or are problems that ask a series of questions to enhance a student's conceptual understanding of the mathematics presented in the section.

6. **Extending the Concepts** exercises can be thought of as problems that go beyond the basics. Within this block of exercises an instructor will find a variety of problems to sharpen students' critical-thinking skills.

7. **Explaining the Concepts** problems require students to think about the big picture concepts of the section and express these ideas in their own words. It is our belief that students need to improve their ability to communicate complicated ideas both orally and in writing. When they are able to explain mathematical methods or concepts to another individual, they have truly mastered the ideas. These problems can serve as a basis for classroom discussion or can be used as writing assignments.

8. Finally, we include coverage of the **graphing calculator.** Instructors' philosophies about the use of graphing devices vary considerably. Because instructors disagree about the value of this tool, we have made an effort to make graphing technology entirely optional. When appropriate, technology exercises are included at the close of a section's exercise set.

Problem Icons In addition to the carefully structured categories of exercises, selected problems are flagged with icons to denote that:

- ⊙ Complete worked-out solutions to these problems are found on the CD Lecture Series.
- △ These problems focus on geometry concepts.
- ▦ A calculator will be useful in working the problem.

What's New to the Second Edition

Quick Check Exercises: Encourage Study Skills that Lead to Independent Learning

What is one of the overarching goals of an education? We believe it is to learn to solve problems independently. In particular, we would like to see students develop the ability to pick up a text or manual and teach themselves the skills they need. In our mathematics classes, however, we are often frustrated because students rarely read the text and often struggle to understand the concepts independently.

To encourage students to use the text more effectively and to help them achieve greater success in the course, we have structured the exercises in the second edition of our text differently from other mathematics textbooks. The aim of this new structure is to get students "into the text" in order to increase their ability and confidence to work any math problem—particularly when they are away from the classroom and an instructor who can help.

With the second edition of *Elementary Algebra*, each section's exercise set begins with the *Quick Check* exercises. The *Quick Checks* are consecutively numbered. The end-of-section exercises begin their numbering scheme based on where the *Quick Checks* end. For example:

- Section 1.2: *Quick Checks* end at Problem 54, so the end-of-section exercise set starts with Problem 55 (see page 17).
- Section 1.3: *Quick Checks* end at Problem 22, so the end-of-section exercise set starts with Problem 23 (see page 26).

You'll recall that the *Quick Checks* follow most examples and provide the platform for students to get "into the text." By integrating these exercises into the exercise set, we direct students to the instructional material in that section. Our hope is that students will then become more aware of the instructional value of the text and will be more likely to succeed when studying away from the classroom and the instructor.

To facilitate this change in numbering of the Quick Checks and end-of-section exercise sets, the following changes have also been made:

- Answer annotations to Quick Checks and exercises have been placed directly next to each problem in the Annotated Instructor's Edition to make it easier for instructors to create assignments.
- We have used the same tan background color for the Quick Checks and the exercise sets to reinforce the connection between them visually. The colored background will also make the Quick Checks easier to find on the page.
- Answers to Selected Exercises at the back of the text now integrate the answers to every Quick Check exercise with the answers to every odd problem from the section exercise sets.

Organizational Changes

Two major changes to the organization of the content have been made from the first edition of *Elementary Algebra*.

- The former Chapter 8, "Introduction to Graphing and Equations of Lines," and Chapter 9, "Systems of Linear Equations and Inequalities," have been moved to Chapters 3 and 4. This change was made based on feedback from reviewers of the first edition and conforms to the more traditional version of the table of contents in *Elementary Algebra*. Instructors may now cover "everything linear" in Chapters 2–4.
- The former Section 8.7, "Variation," is now Section 7.9. This change was made so variation is in the chapter on rational expressions.

Hallmark Features

Study Skills and Student Success

We have included study skills and student success as regular themes throughout this text starting with *Section 1.1, Success in Mathematics.* In addition to this dedicated section that covers many of the basics that are essential to success in any math course, we have included several recurring study aids that appear in the margin. These features are designed to anticipate the student's needs and to provide immediate help—as if the teacher were looking over his or her shoulder. These margin features include *In Words; Work Smart;* and *Work Smart: Study Skills.*

Section 1.1: *Success in Mathematics* focuses the student on basic study skills, including what to do during the first week of the semester; what to do before, during, and after class; how to use the text effectively; and how to prepare for an exam.

In Words helps to address the difficulty that students have in reading mathematically precise definitions and theorems by explaining them in plain English.

Work Smart provides "tricks of the trade" hints, tips, reminders, and alerts. It also identifies some common errors to avoid and helps students work more efficiently.

Work Smart: Study Skills reminds students of study skills that will help them to succeed at various points in the course. Attention to these practices will help them to become better, more proficient learners.

Test Preparation and Student Success

The Chapter Tests in this text and the companion Chapter Test Prep Video CD have been designed to help students make the most of their valuable study time.

Chapter Test In preparation for their classroom test, students should take the practice test to make sure they understand the key topics in the chapter. The exercises in the Chapter Tests have been crafted to reflect the level and types of exercises a student is likely to see on a classroom test.

Chapter Test Prep Video CD Packaged with each new copy of the text, the Chapter Test Prep Video CD provides students with help at the critical juncture when they are studying for a test. The Video CD presents step-by-step solutions to the exact exercises found in each of the book's Chapter Tests. Easy video navigation allows students instant access to the worked-out solutions to the exercises they want to study or review.

Seeing the Connections: The Big Picture

Another important role of the pedagogy in this text is to help students see and understand the connection between the mathematical topics being presented. Several section-opening and margin features help to reinforce connections:

The Big Picture: Putting It Together **(Chapter Opener)** This feature is based on how we start each chapter in the classroom—with a quick sketch of what we plan to cover. Before tackling a chapter, we tie concepts and techniques together by summarizing material covered previously and then relate these ideas to material we are about to discuss. It is important for students to understand that content truly builds from one chapter to the next. We find that students need to be reminded that the familiar operations of addition, subtraction, multiplication, and division are being applied to different or more complex objects.

Preparing for This Section As part of this building process, we think it is important to remind students of specific skills that they will need from earlier in the course to be successful within a given section. The *Preparing for . . .* feature that begins each section not only provides a list of prerequisite skills that a student should understand before tackling the content of a new section but also offers a short quiz to test students' preparedness. Answers to the quiz are provided in a footnote on the same page, and a cross-reference to the material in the text is provided so that the student can remediate when necessary.

Mixed Practice These problems exist within each end-of-section exercise set and draw upon material learned from multiple objectives. Sometimes, these problems simply represent a mixture of problems presented within the section, but they also may include a mixture of problems from various sections. For example, students may need to distinguish between linear and quadratic equations or students may need to distinguish between the direction *simplify* versus *solve*.

Putting the Concepts Together (Mid-Chapter Review) Each chapter has a group of exercises at the appropriate point in the chapter, entitled *Putting the Concepts Together*. These exercises serve as a review—synthesizing material introduced up to that point in the chapter. The exercises in these mid-chapter reviews are carefully chosen to assist students in seeing the "big picture."

Cumulative Review Learning algebra is a building process, and building involves considerable reinforcement. The Cumulative Review exercises at the end of each odd-numbered chapter, starting with Chapter 3, help students to reinforce and solidify their knowledge by revisiting concepts and using them in context. This way, studying for the final exam should be fairly easy. Cumulative Reviews for each even-numbered chapter can be found on the Instructor's Resource Center.

In Closing

When we started writing this textbook, we discussed what improvement we could make in coverage; in staples such as examples and problems; and in any pedagogical features that we found truly useful. After writing and rewriting, and reading many thoughtful reviews from instructors, we focused on the following features of the text to set it apart.

- The **innovative *Sullivan/Struve Examples*** and ***Showcase Examples*** provide students with superior guidance and instruction when they need it most—when they are away from the instructor and the classroom. Each of the margin features *In Words, Work Smart,* and *Work Smart: Study Skills* are designed to improve study skills, make the textbook easier to navigate, and increase student success.

- **Exercise Sets: Paired with Purpose**—The exercise sets are structured to assess student understanding of vocabulary, concepts, drill, problem solving, and applications. The exercise sets are graded in difficulty level to build confidence and to enhance students' mathematical thinking. The *Quick Check* exercises provide students with immediate reinforcement and instant feedback to determine their understanding of the concepts presented in the examples.

- **The Big Picture**—Each section opens with a *Preparing for This Section quiz* that allows students to review material learned earlier in the course that is needed in the upcoming section. **Mixed Practice** problems require students to utilize material learned from multiple objectives to solve a problem. Often, these problems require students to first determine the correct approach to solving the problem prior to actually solving it. *Putting the Concepts Together* helps students see the big picture and provide a structure for learning each new concept and skill in the course.

Student and Instructor Resources

STUDENT RESOURCES

Available for purchase at MyPearsonStore.com

Student's Solutions Manual
(ISBN: 0321589300/9780321589309)

Complete worked solutions to the odd-numbered problems in the end-of-section exercises and all of the Quick Checks and end-of-chapter exercises.

***Do the Math* Workbook**
(ISBN: 032159312X/9780321593122)

A collection of 5-Minute Warm-Up exercises; Guided Practice exercises; and *Do the Math* exercises for each section in the text. These worksheets are designed for students to show their work in homework, during class, or in a lab setting.

Videos on DVD for *Elementary Algebra*, 2/e
(ISBN: 0321593200/9780321593207)

Keyed to each section in the text, mini-lectures provide a 15–20 minute review of the key concepts and step through the solution to the exercises identified with a ⊙ symbol. Videos include optional subtitles in English and Spanish.

MathXL® Tutorials on CD
(ISBN: 0321593146/9780321593146)

Algorithmically generated practice exercises that correlate to exercises at the end of sections with correlated examples and guided solutions. Selected exercises include a video clip.

Chapter Test Prep Video CD (packaged with each new copy of the text)

Includes fully worked-out solutions to every problem in the Chapter Tests.

INSTRUCTOR RESOURCES

Available through your Pearson representative

Annotated Instructor's Edition
(ISBN: 032157592X/9780321575920)

Instructor's Solutions Manual
(ISBN: 0321589572/9780321589576)

Instructor's Resource Manual
(ISBN: 0321589580/9780321589583)

Includes Mini-Lectures—one-page lesson plans at-a-glance for each section in the text that feature key examples and Teaching Tips on how students respond to the material.

PowerPoint Lecture Slides

TestGen® for *Elementary Algebra*, 2/e
(Available for download from the IRC)

ONLINE RESOURCES

MyMathLab® (access code required)

MathXL® (access code required)

Acknowledgments

Textbooks are written by authors but evolve through the efforts of many people. We would like to extend our thanks to the following individuals for their important contributions to the project. From Pearson: Paul Murphy, who saw the vision of this text from its inception and made it happen; Michelle Renda for her innovative marketing ideas; Ann Heath for her dedication, enthusiasm, and attention to detail (quite honestly, Ann was the cement of the project); Chris Hoag for her support and encouragement; Heather Scott and the design team for the attractive and functional design; Karin Kipp and Linda Behrens for keeping a watchful eye and managing countless production details; Tom Benfatti for managing the art program; Ilene Kahn, our operations specialist; and finally, the Pearson Arts & Sciences sales team for their confidence and support of our books.

We would also like to thank Kathleen Miranda, Cindy Trimble, Jon Stockdale, and Rafiq Ladhani for their attention to details and consistency in accuracy checking the text and answer sections. We offer many thanks to all the instructors from across the country who participated in reviewer conferences and focus groups, reviewed or class-tested some aspect of the manuscript, and taught from the first edition. Their insights and ideas form the backbone of this text. Hundreds of instructors contributed their time, energy, and ideas to help us shape this text. We will attempt to thank them all here. We apologize for any omissions.

The following individuals, many of whom reviewed or class-tested the first edition, provided direction and guidance in shaping the second edition.

Marwan Abu–Sawwa, *Florida Community College—Jacksonville*

MaryAnne Anthony, *Santa Ana College*

Darla Aguilar, *Pima State University*

Grant Alexander, *Joliet Junior College*

Philip Anderson, *South Plains College*

Mary Lou Baker, *Columbia State Community College*

Bill Bales, *Rogers State*

Tony Barcellos, *American River College*

John Beachy, *Northern Illinois University*

Donna Beatty, *Ventura College*

David Bell, *Florida Community College—Jacksonville*

Sandy Berry, *Hinds Community College*

Linda Blanco, *Joliet Junior College*

Kevin Bodden, *Lewis and Clark College*

Cherie Bowers, *Santa Ana College*

Becky Bradshaw, *Lake Superior College*

Lori Braselton, *Georgia Southern University*

Tim Britt, *Jackson State Community College*

Beverly Broomell, *Suffolk Community College*

Joanne Brunner, *Joliet Junior College*

Hien Bui, *Hillsborough Community College—Dale Mabry*

Connie Buller, *Metropolitan Community College*

Annette Burden, *Youngstown State University*

James Butterbach, *Joliet Junior College*

Marc Campbell, *Daytona Beach Community College*

Elena Catoiu, *Joliet Junior College*

Nancy Chell, *Anne Arundel Community College*

John F. Close, *Salt Lake Community College*

Bobbi Cook, *Indian River Community College*

Carlos Corona, *San Antonio College*

Faye Dang, *Joliet Junior College*

Shirley Davis, *South Plains College*

Vivian Dennis-Monzingo, *Eastfield College*

Alvio Dominguez, *Miami Dade Community College—Wolfson*

Karen Driskell, *South Plains College*

Thomas Drucker, *University of Wisconsin—Whitewater*

Brenda Dugas, *McNeese State University*

Doug Dunbar, *Okaloosa-Walton Junior College*

Laura Dyer, *Southwestern Illinois State University*

Bill Echols, *Houston Community College—Northwest*

Erica Egizio, *Joliet Junior College*

Laura Egner, *Joliet Junior College*

Jason Eltrevoog, *Joliet Junior College*

Nancy Eschen, *Florida Community College—Jacksonville*

Mike Everett, *Santa Ana College*

Phil Everett, *Ohio State University*

Scott Fallstrom, *Shoreline Community College*

Betsy Farber, *Bucks County Community College*

Fitzroy Farqharson, *Valencia Community College—West*

Jacqueline Fowler, *South Plains College*

Dorothy French, *Community College of Philadelphia*

Randy Gallaher, *Lewis and Clark College*

Sanford Geraci, *Broward Community College*

Donna Gerken, *Miami Dade Community College—Kendall*

Adrienne Goldstein, *Miami Dade Community College—Kendall*

Marion Graziano, *Montgomery County Community College*

Susan Grody, *Broward Community College*

Tom Grogan, *Cincinnati State University*

Barbara Grover, *Salt Lake Community College*

Shawna Haider, *Salt Lake Community College*

Margaret Harris, *Milwaukee Area Technical College*

Teresa Hasenauer, *Indian River Community College*

Mary Henderson, *Okaloosa-Walton Junior College*

Celeste Hernandez, *Richland College*

Paul Hernandez, *Palo Alto College*

Pete Herrera, *Southwestern College*

Bob Hervey, *Hillsborough Community College—Dale Mabry*

Teresa Hodge, *Broward Community College*

Sandee House, *Georgia Perimeter College*

Becky Hubiak, *Tidewater Community College—Virginia Beach*

Sally Jackman, *Richland College*

John Jarvis, *Utah Valley State College*

Nancy Johnson, *Broward Community College*

Steven Kahn, *Anne Arundel Community College*

Linda Kass, *Bergen Community College*

Donna Katula, *Joliet Junior College*

Mohammed Kazemi, *University of North Carolina—Charlotte*

Doreen Kelly, *Mesa Community College*

Mike Kirby, *Tidewater Community College—Virginia Beach*

Keith Kuchar, *College of Dupage*

Carla Kulinsky, *Salt Lake Community College*

Julie Labbiento, *Leigh Carbon Community College*

Kathy Lavelle, *Westchester Community College*

Deanna Li, *North Seattle Community College*

Brian Macon, *Valencia Community College—West*

Lynn Marecek, *Santa Ana College*

Jim Matovina, *Community College of Southern Nevada*

Jean McArthur, *Joliet Junior College*

Michael McComas, *Marshall University*

Mikal McDowell, *Cedar Valley College*

Lee McEwen, *Ohio State University*

David McGuire, *Joliet Junior College*

Angela McNulty, *Joliet Junior College*

Debbie McQueen, *Fullerton College*

Judy Meckley, *Joliet Junior College*

Lynette Meslinsky, *Erie Community College—City Campus*

Kausha Miller, *Lexington Community College*

Chris Mizell, *Okaloosa Walton Junior College*

Jim Moore, *Madison Area Technical College*

Ronald Moore, *Florida Community College—Jacksonville*

Elizabeth Morrison, *Valencia Community College—West*

Roya Namavar, *Rogers State*

Hossein Navid-Tabrizi, *Houston Community College*

Carol Nessmith, *Georgia Southern University*

Kim Neuburger, *Portland Community College*

Larry Newberry, *Glendale Community College*

Elsie Newman, *Owens Community College*

Charlotte Newsome, *Tidewater Community College*

Charles Odion, *Houston Community College*

Viann Olson, *Rochester Community and Technical College*

Linda Padilla, *Joliet Junior College*

Carol Perry, *Marshall Community and Technical College*

Faith Peters, *Miami Dade Community College—Wolfson*

Dr. Eugenia Peterson, *Richard J. Daley College*

Jean Pierre-Victor, *Richard J. Daley College*

Philip Pina, *Florida Atlantic University*

Carol Poos, *Southwestern Illinois University*

Elise Price, *Tarrant County Community College*

R.B. Pruitt, *South Plains College*

William Radulovich, *Florida Community College—Jacksonville*

Pavlov Rameau, *Miami Dade Community College—Wolfson*

David Ray, *University of Tennessee—Martin*

Nancy Ressler, *Oakton Community College*

Michael Reynolds, *Valencia Community College—West*

George Rhys, *College of the Canyons*

Jorge Romero, *Hillsborough Community College—Dale Mabry*

David Ruffato, *Joliet Junior College*

Carol Rychly, *Augusta State University*

David Santos, *Community College of Philadelphia*

Togba Sapolucia, *Houston Community College*

Doug Smith, *Tarrant Community College*

Catherine J. W. Snyder, *Alfred State College*

Gisela Spieler-Persad, *Rio Hondo College*

Raju Sriram, *Okaloosa-Walton Junior College*

Patrick Stevens, *Joliet Junior College*

Bryan Stewart, *Tarrant Community College*

Jennifer Strehler, *Oakton Community College*

Elizabeth Suco, *Miami Dade Community College—Wolfson*

Katalin Szucs, *East Carolina University*

KD Taylor, *Utah Valley State College*

Mary Ann Teel, *University of North Texas*

Suzanne Topp, *Salt Lake Community College*

Suzanne Trabucco, *Nassau Community College*

Jo Tucker, *Tarrant Community College*

Bob Tuskey, *Joliet Junior College*

Mary Vachon, *San Joaquin Delta College*

Carol Walker, *Hinds Community College*

Kim Ward, *Eastern Connecticut State University*

Richard Watkins, *Tidewater Community College*

Natalie Weaver, *Daytona Beach Community College*

Darren Wiberg, *Utah Valley State College*

Rachel Wieland, *Bergen Community College*

Christine Wilson, *Western Virginia University*

Brad Wind, *Miami Dade Community College—North*

Roberta Yellott, *McNeese State University*

Steve Zuro, *Joliet Junior College*

Additional Acknowledgments

We also would like to extend thanks to our colleagues at Joliet Junior College, Columbus State Community College, and Southwestern College, who provided encouragement, support, and the teaching environment where the ideas and teaching philosophies in this text were developed.

Michael Sullivan, III
Katherine R. Struve
Janet Mazzarella

Elementary Algebra

1

Operations on Real Numbers and Algebraic Expressions

In the year 1202, the Italian mathematician Leonardo Fibonacci posed this problem: A certain man put a pair of rabbits in a place surrounded on all sides by a wall. How many pairs of rabbits can be produced from that pair in a year if it is supposed that every month each pair begets a new pair which from the second month on becomes productive?

The answer to Fibonacci's puzzle leads to a sequence of numbers called the *Fibonacci sequence*. See Problem 161 in Section 1.4.

The Big Picture: Putting It Together

Welcome to algebra! This course is taken by a diverse group of individuals. Some of you may never have taken an algebra course, while others may have taken algebra at some time in the past. In any case, we have written this text with both groups in mind.

The first chapter of the text serves as a review of the topics we would learn in an arithmetic course. The material is presented with an eye on the future, which is algebra. This means that we will slowly build our discussion so that the shift from arithmetic to algebra is painless. Take care to study the methods used in this section because these same methods will be used again in later chapters.

1.1 Success in Mathematics

Let's start by having a frank discussion about the "big picture" goals of the course and how this book can help you to be successful at mathematics. Our first "big picture" goal is to develop algebraic skills and gain an appreciation for the power of algebra and mathematics. But there is also a second "big picture" goal. By studying mathematics, we develop a sense of logic and exercise the part of our brains that deals with logical thinking. The examples and problems that appear throughout the text are like the crunches that we do in a gym to exercise our bodies. The goal of running or walking is to get from point A to point B, so doing fifty crunches on a mat does not accomplish that goal, but crunches do make our upper bodies, backs, and heart stronger when we need to run or walk.

Logical thinking can assist us in solving difficult everyday problems, and solving algebra problems "builds the muscles" in the part of our brain that performs logical thinking. So, when you are studying algebra, and getting frustrated with the amount of work that needs to be done, and you say, "My brain hurts," remember the phrase that we all use in the gym, "No pain, no gain."

Another phrase to keep in mind is, "Success breeds success." Mathematics is everywhere. You already are successful at doing some everyday mathematics. With practice, you can take your initial successes and become even more successful. Have you ever done any of the following everyday activities?

- Compare the price per ounce of different sizes of jars of peanut butter or jam.
- Leave a tip at a restaurant.
- Figure out how many calories your bowl of breakfast cereal provides.
- Take an opinion survey along with many other people.
- Measure the distances between cities as you plan a vacation.
- Order the appropriate number of gallons of paint to cover the walls of a room that you are renovating.
- Buy a car and take out a car loan with interest.
- Double a cookie recipe.
- Change American dollars for Canadian dollars.
- Fill up a basketball or soccer ball with air (balls are spheres, after all).
- Coach a Little League team (scores, statistics, catching, and throwing all involve math).
- Check the percentages of saturated and unsaturated fats in a chocolate bar.

We just listed twelve of the many everyday mathematical activities, and you may do five or ten in a single day! The everyday mathematics that you already know is the foundation for your success in this course.

1 What to Do the First Week of the Semester

The first week of the semester gives you the opportunity to prepare for a successful course. Here are the things that you should do:

1. **Pick a good seat.** As you enter the classroom for the first time, choose a seat that gives you a good view of the room. Sit close enough to the front so that you can easily see the board and hear the professor.

2. **Read the syllabus to learn about your instructor and the course.** Be sure to take note of your instructor's name, office location, e-mail address, telephone number, and office hours. Also, pay attention to any additional help that can be found on campus such as tutoring centers, videos in the library, software, online tutorials, and so on. Make sure that you fully understand all of the instructor's policies for the

class. This includes the policy on absences, missed exams or quizzes, and home-work. Ask questions.

3. **Learn the names of some of your classmates and exchange contact information.** One of the best ways to learn math is through group study sessions. Try to create time each week to study with your classmates. Knowing how to get in contact with classmates is also useful if you ever miss class because you can obtain the assignment for the day.

4. **Budget your time.** Most students have a tendency to "bite off more than they can chew." To help with time management, consider the following general rule for studying mathematics: You should plan on studying *at least* two hours outside of class for each hour in class. So, if you enrolled in a four-hour math class, you should set aside at least eight hours each week to study for the course. If this is not your only course, you will have to set aside time for other courses as well. Consider your work schedule and personal life when creating your time budget as well.

Work Smart: Study Skills

Plan on studying two hours outside of class for each hour in class every week. Take a few minutes to plan out the next academic term.

2 What to Do Before, During, and After Class

Now that the semester is under way, we present the following ideas for what to do before, during, and after each class meeting. While these suggestions may sound over-whelming, we guarantee that by following them, you will be successful in mathematics (and other courses). Also, you will find that studying for exams becomes much easier by following this plan.

Before Class Begins

1. Make sure you are mentally prepared for class. This means that your mind should be alert and ready to concentrate for the entire class period. (Invest in a cup of coffee and eat lots of protein for breakfast!)

2. Read the section or sections that will be covered in the upcoming class meeting.

3. Based upon your reading, prepare a list of questions. Jot them down. In many cases, your questions will be answered through the lecture. You can then ask any questions that are not answered completely.

During Class

1. Arrive early enough to prepare your mind and material for the lecture.

2. Stay alert. Do not doze off or daydream during class. It will be very difficult to understand the lecture when you "return to class."

3. Take thorough notes. It is normal not to understand certain topics the first time that you hear them in a lecture. However, this does not mean that you throw your hands up in despair. Rather, continue to take class notes.

Work Smart: Study Skills

Be sure to ask questions during class.

4. You can ask questions when appropriate. Do not be afraid to ask questions. In fact, instructors love when students ask questions, for two reasons. First, we know as teachers that if one student has a question, there are many more in class with the same question. Second, by asking questions, you are teaching the teacher what topics cause difficulty.

After Class

1. Reread (and possibly rewrite) your class notes. In our experience as students, we were amazed how often confusion that existed during class went away after studying our in-class notes later when we had more time to absorb the material.

2. Reread the section. This is an especially important step. Once you have heard the lecture, the section will make more sense and you will understand much more.

3. Do your homework. **Homework is not optional.** There is an old Chinese proverb that says,

I hear … and I forget

I see … and I remember

I do … and I understand

This proverb applies to any situation in life in which you want to succeed. Would a pianist expect to be the best if she didn't practice? The only way you are going to learn algebra is by doing algebra. Remember: Success breeds success.

4. And don't forget, when you get a problem wrong, try to figure out why you got the problem wrong. If you can't discover your error, be sure to ask for help.

5. If you have questions, visit your professor during office hours. You can also ask someone in your study group or go to the tutoring center on campus, if available.

Math Courses: No Brain Freezes Here!

Learning algebra is a building process. Learning is the art of making connections between thousands of neurons (specialized cells) in the brain. Memory is the ability to reactivate these neural networks—it is a conversation among neurons.

Math isn't a mystery. You already know some math. But you do have to practice what you know and expand your knowledge. Why? The brain contains thousands of neurons. Through repeated practice, a special coating forms that allows the signals to travel faster and reduces interference. The cells "fire" more quickly and connections are made faster and with less effort. Practice forms the pathways that allow us to retrieve concepts and facts at test time. Remember those crunches, which are a way of making your body more robust and nimble—learning does the same to your brain.

Have We Mentioned Asking Questions?

To move information from short-term memory to long-term memory, we need to think about the information, comprehend its meaning, and ask questions about it.

⎡3⎤ How to Use the Text Effectively

When we sat down to write this text, we knew based upon experience from teaching our own students that students typically do not read their mathematics text. Rather than saying to you, "Ah, but our book is different—it can be read!," we decided to accept how students study math.

Students usually go through the following steps:

1. Attend the lecture and watch the instructor do some problems on the board. Perhaps work some problems in class.

2. Go home and work on the homework assignment.

3. After each problem, check the answer in the back of the text. If right, move on, but if wrong, go back and see where the solution went wrong.

4. Maybe the mistake can be identified, but if not, go to the class notes or try to find a similar example in the text. With a little luck, a similar example can be found and the student can determine where the solution went wrong in the problem.

5. If not, mark the problem and ask about it in the next class meeting, which leads us back to step 1.

So with this model in mind, we started to develop this text so that there is more than one way to extract the information you need from it.

All of the features have been included in the text to help you succeed. The features are based on time-tested techniques we use in class. We list the features in the order they appear and briefly explain the purpose of each feature and how it can be used to help you succeed in this course:

Preparing for This Section: Warming Up

Immediately after the title of the section, each section (after Section 1.2) begins with a short "readiness quiz." The readiness quiz asks questions about material that was presented earlier in the course and is needed for the upcoming section. You should take the readiness quiz to be sure that you understand the material that the new section will be based on. Answers to the readiness quiz appear as footnotes on the page of the quiz. Check your answers. If you get a problem wrong, or don't know how to do a problem, go back to the section listed and review the material.

Objectives: A "Road Map" through the Course

To the left of the readiness quiz, we present a list of objectives to be covered in the section. If you follow the objectives, you will get a good idea of the section's "big picture" — the important concepts, techniques, and procedures.

The objectives are numbered. (See the numbered headline at the beginning of this section.) When we begin discussing a particular objective within the section, the objective number appears along with the stated objective.

Examples: Where to Look for Information

You look to examples to provide you with guidance and instruction when you need it most — when you are away from the instructor and the classroom. With this in mind, we have developed two special example formats.

Step-by-Step Examples have a three-column format where the left column describes a step, the middle column provides a brief explanation of the step, and the right column presents the algebra. With this format, the left and middle columns can be thought of as your instructor's voice during a lecture. *Step-by-Step Examples* are used to introduce key topics or important problem-solving strategies. They are meant to provide easy-to-understand, practical instructions by including the words "how to" in the examples' headline.

Annotated Examples have a two-column format in which explanations are provided to the left of the algebra. Because we read from left to right, placing the explanation on the left clearly describes what we are about to do in the order that we will do it. Again, the annotations can be thought of as your instructor's voice right before he or she writes each step of the solution on the board.

In Words: Math in Everyday Language

Have you ever been given a math definition in class and said, "What in the world does that mean?" As teachers, we have heard that from our students. So we added the "In Words" feature, which takes a definition in mathematical form and restates it in everyday language. This margin feature will help you to understand the language of mathematics better.

Work Smart

These "tricks of the trade" that appear in the margin can be used to help you solve problems. They also show alternative approaches to solving problems. Yes, there is more than one way to solve a math problem!

Work Smart: Study Skills

Working smart also means studying smart. We provide study skill tips in the margin throughout the text to help you understand the study skills required for success in this and other mathematics courses.

Exercises: A Unique Numbering Scheme

We know from our own experiences as teachers that students typically jump right to the exercises after attending a lecture. So, all of the examples and explanation of concepts that are contained within the section are glossed over, or skipped entirely. In the interest of helping you use the book most effectively to learn the math, we have structured the exercises differently from textbooks you have experienced thus far in your mathematics career. Our structure is designed to increase your confidence and ability to work any mathematical problem while decreasing your dependence on the bad habit of looking back in the book for an example that mimics the exact problem you are currently working. Consequently, the exercises in each section are broken into as many as seven parts. Each exercise set will have some, or all, of the following exercise types.

1. Quick Checks
2. Building Skills
3. Mixed Practice
4. Applying the Concepts
5. Extending the Concepts
6. Explaining the Concepts
7. The Graphing Calculator

1. **Quick Checks: Learning to Ride a Bicycle with Training Wheels** Do you remember when you were first learning to ride a bicycle? Training wheels were placed on the bicycle to assist you in learning balance. The Quick Checks can be thought of as exercises with training wheels. What are the training wheels? Well, Quick Check exercises appear right after the example or examples that illustrate the concept being taught. So, if you get stuck on a Quick Check problem, you simply need to consult the example immediately preceding the Quick Check problems. You don't have to search back through the text. The Quick Check exercises also verify your understanding of the vocabulary introduced in the section. See page 9 in Section 1.2.

2. **Building Skills: Learning to Ride a Bicycle with Assistance** Let's continue with the bicycle analogy. Once you felt ready to ride without training wheels, you likely had an adult follow closely behind you holding the bicycle for balance and helping build your confidence in your ability. The Building Skills problems serve a similar purpose. They are keyed to the objectives within the section, so the directions for the problem indicate which objective is being developed. As a result, you know exactly what part of the text to consult if you get stuck. (But you won't necessarily know exactly which example to read.) See page 17 in Section 1.2.

3. **Mixed Practice: Now You Are Ready to Ride!** You have mastered training wheels and have learned to balance with assistance. Now you are ready to go off on your own. This stage is the Mixed Practice portion of the exercises. These exercises are composed of a potpourri of problems from the section. They may also include problems that develop your ability to see the big picture of mathematics. They are not keyed to a particular objective and require you to determine the appropriate approach to solving a problem on your own. See page 27 in Section 1.3.

4. **Applying the Concepts: Where Will I Ever Use This Stuff?** The Applying the Concepts part not only presents problems that illustrate the application of mathematics in your life, but also provides some problems that test your conceptual understanding of the mathematics. See page 19 in Section 1.2.

5. **Extending the Concepts: Stretching Your Mind** Sometimes we need to be challenged. These exercises extend your skills to a new level and provide further insight into where mathematics can be used. See page 28 in Section 1.3.

6. **Explaining the Concepts: Verbalize Your Understanding** These problems require you to think about the big-picture concepts of the section and express these concepts in your own words. It is our belief that students need to improve their ability to communicate complicated ideas (both oral and written communication). These problems can serve as a basis for classroom discussion, or can be used as writing assignments. If you truly understand the material in the section, you should be able to clearly articulate the concepts. See page 28 in Section 1.3.

7. The Graphing Calculator The graphing calculator is a great tool for verifying answers, but it is also very useful in helping us to visualize results. These exercises illustrate how the graphing calculator can be incorporated into the material of the section. See page 266 in Section 4.1.

Chapter Review

The chapter review is arranged section by section. For each section, we state key concepts, key terms, and objectives. For each objective, we list the examples from the text, along with page references, that illustrate the objective. Also, for each objective, we list the problems in the review exercises that test your understanding. If you get a problem wrong, use this feature to determine where to look in the book to help you to work the problem.

Chapter Test

We have included a chapter test. Once you think that you are prepared for the exam, take the chapter test. If you do well on the chapter test, chances are you will do well on your in-class exam. Be sure to take the chapter test under the conditions that you will face in class. If you are unsure how to solve a problem in the chapter test, watch the Chapter Test Prep Video CD, which is a video of an instructor solving each problem in the chapter test.

Cumulative Review: Reinforcing Your Knowledge

As we mentioned, learning algebra is a building process. Building involves a lot of reinforcement. To do so, we provide cumulative reviews at the end of every odd-numbered chapter starting with Chapter 3. Do these cumulative reviews after each chapter test, so that you are always refreshing your memory—making those neurons do their calisthenics. This way, studying for the final exam should be fairly easy.

⌐4⌐ How to Prepare for an Exam

The following steps are time-tested suggestions to help you prepare for an exam.

Step 1: **Revisit your homework and the chapter review problems** Beginning about one week before your exam, start to redo your homework assignments. If you don't understand a topic, be sure to seek out help. You should also work the problems given in the chapter review. The problems are keyed to the objectives in the course. If you get a problem wrong, identify the objective and examples that illustrate the objective. Then review this material and try the problem in the chapter review again. If you get the problem wrong again, seek out help.

Step 2: **Test yourself** A day or two before the exam, take the chapter test under test conditions. Be sure to check your answers. If you got any problems wrong, determine why you got them wrong and remedy the situation.

Step 3: **View the Chapter Test Prep Video CD** These videos provide you with step-by-step solutions to the exact exercises found in each of the book's chapter tests. To get the most from this valuable resource, follow the worked-out solutions to any of the exercises on the chapter test that you want to study or review.

Work Smart: Study Skills

Do not "cram" for an exam by pulling an "all-nighter."

Step 4: **Follow these rules as you train** Be sure to arrive early at the location of the exam. Prepare your mind for the exam. Also, be sure that you are well rested. Don't try to pull "all-nighters." If you need to study all night long for an exam, then your time management is poor and you should rethink how you are using your time or whether you have enough time set aside for the course.

1.1 EXERCISES

PRACTICE   WATCH   DOWNLOAD   READ   REVIEW

1. Why do you want to be successful in mathematics? Are your goals positive or negative? If you stated your goal negatively ("Just get me out of this course!"), can you restate it positively?

2. Name three activities in your daily life that involve the use of math (for instance, playing cards, operating your computer, or reading a credit-card bill).

3. What is your instructor's name?

4. What are your instructor's office hours? Where is your instructor's office?

5. Does your instructor have an e-mail address? If so, what is it?

6. Does your class have a website? Do you know how to access it? What information is located on the website?

7. Are there tutors available for this course? If so, where are they located? When are they available?

8. Name two other students in your class. What is their contact information? When can you meet with them to study?

9. List some of the things that you should do before class begins.

10. List some of the things that you should do during class.

11. List some of the things that you should do after class.

12. What is the point of the Chinese proverb on page 4?

13. What is the "readiness quiz"? How should it be used?

14. Name three features that appear in the margins. What is the purpose of each of them?

15. Name the categories of exercises that appear in this book.

16. How should the chapter review material be used?

17. How should the chapter test be used? What is the Chapter Test Prep Video CD?

18. How should the cumulative review be used?

19. List the four steps that should be followed when preparing for an exam. Can you think of other methods of preparing for an exam that have worked for you?

---

20. Use the chart below to help manage your time. Be sure to fill in time allocated to various activities in your life including school, work, and leisure.

	Monday	Tuesday	Wednesday	Thursday	Friday	Saturday	Sunday
7 A.M.							
8 A.M.							
9 A.M.							
10 A.M.							
11 A.M.							
Noon							
1 P.M.							
2 P.M.							
3 P.M.							
4 P.M.							
5 P.M.							
6 P.M.							
7 P.M.							
8 P.M.							
9 P.M.							

1.2 Fractions, Decimals, and Percents

We begin this section by reviewing two concepts from arithmetic: *factoring* a number as a product of primes and finding the *least common multiple* of a list of numbers. We base our discussion in this section on *natural numbers*. **Natural numbers** are the numbers 1, 2, 3, 4, and so on.

1̄ Factor a Number as a Product of Prime Factors

When we multiply, the numbers that are multiplied together are called **factors** and the answer is called the **product.**

$$\underset{\text{factor}}{7} \cdot \underset{\text{factor}}{5} = \underset{\text{product}}{35}$$

When we write a number as a product, we say that we **factor** the number. For example, when we write 20 as the product $10 \cdot 2$, we say that we have factored 20.

Some natural numbers are *prime* numbers and others are *composite*.

> **DEFINITION**
>
> A natural number is **prime** if its only factors are one and itself. Natural numbers that are not prime are called **composite.** The number 1 is neither prime nor composite.

Examples of prime numbers are 2, 3, 5, 7, 11, and 13. We use a *factor tree* to find the prime factorization of a number. The process begins with finding two factors of the given number. Continue to factor until all factors are prime.

When a composite number is written as the product of prime numbers, we say that we are writing the **prime factorization** of the number. One technique that may be used to write the prime factorization of a number is shown below.

Work Smart

The first six primes are 2, 3, 5, 7, 11, and 13.

Work Smart

We could have begun the factorization of 24 with the factors 8 and 3 instead of 4 and 6. Try this for yourself.

> **EXAMPLE 1** **Finding the Prime Factorization**
>
> Write the prime factorization of 24.
>
> **Solution**
>
>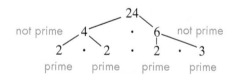
>
> All the numbers in the last row are prime, so we are done. The prime factorization of 24 is $2 \cdot 2 \cdot 2 \cdot 3$. Order is not important in multiplying factors. The product could also be written as $3 \cdot 2 \cdot 2 \cdot 2$ or $2 \cdot 3 \cdot 2 \cdot 2$. ∎

> Quick ✔
>
> **1.** In the statement $6 \cdot 8 = 48$, 6 and 8 are called _____ and 48 is called the _____.
>
> *In Problems 2–7, find the prime factorization of each of the following:*
>
> **2.** 12   **3.** 18   **4.** 75
>
> **5.** 120   **6.** 131   **7.** 459

2̄ Find the Least Common Multiple of Two or More Numbers

A **multiple** of a number is the product of that number and any natural number. For example, the multiples of 2 are

$$2 \cdot 1 = 2, 2 \cdot 2 = 4, 2 \cdot 3 = 6, 2 \cdot 4 = 8, 2 \cdot 5 = 10, 2 \cdot 6 = 12, \text{ and so on.}$$

Multiples of 3 are

$$3 \cdot 1 = 3, 3 \cdot 2 = 6, 3 \cdot 3 = 9, 3 \cdot 4 = 12, 3 \cdot 5 = 15, 3 \cdot 6 = 18, \text{ and so on.}$$

Notice that the numbers 2 and 3 share two common multiples in this list: 6 and 12. The smallest common multiple, called the *least common multiple,* of 2 and 3 is 6.

> **DEFINITION**
>
> The **least common multiple (LCM)** of two or more natural numbers is the smallest number that is a multiple of each of the numbers.

For example, suppose we wanted to find the least common multiple of 6 and 15. We could find the least common multiple by listing the multiples of each number until we find the smallest common multiple as follows:

Multiples of 6:   6, 12, 18, 24, 30, 36, 42, . . .
Multiples of 15:   15, 30, 45, 60, . . .

The least common multiple is 30 (indicated in red). This approach works just fine for numbers, but does not work for algebra. For this reason, it is recommended that you follow the steps used in Example 2 to find the least common multiple of two or more numbers so that you are better prepared when we discuss the least common multiple again later in the text.

EXAMPLE 2 How to Find the Least Common Multiple

Find the least common multiple of the numbers 6 and 15.

Step-by-Step Solution

Step 1: Write each number as the product of prime factors, aligning common factors vertically.	Arrange the common factor of 3 in its own column	$6 = 2 \cdot 3$ $15 = \quad 3 \cdot 5$
Step 2: Write down the factor(s) that the numbers share, if any. Then write down the remaining factors the greatest number of times that the factors appear in any number.		The common factor is 3. The remaining factors are 2 and 5.
Step 3: Multiply the factors listed in Step 2. The product is the least common multiple (LCM).		The LCM is $2 \cdot 3 \cdot 5 = 30$

The least common multiple of 6 and 15 is 30. We see that 30 is a multiple of 6 because $6 \cdot 5 = 30$, and 30 is a multiple of 15 because $15 \cdot 2 = 30$. ∎

EXAMPLE 3 Finding the Least Common Multiple

Find the LCM of the numbers 18 and 15.

Solution

We first write each number as the product of prime factors.

$$18 = 2 \cdot 3 \cdot 3$$
$$15 = \quad 3 \cdot \quad 5$$
$$2 \cdot 3 \cdot 3 \cdot 5$$

Write the factors in each column that the numbers share, if any. Then write down the remaining factors the greatest number of times that the factors appear in any number.

Find the product of the factors.   The LCM is $2 \cdot 3 \cdot 3 \cdot 5 = 90$. ∎

Quick ✔ *In Problems 8–12, find the LCM of the numbers.*

8. 6 and 8   **9.** 5 and 10   **10.** 45 and 72

11. 7 and 3   **12.** 12, 18, and 30

⎾3⏋ Write Equivalent Fractions

A fraction represents a part of a whole. For example, the fraction $\frac{5}{8}$ means "5 parts out of 8 parts." A fraction also indicates division: $\frac{5}{8}$ means "five divided by eight." Since $\frac{5}{8}$ indicates division, $\frac{5}{8}$ may be written as $8\overline{)5}$. Figure 1 shows the fraction $\frac{5}{8}$ visually.

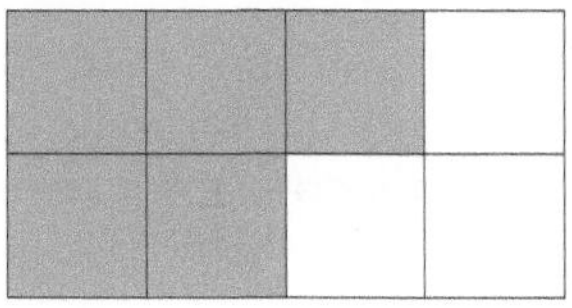

In the fraction $\frac{5}{8}$, the number 5 is called the **numerator** and the number 8 is called the **denominator.** The denominator tells the number of equal parts that the whole is divided into, and the numerator tells the number of equal parts that are shaded. For example, in Figure 1 the box is divided into 8 equal parts, 5 of which are shaded.

We use **whole numbers,** the natural numbers plus 0, for the numerator of a fraction and natural numbers for the denominator.

Fractions without common denominators can be rewritten in equivalent forms so they have the same denominator.

Figure 1

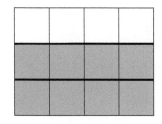

Work Smart

The denominator of a number such as 7 is 1 because $7 = \frac{7}{1}$.

> **DEFINITION**
> **Equivalent fractions** are fractions that represent the same part of a whole.

Figure 2

For example, $\frac{2}{3}$ and $\frac{8}{12}$ are equivalent fractions. To understand why, consider Figure 2. If we break the whole into 12 parts and shade 8 of these parts, the shaded region represents $\frac{8}{12}$ of the rectangle. If we only consider the 3 parts separated by the thick black lines, we can see that 2 parts are shaded for a fraction of $\frac{2}{3}$. In each case, the same portion of the rectangle is shaded, so $\frac{2}{3}$ and $\frac{8}{12}$ are equivalent fractions.

Now the question becomes, how do we obtain equivalent fractions? The answer lies in the following property.

If *a*, *b*, and *c* are whole numbers, then

$$\frac{a}{b} = \frac{a \cdot c}{b \cdot c} \qquad \text{if } b \neq 0, c \neq 0$$

Let's see how this property works.

In Words

We can obtain an equivalent fraction by multiplying the numerator and denominator of the fraction by the same nonzero number.

⎾EXAMPLE 4⏋ Writing an Equivalent Fraction

Write the fraction $\frac{3}{4}$ as an equivalent fraction with a denominator of 20.

Solution

We want to know $\frac{3}{4}$ equals "what" over 20, or $\frac{3}{4} = \frac{?}{20}$. To write the fraction $\frac{3}{4}$ with a denominator of 20, we multiply the numerator and denominator of $\frac{3}{4}$ by 5. Do you see why?

$$\frac{3}{4} = \frac{3 \cdot 5}{4 \cdot 5}$$
$$= \frac{15}{20}$$

Quick ✔

13. Fractions which represent the same portion of a whole are called _____ _____.

In Problems 14 and 15, rewrite each fraction with the denominator indicated.

14. $\frac{1}{2}$; 10   **15.** $\frac{5}{8}$; 48

It is sometimes necessary to rewrite two or more fractions so that each has the same denominator. For example, we could rewrite the fractions $\frac{5}{6}$ and $\frac{3}{8}$ so that they have a common denominator of 24, 48, 96 and so on because these are common multiples of the denominators 6 and 8. Notice that 24 is the least common multiple of 6 and 8. When talking about the least common multiple as it applies to denominators of fractions, we use the phrase *least common denominator*.

DEFINITION

The **least common denominator (LCD)** is the least common multiple of the denominators of a group of fractions.

EXAMPLE 5 **How to Write Two Fractions as Equivalent Fractions with the LCD**

Write $\frac{5}{8}$ and $\frac{9}{20}$ as equivalent fractions with the least common denominator.

Step-by-Step Solution

Step 1: Find the least common denominator of the fractions.

The denominators of $\frac{5}{8}$ and $\frac{9}{20}$ are 8 and 20.

Write each denominator as the product of prime factors: $8 = 2 \cdot 2 \cdot 2$

$$20 = 2 \cdot 2 \cdot \quad 5$$

$$\text{LCD} = 2 \cdot 2 \cdot 2 \cdot 5$$
$$= 40$$

Step 2: Rewrite each fraction with the least common denominator.

Multiply the numerator and denominator of $\frac{5}{8}$ by 5: $\dfrac{5}{8} = \dfrac{5 \cdot 5}{8 \cdot 5}$

$$= \dfrac{25}{40}$$

Multiply the numerator and denominator of $\frac{9}{20}$ by 2: $\dfrac{9}{20} = \dfrac{9 \cdot 2}{20 \cdot 2}$

$$= \dfrac{18}{40}$$

So $\dfrac{5}{8} = \dfrac{25}{40}$ and $\dfrac{9}{20} = \dfrac{18}{40}$.

Quick ✔ *In Problems 16–18, write the equivalent fractions with the least common denominator.*

16. $\frac{1}{4}$ and $\frac{5}{6}$ **17.** $\frac{5}{12}$ and $\frac{4}{15}$ **18.** $\frac{9}{20}$ and $\frac{11}{16}$

4 Write a Fraction in Lowest Terms

DEFINITION

A fraction is written in **lowest terms** if the numerator and the denominator share no common factor other than 1.

We can write fractions in lowest terms using the fact that

$$\frac{a \cdot c}{b \cdot c} = \frac{a}{b}$$

So, to write a fraction in lowest terms, we write the numerator and the denominator as a product of primes, and then divide out common factors.

EXAMPLE 6 Writing a Fraction in Lowest Terms

Write $\dfrac{24}{40}$ in lowest terms.

Solution

Write the numerator and the denominator as the product of primes and divide out common factors.

$$\frac{24}{40} = \frac{2 \cdot 2 \cdot 2 \cdot 3}{2 \cdot 2 \cdot 2 \cdot 5}$$

Divide out common factors:
$$= \frac{\cancel{2} \cdot \cancel{2} \cdot \cancel{2} \cdot 3}{\cancel{2} \cdot \cancel{2} \cdot \cancel{2} \cdot 5}$$

$$= \frac{3}{5}$$

So $\dfrac{24}{40} = \dfrac{3}{5}$.

Work Smart

Use different slash marks to keep track of factors that have divided out. Also, you may wish to use nonprime factors when writing a fraction in lowest terms. In Example 6 we could have written $\dfrac{24}{40}$ in lowest terms as follows:

$$\frac{24}{40} = \frac{8 \cdot 3}{8 \cdot 5} = \frac{3}{5}$$

Quick ✔ *In Problems 19–22, write each fraction in lowest terms.*

19. $\dfrac{45}{80}$ **20.** $\dfrac{4}{9}$ **21.** $\dfrac{20}{50}$ **22.** $\dfrac{30}{105}$

5 Round Decimals

Decimals and percentages commonly occur in everyday life. You received a 92% on your test, there is a 10% discount on jeans, we pay 7.75% in sales tax, 45% of the people polled support a proposition. Before we discuss decimals and percents, let us consider place value.

Figure 3 shows how we interpret the place value of each digit in the number 9186.347. For example, the 7 is in the "thousandths" position, 3 is in the "tenths" position, and the 8 is in the "tens" position.

Figure 3

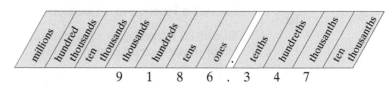

The number 9186.347 is read "nine thousand, one hundred eighty-six and three hundred forty-seven thousandths."

Quick ✔ *In Problems 23–28, tell the place value of the digit in the given number.*

23. 235.71; the 1
24. 56,701.28; the 2
25. 278,403.95; the 8
26. 0.189; the 9
27. 3.590; the 3
28. 9,021,458.5; the 2

We round decimals in the same way we round whole numbers. First, identify the specified place value in the decimal. If the digit to the right is 5 or more, add 1 to the digit; if the digit to the right is 4 or less, leave the digit as it is. Then drop the digits to the right of the specified place value.

EXAMPLE 7 Rounding a Decimal Number

Round 8.726 to the nearest hundredth.

Solution

To round to the nearest hundredth, we determine that the number 2 is in the hundredths place: 8.7<u>2</u>6. The number to the right of 2 is 6. Since 6 is greater than 5, we round 8.726 to 8.73. ∎

EXAMPLE 8 Rounding a Decimal Number

Round 0.9451 to the nearest thousandth.

Solution

To round 0.9451 to the nearest thousandth, we see that the number 5 is in the thousandths place: 0.94<u>5</u>1. The number to the right of 5 is 1. Since 1 is less than 5, we round 0.9451 to 0.945. ∎

Quick ✔ *In Problems 29–34, round each number to the given decimal place.*

29. 0.17 to the nearest tenth
30. 0.932 to the nearest hundredth
31. 1.396 to the nearest hundredth
32. 14.3983 to the nearest thousandth
33. 690.004 to the nearest hundredth
34. 59.98 to the nearest tenth

⌈6⌉ Convert a Fraction to a Decimal and a Decimal to a Fraction

Convert a Fraction to a Decimal

To convert a fraction to a decimal, divide the numerator of the fraction by the denominator of the fraction until the remainder is 0 or the remainder repeats.

EXAMPLE 9 **Converting a Fraction to a Decimal**

Convert $\dfrac{9}{20}$ to a decimal.

Solution

$$\frac{9}{20} = 20\overline{)\begin{array}{l} 0.45 \\ 9.00 \end{array}}$$
$$\begin{array}{r} 8\,0 \\ \hline 100 \\ 100 \\ \hline 0 \end{array}$$

Therefore, $\dfrac{9}{20} = 0.45$. ■

EXAMPLE 10 **Converting a Fraction to a Decimal**

Convert $\dfrac{2}{3}$ to a decimal.

Solution

$$\frac{2}{3} = 3\overline{)\begin{array}{l} 0.666 \\ 2.000 \end{array}}$$
$$\begin{array}{r} 1\,8 \\ \hline 20 \\ 18 \\ \hline 20 \\ 18 \\ \hline 2 \end{array}$$

Notice that the remainder, 2, repeats. So $\dfrac{2}{3} = 0.666\ldots$. ■

In Example 9, the decimal 0.45 is called a **terminating decimal** because the decimal stops after the 5. In Example 10, the number $0.666\ldots$ is called a **repeating decimal** because the 6 continues repeating indefinitely. The decimal $0.666\ldots$ can also be written as $0.\overline{6}$. The bar over the 6 means the 6 repeats.

Quick ✔ *In Problems 35–39, write the fraction as a decimal.*

35. $\dfrac{2}{5}$ **36.** $\dfrac{3}{7}$ **37.** $\dfrac{11}{8}$

38. $\dfrac{5}{6}$ **39.** $\dfrac{5}{9}$

Based on Examples 9 and 10 and Quick Check Problems 35–39, you should notice that **every fraction has a decimal representation that either terminates or repeats.**

Convert a Decimal to a Fraction

To convert a decimal to a fraction, identify the place value of the last digit in the decimal. Write the decimal as a fraction using the place value of the last digit as the denominator, and write in lowest terms.

EXAMPLE 11 Writing a Decimal as a Fraction

Convert each decimal to a fraction and write in lowest terms, if possible.

   (a) 0.8   **(b)** 0.77

Solution

(a) 0.8 is equivalent to 8 tenths, or $\dfrac{8}{10}$. Because $\dfrac{8}{10} = \dfrac{4 \cdot 2}{5 \cdot 2} = \dfrac{4}{5}$, we write $0.8 = \dfrac{4}{5}$.

(b) 0.77 is equivalent to 77 hundredths, or $\dfrac{77}{100}$.

Quick ✔ *In Problems 40–42, write the decimal as a fraction and write in lowest terms.*

40. 0.65   **41.** 0.2   **42.** 0.625

---

7 Convert a Percent to a Decimal and a Decimal to a Percent

When computing with percents, it is convenient to write percents as decimals. How is a percent converted to a decimal? Let's see.

Convert a Percent to a Decimal

DEFINITION

The word **percent** means **parts per hundred** or **parts out of one hundred.**

So 25% means 25 parts out of 100 parts. Therefore, $25\% = \dfrac{25}{100} = \dfrac{1 \cdot 25}{4 \cdot 25} = \dfrac{1}{4}$.

    Since the word percent means "parts per hundred," we have that 100% means "100 parts per 100," so 100% = 1. Therefore, to convert from a percent to a decimal, multiply the percent by $\dfrac{1}{100\%}$.

EXAMPLE 12 Writing a Percent as a Decimal

Write the following percents as decimals:

   (a) 17%   **(b)** 150%

Solution

Work Smart

To convert from a percent to a decimal, move the decimal point two places to the left and drop the % symbol.

(a) $17\% = 17\% \cdot \dfrac{1}{100\%}$

$\qquad = \dfrac{17}{100}$

$\qquad = 0.17$

(b) $150\% = 150\% \cdot \dfrac{1}{100\%}$

$\qquad = \dfrac{150}{100}$

$\qquad = 1.5$

Quick ✔

43. The word percent means parts per _____ , so 35% means __ parts out of 100 parts or $\overline{}{100}$.

In Problems 44–48, write the percent as a decimal.

44. 23%　　　**45.** 1%　　　**46.** 72.4%

47. 127%　　　**48.** 89.26%

Convert a Decimal to a Percent

Because 100% = 1, to convert a decimal to a percent, multiply the decimal by $\dfrac{100\%}{1}$.

EXAMPLE 13　Writing a Decimal as a Percent

Write the following decimals in percent form:

　(a) 0.445　　　　　　**(b)** 1.42

Solution

(a) $0.445 = 0.445 \cdot \dfrac{100\%}{1}$
$= 44.5\%$

(b) $1.42 = 1.42 \cdot \dfrac{100\%}{1}$
$= 142\%$

Work Smart

To convert from a decimal to a percent, move the decimal point two places to the right and add the % symbol.

Quick ✔

49. To convert a decimal to a percent, multiply the decimal by ____ .

In Problems 50–54, write the decimal as a percent.

50. 0.15　　　**51.** 0.8　　　**52.** 1.3

53. 0.398　　　**54.** 0.004

1.2 EXERCISES

 MyMathLab

| 　PRACTICE | 　WATCH | 　DOWNLOAD | 　READ | 　REVIEW |

1–54. *are the* Quick ✔s *that follow each* EXAMPLE

Building Skills

In Problems 55–72, find the prime factorization of each number. See Objective 1.

55. 25　　**56.** 9　　**57.** 28　　**58.** 100

59. 21　　**60.** 35　　**61.** 36　　**62.** 54

63. 20　　**64.** 63　　**65.** 30　　**66.** 45

67. 50　　**68.** 70　　**69.** 53　　**70.** 79

71. 252　　**72.** 315

In Problems 73–84, find the LCM of each set of numbers. See Objective 2.

73. 6 and 21　　**74.** 10 and 14　　**75.** 12 and 10

76. 21 and 18　　**77.** 15 and 14　　**78.** 55 and 6

79. 30 and 45　　**80.** 8 and 70　　**81.** 5, 6, and 12

82. 9, 15, and 20　　**83.** 3, 8, and 9　　**84.** 4, 18, and 20

In Problems 85–90, write each fraction with the given denominator. See Objective 3.

85. Write $\dfrac{2}{3}$ with denominator 12.

86. Write $\dfrac{4}{5}$ with denominator 15.

87. Write $\dfrac{3}{4}$ with denominator 24.

88. Write $\dfrac{5}{14}$ with denominator 28.

89. Write 7 with denominator 3.

90. Write 4 with denominator 10.

In Problems 91–100, write the equivalent fractions with the least common denominator. See Objective 3.

91. $\dfrac{1}{2}$ and $\dfrac{3}{8}$　**92.** $\dfrac{3}{4}$ and $\dfrac{5}{12}$　**93.** $\dfrac{3}{5}$ and $\dfrac{2}{3}$　**94.** $\dfrac{1}{4}$ and $\dfrac{2}{9}$

95. $\frac{5}{6}$ and $\frac{5}{8}$

96. $\frac{1}{12}$ and $\frac{5}{18}$

97. $\frac{11}{15}$ and $\frac{7}{20}$

98. $\frac{5}{12}$ and $\frac{7}{15}$

99. $\frac{2}{9}$ and $\frac{7}{18}$ and $\frac{7}{30}$

100. $\frac{7}{10}$ and $\frac{1}{4}$ and $\frac{5}{6}$

In Problems 101–108, write each fraction in lowest terms. See Objective 4.

101. $\frac{14}{21}$

102. $\frac{9}{15}$

103. $\frac{38}{18}$

104. $\frac{81}{36}$

105. $\frac{22}{44}$

106. $\frac{24}{27}$

107. $\frac{32}{40}$

108. $\frac{49}{63}$

In Problems 109–114, tell the place value of the digit in the given number. See Objective 5.

109. 3465.902; the 0

110. 549,813.0267; the 8

111. 357.469; the 5

112. 9124.786; the 7

113. 2018.3764; the 6

114. 539.016; the 9

In Problems 115–122, round each number to the given place. See Objective 5.

115. 578.206 to the nearest tenth

116. 7298.0845 to the nearest hundred

117. 354.678 to the nearest ten

118. 543.06 to the nearest one (unit)

119. 3682.0098 to the nearest thousandth

120. 683.098 to the nearest hundredth

121. 29.96 to the nearest one (unit)

122. 37.439 to the nearest tenth

In Problems 123–132, write each fraction as a terminating or repeating decimal. See Objective 6.

123. $\frac{5}{8}$

124. $\frac{3}{4}$

125. $\frac{2}{7}$

126. $\frac{2}{9}$

127. $\frac{5}{16}$

128. $\frac{11}{32}$

129. $\frac{3}{13}$

130. $\frac{6}{13}$

131. $\frac{29}{25}$

132. $\frac{57}{50}$

In Problems 133–138, write each fraction as a decimal, rounded to the indicated place. See Objective 6.

133. $\frac{13}{6}$ to the nearest tenth

134. $\frac{15}{8}$ to the nearest tenth

135. $\frac{8}{3}$ to the nearest hundredth

136. $\frac{9}{7}$ to the nearest hundredth

137. $\frac{14}{27}$ to the nearest thousandth

138. $\frac{18}{31}$ to the nearest thousandth

In Problems 139–146, write each decimal as a fraction in lowest terms. See Objective 6.

139. 0.75

140. 0.25

141. 0.9

142. 0.4

143. 0.982

144. 0.358

145. 0.2525

146. 0.3334

In Problems 147–152, write each percent as a decimal. See Objective 7.

147. 37%

148. 59%

149. 6.02%

150. 8.25%

151. 0.1%

152. 0.5%

In Problems 153–158, write each decimal as a percent. See Objective 7.

153. 0.2

154. 0.5

155. 0.275

156. 0.349

157. 2

158. 1

Applying the Concepts

159. Planets in Our Solar System At a certain point, Mercury, Venus, and Earth lie on a straight line. If it takes each planet 3, 7, and 12 months, respectively, to revolve around the sun, what is the fewest number of months until they align this way again?

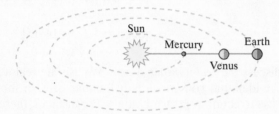

160. Talladega Raceway At Talladega one of the crew chiefs discovered that in a given time interval, Jeff Gordon completed 21 laps, Dale Earnhardt Jr. completed 18 laps, and Robby Gordon completed 15 laps. Suppose all three drivers begin at the same time. How many laps would need to be completed so that all three drivers were at the finish line at exactly the same time?

161. Sam's Medication Bob gives his dog Sam one type of medication every 4 days, and a second type of medication every 10 days. How often does Bob give Sam both types of medication on the same day?

162. Visiting Columbus Pamela and Geoff both visit Columbus on business. Pamela flies to Columbus from Atlanta every 14 days, and Geoff takes the train to Columbus from Cincinnati every 20 days. How often are both Pamela and Geoff in Columbus on business?

163. Survey Data In a survey of 500 students, 325 stated that they work at least 25 hours per week. Express the fraction of students that work at least 25 hours per week as a fraction in lowest terms.

164. Survey Data In a survey of 750 students, 450 stated that they are enrolled in 15 or more semester hours. Express the fraction of students who are enrolled in 15 or more semester hours as a fraction in lowest terms.

In Problems 165–172, express answers to the nearest hundredth of a percent, if necessary.

165. Eating Healthy? In a poll conducted by Zogby International of 1200 adult Americans, 840 stated that they believe that they eat healthy foods. What percentage of adult Americans believe that they eat healthy foods?

166. Ghosts In a survey of 1100 adult women conducted by Harris Interactive, it was determined that 640 believe in ghosts. What percentage of adult women believe in ghosts?

167. Test Score A student earns 85 points out of a total of 110 points on an exam. Express this score as a percent.

168. Test Score A student earns 80 points out of a total of 115 points on an exam. Express this score as a percent.

169. Time Utilization In a 24-hour day, Jackson sleeps for 8 hours, works for 4 hours, and goes to school and studies for 6 hours.

  (a) What percent of the time does Jackson sleep?
  (b) What percent of the time does Jackson work?
  (c) What percent of the time does Jackson go to school and study?

170. Tree Inventory An arborist counted the number of ash trees in Whetstone Park. He found that there were 48 white ash trees, 51 green ash trees, and 2 blue ash trees.

  (a) What percent of the ash trees in Whetstone Park were white ashes?
  (b) What percent of the ash trees in Whetstone Park were green ashes?
  (c) What percent of the ash trees in Whetstone Park were blue ashes?

171. Cashews A single serving of cashews contains 14 grams of fat. Of this, 3 grams is saturated fat. What percentage of fat grams is saturated fat in a single serving of cashews?

172. Cheese Pizza A single serving of cheese pizza contains 11 grams of fat. Of this, 5 grams are saturated fat. What percentage of fat grams is saturated fat in a single serving of cheese pizza?

Extending the Concepts

173. The Sieve of Eratosthenes Eratosthenes (276 B.C.–194 B.C.) was born in Cyrene, which is now in Libya in North Africa. He devised an algorithm (a series of steps that are followed to solve a problem) for identifying prime numbers. The algorithm works as follows:

Step 1: List all the natural numbers that are greater than or equal to 2.
Step 2: The first number in the list, 2, is prime. Cross out all multiples of 2. For example, cross out 2, 4, 6, ...
Step 3: Identify the next number in the list after the most recently identified prime number. For example, we already know 2 is a prime number, so the next number in the list, 3, is also prime. Cross out all multiples of this number.
Step 4: Repeat Step 3.

Use the algorithm to find all the prime numbers less than 100.

1.3 The Number Systems and the Real Number Line

OBJECTIVES

1. Classify Numbers
2. Plot Points on a Real Number Line
3. Use Inequalities to Order Real Numbers
4. Compute the Absolute Value of a Real Number

Work Smart

The use of the word "real" to describe numbers leads us to question "Are there 'nonreal' numbers?" The answer is "yes." We use the word "imaginary" to describe nonreal numbers. Imaginary does not mean that these numbers are made up, however. Imaginary numbers have many interesting applications in areas such as biology and the development of high-definition antennas. We will discuss imaginary numbers in Section 9.5. For most of the text, we concentrate on real numbers.

Preparing for the Number Systems and the Real Number Line
Before getting started, take the following readiness quiz. If you get a problem wrong, go to the section cited and review the material.

P1. Write $\dfrac{5}{8}$ as a decimal. [Section 1.2, pp. 14–15]

P2. Write $\dfrac{9}{11}$ as a decimal. [Section 1.2, pp. 14–15]

The goal of this section is to discuss the *real number system.* We use the real numbers every day in our lives, so it is an idea that you are already familiar with. In short, real numbers are numbers that we use to count or measure things: For instance, there might be 25 students in your class. Your car might get 18.4 miles per gallon. You might have a $130 debt.

As we proceed through the course, we will be dealing with various types of numbers. The kinds of numbers that we deal with are organized in *sets.* A **set** is a well-defined collection of objects. For example, we can identify the students enrolled in Elementary Algebra at your college as a set. The collection of numbers $0, 1, 2, 3, 4, 5, 6, 7, 8,$ and 9 may also be identified as a set. If we let A represent this set of numbers, then we can write

$$A = \{0, 1, 2, 3, 4, 5, 6, 7, 8, 9\}$$

In this notation, braces $\{\ \}$ are used to enclose the objects, or **elements,** in the set. When a set has no elements in it, we say that the set is an **empty set.** Empty sets are denoted by the symbol $\varnothing$ or $\{\ \}$.

EXAMPLE 1 Writing a Set

Write the set that represents the vowels.

Solution

The vowels are $a, e, i, o,$ and $u.$ If we let V represent this set, then

$$V = \{a, e, i, o, u\}$$ ∎

Quick ✔

1. Write the set that represents the first 4 positive, odd numbers.
2. Write the set that represents the states in the United States with names that begin with the letter A.
3. Write the set that represents the states in the United States with names that begin with the letter Z.

1 Classify Numbers

We will develop the real number system by looking at the history of numbers. The first types of numbers that humans worked with are called the *natural numbers* or *counting numbers.* We introduced natural numbers in Section 1.2. We now present a formal definition using a set.

DEFINITION

The **natural numbers,** or **counting numbers,** are the numbers in the set $\{1, 2, 3, \dots\}$. The three dots, called an *ellipsis*, indicate that the pattern continues indefinitely.

Figure 4
The natural numbers.

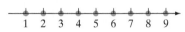

As their name implies, the counting numbers are often used to count things. For example, we can count the number of cars that arrive at a Wendy's drive-thru between 12 noon and 1:00 P.M. We can represent the counting numbers graphically using a number line. See Figure 4. The arrow on the right is used to indicate the direction in which the numbers increase.

Since we do not count the number of cars waiting in the drive-thru by saying, "zero, one, two, three . . . ," zero is not a natural, or counting, number. When we add the number 0 to the set of counting numbers, we get the set of *whole numbers*.

DEFINITION

The **whole numbers** are the numbers in the set $\{0, 1, 2, 3, \dots\}$.

Figure 5
The whole numbers.

Figure 5 represents the whole numbers on the number line. Notice that the set of natural numbers, $\{1, 2, 3, \dots\}$ is included in the set of whole numbers.

By expanding the numbers to the left of zero on the number line, we have the set called *integers*.

DEFINITION

The **integers** are the numbers in the set $\{\dots, -3, -2, -1, 0, 1, 2, 3, \dots\}$.

Figure 6
The integers.

Figure 6 represents the integers on the number line. Notice that the whole numbers and natural numbers are included in the set of integers.

Integers are useful in many situations. For example, we could not discuss temperatures above 0°F (positive counting numbers) and temperatures below 0°F (negative counting numbers) without integers. A debt of 300 dollars can be represented as an integer by -300 dollars.

How can you represent a part of a whole? For example, how do you represent a part of last night's leftover pizza or part of a dollar? To address this problem, we enlarge our number system to include *rational numbers*.

DEFINITION

A **rational number** is a number that can be expressed as a fraction where the numerator is any integer and the denominator is any nonzero integer. That is, a rational number is a number that can be written in the form $\dfrac{p}{q}$, where p and q are integers. However, q cannot equal zero.

Work Smart

Remember, all integers are also rational numbers. For example $42 = \dfrac{42}{1}$.

Examples of rational numbers are $\dfrac{2}{5}, \dfrac{5}{2}, \dfrac{0}{8}, -\dfrac{7}{9}$, and $\dfrac{31}{4}$. Because $\dfrac{p}{1} = p$ for any integer p, it follows that all integers are also rational numbers. For example, 7 is an integer, but it is also a rational number because it can be written as $\dfrac{7}{1}$. We illustrate this idea below.

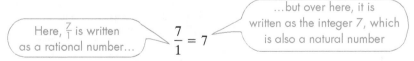

Here, $\frac{7}{1}$ is written as a rational number... $\quad \dfrac{7}{1} = 7 \quad$ ...but over here, it is written as the integer 7, which is also a natural number

In addition to representing rational numbers as fractions, we can also represent rational numbers in decimal form as either repeating decimals or terminating decimals. Table 1 shows various rational numbers in fraction form and decimal form.

Table 1		
Fraction Form of Rational Number	Decimal Form of Rational Number	Terminating or Repeating Decimal
$\dfrac{7}{2}$	3.5	Terminating
$\dfrac{5}{11}$	$0.454545\ldots = 0.\overline{45}$	Repeating
$-\dfrac{3}{8}$	-0.375	Terminating
$-\dfrac{23}{21}$	$-1.095238095238\ldots = -1.\overline{095238}$	Repeating

The repeating decimal $0.\overline{3}$ and the terminating decimal 0.27 are rational numbers because they represent fractions (see Section 1.2). The repeating decimal $0.\overline{3}$ is equivalent to the fraction $\dfrac{1}{3}$. The terminating decimal 0.27 is equivalent to the fraction $\dfrac{27}{100}$.

Some decimals neither terminate nor repeat, which means they cannot be written as the quotient of two integers. These types of numbers are called *irrational numbers*.

> **DEFINITION**
>
> An **irrational number** is a number that has a decimal representation that neither terminates nor repeats. Therefore, irrational numbers cannot be written as the quotient (ratio) of two integers.

In Words

Numbers that cannot be written as the ratio of two integers are irrational.

An example of an irrational number is the symbol π, whose value is approximately 3.141593. Another example of an irrational number is the symbol $\sqrt{2}$, whose value is approximately 1.41421.

Now that we have defined the set of rational numbers and the set of irrational numbers, we are ready for a formal definition of the set of *real numbers*.

> **DEFINITION**
>
> The set of rational numbers combined with the set of irrational numbers is called the set of **real numbers.**

Figure 7 shows the relationships among the various types of numbers. Notice the oval that represents the whole numbers surrounds the oval that represents the natural numbers. This means the whole numbers include all the natural numbers.

Figure 7

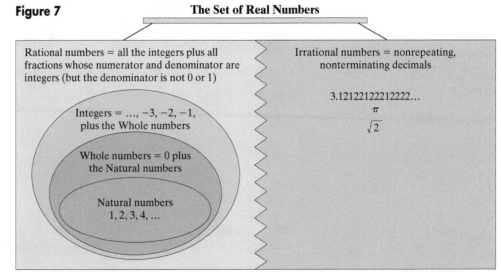

The Set of Real Numbers is composed of the set of rational numbers and the set of irrational numbers

Summary of the Set of Real Numbers		
Classification	Elements of the Set	Description
Natural numbers (also called counting numbers)	$\{1, 2, 3, \dots\}$	
Whole numbers	$\{0, 1, 2, 3, \dots\}$	Natural numbers and 0
Integers	$\{\dots, -3, -2, -1, 0, 1, 2, 3, \dots\}$	Positive and negative natural numbers and 0
Rational numbers	A number that can be written in the form $\frac{p}{q}$ where p and q are integers. However, q cannot equal zero. Examples: $3, -11, -\frac{4}{5}, 7.\overline{16}, 4.125$	Any number that can be written as the quotient of two integers with the denominator not equal to 0 Terminating decimals or nonterminating, repeating decimals
Irrational numbers	Numbers that **cannot** be written as the quotient of two integers with a nonzero denominator. Examples: $1.1121231234\dots, 3.14159\dots, 1.8975314253648607\dots$	Nonrepeating, nonterminating decimals
Real numbers	Set of rational numbers combined with the set of irrational numbers.	Rational numbers (any number that can be written as the quotient of two integers with the denominator not equal to 0; terminating decimals or nonterminating, repeating decimals) and irrational numbers (nonrepeating, nonterminating decimals.)

⌐**EXAMPLE 2** **Classifying Numbers in a Set**

List the numbers in the set

$$\left\{ 9, -\frac{2}{7}, -4, 0, -4.010010001\dots, 3.\overline{632}, 18.3737\dots \right\}$$

that are

(a) Natural numbers   (b) Whole numbers

(c) Integers   (d) Rational numbers

(e) Irrational numbers   (f) Real numbers

Solution

(a) 9 is the only natural number

(b) 0 and 9 are the whole numbers

(c) 9, −4, and 0 are the integers

(d) $9, -\frac{2}{7}, -4, 0, 3.\overline{632}$, and $18.3737\dots$ are the rational numbers.

(e) $-4.010010001\dots$ is the only irrational number because the decimal does not repeat, nor does it terminate.

(f) All the numbers listed are real numbers. Real numbers consist of rational numbers together with irrational numbers.

Quick ✔

4. *True or False:* Every integer is a rational number.

5. Real numbers that can be represented with a terminating decimal are called _____ numbers.

In Problems 6–11, list the numbers in the set $\left\{ \dfrac{11}{5}, -5, 12, 2.\overline{76}, 0, \pi, \dfrac{18}{4} \right\}$ that are

6. Natural numbers

7. Whole numbers

8. Integers

9. Rational numbers

10. Irrational numbers

11. Real numbers

2 Plot Points on a Real Number Line

Look back at Figure 6. Notice that there are gaps between the integers plotted on the number line. These gaps are filled in with the real numbers that are not integers.

To construct a **real number line,** pick a point on a line somewhere in the center, and label it O. This point, called the **origin,** corresponds to the real number 0. See Figure 8.

Figure 8
The real number line.

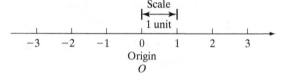

The point 1 unit to the right of O corresponds to the real number 1. The distance between 0 and 1 determines the **scale** of the number line. For example, the point associated with the number 2 is twice as far from O as 1 is. Notice that an arrowhead on the right end of the line indicates the direction in which the numbers increase. Points to the left of the origin correspond to the real numbers $-1, -2$, and so on.

DEFINITION

The real number associated with a point P is called the **coordinate** of P.

EXAMPLE 3 Plotting Points on a Real Number Line

On a real number line, label the points with coordinates $0, 6, -2, 2.5, -\dfrac{1}{2}$.

Solution

We draw a real number line and then plot the points. See Figure 9. Notice that 2.5 is midway between 2 and 3. Also notice that $-\dfrac{1}{2}$ is midway between -1 and 0.

Figure 9

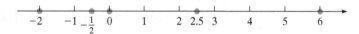

Quick ✔

12. On a real number line, label the points with coordinates $0, 3, -2, \dfrac{1}{2}$, and 3.5.

The real number line consists of three classes (or categories) of real numbers, as shown in Figure 10.

Figure 10

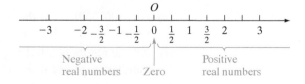

- The **negative real numbers** are the coordinates of points to the left of the origin, O.
- The real number **zero** is the coordinate of the origin denoted O.
- The **positive real numbers** are the coordinates of points to the right of the origin, O.

The **sign** of a number refers to whether the number is a positive real number or a negative real number. For example, the sign of -4 is negative while the sign of 100 is positive.

Figure 11

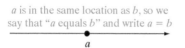

a is to the left of b, so we say that "a is less than b" and write $a < b$

a is in the same location as b, so we say that "a equals b" and write $a = b$

a is to the right of b, so we say that "a is greater than b" and write $a > b$

⌐3⌐ Use Inequalities to Order Real Numbers

An important property of a real number line follows from the fact that given two numbers (points) a and b, either a is to the left of b, denoted $a < b$, a is the same as b, denoted $a = b$, or a is to the right of b, denoted $a > b$. See Figure 11.

If a is either less than or equal to b, we write $a \le b$. Similarly, $a \ge b$ means that a is either greater than or equal to b. Collectively, the symbols $<$, $>$, $\le$, and $\ge$ are called **inequality symbols.** The "arrowhead" in an inequality always points to the smaller number. For $3 < 5$, the "arrowhead" points to the 3.

Note that $a < b$ and $b > a$ mean the same thing. For example, it does not matter whether we write $2 < 3$ (2 is to the left of 3) or $3 > 2$ (3 is to the right of 2).

⌐EXAMPLE 4⌐ Using Inequality Symbols

(a) We know that having \$3 is less than having \$7 or having 3 apples is fewer than having 7 apples. Using the real number line, we say $3 < 7$ because the coordinate 3 lies to the left of the coordinate 7 on a real number line.

(b) Being \$2 in debt is not as bad as being \$5 in debt, so $-2 > -5$. Using the real number line, $-2 > -5$ because the coordinate -2 lies to the right of the coordinate -5 on a real number line.

(c) $2.7 > \dfrac{5}{2}$ because $\dfrac{5}{2} = 2.5$ and $2.7 > 2.5$.

(d) $\dfrac{5}{6} > \dfrac{4}{5}$ because $\dfrac{5}{6} = \dfrac{25}{30}$ and $\dfrac{4}{5} = \dfrac{24}{30}$. Having 25 parts out of 30 is more than having 24 parts out of 30. We could also write $\dfrac{5}{6} = 0.8\overline{3}$ and $\dfrac{4}{5} = 0.8$.

Since $0.8\overline{3}$ is greater than 0.80, $\dfrac{5}{6} > \dfrac{4}{5}$. ∎

Work Smart

Write fractions with a common denominator or change fractions to decimals to compare the location of the numbers on the number line.

Quick ✔

13. The symbols $<$, $>$, $\le$, $\ge$ are called _____ symbols.

In Problems 14–19, replace the question mark by $<$, $>$, or $=$, whichever is correct.

14. $2 \, ? \, 9$

15. $-5 \, ? \, -3$

16. $\dfrac{4}{5} \, ? \, \dfrac{1}{2}$

17. $\dfrac{4}{7} \, ? \, 0.5$

18. $\dfrac{4}{3} \, ? \, \dfrac{20}{15}$

19. $-\dfrac{4}{3} \, ? \, -\dfrac{5}{4}$

If you look carefully at the results of Example 4, you should notice that the direction of the inequality symbol always points to the smaller number.

Based upon the discussion so far, we conclude that

$$a > 0 \quad \text{is equivalent to} \quad a \text{ is positive}$$
$$a < 0 \quad \text{is equivalent to} \quad a \text{ is negative}$$

We sometimes read $a > 0$ by saying that "a is positive." If $a \ge 0$, then either $a > 0$ or $a = 0$, and we may read this as "a is nonnegative" or "a is greater than or equal to zero."

⌈4⌉ Compute the Absolute Value of a Real Number

The real number line can be used to describe the concept of *absolute value*.

> **DEFINITION**
>
> The **absolute value** of a number a, written $|a|$, is the distance from 0 to a on a real number line.

For example, because the distance from 0 to 3 on a real number line is 3, the absolute value of 3, $|3|$, is 3. Because the distance from 0 to -3 on a real number line is 3, the absolute value of -3, $|-3|$, is 3. See Figure 12.

Figure 12

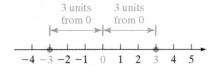

EXAMPLE 5 Computing Absolute Value

Evaluate each of the following:

(a) $|-7|$ (b) $|-1.5|$ (c) $|6|$ (d) $|0|$

Solution

(a) $|-7| = 7$ because the distance from 0 to -7 on a real number line is 7.

(b) $|-1.5| = 1.5$ because the distance from 0 to -1.5 on a real number line is 1.5.

(c) $|6| = 6$ because the distance from 0 to 6 on a real number line is 6.

(d) $|0| = 0$ because the distance from 0 to 0 on a real number line is 0. ∎

Quick ✔

20. The distance from zero to a point on a real number line whose coordinate is a is called the _____ ____ of a.

In Problems 21 and 22, evaluate each expression.

21. $|-15|$ **22.** $\left|\dfrac{3}{4}\right|$

1.3 EXERCISES

PRACTICE   WATCH   DOWNLOAD   READ   REVIEW

1–22. are the Quick ✔s that follow each EXAMPLE

Building Skills

In Problems 23–28, write each set. See Objective 1.

23. A is the set of *whole* numbers less than 5.

24. B is the set of *natural* numbers less than 25.

25. D is the set of *natural* numbers less than 5.

26. C is the set of *integers* between -6 and 4, not including -6 or 4.

27. E is the set of even *natural* numbers between 4 and 15, not including 4 or 15.

28. F is the set of odd *natural* numbers less than 1.

In Problems 29–34, list the elements in the set
$$\left\{-4, 3, -\frac{13}{2}, 0, 2.303003000\ldots\right\}$$
that are described. See Objective 1.

29. natural numbers   **30.** whole numbers

🌀 **31.** integers   **32.** rational numbers

33. irrational numbers   **34.** real numbers

In Problems 35–40, list the elements in the set $\left\{-4.2, 3.\overline{5}, \pi, \dfrac{5}{5}\right\}$ *that are described. See Objective 1.*

35. real numbers   **36.** rational numbers

37. irrational numbers   **38.** integers

39. whole numbers   **40.** natural numbers

In Problems 41 and 42, plot the points in each set on a real number line. See Objective 2.

41. $\left\{0, \dfrac{3}{3}, -1.5, -2, \dfrac{4}{3}\right\}$

42. $\left\{\dfrac{3}{4}, \dfrac{0}{2}, -\dfrac{5}{4}, -0.5, 1.5\right\}$

In Problems 43–50, determine whether the statement is True or False. See Objective 3.

43. $-2 > -3$

44. $0 < -5$

45. $-6 \leq -6$

46. $-3 \geq -5$

47. $\dfrac{3}{2} = 1.5$

48. $4.7 = 4.\overline{7}$

49. $\pi = 3.14$

50. $\dfrac{1}{3} = 0.33$

In Problems 51–58, replace the ? with the correct symbol: $>, <, =$. See Objective 3.

51. $-1\ ?\ 0$

52. $-8\ ?\ -8.5$

53. $\dfrac{5}{8}\ ?\ \dfrac{6}{11}$

54. $\dfrac{5}{12}\ ?\ \dfrac{2}{3}$

55. $\dfrac{6}{13}\ ?\ 0.46$

56. $\dfrac{5}{11}\ ?\ 0.\overline{45}$

57. $\dfrac{42}{6}\ ?\ 7$

58. $\dfrac{3}{4}\ ?\ \dfrac{3}{5}$

In Problems 59–66, evaluate each expression. See Objective 4.

59. $|-12|$

60. $|-8|$

61. $|4|$

62. $|7|$

63. $\left|-\dfrac{3}{8}\right|$

64. $\left|-\dfrac{13}{9}\right|$

65. $|-2.1|$

66. $|-3.2|$

Mixed Practice

In Problems 67 and 68, (a) plot the points on a real number line, (b) write the numbers in ascending order, and (c) list the numbers that are (i) integers, (ii) rational numbers.

67. $\left\{\dfrac{3}{5}, -1, -\dfrac{1}{2}, 1, 3.5, |-7|, -4.5\right\}$

68. $\left\{8, -2, |-4|, -1.5, -\dfrac{4}{3}, 0, -\dfrac{15}{3}\right\}$

Applying the Concepts

In Problems 69–76, place a ✓ in the box if the given number belongs to the set.

		Natural	Whole	Integers	Rational	Irrational	Real
69.	-100						
70.	0						
71.	-10.5						
72.	π						
73.	$\dfrac{75}{25}$						
74.	4						
75.	$7.56556555\ldots$						
76.	$6.\overline{45}$						

In Problems 77–86, determine whether the statement is True or False.

77. Every *whole* number is also an *integer*.

78. Every decimal number is a *rational* number.

79. There are numbers which are both *rational* and *irrational*.

80. 0 is a positive number.

81. Every *natural* number is also a *whole* number.

82. Every *integer* is also a *real* number.

83. Every terminating decimal is a *rational* number.

84. Some numbers in the form $\frac{p}{q}$, $q \neq 0$ are *integers*.

85. 0 is a nonnegative *integer*.

86. -1 is a nonpositive *integer*.

In Problems 87–92, give the name of the set or elements of the set that matches the following description:

87. nonterminating and nonrepeating decimals

88. nonnegative integers

89. the set of rational numbers combined with the set of irrational numbers

90. terminating or repeating decimals

91. numbers which are both nonnegative and nonpositive

92. numbers which are both negative and positive

Extending the Concepts

If every element of set A is also an element of set B, we say A is a **subset** *of B and we write $A \subseteq B$. In Problems 93–96, use this definition and the following sets to answer True or False to each statement.*

$$X = \{a, b, c, d, e\} \quad Y = \{c, e\} \quad Z = \{c, e, f\}$$

93. $Y \subseteq X$

94. $Z \subseteq Y$

95. $Y \subseteq Z$

96. $Z \subseteq X$

The **intersection** *of two sets is the set that contains the elements common to both A and B and is written $A \cap B$. The* **union** *of two sets is the set of all elements that are in either A or B and is written $A \cup B$. In Problems 97–102, write the elements of each set, using sets A, B, and C below.*

$$A = \{7, 8, 9, 10, 11, 12\} \quad B = \{10, 11, 12, 13, 14, 15\}$$
$$C = \{11, 12, 13, 14, 15\}$$

97. $A \cup B$

98. $A \cap B$

99. $B \cup C$

100. $B \cap C$

101. $A \cap C$

102. $A \cup C$

103. If $A = \{$even integers$\}$ and $B = \{$whole numbers less than 11$\}$, find $A \cap B$.

104. If $X = \{48, 49, 50, \ldots\}$ and $Y = \{60, 62, 64, \ldots, 80\}$, find $X \cap Y$.

105. When writing subsets, it is important to be orderly when creating the list. Think of a pattern and then answer the following:

   (a) List all possible subsets of set Z where $Z = \{1, 2, 3, 4\}$. *Hint:* The empty set is a subset of every set.

   (b) How many subsets did you find?

106. Use the set $M = \{a, b, c\}$ to answer the following:

   (a) List all possible subsets of M. *Hint:* The empty set is a subset of every set.

   (b) How many subsets did you find?

   (c) Determine a rule for finding the number of subsets of a set that has n elements.

Explaining the Concepts

107. Write a definition of "rational number" in your own words. Describe the characteristics to look for when deciding whether a number is in this set.

108. Write a definition of "irrational number" in your own words. Describe the characteristics to look for when deciding whether a number is in this set.

1.4 Adding, Subtracting, Multiplying, and Dividing Integers

OBJECTIVES

1. Add Integers
2. Determine the Additive Inverse of a Number
3. Subtract Integers
4. Multiply Integers
5. Divide Integers

Preparing for Adding, Subtracting, Multiplying, and Dividing Integers
Before getting started, take the following readiness quiz. If you get a problem wrong, go back to the section cited and review the material.

P1. Write $\frac{16}{36}$ as a fraction in lowest terms.   [Section 1.2, p. 13]

In this section, we perform addition, subtraction, multiplication, and division, called **operations,** on integers. The symbols used in algebra for addition, subtraction, multiplication, and division are $+$, $-$, $\cdot$, and $/$, respectively. The words used to describe the results of these four operations are **sum, difference, product,** and **quotient.** Table 2 summarizes these ideas.

Preparing for...Answer **P1.** $\frac{4}{9}$

Table 2		
Operation	Symbols	Words
Addition	$a + b$	Sum: a plus b
Subtraction	$a - b$	Difference: a minus b
Multiplication	$a \cdot b$, $(a) \cdot b$, $a \cdot (b)$, $(a) \cdot (b)$, ab, $(a)b$, $a(b)$, $(a)(b)$	Product: a times b
Division	a/b or $\dfrac{a}{b}$	Quotient: a divided by b

In algebra, we avoid using the multiplication sign $\times$ used in arithmetic. Instead, when two expressions are placed next to each other without an operation symbol, as in ab, or in parentheses, as in $(a)(b)$, we know that the expressions are to be multiplied.

A **mixed number** is a whole number followed by a fraction. We do not use mixed numbers in algebra. When mixed numbers are used, addition is understood. For example, $3\dfrac{2}{5}$ means $3 + \dfrac{2}{5}$.

When you see a mixed number, rewrite it as a fraction. Do you remember how to do this? To write $3\dfrac{2}{5}$ as a fraction, we multiply the whole number 3 by the denominator 5 and obtain 15. Then add this result to the numerator 2 and obtain 17. This result is the numerator of the fraction. The denominator remains 5. So

$$3\frac{2}{5} = \frac{17}{5}$$

In algebra, using mixed numbers becomes confusing because we interpret the lack of an operation symbol between two terms to mean multiplication. To avoid confusion, write $3\dfrac{2}{5}$ as 3.4 or as $\dfrac{17}{5}$.

⌐1⌐ Add Integers

Adding Integers with the Same Sign Using a Number Line

We will use a real number line to discover a pattern for adding integers. When we add a positive integer, we move to the right on the number line, and when we add a negative integer, we move to the left on the number line.

Remember, the *sign* of a number refers to whether the number is positive or negative. For example, the sign of 4 is positive, while the sign of -12 is negative. We will first consider adding integers with the same sign.

⌐EXAMPLE 1⌐ Adding Two Positive Integers Using a Number Line

Find the sum: $5 + 3$

Solution

We begin at 5 on the number line and move 3 spaces to the right, so $5 + 3 = 8$. See Figure 13.

Figure 13

EXAMPLE 2 Adding Two Negative Integers Using a Number Line

Find the sum: $-7 + (-4)$

Solution

We begin at -7 on the number line and move 4 spaces to the left, so $-7 + (-4) = -11$.
See Figure 14.

Figure 14

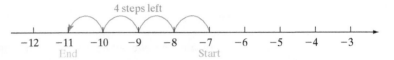

Quick ✔
1. The answer to an addition problem is called the _____.
In Problems 2–6, use a number line to find each sum.
2. $8 + 19$ 3. $-3 + (-5)$ 4. $8 + 6$
5. $-3 + (-4)$ 6. $-5 + (-12)$

Adding Integers with Different Signs Using a Number Line

We now consider the sum of two integers with different signs.

EXAMPLE 3 Adding Integers with Different Signs Using a Number Line

Find the sum: $-5 + 3$

Solution

We begin at -5 and then move 3 units to the right. From Figure 15 we see that
$-5 + 3 = -2$.

Figure 15

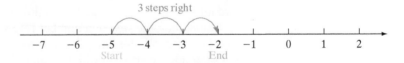

EXAMPLE 4 Adding Integers with Different Signs Using a Number Line

Find the sum: $7 + (-4)$

Solution

We begin at 7 and move 4 spaces to the left. We see that $7 + (-4) = 3$. See Figure 16.

Figure 16

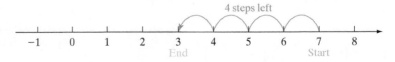

Quick ✔ *In Problems 7–13, use a number line to find each sum.*

7. $-1 + 4$ **8.** $3 + (-4)$ **9.** $-8 + 10$

10. $-8 + 4$ **11.** $17 + (-3)$ **12.** $-12 + 6$

13. $15 + (-5)$

Adding Integers Using Absolute Value

Did you discover a pattern for adding integers from Examples 1–4? When we add integers with the same sign (both positive or both negative), we add the absolute values of the integers and attach the common sign. When we add integers with different signs (one positive and one negative), we subtract the smaller absolute value from the larger absolute value and attach the sign of the integer having the larger absolute value.

EXAMPLE 5   How to Add Integers with the Same Sign Using Absolute Value

Find $-16 + (-24)$ using absolute value.

Step-by-Step Solution

Step 1: Add the absolute values of the two integers.	We have $\lvert -16 \rvert = 16$ and $\lvert -24 \rvert = 24$. So $$16 + 24 = 40$$
Step 2: Attach the common sign, either positive or negative.	Both integers are negative in the original problem, so $$-16 + (-24) = -40$$

EXAMPLE 6   How to Add Integers with Different Signs Using Absolute Value

Find $-31 + 16$ using absolute value.

Step-by-Step Solution

Step 1: Subtract the smaller absolute value from the larger absolute value.	We have $\lvert -31 \rvert = 31$ and $\lvert 16 \rvert = 16$. The smaller absolute value is 16, so we compute $$31 - 16 = 15$$
Step 2: Attach the sign of the integer with the larger absolute value.	The larger absolute value is 31, which was a negative number in the original problem. So, the sum is negative. Therefore, $$-31 + 16 = -15$$

SUMMARY   STEPS TO ADD TWO NONZERO INTEGERS USING ABSOLUTE VALUE

To add integers with the same sign (both positive or both negative),

Step 1: Add the absolute values of the two integers.

Step 2: Attach the common sign, either positive or negative.

To add integers with different signs (one positive and one negative),

Step 1: Subtract the smaller absolute value from the larger absolute value.

Step 2: Attach the sign of the integer with the larger absolute value.

Quick ✔

14. The sum of two negative integers will be _____.

In Problems 15–18, use absolute value to find each sum.

15. $-11 + 7$ **16.** $5 + (-8)$

17. $-8 + (-16)$ **18.** $-94 + 38$

⌐2 Determine the Additive Inverse of a Number

What is $3 + (-3)$? What is $10 + (-10)$? What is $-143 + 143$? The answer to all three of these questions is 0! In fact, these results are true in general.

Work Smart

The additive inverse of a, $-a$, is sometimes called the *negative* of a. Be careful when using this term because it suggests that the opposite is a negative number, which may not be true! For example, the additive inverse of -11 is 11, a positive number.

ADDITIVE INVERSE PROPERTY

For any real number a other than 0, there is a real number $-a$, called the **additive inverse**, or **opposite**, of a, having the following property.

$$a + (-a) = -a + a = 0$$

Any two numbers whose sum is zero are additive inverses, or opposites.

EXAMPLE 7 Finding an Additive Inverse

   (a) The additive inverse of 9 is -9 because $9 + (-9) = 0$.

   (b) The additive inverse of -12 is $-(-12) = 12$ because $-12 + 12 = 0$.   ■

Notice from Example 7(b) that $-(-a) = a$ **for any real number** a.

Quick ✔ *In Problems 19–23, determine the additive inverse of the given real number.*

19. 7   **20.** $\dfrac{3}{7}$ **21.** -21

22. $-\dfrac{8}{5}$ **23.** -5.75

⌐3 Subtract Integers

Now that we understand addition and have the ability to determine the additive inverse of a number, we can proceed to subtract integers. Good news! There is not a new set of rules to follow for subtracting integers. We simply rewrite the subtraction problem as an addition problem and use the addition rules that were presented earlier.

From arithmetic, we write $10 - 6 = 4$. Using the additive inverse, we can write $10 - 6 = 4$ as $10 + (-6) = 4$.

DEFINITION

The **difference** $a - b$, read "a minus b" or "a less b," is defined as

$$a - b = a + (-b)$$

In words, to subtract b from a, add the opposite of b to a.

EXAMPLE 8   How to Subtract Integers

Compute the difference: $-18 - (-40)$

Step-by-Step Solution

Step 1: Change the subtraction problem to an equivalent addition problem. $-18 - (-40) = -18 + 40$

Step 2: Find the sum. $= 22$

In Words

The problem in Example 8 is read "negative eighteen minus negative 40" not "negative 18 minus minus 40."

SUMMARY STEPS TO SUBTRACT NONZERO INTEGERS

1. Change the subtraction problem to an equivalent addition problem using
   $a - b = a + (-b)$.
2. Find the sum.

Quick ✔

24. The answer to a subtraction problem is called the _____.

25. The subtraction problem $-3 - 10$ is equivalent to $-3 +$ ____.

In Problems 26–29, find the value of each expression.

26. $59 - (-21)$ **27.** $-32 - 146$

28. 17 minus 35   **29.** -382 subtracted from -2954

For the remainder of this text, the direction **evaluate** will mean to find the numerical value of an expression. When we evaluate a numerical expression in which there is both addition and subtraction, change all subtraction to addition. Then add from left to right.

EXAMPLE 9   Evaluating an Expression Containing Three Integers

Evaluate the expression: $10 - 18 + 25$

Solution

$$10 - 18 + 25 = 10 + (-18) + 25$$

Add from left to right: $= -8 + 25$

$$= 17$$

Work Smart

When adding and subtracting more than two numbers, add in order from left to right.

EXAMPLE 10   Evaluating an Expression Containing Four Integers

Evaluate the expression: $162 - (-46) + 80 - 274$

Solution

$$162 - (-46) + 80 - 274 = 162 + 46 + 80 + (-274)$$

Add from left to right: $= 208 + 80 + (-274)$

$$= 288 + (-274)$$

$$= 14$$

Quick ✔ *In Problems 30–33, evaluate each expression.*

30. $8 - 13 + 5 - 21$ **31.** $-27 - 49 + 18$

32. $3 - (-14) - 8 + 3$ **33.** $-825 + 375 - (-735) + 265$

4 Multiply Integers

A quick review of the language of multiplication is needed: In the multiplication statement $9 \cdot 2 = 18$, the numbers 9 and 2 are called **factors** and the number 18 is the **product**.

$$\underbrace{9}_{\text{factor}} \cdot \underbrace{2}_{\text{factor}} = \underbrace{18}_{\text{product}}$$

When we first learned how to multiply natural numbers, we were told that we can think of multiplication as repeated addition. For example, $3 \cdot 4$ is equivalent to adding 4 three times. That is,

$$3 \cdot 4 = \underbrace{4 + 4 + 4}_{\substack{\text{Add } 4 \\ \text{three times}}} = 12$$

Notice that the product of two positive factors produces a positive product. We knew that from arithmetic! But what is the product $3 \cdot (-4)$?

$$3 \cdot (-4) = \underbrace{-4 + (-4) + (-4)}_{\substack{\text{Add } -4 \\ \text{three times}}} = -12$$

We conclude that the product of two real numbers with *different signs* is negative.

What about the product of two negative numbers? Consider the pattern shown below.

$$-4 \cdot 3 = -12$$
$$-4 \cdot 2 = -8$$
$$-4 \cdot 1 = -4$$
$$-4 \cdot 0 = 0$$

Notice that each time the second factor decreases by 1, the product increases by four. Assuming this pattern continues, we would have

$$-4 \cdot -1 = 4$$
$$-4 \cdot -2 = 8$$

The pattern suggests that the product of two negative numbers is a positive number.

In Words

The sign of the product is *positive* if the signs of the two factors are the *same* and *negative* if the signs of the two factors are *different*.

RULES OF SIGNS FOR MULTIPLYING TWO INTEGERS

1. If we multiply two positive integers, the product is positive.

2. If we multiply one positive integer and one negative integer, the product is negative.

3. If we multiply two negative integers, the product is positive.

EXAMPLE 11 Multiplying Integers

(a) $2(-4) = -8$ **(b)** $-6(5) = -30$

(c) $(-7)(-8) = 56$ **(d)** $-25(18) = -450$ ∎

Quick ✔

34. The product of two integers with the same sign is _____.

In Problems 35–39, find the product.

35. $-3(7)$ **36.** $13(-4)$ **37.** $5 \cdot 16$

38. $-9(-12)$ **39.** $(-13)(-25)$

Find the Product of Several Integers

When we find the product of more than two integers, we multiply in order, from left to right.

| EXAMPLE 12 | Multiplying Three Integers

Find the product: $3 \cdot (-4) \cdot 7$

Solution

Multiply from left to right:
$$3 \cdot (-4) \cdot 7 = -12 \cdot 7$$
$$= -84$$

| EXAMPLE 13 | Multiplying Four Integers

Find the product: $-8 \cdot (-1) \cdot 4 \cdot (-5)$

Solution

Multiply from left to right:
$$-8 \cdot (-1) \cdot 4 \cdot (-5) = 8 \cdot 4 \cdot (-5)$$
$$= 32 \cdot (-5)$$
$$= -160$$

Work Smart

If we multiply an *even* number of negative factors the product is *positive*.

If we multiply an *odd* number of negative factors the product is *negative*.

Quick ✔

40. *True or False:* The product of thirteen negative factors is negative.

In Problems 41 and 42, find the product.

41. $-3 \cdot 9 \cdot (-4)$

42. $(-3) \cdot (-4) \cdot (-5) \cdot (-6)$

| 5 | Divide Integers

When we divide, the numerator is called the **dividend,** the denominator is called the **divisor,** and the answer is called the **quotient.**

$$\text{dividend} \rightarrow \frac{28}{7} = 4 \leftarrow \text{quotient} \quad \text{or} \quad \underbrace{28}_{\text{dividend}} \div \underbrace{7}_{\text{divisor}} = \underbrace{4}_{\text{quotient}}$$

To discuss division of integers, we need to introduce the idea of a *multiplicative inverse,* which is a property that applies to all real numbers.

In Words

Any two numbers whose product is 1 are called multiplicative inverses or reciprocals of each other.

MULTIPLICATIVE INVERSE (RECIPROCAL) PROPERTY

For each *nonzero* real number a, there is a real number $\frac{1}{a}$, called the **multiplicative inverse** or **reciprocal** of a, having the following property:

$$a \cdot \frac{1}{a} = \frac{1}{a} \cdot a = 1 \quad a \neq 0$$

| EXAMPLE 14 | Finding the Multiplicative Inverse (or Reciprocal) of an Integer

(a) The multiplicative inverse or reciprocal of 5 is $\frac{1}{5}$.

(b) The multiplicative inverse or reciprocal of -8 is $-\frac{1}{8}$.

Quick ✔ *In Problems 43 and 44, find the reciprocal of each integer.*

43. 6   **44.** −2

Now we can define division of integers.

DEFINITION

If b is a nonzero integer, the **quotient** $\dfrac{a}{b}$, read as "a divided by b" or "the **ratio** of a to b," is defined as

$$\frac{a}{b} = a \cdot \frac{1}{b} \qquad \text{if } b \neq 0$$

For example, $\dfrac{40}{8} = 40 \cdot \dfrac{1}{8}$ and $\dfrac{12}{7} = 12 \cdot \dfrac{1}{7}$. Because division can be represented as multiplication, the same rules of signs that apply to multiplication also apply to division.

In Words

These are the same rules we saw in multiplying integers . . . a positive divided by a positive is positive; positive divided by negative is negative, and so on.

RULES OF SIGNS FOR DIVIDING TWO INTEGERS

1. If we divide two positive integers, the quotient is positive. That is, $\dfrac{+a}{+b} = \dfrac{a}{b}$.
2. If we divide one positive integer and one negative integer, the quotient is negative. That is, $\dfrac{-a}{b} = \dfrac{a}{-b} = -\dfrac{a}{b}$.
3. If we divide two negative integers, the quotient is positive. That is, $\dfrac{-a}{-b} = \dfrac{a}{b}$.

Finding the quotient of two integers is identical to writing a fraction in lowest terms.

|EXAMPLE 15 Finding the Quotient of Two Integers

Find each quotient:

     (a) $\dfrac{-90}{20}$ **(b)** $200 \div (-5)$

Solution

(a)

$$\frac{-90}{20} = \frac{-9 \cdot 10}{2 \cdot 10}$$

Divide out the common factor:
$$= \frac{-9 \cdot \cancel{10}}{2 \cdot \cancel{10}}$$
$$= \frac{-9}{2}$$

$\dfrac{-a}{b} = -\dfrac{a}{b}\text{:}$
$$= -\frac{9}{2}$$

(b)

$$200 \div (-5) = \frac{200}{-5}$$
$$= \frac{40 \cdot 5}{-1 \cdot 5}$$

Divide out the common factor:
$$= \frac{40 \cdot \cancel{5}}{-1 \cdot \cancel{5}}$$
$$= -40$$

Quick ✔

45. *True or False:* The quotient of two negative numbers is positive.

In Problems 46–48, find the quotient.

46. $\dfrac{20}{-4}$ **47.** $\dfrac{-707}{101}$ **48.** $-63 \div -7$

1.4 EXERCISES

PRACTICE   WATCH   DOWNLOAD   READ   REVIEW

1–48. *are the* Quick ✔*s that follow each* EXAMPLE

Building Skills

In Problems 49–64, find the sum. See Objective 1.

49. $8 + 7$ **50.** $6 + 4$ **51.** $-5 + 9$

52. $-4 + 12$ **53.** $9 + (-5)$ **54.** $13 + (-7)$

⊜ **55.** $-11 + (-8)$ **56.** $-13 + (-5)$ **57.** $-16 + 37$

58. $-32 + 49$ **59.** $-119 + (-209)$

60. $-145 + (-68)$ **61.** $-14 + 21 + (-18)$

62. $(-13) + 37 + (-22)$

63. $74 + (-13) + (-23) + 5$

64. $-34 + 46 + (-12) + 72$

In Problems 65–68, determine the additive inverse of each real number. See Objective 2.

65. -325 **66.** -34

67. 125 **68.** 7

In Problems 69–84, find the difference. See Objective 3.

69. $23 - 12$ **70.** $35 - 23$ ⊜ **71.** $9 - 17$

72. $12 - 19$ **73.** $-20 - 8$ **74.** $-15 - 9$

75. $13 - (-41)$ **76.** $14 - (-18)$ **77.** $-36 - (-36)$

78. $-15 - (-15)$ **79.** $0 - 41$ **80.** $0 - 18$

81. $-93 - (-62)$ **82.** $46 - (-25)$ **83.** $86 - (-86)$

84. $49 - (-49)$

In Problems 85–100, find the product. See Objective 4.

85. $5 \cdot 8$ **86.** $7 \cdot 9$ **87.** $8(-7)$

88. $9(-7)$ **89.** $(0)(-21)$ **90.** $-21 \cdot 0$

⊜ **91.** $(-48)(-3)$ **92.** $(-22)(-5)$ **93.** $(-42)3$

94. $(-128)7$ **95.** $-5 \cdot 6 \cdot 3$ **96.** $-6 \cdot 4 \cdot 8$

97. $-10(3)(-7)$ **98.** $-8(2)(-9)$

99. $(-2)(4)(-1)(3)(5)$ **100.** $(-3)(-4)(6)(-1)$

In Problems 101–106, find the multiplicative inverse (or reciprocal) of each number. See Objective 5.

101. 8 **102.** 10 **103.** -4

104. -3 **105.** 1 **106.** 2

In Problems 107–118, find the quotient. See Objective 5.

107. $10 \div 2$ **108.** $36 \div 9$ **109.** $\dfrac{-56}{-8}$

110. $\dfrac{-63}{-7}$ ⊜ **111.** $\dfrac{-45}{3}$ **112.** $\dfrac{-144}{6}$

113. $\dfrac{35}{10}$ **114.** $\dfrac{20}{16}$ **115.** $\dfrac{60}{-42}$

116. $\dfrac{120}{-66}$ **117.** $\dfrac{-105}{-12}$ **118.** $\dfrac{-80}{-12}$

Mixed Practice

In Problems 119–134, evaluate the expression.

119. $-4 \cdot 18$ **120.** $7 \cdot (-15)$

121. $-16 - (-76)$ **122.** $87 - 19$

123. $-9 \cdot (-19)$ **124.** $7 \cdot 209$

125. $\dfrac{120}{-8}$ **126.** $\dfrac{-156}{-26}$

127. $-98 + 56$ **128.** $103 + (-66)$

129. $\dfrac{75}{|-20|}$ **130.** $\dfrac{|-42|}{12}$

131. $|-14| + |-26|$ **132.** $|-10| + (-62)$

133. $|-389| - 627$ **134.** $|-193| - (-20)$

In Problems 135–142, write each expression using mathematical symbols. Then evaluate the expression.

135. the sum of 28 and -21 **136.** the sum of 32 and -64

137. -21 minus 47   **138.** -16 minus -85

139. −12 multiplied by 18   **140.** 32 multiplied by −8

141. −36 divided by −108   **142.** −40 divided by 100

Applying the Concepts

In Problems 143–148, write the positive or negative number for each of the following.

143. Stock The price of IBM stock fell by 3.25 dollars.

144. Temperature The current temperature in Juneau, Alaska, is 14° below zero.

145. Chargers Football The Chargers lost 6 yards on the play.

146. Profit Mark's BMW dealership showed a profit of $125,000 this quarter.

147. Checking Account Leila's checking account is now overdrawn by $48.

148. Census The number of people in Brian's hometown grew by 12,368.

149. Hiking Loren and Richard went on a hiking trip. They walked 8 miles to the base of Snow Creek Falls, where they set up camp. They went another 3 miles to see the Falls and then returned to their campsite. How many miles did they walk that day?

150. Football The Cary High School Eagles took over possession of the ball on their own 15-yard line. The following plays occurred: QB sack, loss of 7 yards; Jon Anderson ran for 14 yards; Juan Ramirez caught a pass for 26 yards. What yard marker is the ball on now?

151. Bank Balance When Martha balanced her checkbook, she had $563 in the account. Then the following transactions occurred: She wrote a check to Home Depot for $46; deposited $233; wrote a check to Vons for $63; and wrote a check to Petco for $32. What is Martha's new balance?

152. Checkbook Balance Josie began the month with $399 in her bank account. She deposited her paycheck of $839. She paid her $69 telephone bill, the electric bill for $78, and rent of $739. How much does she have left for spending money?

153. Warehouse Inventory The warehouse began the month with 725 cases of soda. During the month the following transactions occurred: 120 cases were shipped out, 590 cases were shipped out, and 310 cases were delivered to the warehouse. Does the warehouse have enough stock on hand to fill an order for 450 cases of soda? What is the difference between what it has and what has been requested?

154. Altitude of an Airplane A pilot leveled off his airplane at 35,000 feet at the beginning of the flight. The following adjustments were made during the trip: gained 4290 feet, dropped 10,400 feet, and then dropped 2605 feet. At what altitude is the plane currently flying?

155. Distance An airplane flying at 25,350 feet is directly over a submarine that is 375 feet below sea level. What is the distance between a person in the plane and a person in the submarine?

156. Elevation The highest point in California is Mt. Whitney at an elevation of 14,495 feet and the lowest point is in Death Valley at 280 feet below sea level. What is the maximum difference in elevation between the two points in California?

Extending the Concepts

157. Find two integers whose sum is −8 and whose product is 15.

158. Find two integers whose sum is 2 and whose product is −24.

159. Find two integers whose sum is −10 and whose product is −24.

160. Find two integers whose sum is −18 and whose product is 45.

161. The Fibonacci Sequence The numbers in the Fibonacci sequence are 1, 1, 2, 3, 5, 8, 13, 21, 34, 55, . . . where each term after the second term is the sum of the two preceding terms. This famous sequence of numbers can be used to model many phenomena in nature.

(a) Form fractions of consecutive terms in the sequence. Find the decimal approximations to $\frac{1}{1}, \frac{2}{1}, \frac{3}{2}, \frac{5}{3}$, and so on.

(b) What number do the ratios get close to? This number is called the **golden ratio** and has application in many different areas.

(c) Research Fibonacci numbers and cite three different applications.

Explaining the Concepts

162. Write a sentence or two that justifies the fact that the product of a positive number and a negative number is a negative number. You may use an example.

163. Explain how 42 ÷ 4 may be written as a multiplication problem.

1.5 Adding, Subtracting, Multiplying, and Dividing Rational Numbers Expressed as Fractions and Decimals

OBJECTIVES

1. Multiply Rational Numbers Expressed as Fractions
2. Divide Rational Numbers Expressed as Fractions
3. Add and Subtract Rational Numbers Expressed as Fractions
4. Add, Subtract, Multiply, and Divide Rational Numbers Expressed as Decimals

Preparing for Adding, Subtracting, Multiplying, and Dividing Rational Numbers Expressed as Fractions and Decimals

Before getting started, take the following readiness quiz. If you get a problem wrong, go to the section cited and review the material.

P1. Find the least common denominator   [Section 1.2, p. 12]
of $\frac{5}{12}$ and $\frac{3}{16}$.

P2. Rewrite $\frac{4}{5}$ as an equivalent fraction with   [Section 1.2, pp. 11–12]
a denominator of 30.

Now that we are comfortable with operations on integers, we expand our skill set so that we can perform operations on rational numbers. Remember, a rational number can be expressed either as a fraction, as a terminating decimal, or as a nonterminating, repeating decimal. We begin with operations on rational numbers expressed as fractions and end the section with the operations on rational numbers in decimal form. All of the properties included for integers in Section 1.4 apply to rational numbers as well. In fact, these properties apply to all real numbers.

Finding the quotient of two integers is identical to writing a fraction in lowest terms. So, the direction to "find the quotient $\frac{-90}{20}$" is the same as "write $\frac{-90}{20}$ in lowest terms."

For example, the rational number $\frac{-90}{20}$ is written in lowest terms as $-\frac{9}{2}$.

Quick ✔ *In Problems 1–3, write each rational number in lowest terms.*

1. $-\frac{4}{14}$ **2.** $-\frac{18}{30}$ **3.** $-\frac{24}{4}$

1 Multiply Rational Numbers Expressed as Fractions

The following property tells us how to multiply two rational numbers when they are in fractional form:

In Words

When finding the product of two or more fractions, multiply the numerators together. Then multiply the denominators together. Write the fraction in lowest terms, if necessary.

MULTIPLYING FRACTIONS

$$\frac{a}{b} \cdot \frac{c}{d} = \frac{a \cdot c}{b \cdot d}, \text{ where } b \text{ and } d \neq 0$$

The rules of signs that apply to integers also apply to rational numbers: The product of two positive rational numbers is positive; the product of a positive rational number and a negative rational number is negative, and so on.

Preparing for...Answers **P1.** LCD = 48
P2. $\frac{4}{5} = \frac{24}{30}$

EXAMPLE 1 **Multiplying Rational Numbers (Fractions)**

Find the product: $\dfrac{2}{9} \cdot \left(-\dfrac{15}{19}\right)$

Solution

We begin by rewriting the rational number $-\dfrac{15}{19}$ as $\dfrac{-15}{19}$. Then we multiply the numerators and multiply the denominators.

$$\frac{2}{9} \cdot \left(\frac{-15}{19}\right) = \frac{2 \cdot (-15)}{9 \cdot 19}$$

Write the numerator and the denominator as products of prime factors: $\quad = \dfrac{2 \cdot 3 \cdot (-5)}{3 \cdot 3 \cdot 19}$

Divide out common factors: $\quad = \dfrac{2 \cdot \cancel{3} \cdot (-5)}{\cancel{3} \cdot 3 \cdot 19}$

$$= \frac{2 \cdot (-5)}{3 \cdot 19}$$

Perform the multiplication: $\quad = -\dfrac{10}{57}$

> **Work Smart**
>
> Notice that we do not carry out the multiplication in the numerator or denominator until the last step. This makes it easier to divide out common factors. Once the common factors are divided out, we perform the multiplication.

Quick ✔ *In Problems 4–8, find each product, and write in lowest terms.*

4. $\dfrac{3}{4} \cdot \dfrac{9}{8}$ **5.** $\dfrac{-5}{7} \cdot \dfrac{56}{15}$ **6.** $\dfrac{12}{45} \cdot \left(-\dfrac{18}{20}\right)$

7. $-\dfrac{25}{75} \cdot \left(-\dfrac{9}{4}\right)$ **8.** $\dfrac{7}{3} \cdot \dfrac{1}{14} \cdot \left(-\dfrac{9}{11}\right)$

▢2 Divide Rational Numbers Expressed as Fractions

To divide rational numbers, we must know how to determine the reciprocal of a rational number. We introduced the term *reciprocal* in Section 1.4 by saying that two numbers are reciprocals, or multiplicative inverses, if the product of the numbers is 1. This definition applies to any nonzero real number. So, $\dfrac{3}{2}$ and $\dfrac{2}{3}$ are reciprocals because $\dfrac{3}{2} \cdot \dfrac{2}{3} = 1$; 9 and $\dfrac{1}{9}$ are reciprocals because $9 \cdot \dfrac{1}{9} = 1$; $-\dfrac{4}{7}$ and $-\dfrac{7}{4}$ are reciprocals because $-\dfrac{4}{7} \cdot \left(-\dfrac{7}{4}\right) = 1$.

Quick ✔

9. Two numbers are called multiplicative inverses, or reciprocals, if their product is equal to____.

In Problems 10–13, find the reciprocal of each number.

10. 12   **11.** $\dfrac{7}{5}$ **12.** $-\dfrac{1}{4}$ **13.** $-\dfrac{31}{20}$

We divide rational numbers by rewriting the division as an equivalent multiplication problem, according to the following.

DIVIDING RATIONAL NUMBERS EXPRESSED AS FRACTIONS

$$\frac{a}{b} \div \frac{c}{d} = \frac{a}{b} \cdot \frac{d}{c} = \frac{a \cdot d}{b \cdot c}, \quad \text{where } b, c, d \neq 0$$

EXAMPLE 2 How to Divide Rational Numbers (Fractions)

Find the quotient: $\dfrac{3}{10} \div \dfrac{12}{25}$

Step-by-Step Solution

Step 1: Write the equivalent multiplication problem.	$\dfrac{3}{10} \div \dfrac{12}{25} = \dfrac{3}{10} \cdot \dfrac{25}{12}$
Step 2: Write the product in factored form and divide out common factors.	$= \dfrac{3 \cdot 25}{10 \cdot 12}$ $= \dfrac{3 \cdot 5 \cdot 5}{5 \cdot 2 \cdot 4 \cdot 3}$ $= \dfrac{\cancel{3} \cdot \cancel{5} \cdot 5}{\cancel{5} \cdot 2 \cdot 4 \cdot \cancel{3}}$ $= \dfrac{5}{2 \cdot 4}$
Step 3: Multiply the remaining factors.	$= \dfrac{5}{8}$

So $\dfrac{3}{10} \div \dfrac{12}{25} = \dfrac{5}{8}$.

Quick ✔ *In Problems 14–17, find the quotient.*

14. $\dfrac{5}{7} \div \dfrac{7}{10}$

15. $-\dfrac{9}{12} \div \dfrac{14}{7}$

16. $\dfrac{8}{35} \div \left(\dfrac{-1}{10}\right)$

17. $-\dfrac{18}{63} \div \left(-\dfrac{54}{35}\right)$

⌐3 Add and Subtract Rational Numbers Expressed as Fractions

Figure 17

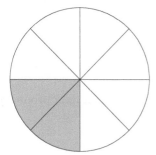

Consider Figure 17, which shows a circle divided into 8 equal parts. We have two regions shaded, each of which represents the fraction $\dfrac{1}{8}$. Together, the two shaded regions make up $\dfrac{1}{4}$ of the circle. This implies that

$$\frac{1}{8} + \frac{1}{8} = \frac{1+1}{8}$$
$$= \frac{2}{8}$$
$$= \frac{1}{4}$$

Or, suppose Bobby has \$0.25 and his grandma gives him \$0.50. How much does he now have? Of course, \$0.25 + \$0.50 = \$0.75 or $\dfrac{3}{4}$ of a dollar. Because $0.25 = \dfrac{1}{4}$ and $0.50 = \dfrac{1}{2}$, we can determine Bobby's good fortune using fractions:

$$\frac{1}{4} + \frac{1}{2} = \frac{1}{4} + \frac{2}{4}$$
$$= \frac{3}{4}$$

Based on these results, we might conclude that to add fractions with the same denominators, we add the numerators and write the result over the common denominator. This conclusion is correct. Also, because we can write any subtraction problem as an equivalent addition problem, we have the following methods for adding and subtracting rational numbers.

In Words

When adding or subtracting fractions with a common denominator, you add or subtract the numerators and retain the denominator.

ADDING OR SUBTRACTING RATIONAL NUMBERS (FRACTIONS) WITH THE SAME DENOMINATOR

$$\frac{a}{c} + \frac{b}{c} = \frac{a+b}{c} \quad \text{where } c \neq 0 \qquad \frac{a}{c} - \frac{b}{c} = \frac{a-b}{c} = \frac{a+(-b)}{c} \quad \text{where } c \neq 0$$

EXAMPLE 3 Adding Rational Numbers (Fractions) with the Same Denominator

Find the sum and write in lowest terms: $-\frac{1}{8} + \frac{3}{8}$

Solution

$$-\frac{1}{8} + \frac{3}{8} = \frac{-1}{8} + \frac{3}{8}$$

Write the numerators as a sum over the common denominator: $= \frac{-1+3}{8}$

Add the numerators: $= \frac{2}{8}$

Factor 8: $= \frac{1 \cdot 2}{4 \cdot 2}$

Divide out the 2s: $= \frac{1 \cdot \cancel{2}}{4 \cdot \cancel{2}}$

$$= \frac{1}{4}$$

So $-\frac{1}{8} + \frac{3}{8} = \frac{1}{4}$.

EXAMPLE 4 Subtracting Rational Numbers (Fractions) with the Same Denominator

Find the difference and write in lowest terms: $\frac{9}{16} - \frac{3}{16}$

Solution

$$\frac{9}{16} - \frac{3}{16} = \frac{9-3}{16}$$

Rewrite as an addition problem: $= \frac{9+(-3)}{16}$

Add the numerators: $= \frac{6}{16}$

Factor 6; factor 16: $= \frac{3 \cdot 2}{8 \cdot 2}$

Divide out the 2s: $= \frac{3 \cdot \cancel{2}}{8 \cdot \cancel{2}}$

$$= \frac{3}{8}$$

So $\frac{9}{16} - \frac{3}{16} = \frac{3}{8}$.

Quick ✔

18. $\dfrac{-5}{7} + \dfrac{3}{7} = \dfrac{-5 + 3}{\underline{}}$

In Problems 19–22, find the sum or difference, and write in lowest terms.

19. $-\dfrac{9}{10} - \dfrac{3}{10}$

20. $\dfrac{8}{11} + \dfrac{2}{11}$

21. $-\dfrac{18}{35} + \dfrac{3}{35}$

22. $\dfrac{19}{63} - \dfrac{10}{63}$

Work Smart: Study Skills

Notice the title of Example 5: "How to Add Rational Numbers with Unlike Denominators." This three-column example provides a guided, step-by-step approach to solving a problem so you can immediately see each of the steps. Cover the third column and try to work the example yourself. Then look at the entries in the third column and check your solution. Was it correct?

Adding and Subtracting Rational Numbers (Fractions) with Unlike Denominators

How do we add rational numbers with different denominators? We must find the least common denominator of the two rational numbers. Recall from Section 1.2 that the **least common denominator (LCD)** is the smallest number that each denominator has as a common multiple.

EXAMPLE 5 **How to Add Rational Numbers (Fractions) with Unlike Denominators**

Find the sum: $\dfrac{5}{6} + \dfrac{3}{8}$

Step-by-Step Solution

Step 1: Find the least common denominator of the fractions.

Write each denominator as the product of prime factors, arranging like factors vertically:

$$6 = 2 \qquad \cdot 3$$
$$8 = 2 \cdot 2 \cdot 2$$

Find the product of each of the prime factors the greatest number of times they appear in any factorization:

$$\text{LCD} = 2 \cdot 2 \cdot 2 \cdot 3$$
$$= 24$$

Step 2: Write each rational number with the denominator found in Step 1.

Use $1 = \dfrac{4}{4}$ to change the denominator 6 to 24, and use $1 = \dfrac{3}{3}$ to change the denominator 8 to 24:

$$\dfrac{5}{6} + \dfrac{3}{8} = \dfrac{5}{6} \cdot \dfrac{4}{4} + \dfrac{3}{8} \cdot \dfrac{3}{3}$$
$$= \dfrac{20}{24} + \dfrac{9}{24}$$

Step 3: Add the numerators and write the result over the common denominator.

$$= \dfrac{20 + 9}{24}$$
$$= \dfrac{29}{24}$$

Step 4: Write in lowest terms.

The rational number is in lowest terms.

Thus, $\dfrac{5}{6} + \dfrac{3}{8} = \dfrac{29}{24}$.

EXAMPLE 6 How to Subtract Rational Numbers (Fractions) with Unlike Denominators

Find the difference: $-\dfrac{9}{14} - \dfrac{1}{6}$

Step-by-Step Solution

Step 1: Find the least common denominator of the fractions.

Write each denominator as the product of prime factors, aligning like factors vertically:

Find the product of each of the prime factors the greatest number of times it appears in any factorization:

$$14 = 2 \cdot 7$$
$$6 = 2 \quad \cdot 3$$
$$\text{LCD} = 2 \cdot 7 \cdot 3$$
$$= 42$$

Step 2: Write each rational number with the denominator found in Step 1.

Use $1 = \dfrac{3}{3}$ to change the denominator 14 to 42, and use $1 = \dfrac{7}{7}$ to change the denominator 6 to 42:

$$-\dfrac{9}{14} - \dfrac{1}{6} = \dfrac{-9}{14} \cdot \dfrac{3}{3} - \dfrac{1}{6} \cdot \dfrac{7}{7}$$

$$= \dfrac{-27}{42} - \dfrac{7}{42}$$

Step 3: Subtract the numerators and write the result over the common denominator.

$$= \dfrac{-27 - 7}{42}$$

$$= \dfrac{-34}{42}$$

Step 4: Write in lowest terms.

Factor -34 and 42:

$$= \dfrac{2 \cdot (-17)}{2 \cdot 21}$$

Divide out like factors:

$$= \dfrac{\cancel{2} \cdot (-17)}{\cancel{2} \cdot 21}$$

$$= -\dfrac{17}{21}$$

We see that $-\dfrac{9}{14} - \dfrac{1}{6} = -\dfrac{17}{21}$.

SUMMARY STEPS TO ADD OR SUBTRACT RATIONAL NUMBERS (FRACTIONS) WITH UNLIKE DENOMINATORS

Step 1: Find the LCD of the rational numbers.

Step 2: Write each rational number with the LCD.

Step 3: Add or subtract the numerators and write the result over the common denominator.

Step 4: Write the result in lowest terms.

Quick ✔ *In Problems 23–26, find each sum or difference, and write in lowest terms.*

23. $\dfrac{5}{12} - \dfrac{5}{18}$

24. $\dfrac{3}{14} + \dfrac{10}{21}$

25. $-\dfrac{23}{6} + \dfrac{7}{12}$

26. $\dfrac{3}{5} + \left(-\dfrac{4}{11}\right)$

Remember, the direction "evaluate" means to find the value of the expression, so the direction "evaluate $4 - \frac{2}{3}$" means to find the difference between 4 and $\frac{2}{3}$.

EXAMPLE 7 Evaluating an Expression Containing Rational Numbers

Evaluate and write in lowest terms: $4 - \frac{2}{3}$

Solution

The key is to remember that $4 = \frac{4}{1}$.

$$4 - \frac{2}{3} = \frac{4}{1} - \frac{2}{3}$$

Rewrite each fraction with LCD = 3:
$$= \frac{4}{1} \cdot \frac{3}{3} - \frac{2}{3}$$

$$= \frac{12}{3} - \frac{2}{3}$$

$$= \frac{10}{3}$$

Quick ✔ *In Problems 27 and 28, evaluate and write in lowest terms.*

27. $-2 + \frac{7}{16}$ **28.** $6 + \left(-\frac{9}{4}\right)$

4 Add, Subtract, Multiply, and Divide Rational Numbers Expressed as Decimals

Adding and Subtracting Decimals

To add or subtract decimals, we arrange the numbers in a column with the decimal points aligned. Then add or subtract the digits in the like place values, and place the decimal point in the answer directly below the decimal point in the problem.

EXAMPLE 8 Adding and Subtracting Decimals That Are the Same Sign

Evaluate each expression:

    (a) $2.93 + 7.2 + 3.026$ **(b)** $76.4 - 4.95$

Solution

    (a) Add zeros as placeholders:

$$\begin{array}{r} 2.930 \\ 7.200 \\ +\,3.026 \\ \hline 13.156 \end{array}$$

Work Smart

A whole number has an implied decimal point. For example,

$$74 = 74.000$$

    (b) Add a zero as a placeholder:

$$\begin{array}{r} \overset{5\ \ 13\ \ 10}{76.40} \\ -\,4.95 \\ \hline 71.45 \end{array}$$

EXAMPLE 9 Adding and Subtracting Decimals That Have Different Signs

Evaluate each expression:

(a) $100.32 - (-32.015)$ (b) $-23.03 + 18.49$

Solution

(a) Remember, $a - (-b) = a + b$, so we can write $100.32 - (-32.015)$ as $100.32 + 32.015$.

$$\begin{array}{r} 100.320 \\ +32.015 \\ \hline 132.335 \end{array}$$

(b) Recall that to add real numbers with different signs (one positive and one negative), we subtract the smaller absolute value from the larger absolute value and attach the sign of the larger absolute value. Because $|-23.03| = 23.03$ and $|18.49| = 18.49$, we compute $23.03 - 18.49$ and attach a negative sign to the difference.

$$\begin{array}{r} 23.03 \\ -18.49 \\ \hline 4.54 \end{array}$$

So $-23.03 + 18.49 = -4.54$. ■

Quick ✔ *In Problems 29–34, find the sum or difference.*

29. $9.67 + 11.344$

30. $81.96 - 17.39$

31. $14.95 + 7.118 + 0.3$

32. $345.67 - 8.0912$

33. $-180.782 + 100.3 + 9.07$

34. $-74.28 - 14.832$

Multiplying Decimals

The rules for multiplying decimals come from the rules for multiplying rational numbers written as fractions. For example,

$$\underbrace{-0.7}_{\substack{1 \text{ decimal} \\ \text{place}}} \cdot \underbrace{0.03}_{\substack{2 \text{ decimal} \\ \text{places}}} = \frac{-7}{10} \cdot \frac{3}{100} = \frac{-21}{1000} = \underbrace{-0.021}_{\substack{3 \text{ decimal} \\ \text{places}}}$$

Notice that there are three digits to the right of the decimal point in the answer. This is equal to the sum of the number of digits to the right of the decimal point in the factors.

Notice also that the rules of signs that we learned in Section 1.4 apply to decimals as well. We use this result to demonstrate how to multiply decimals.

EXAMPLE 10 Multiplying Decimals

Find the product:

(a) $3.43 \cdot 2.6$ (b) $-3.17 \cdot 0.02$

Solution

(a)

two digits to the right of the decimal point

three digits to the right of the decimal point

one digit to the right of the decimal point

$$\begin{array}{r} 3.43 \\ \times 2.6 \\ \hline 2\,0\,5\,8 \\ 6\,8\,6 \\ \hline 8.9\,1\,8 \end{array}$$

(b)

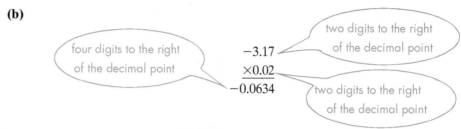

We summarize the procedure for multiplying decimals.

SUMMARY STEPS TO MULTIPLY DECIMALS

Step 1: Multiply the factors as if they were whole numbers.

Step 2: Count the total number of digits to the right of the decimal point in the factors.

Step 3: Place the decimal point so the number of digits to the right of the decimal point in the product equals the *sum* of the number of digits to the right of the decimal point in the factors.

Quick ✔ *In Problems 35–40, find the product.*

35. $23.9 \cdot 0.2$

36. $9.1 \cdot 7.24$

37. $-3.45 \cdot 0.03$

38. $257 \cdot (-3.5)$

39. $-0.03 \cdot (-0.45)$

40. $9.9 \cdot 0.002$

Dividing Decimals

First, we review vocabulary. In the division problem $2\overline{)7.94}$ with quotient 3.97, the number 2 is called the *divisor,* 7.94 is called the *dividend,* and 3.97 is the *quotient.* You see from this example that when we divide by a whole number, we place the decimal point in the quotient directly above the decimal point in the dividend. In algebra, we typically write this division problem as $\dfrac{7.94}{2} = 3.97$.

To divide decimals, we want the divisor to be a whole number, so we multiply the dividend and the divisor by a power of 10 that will make the divisor a whole number. Then divide as though we were working with whole numbers. The decimal point in the quotient lies directly above the decimal point in the dividend.

EXAMPLE 11 Dividing Decimals

(a) Divide: $\dfrac{22.26}{15.9}$

(b) Divide: $\dfrac{0.03724}{-0.38}$

Solution

(a) Since the divisor 15.9 is fifteen and nine-tenths, we multiply $\dfrac{22.26}{15.9}$ by $\dfrac{10}{10}$ to make the divisor a whole number and obtain $\dfrac{22.26}{15.9} \cdot \dfrac{10}{10} = \dfrac{222.6}{159}$. Now we divide.

$$
\begin{array}{r}
1.4 \\
159\overline{)222.6} \\
159 \\
\hline
63\,6 \\
63\,6 \\
\hline
0
\end{array}
$$

So $\dfrac{22.26}{15.9} = 1.4$.

(b) Because we have a positive number divided by a negative number, the quotient will be negative. Now, perform the division $\dfrac{0.03724}{0.38}$. Once we obtain this quotient, we will make it negative. The divisor 0.38 is thirty-eight hundredths so we multiply $\dfrac{0.03724}{0.38}$ by $\dfrac{100}{100}$ to make the divisor a whole number and obtain $\dfrac{0.03724}{0.38} \cdot \dfrac{100}{100} = \dfrac{3.724}{38}$. Now we divide.

$$
\begin{array}{r}
0.098 \\
38\overline{)3.724} \\
\underline{3\ 42} \\
304 \\
\underline{304} \\
0
\end{array}
$$

Therefore, $\dfrac{0.03724}{-0.38} = -0.098$. ∎

We generalize the process for dividing decimals.

In Words
To divide decimals, change the divisor to a whole number and divide.

STEPS TO DIVIDE DECIMALS

Step 1: Multiply the dividend and divisor by a power of ten that will make the divisor a whole number.

Step 2: Divide as though working with whole numbers.

Work Smart: Study Skills
Selected problems in the exercise sets are identified by a 💿 symbol. For extra help, view the worked solutions to these problems on the book's CD Lecture Series.

Quick ✔ *In Problems 41–44, find the quotient.*

41. $\dfrac{18.25}{73}$

42. $\dfrac{1.0032}{0.12}$

43. $\dfrac{-4.2958}{45.7}$

44. $\dfrac{0.1515}{-5.05}$

1.5 EXERCISES

PRACTICE · WATCH · DOWNLOAD · READ · REVIEW

1–44. *are the* Quick ✔*s that follow each* EXAMPLE

Building Skills

In Problems 45–52, write each rational number in lowest terms.

45. $\dfrac{14}{21}$

46. $\dfrac{9}{15}$

💿**47.** $\dfrac{38}{-18}$

48. $-\dfrac{81}{36}$

49. $-\dfrac{22}{44}$

50. $-\dfrac{24}{27}$

51. $\dfrac{32}{40}$

52. $\dfrac{49}{63}$

In Problems 53–64, find the product, and write in lowest terms. See Objective 1.

53. $\dfrac{6}{5} \cdot \dfrac{2}{5}$

54. $\dfrac{7}{8} \cdot \dfrac{10}{21}$

55. $-\dfrac{5}{2} \cdot 10$

56. $-\dfrac{3}{7} \cdot 63$

57. $-\dfrac{3}{2} \cdot \dfrac{4}{9}$

58. $-\dfrac{5}{2} \cdot \dfrac{16}{25}$

59. $-\dfrac{22}{3} \cdot \left(-\dfrac{12}{11}\right)$

60. $-\dfrac{60}{75} \cdot \left(-\dfrac{25}{36}\right)$

61. $5 \cdot \dfrac{31}{15}$

62. $9 \cdot \dfrac{5}{18}$

63. $\dfrac{3}{4} \cdot \dfrac{8}{11}$

64. $\dfrac{4}{7} \cdot \dfrac{9}{16}$

In Problems 65–68, find the reciprocal of each number.
See Objective 2.

65. $\dfrac{3}{5}$

66. $\dfrac{9}{4}$

67. -5

68. -8

In Problems 69–80, find the quotient, and write in lowest terms.
See Objective 2.

69. $\dfrac{4}{9} \div \dfrac{8}{15}$

70. $\dfrac{1}{2} \div \dfrac{3}{6}$

71. $-\dfrac{1}{3} \div 3$

72. $-\dfrac{1}{4} \div 4$

73. $\dfrac{5}{6} \div \left(-\dfrac{5}{4}\right)$

74. $\dfrac{4}{3} \div \left(-\dfrac{9}{10}\right)$

75. $\dfrac{36}{28} \div \dfrac{22}{14}$

76. $\dfrac{44}{63} \div \dfrac{11}{21}$

77. $-8 \div \dfrac{2}{3}$

78. $-3 \div \dfrac{7}{9}$

79. $-8 \div \left(-\dfrac{1}{4}\right)$

80. $-3 \div \left(-\dfrac{1}{6}\right)$

In Problems 81–104, find the sum or difference and write in lowest terms. See Objective 3.

81. $\dfrac{3}{4} + \dfrac{3}{4}$

82. $\dfrac{6}{11} + \dfrac{16}{11}$

83. $\dfrac{9}{8} - \dfrac{5}{8}$

84. $\dfrac{12}{5} - \dfrac{2}{5}$

85. $\dfrac{6}{7} - \left(-\dfrac{8}{7}\right)$

86. $\dfrac{2}{3} - \left(-\dfrac{7}{3}\right)$

87. $-\dfrac{5}{3} + 2$

88. $-\dfrac{7}{8} + 4$

89. $6 - \dfrac{7}{2}$

90. $3 - \dfrac{5}{3}$

91. $-\dfrac{4}{3} + \dfrac{1}{4}$

92. $-\dfrac{2}{5} + \left(-\dfrac{2}{3}\right)$

93. $\dfrac{7}{5} + \left(-\dfrac{23}{20}\right)$

94. $\dfrac{3}{4} + \left(-\dfrac{3}{8}\right)$

95. $\dfrac{7}{15} - \left(-\dfrac{4}{3}\right)$

96. $\dfrac{8}{3} - \left(-\dfrac{29}{9}\right)$

97. $\dfrac{8}{15} - \dfrac{7}{10}$

98. $\dfrac{17}{6} - \dfrac{13}{9}$

99. $-\dfrac{33}{10} - \left(-\dfrac{33}{8}\right)$

100. $-\dfrac{29}{6} - \left(-\dfrac{29}{20}\right)$

101. $\dfrac{19}{12} - \left(-\dfrac{41}{18}\right)$

102. $\dfrac{13}{12} - \dfrac{35}{16}$

103. $-\dfrac{2}{3} + \left(-\dfrac{5}{9}\right) + \dfrac{5}{6}$

104. $-\dfrac{1}{2} + \dfrac{3}{8} + \left(-\dfrac{3}{4}\right)$

In Problems 105–124, perform the indicated operation(s).
See Objective 4.

105. $-10.5 + 4$

106. $-13.2 + 7$

107. $-(-3.5) + 4.9$

108. $-(-32.9) + 10.3$

109. $39.1 - (-16.82)$

110. $29.23 - (-12.98)$

111. $-5.21 - (-6.7)$

112. $-4.94 - (-3.87)$

113. $45 - 2.45$

114. $32 - 5.68$

115. $4.3 \cdot 5.8$

116. $3.1 \cdot 10.9$

117. $0.075 \cdot 120$

118. $0.065 \cdot 340$

119. $\dfrac{136.08}{5.6}$

120. $\dfrac{332.59}{7.9}$

121. $\dfrac{25.48}{0.052}$

122. $\dfrac{48}{0.03}$

123. $-1.25 - (-0.6) + 1.6$

124. $-5.82 - (-2.9) + (-2.74)$

Mixed Practice

In Problems 125–156, evaluate and write in lowest terms.

125. $-\dfrac{5}{6} + \dfrac{7}{15}$

126. $-\dfrac{8}{9} + \left(-\dfrac{16}{21}\right)$

127. $-\dfrac{10}{21} \cdot \dfrac{14}{5}$

128. $\dfrac{24}{5} \cdot \left(-\dfrac{35}{4}\right)$

129. $\dfrac{3}{8} \div \left(-\dfrac{9}{16}\right)$

130. $-\dfrac{12}{7} \div \left(-\dfrac{4}{21}\right)$

131. $-\dfrac{5}{12} + \dfrac{2}{12}$

132. $-\dfrac{4}{9} + \dfrac{1}{9}$

133. $-\dfrac{2}{7} - \dfrac{17}{5}$

134. $-\dfrac{3}{4} - \dfrac{1}{5}$

135. $-8.7 - (-10.3)$

136. $-4.63 - (-12.9)$

137. $\dfrac{1}{12} + \left(-\dfrac{5}{28}\right)$

138. $\dfrac{3}{16} + \left(-\dfrac{7}{40}\right)$

139. $-12.03 \cdot 4.2$

140. $34.2 \cdot (-8.43)$

141. $36 \cdot \left(-\dfrac{4}{9}\right)$

142. $-\dfrac{8}{3} \cdot 15$

143. $-27 \div \dfrac{9}{5}$

144. $-24 \div \dfrac{8}{7}$

145. $3.62 - 10.2$

146. $4.75 - 6.2$

147. $\dfrac{-145.518}{18.42}$

148. $\dfrac{-297.078}{22.17}$

149. $\dfrac{12}{7} - \dfrac{17}{14} - \dfrac{48}{21}$

150. $\dfrac{9}{4} - \dfrac{21}{6} - \dfrac{11}{8}$

151. $54.2 - 18.78 - (-2.5) + 20.47$

152. $90.3 - 100.9 - (-34.26) + 32.95$

153. $400 \times 25.8 \times 0.003$

154. $500 \times 12.4 \times 0.02$

155. $-\dfrac{11}{12} - \left(-\dfrac{1}{6}\right) + \dfrac{7}{8}$

156. $\dfrac{8}{15} - \left(-\dfrac{7}{9}\right) + \dfrac{2}{3}$

Applying the Concepts

157. Watching TV If Rachel spends $\dfrac{1}{8}$ of her life watching TV, how many hours of TV does she watch in one week?

158. Halloween Candy Henry decided to make $\dfrac{2}{3}$-oz bags of candy for treats at Halloween. If he bought 16 oz of candy, how many bags will he have to give away?

159. Biology Class Susan's biology class begins with 36 students. If $\dfrac{2}{3}$ will finish the course and $\dfrac{3}{4}$ of those get a passing grade, how many students will pass Susan's biology class this term?

160. Pizza Time Joyce and Ramie bought a pizza. Joyce ate $\dfrac{2}{5}$ of the pizza and Ramie ate $\dfrac{1}{9}$ of what was left. What fraction of the pizza remains uneaten?

161. Overdrawn Maria's checking account was overdrawn by $43.29. The bank charged overdraft fees amounting to $25.50. What is the balance in Maria's checking account now?

162. Temperature The temperature in Yellowstone National Park fell from 25.6° above zero to 13.7° below zero. How much did the temperature drop?

163. Stock Prices The price per share of Intel stock has been up and down lately. On Monday it rose 2.75; on Tuesday it rose 0.87; on Wednesday it dropped 1.12; on Thursday it rose 0.52; and on Friday it fell 0.62. What was the net change in Intel's stock price per share for the week?

164. Bank Balance Henry started the month with $43.68 in his checking account. During the month the following transactions occurred: He deposited his paycheck of $929.30; and he wrote checks for rent $650, phone $33.49, credit card $229.50, cable service $75.50, and groceries $159.30. How much does he have in his account now?

Extending the Concepts

Problems 165–168 use the following definition.

If P and Q are two points on a real number line with coordinates a and b, respectively, the **distance between P and Q**, denoted by $d(P, Q)$, is

$$d(P, Q) = |b - a|$$

165. Find the distance between the points P and Q on the real number line if $P = -9.7$ and $Q = 3.5$.

166. Find the distance between the points P and Q on the real number line if $P = -12.5$ and $Q = 2.6$.

167. Find the distance between the points P and Q on the real number line if $P = -\dfrac{13}{3}$ and $Q = \dfrac{7}{5}$.

168. Find the distance between the points P and Q on the real number line if $P = -\dfrac{5}{6}$ and $Q = 4$.

PUTTING THE CONCEPTS TOGETHER (Sections 1.2–1.5)

These problems cover important concepts from Sections 1.2 through 1.5. We designed these problems so that you can review the chapter so far and show your mastery of the concepts. Take time to work these problems before proceeding with the next section. The answers to these problems are located at the back of the text on page AN-2.

1. Write $\frac{7}{8}$ and $\frac{9}{20}$ as equivalent fractions with the least common denominator.

2. Write $\frac{21}{63}$ as a fraction in lowest terms.

3. Convert $\frac{2}{7}$ to a decimal.

4. Write 0.375 as a fraction in lowest terms.

5. Write 12.3% as a decimal.

6. Write 0.0625 as a percent.

7. Use the set $\left\{ -12, -\frac{14}{7}, -1.25, 0, \sqrt{2}, 3, 11.2 \right\}$ to list all of the elements that are:
   (a) integers
   (b) rational numbers
   (c) irrational numbers
   (d) real numbers

8. Replace the ? with the correct symbol $>, <, =: \frac{1}{8} ? 0.5$

In Problems 9–30, perform the indicated operation and write in lowest terms.

9. $17 + (-28)$

10. $-23 + (-42)$

11. $18 - 45$

12. $3 - (-24)$

13. $-18 - (-12.5)$

14. $(-5)(2)$

15. $25(-4)$

16. $(-8)(-9)$

17. $\frac{-35}{7}$

18. $\frac{-32}{-2}$

19. $27 \div -3$

20. $-\frac{4}{5} - \frac{11}{5}$

21. $7 - \frac{4}{5}$

22. $\frac{7}{12} + \frac{5}{18}$

23. $-\frac{5}{12} - \frac{1}{18}$

24. $\frac{6}{25} \cdot 15 \cdot \frac{1}{2}$

25. $\frac{2}{7} \div (-8)$

26. $\frac{0}{-8}$

27. $3.56 - (-7.2)$

28. $18.946 - 11.3$

29. $62.488 \div 42.8$

30. $(7.94)(2.8)$

1.6 Properties of Real Numbers

OBJECTIVES

1. Understand and Use the Identity Properties of Addition and Multiplication

2. Understand and Use the Commutative Properties of Addition and Multiplication

3. Understand and Use the Associative Properties of Addition and Multiplication

4. Understand the Multiplication and Division Properties of 0

Preparing for Properties of Real Numbers

Before getting started, take the following readiness quiz. If you get a problem wrong, go to the section cited and review the material.

P1. Find the sum: $12 + 3 + (-12)$ [Section 1.4, pp. 29–32]

P2. Find the product: $\frac{3}{4} \cdot 11 \cdot \frac{4}{3}$ [Section 1.5, pp. 39–40]

This section is dedicated to presenting properties of real numbers. A property in mathematics is a rule that is always true. These properties will be used throughout this course and in future math courses, so it is extremely important that you understand these properties and know how to use them.

1   Understand and Use the Identity Properties of Addition and Multiplication

The real number 0 has an interesting property. It turns out that 0 is the only number that when added to any real number a results in the same real number a.

IDENTITY PROPERTY OF ADDITION

For any real number a,

$$0 + a = a + 0 = a$$

That is, the sum of any number and 0 is that number. We call 0 the **additive identity.**

The real number 1 also has an interesting property. Recall that the expression $3 \cdot 5$ is equivalent to adding 5 three times. That is, $3 \cdot 5 = 5 + 5 + 5$. Therefore, $1 \cdot 5$ means to add 5 once, so, $1 \cdot 5 = 5$. This result is true in general.

IDENTITY PROPERTY OF MULTIPLICATION

For any real number a,

$$a \cdot 1 = 1 \cdot a = a$$

That is, the product of any number and 1 is that number. We call 1 the **multiplicative identity.**

We also use the multiplicative identity throughout our math careers to create new expressions that are equivalent to previous expressions. For example, the expressions

$$\frac{4}{5} \quad \text{and} \quad \frac{4}{5} \cdot \frac{3}{3}$$

are equivalent because $\frac{3}{3} = 1$.

Conversion

A practical use of the multiplicative identity is conversion. **Conversion** is changing the units of measure (such as inches or pounds) from one measure to a different measure. For example, we might change a length from inches to feet or a weight from ounces to pounds.

EXAMPLE 1 Converting from Inches to Feet

Janice measures her family room and finds that its length is 184 inches. How many feet long is Janice's family room? (*Note*: 12 inches = 1 foot)

Solution

The trick in doing conversions is to make sure that the units of measure that you are trying to remove get divided out and the new units of measure remain. In this problem, we want the inches to divide out with feet remaining. Because 12 inches equals 1 foot, multiplying 184 inches by $\dfrac{1 \text{ foot}}{12 \text{ inches}}$ is the same as multiplying by one.

$$184 \text{ inches} = 184 \text{ inches} \cdot \overbrace{\frac{1 \text{ foot}}{12 \text{ inches}}}^{\text{Multiplying by 1}}$$

The inches "divide out": $\quad = \dfrac{184}{12} \text{ feet}$

$184 = 2 \cdot 2 \cdot 2 \cdot 23;\ 12 = 2 \cdot 2 \cdot 3: \quad = \dfrac{2 \cdot 2 \cdot 2 \cdot 23}{2 \cdot 2 \cdot 3} \text{ feet}$

Divide out common factors: $\quad = \dfrac{\cancel{2} \cdot \cancel{2} \cdot 2 \cdot 23}{\cancel{2} \cdot \cancel{2} \cdot 3} \text{ feet}$

$$= \dfrac{46}{3} \text{ feet}$$

Work Smart

$$\begin{array}{r} 15 \\ 3\overline{)46} \\ -3 \\ \hline 16 \\ -15 \\ \hline 1 \end{array}$$

So 184 inches equals $\dfrac{46}{3}$ feet. Because 46 divided by 3 is 15 with a remainder of 1 (Why? See the Work Smart), $\dfrac{46}{3}$ feet is equivalent to $15\dfrac{1}{3}$ feet. Since $\dfrac{1}{3}$ foot $\cdot \dfrac{12 \text{ inches}}{1 \text{ foot}} = 4$ inches, we have that $\dfrac{46}{3}$ feet is equivalent to 15 feet, 4 inches. ∎

Quick ✔

1. The product of any real number and the number ___ is that number.

In Problems 2–4, convert each measurement to the indicated unit of measurement.

2. 96 inches = ? feet [1 foot = 12 inches]

3. 500 minutes = ? hours [60 minutes = 1 hour]

4. 88 ounces = ? pounds [16 ounces = 1 pound]

⌐2⌐ Understand and Use the Commutative Properties of Addition and Multiplication

We illustrate another property of real numbers in the next example.

EXAMPLE 2 Illustrating the Commutative Properties

(a) $4 + 7 = 11$ and
$7 + 4 = 11$ so
$4 + 7 = 7 + 4$

(b) $3 \cdot 8 = 24$ and
$8 \cdot 3 = 24$ so
$3 \cdot 8 = 8 \cdot 3$ ∎

The results of Example 2 are true in general.

COMMUTATIVE PROPERTIES OF ADDITION AND MULTIPLICATION

If a and b are real numbers, then

$$a + b = b + a \quad \text{and} \quad a \cdot b = b \cdot a$$

In Words

The Commutative Property of real numbers states that the order in which we add or multiply real numbers does not affect the final result.

We add real numbers from left to right. We multiply real numbers from left to right. The **Commutative Property** allows us to write $3 + 5$ as $5 + 3$ or $3 \cdot 5$ as $5 \cdot 3$ without affecting the value of the expression. Why is this important? As the next example illustrates, by rearranging addition or multiplication problems, some expressions become much easier to evaluate.

EXAMPLE 3 Using the Commutative Property of Addition

Evaluate the expression: $18 + 3 + (-18)$

Solution

$$18 + 3 + (-18) = 18 + (-18) + 3$$
$$\text{Add } 18 + (-18)\text{:} = 0 + 3$$
$$\text{Add } 0 + 3\text{:} = 3$$

It is also true here that if we add in order, from left to right, we obtain the sum $18 + 3 + (-18) = 21 + (-18) = 3$. Notice that rearranging the numbers made the problem easier! ∎

Does subtraction obey the Commutative Property? In other words, does $3 - 14 = 14 - 3$? Because $3 - 14 = 3 + (-14) = -11$ while $14 - 3 = 14 + (-3) = 11$, we see that **subtraction is not commutative.**

Quick ✔

5. The Commutative Property of Addition states that for any real numbers a and b, $a + b =$ __ $+$ __.

6. The sum of any real number and its opposite is equal to _____.

In Problems 7–9, use the Commutative Property of Addition and the Additive Inverse Property to find the sum of the real numbers.

7. $(-8) + 22 + 8$

8. $\dfrac{8}{15} + \dfrac{3}{20} + \left(-\dfrac{8}{15}\right)$

9. $2.1 + 11.98 + (-2.1)$

EXAMPLE 4 **Using the Commutative Property of Multiplication**

Find each product.

(a) $-27 \cdot 7 \cdot \left(-\dfrac{2}{9}\right)$

(b) $100 \cdot 307.5 \cdot 0.01$

Solution

(a) $-27 \cdot 7 \cdot \left(-\dfrac{2}{9}\right) = -27 \cdot \left(-\dfrac{2}{9}\right) \cdot 7$

$$= -\overset{3}{\cancel{27}} \cdot \left(-\dfrac{2}{\underset{1}{\cancel{9}}}\right) \cdot 7$$

$$= -3 \cdot (-2) \cdot 7$$

$$= 6 \cdot 7$$

$$= 42$$

(b) $100 \cdot 307.5 \cdot 0.01 = 100 \cdot 0.01 \cdot 307.5$

$$= 1 \cdot 307.5$$

$$= 307.5$$

Quick ✔ *In Problems 10–12, find the product of the real numbers.*

10. $-8 \cdot (-13) \cdot \left(-\dfrac{3}{4}\right)$

11. $\dfrac{5}{22} \cdot \dfrac{18}{331} \cdot \left(-\dfrac{44}{5}\right)$

12. $100{,}000 \cdot 349 \cdot 0.00001$

Work Smart

Neither division nor subtraction is commutative.

Does division obey the Commutative Property? That is, does $a \div b = b \div a$? To see the answer, we ask does $8 \div 2 = 2 \div 8$? Because $8 \div 2 = \dfrac{8}{2} = 4$, but $2 \div 8 = \dfrac{2}{8} = \dfrac{1}{4}$, we conclude that **division is not commutative.**

⌐3 Understand and Use the Associative Properties of Addition and Multiplication

Sometimes **grouping symbols** such as parentheses ( ), brackets [ ], or braces { } are used to indicate that the operation within the grouping symbols is to be performed first. For example, $3 \cdot (8 + 3)$ indicates that we should first add 8 and 3 and then multiply this sum by 3.

Earlier we mentioned that addition is to be performed from left to right. We also stated that multiplication should be performed from left to right. But does the order in which we add (or multiply) three or more numbers matter? Let's see.

EXAMPLE 5 Illustrating the Associative Properties

 (a) $2 + (8 + 6) = 2 + 14 = 16$ and $(2 + 8) + 6 = 10 + 6 = 16$
 so
$$2 + (8 + 6) = (2 + 8) + 6$$
 (b) $-4 \cdot (9 \cdot 2) = -4 \cdot (18) = -72$ and $(-4 \cdot 9) \cdot 2 = -36 \cdot 2 = -72$
 so
$$-4 \cdot (9 \cdot 2) = (-4 \cdot 9) \cdot 2$$

Examples 5(a) and (b) illustrate the **Associative Properties of Addition and Multiplication**.

ASSOCIATIVE PROPERTIES OF ADDITION AND MULTIPLICATION

If $a, b,$ and c are real numbers, then
$$a + (b + c) = (a + b) + c = a + b + c$$
$$a \cdot (b \cdot c) = (a \cdot b) \cdot c = a \cdot b \cdot c$$

EXAMPLE 6 Using the Associative Property of Addition

Use the Associative Property of Addition to evaluate $23 + 453 + (-453)$.

Solution

There are three numbers to be added. However, we see that the second and third numbers are additive inverses, so we use the Associative Property of Addition and insert parentheses around $453 + (-453)$ and perform this operation first.
$$23 + 453 + (-453) = 23 + (453 + (-453))$$
$$= 23 + 0$$
$$= 23$$

EXAMPLE 7 Using the Associative Property of Multiplication

Use the Associative Property of Multiplication to evaluate $-\dfrac{3}{11} \cdot \dfrac{9}{4} \cdot \dfrac{8}{3}$.

Solution

There are three factors. If we look carefully at the problem, we notice that the second and third factors have common factors that can be divided out. So, we use the Associative Property of Multiplication and insert parentheses around $\dfrac{9}{4} \cdot \dfrac{8}{3}$ and perform this operation first.

$$-\frac{3}{11} \cdot \frac{9}{4} \cdot \frac{8}{3} = -\frac{3}{11} \cdot \left(\frac{9}{4} \cdot \frac{8}{3} \right)$$
$$= -\frac{3}{11} \cdot \frac{\overset{3}{\cancel{9}}}{\underset{1}{\cancel{4}}} \cdot \frac{\overset{2}{\cancel{8}}}{\underset{1}{\cancel{3}}}$$
$$= -\frac{3}{11} \cdot (3 \cdot 2)$$
$$= -\frac{3}{11} \cdot 6$$
$$= -\frac{18}{11}$$

Quick ✔ *In Problems 13–16, use an Associative Property to evaluate each expression.*

13. $14 + 101 + (-101)$

14. $14 \cdot \dfrac{1}{5} \cdot 5$

15. $-34.2 + 12.6 + (-2.6)$

16. $\dfrac{19}{2} \cdot \dfrac{4}{38} \cdot \dfrac{50}{13}$

⌐4⌐ Understand the Multiplication and Division Properties of 0

We know that when we multiply any real number a by 1, the product is a. Now let's look at multiplication by zero.

MULTIPLICATION PROPERTY OF ZERO

For any real number a, the product of a and 0 is always 0; that is,

$$a \cdot 0 = 0 \cdot a = 0$$

We now introduce some division properties of the number 0.

DIVISION PROPERTIES OF ZERO

For any nonzero real number a,

1. The quotient of 0 and a is 0. That is, $\dfrac{0}{a} = 0$.

2. The quotient of a and 0 is **undefined.** That is, $\dfrac{a}{0}$ is undefined.

Work Smart

Division by zero is not allowed. That is, 0 cannot be used as a divisor.

To see why these statements are true, consider the following. When we divide, we can check the quotient by multiplication. For example, $\dfrac{12}{4} = 3$ because $4 \cdot 3 = 12$. In the same way, $\dfrac{0}{4} = 0$ because $4 \cdot 0 = 0$. However, what is the value of $\dfrac{12}{0}$? To determine this quotient, we should be able to determine a real number such that $0 \cdot \square = 12$. But since the product of 0 and every real number is 0, there is no replacement value for $\square$.

EXAMPLE 8 Using Zero as a Divisor and a Dividend

Find the quotient:

(a) $\dfrac{23}{0}$

(b) $\dfrac{0}{17}$

Solution

(a) $\dfrac{23}{0}$ is undefined because 0 is the divisor.

(b) $\dfrac{0}{17} = 0$ because 0 is the dividend. ∎

Quick ✔ *In Problems 17–20, tell if the quotient is zero or undefined.*

17. $\dfrac{0}{22}$

18. $\dfrac{-11}{0}$

19. $-\dfrac{0}{5}$

20. $\dfrac{5678}{0}$

We conclude this section with a summary of the properties of addition, multiplication, and division.

SUMMARY PROPERTIES OF ADDITION

Identity Property of Addition   For any real number $a, 0 + a = a + 0 = a.$

Commutative Property of Addition   If a and b are real numbers, then $a + b = b + a.$

Additive Inverse Property   For any real number $a, a + (-a) = -a + a = 0.$

Associative Property of Addition   If $a, b,$ and c are real numbers, then $a + (b + c) = (a + b) + c.$

SUMMARY PROPERTIES OF MULTIPLICATION AND DIVISION

Identity Property of Multiplication $a \cdot 1 = 1 \cdot a = a$ for any real number a.

Commutative Property of Multiplication   If a and b are real numbers, then $a \cdot b = b \cdot a.$

Multiplicative Inverse Property

$$a \cdot \frac{1}{a} = \frac{1}{a} \cdot a = 1 \quad \text{provided that } a \neq 0$$

Associative Property of Multiplication   If $a, b,$ and c are real numbers, then $a \cdot (b \cdot c) = (a \cdot b) \cdot c.$

Multiplication Property of Zero   For any real number a, the product of a and 0 is always 0; that is, $a \cdot 0 = 0 \cdot a = 0.$

Division Properties of Zero   For any nonzero number a,

1. The quotient of 0 and a is 0. That is, $\dfrac{0}{a} = 0.$

2. The quotient of a and 0 is undefined. That is, $\dfrac{a}{0}$ is undefined.

1.6 EXERCISES

PRACTICE   WATCH   DOWNLOAD   READ   REVIEW

1–20. *are the* Quick ✔*s that follow each* EXAMPLE

Building Skills

In Problems 21–30, convert each measurement to the indicated unit of measurement. See Objective 1. Use the following conversions:

1 foot = 12 inches   3 feet = 1 yard
1 gallon = 4 quarts   100 centimeters = 1 meter
16 ounces = 1 pound

21. 13 feet to inches

22. 130 feet to yards

⊜ **23.** 4500 centimeters to meters

24. 5900 centimeters to meters

25. 42 quarts to gallons

26. 58 quarts to gallons

27. 180 ounces to pounds

28. 120 ounces to pounds

29. 16,200 seconds to hours

30. 22,500 seconds to hours

In Problems 31–46, state the property of real numbers that is being illustrated. See Objectives 2, 3, and 4.

31. $16 + (-16) = 0$

32. $4 \cdot 63 \cdot \dfrac{1}{4} = 4 \cdot \dfrac{1}{4} \cdot 63$

33. $\dfrac{3}{4}$ is equivalent to $\dfrac{3}{4} \cdot \dfrac{5}{5}$

34. $4 + 5 + (-4)$ is equivalent to $4 + (-4) + 5$

35. $12 \cdot \dfrac{1}{12} = 1$

36. $-236 + 236 = 0$

37. $34.2 + (-34.2) = 0$

38. $(4 \cdot 5) \cdot 7 = 4 \cdot (5 \cdot 7)$

39. $\dfrac{0}{17}$

40. $\dfrac{-8}{0}$

41. $\dfrac{2}{3} \cdot \left(-\dfrac{12}{43}\right) \cdot \dfrac{3}{2} = \dfrac{2}{3} \cdot \dfrac{3}{2} \cdot \left(-\dfrac{12}{43}\right)$

42. $\dfrac{5}{12} \cdot \dfrac{12}{5} = 1$

43. $5.23 + 4.98 + (-5.23) = 5.23 + (-5.23) + 4.98$

44. $16.4 \cdot 0 = 0$

45. $\dfrac{21}{0}$

46. $\dfrac{0}{106}$

Mixed Practice

In Problems 47–66, evaluate each expression by using the properties of real numbers.

47. $54 + 29 + (-54)$

48. $46 + 59 + (-46)$

49. $\dfrac{9}{5} \cdot \dfrac{5}{9} \cdot 18$

50. $\dfrac{4}{9} \cdot \dfrac{9}{4} \cdot 28$

51. $-25 \cdot 13 \cdot \dfrac{1}{5}$

52. $36 \cdot (-12) \cdot \dfrac{1}{6}$

53. $347 + 456 + (-456)$

54. $593 + 306 + (-306)$

55. $\dfrac{9}{2} \cdot \left(-\dfrac{10}{3}\right) \cdot 6$

56. $\dfrac{13}{2} \cdot \dfrac{8}{39} \cdot \dfrac{39}{4}$

57. $\dfrac{7}{0}$

58. $\dfrac{0}{100}$

59. $100(-34)(0.01)$

60. $4000(0.5)(0.001)$

61. $569.003 \cdot 0$

62. $104 \cdot \dfrac{1}{104}$

63. $\dfrac{45}{3902} + \left(-\dfrac{45}{3902}\right)$

64. $30 \cdot \dfrac{4}{4}$

65. $-\dfrac{5}{44} \cdot \dfrac{80}{3} \cdot \dfrac{11}{5}$

66. $\dfrac{7}{48} \cdot \left(-\dfrac{21}{4}\right) \cdot \dfrac{12}{7}$

Applying the Concepts

67. Balancing the Checkbook Alberto's checking account balance at the start of the month was $321.03. During the month, he wrote checks for $32.84, $85.03, and $120.56. He also deposited a check for $120.56. What is Alberto's balance at the end of the month?

68. Stock Price Before the opening bell on Monday, a certain stock was priced at $32.04. On Monday the stock was up $0.54, on Tuesday it was down $0.32, and on Wednesday it was down $0.54. What was the closing price of the stock on Wednesday?

Extending the Concepts

In Problems 69–72, insert parentheses to make the statement true.

69. $-3 - 4 - 10 = 3$

70. $-6 - 4 + 10 = -20$

71. $-15 + 10 - 4 - 8 = -1$

72. $25 - 6 - 10 - 1 = 28$

73. Convert 30 miles per hour to feet per second. (*Note*: 1 mile = 5280 feet)

74. Convert 40 miles per hour to feet per second. (*Note*: 1 mile = 5280 feet)

Explaining the Concepts

75. In your own words, explain why 0 does not have a multiplicative inverse.

76. Why does $2(4 \cdot 5)$ not equal $(2 \cdot 4) \cdot (2 \cdot 5)$?

77. Why does $\dfrac{0}{4} = 0$? Why is $\dfrac{4}{0}$ undefined?

78. How is the Identity Property of Addition related to the Additive Inverse Property?

79. How is the Identity Property of Multiplication related to the Multiplicative Inverse Property?

1.7 Exponents and the Order of Operations

OBJECTIVES

1. Evaluate Exponential Expressions
2. Apply the Rules for Order of Operations

Preparing for Exponents and the Order of Operations
Before getting started, take this readiness quiz. If you get a problem wrong, go back to the section cited and review the material.

P1. Find the sum: $9 + (-19)$ [Section 1.4, pp. 29–32]

P2. Find the difference: $28 - (-7)$ [Section 1.4, pp. 32–33]

P3. Find the product: $-7 \cdot \dfrac{8}{3} \cdot 36$ [Section 1.5, pp. 39–40]

P4. Find the quotient: $\dfrac{100}{-15}$ [Section 1.4, pp. 35–37]

1 Evaluate Exponential Expressions

Suppose that we wanted to multiply 2 eight times. We would write this as

$$2 \cdot 2 \cdot 2 \cdot 2 \cdot 2 \cdot 2 \cdot 2 \cdot 2$$

That's a lot of writing! To reduce the amount of writing that is needed to represent this repeated multiplication, we introduce a new notation. Using this new notation, called **exponential notation,** we would write $2 \cdot 2 \cdot 2 \cdot 2 \cdot 2 \cdot 2 \cdot 2 \cdot 2$ as 2^8. The number 2 is called the **base** and the number 8 is called the **exponent**.

EXPONENTIAL NOTATION

If n is a natural number and a is a real number, then

$$a^n = \underbrace{a \cdot a \cdot a \cdot \,\cdots\, \cdot a}_{n \text{ factors}}$$

where a is called the **base** and the natural number n is called the **exponent** or **power.** The exponent tells the number of times the base is used as a factor.

An expression written in the form a^n is said to be in **exponential form.** The expression 6^2 is read "six squared," 8^3 is read "eight cubed," and the expression 11^4 is read "eleven to the fourth power." In general, we read a^n as "a to the nth power."

EXAMPLE 1 **Writing a Numerical Expression in Exponential Form**

Write each expression in exponential form.

    (a) $5 \cdot 5 \cdot 5$ **(b)** $(-4) \cdot (-4) \cdot (-4) \cdot (-4) \cdot (-4) \cdot (-4)$

Solution

    (a) The expression $5 \cdot 5 \cdot 5$ contains three factors of 5, so $5 \cdot 5 \cdot 5 = 5^3$.

    (b) The expression $(-4) \cdot (-4) \cdot (-4) \cdot (-4) \cdot (-4) \cdot (-4)$ contains 6 factors of -4, so $(-4) \cdot (-4) \cdot (-4) \cdot (-4) \cdot (-4) \cdot (-4) = (-4)^6$. ∎

Quick ✔ *In Problems 1–3, write each expression in exponential form.*
  1. $11 \cdot 11 \cdot 11 \cdot 11 \cdot 11$ **2.** $(-7) \cdot (-7) \cdot (-7) \cdot (-7)$ **3.** $(-2) \cdot (-2) \cdot (-2)$

Preparing for...Answers **P1.** -10
P2. 35 **P3.** -672 **P4.** $-\dfrac{20}{3}$

To evaluate an exponential expression, we write the expression in **expanded form.** For example, 2^8 in expanded form would be $2 \cdot 2 \cdot 2 \cdot 2 \cdot 2 \cdot 2 \cdot 2 \cdot 2$. We then perform the multiplication.

EXAMPLE 2 **Evaluating an Exponential Expression**

Evaluate each exponential expression:

(a) 6^4 (b) $\left(\dfrac{5}{3}\right)^5$

Solution

(a) $6^4 = 6 \cdot 6 \cdot 6 \cdot 6$

$= 1296$

(b) $\left(\dfrac{5}{3}\right)^5 = \left(\dfrac{5}{3}\right)\left(\dfrac{5}{3}\right)\left(\dfrac{5}{3}\right)\left(\dfrac{5}{3}\right)\left(\dfrac{5}{3}\right)$

$= \dfrac{5 \cdot 5 \cdot 5 \cdot 5 \cdot 5}{3 \cdot 3 \cdot 3 \cdot 3 \cdot 3}$

$= \dfrac{3125}{243}$

EXAMPLE 3 **Evaluating an Exponential Expression—Odd Exponent**

Evaluate each exponential expression:

(a) $(-5)^3$ (b) -5^3

Solution

(a) $(-5)^3 = (-5) \cdot (-5) \cdot (-5)$

$= -125$

(b) $-5^3 = -(5 \cdot 5 \cdot 5)$

$= -125$

EXAMPLE 4 **Evaluating an Exponential Expression—Even Exponent**

Evaluate each exponential expression:

(a) $(-5)^4$ (b) -5^4

Solution

(a) $(-5)^4 = (-5) \cdot (-5) \cdot (-5) \cdot (-5)$

$= 625$

(b) $-5^4 = -(5 \cdot 5 \cdot 5 \cdot 5)$

$= -625$

Work Smart

There is a difference between finding $(-5)^4$ and -5^4.

The parentheses around (-5) tell us to use four factors of -5. However, in the expression -5^4, we use 5 as a factor four times and then multiply the result by -1. We could also read -5^4 as "Take the opposite of the quantity 5^4."

Quick ✔ *In Problems 4–9, evaluate each exponential expression.*

4. 2^4 **5.** $(-7)^2$ **6.** $\left(-\dfrac{1}{6}\right)^3$

7. $(0.9)^2$ **8.** -2^4 **9.** $(-2)^4$

⌐2 Apply the Rules for Order of Operations

Suppose you wish to evaluate the mathematical expression $3 \cdot 5 + 4$. Do you multiply first, then add to get $15 + 4 = 19$ *or* add first, then multiply to get $3 \cdot 9 = 27$?

Because $3 \cdot 5$ is equivalent to $5 + 5 + 5$, we have

In Words

Multiply first, then add.

$$3 \cdot 5 + 4 = 5 + 5 + 5 + 4$$
$$= 19$$

Based on this, **whenever the two operations of addition and multiplication appear in the same expression, the multiplication operation is always performed first, followed by the addition operation.**

Because any division problem can be written as a multiplication problem, we perform division before addition as well. Also, because any subtraction problem can be written as an addition problem, we perform multiplication and division before addition and subtraction.

EXAMPLE 5   Finding the Value of an Expression Containing Multiplication, Division, and Addition

Evaluate each expression:

   (a) $11 + 2 \cdot (-6)$ **(b)** $7 + 12 \div 3 \cdot 5$

Solution

   (a)   Multiply first: $11 + 2 \cdot (-6) = 11 + (-12)$

                     Add: $= -1$

   (b)   Multiply/divide left to right: $7 + 12 \div 3 \cdot 5 = 7 + 4 \cdot 5$

                     Multiply: $= 7 + 20$

                                        $= 27$

Quick ✔ *In Problems 10–14, evaluate each expression.*

10. $1 + 7 \cdot 2$ **11.** $-11 \cdot 3 + 2$ **12.** $18 + 3 \div \left(-\dfrac{1}{2}\right)$

13. $9 \cdot 4 - 5$ **14.** $\dfrac{15}{2} \div (-5) - \dfrac{3}{2}$

Parentheses

If we want to add two numbers first and then multiply, we use parentheses and write $(3 + 5) \cdot 4$. In other words, **the expression in parentheses is always evaluated first.**

EXAMPLE 6   Finding the Value of an Expression Containing Parentheses

Evaluate each expression:

   (a) $(5 + 3) \cdot 2$ **(b)** $\left(\dfrac{3}{2} - \dfrac{5}{2}\right)\left(\dfrac{7}{3} + \dfrac{2}{3}\right)$

Solution

   (a) $(5 + 3) \cdot 2 = 8 \cdot 2$

                  $= 16$

   (b) $\left(\dfrac{3}{2} - \dfrac{5}{2}\right)\left(\dfrac{7}{3} + \dfrac{2}{3}\right) = \left(-\dfrac{2}{2}\right)\left(\dfrac{9}{3}\right)$

                        $= (-1)(3)$

                        $= -3$

Quick ✔ *In Problems 15–17, evaluate each expression.*

15. $8(2 + 3)$ **16.** $(2 - 9) \cdot (5 + 4)$ **17.** $\left(\dfrac{6}{7} + \dfrac{8}{7}\right) \cdot \left(\dfrac{11}{8} + \dfrac{5}{8}\right)$

The Division Bar

Another type of problem involves dividing numerical expressions that contain a division bar. When we divide numerical expressions in this form, we agree to treat the terms above and below the division bar as if they were in parentheses. To evaluate the numerical expression $\dfrac{3+5}{9+7}$, we see that

$$\frac{3+5}{9+7} = \frac{(3+5)}{(9+7)} = \frac{8}{16} = \frac{8 \cdot 1}{8 \cdot 2} = \frac{1}{2}$$

EXAMPLE 7 Finding the Value of an Expression That Contains a Division Bar

Evaluate each expression:

(a) $\dfrac{7 \cdot 3}{3 + 9 \cdot 2}$

(b) $\dfrac{1 + 7 \div \frac{1}{5}}{-6 \cdot 2 + 8}$

Solution

(a) Multiply: $\dfrac{7 \cdot 3}{3 + 9 \cdot 2} = \dfrac{21}{3 + 18}$

Add: $\qquad\qquad = \dfrac{21}{21}$

$\qquad\qquad = 1$

(b) Write division as multiplication: $\dfrac{1 + 7 \div \frac{1}{5}}{-6 \cdot 2 + 8} = \dfrac{1 + 7 \cdot 5}{-6 \cdot 2 + 8}$

Multiply: $\qquad\qquad = \dfrac{1 + 35}{-12 + 8}$

Add: $\qquad\qquad = \dfrac{36}{-4}$

$\qquad\qquad = \dfrac{9 \cdot 4}{-1 \cdot 4}$

$\qquad\qquad = -9$

Quick ✔ *In Problems 18–20, evaluate each expression.*

18. $\dfrac{2 + 5 \cdot 6}{-3 \cdot 8 - 4}$

19. $\dfrac{(12 + 14) \cdot 2}{13 \cdot 2 + 13 \cdot 5}$

20. $\dfrac{4 + 3 \div \frac{1}{7}}{2 \cdot 9 - 3}$

Embedded Grouping Symbols

Grouping symbols include parentheses ( ), brackets [ ], braces { }, and absolute value symbols, | |. They are used to group numbers and mathematical expressions together so that operations within the grouping symbols are performed first. **When multiple pairs of grouping symbols exist and are nested inside one another, we evaluate the information in the innermost grouping symbols first and work our way outward.**

EXAMPLE 8 Finding the Value of an Expression Containing Grouping Symbols

Evaluate each expression:

(a) $2 \cdot [3 \cdot (6 + 3) - 7]$

(b) $\left[4 + \left(\dfrac{2}{3} \cdot (-9) \right) \right] \cdot 3$

Solution

(a) Perform the operation in parentheses first: $2 \cdot [3 \cdot (6 + 3) - 7] = 2 \cdot [3 \cdot 9 - 7]$

Perform the operations in brackets, $= 2 \cdot [27 - 7]$
multiply first: $= 2 \cdot [20]$

$= 40$

(b) Perform the operation in parentheses first: $\left[4 + \left(\dfrac{2}{3} \cdot (-9)\right)\right] \cdot 3 = [4 + (-6)] \cdot 3$

Perform the operation in brackets: $= -2 \cdot 3$

$= -6$ ∎

Quick ✔ *In Problems 21 and 22, evaluate each expression.*

21. $4 \cdot [2 \cdot (3 + 7) - 15]$ **22.** $2 \cdot \{4 \cdot [26 - (9 + 7)] - 15\} - 10$

When do we evaluate exponents in the order of operations? Consider the expression $2 \cdot 4^3$. Do we multiply first and then evaluate the exponent to obtain $2 \cdot 4^3 = 8^3 = 512$, or do we evaluate the exponent first and then multiply to obtain $2 \cdot 4^3 = 2 \cdot 64 = 128$? Because $2 \cdot 4^3 = 2 \cdot 4 \cdot 4 \cdot 4 = 128$, we **evaluate exponents before multiplication.**

EXAMPLE 9 Finding the Value of an Expression Containing Exponents

Evaluate each of the following:

(a) $2 + 7(-4)^2$ **(b)** $\dfrac{2 \cdot 3^2 + 4}{3(2 - 6)}$

Solution

(a) Evaluate the exponent: $2 + 7(-4)^2 = 2 + 7 \cdot 16$

Multiply: $= 2 + 112$

Add: $= 114$

(b) Evaluate the exponent: $\dfrac{2 \cdot 3^2 + 4}{3(2 - 6)} = \dfrac{2 \cdot 9 + 4}{3(-4)}$

Find products: $= \dfrac{18 + 4}{-12}$

Add terms in numerator: $= \dfrac{22}{-12}$

Write in lowest terms: $= \dfrac{\cancel{2} \cdot 11}{\cancel{2} \cdot -6}$

$= -\dfrac{11}{6}$ ∎

Quick ✔ *In Problems 23–26, evaluate each of the following:*

23. $\dfrac{7 - 5^2}{2}$ **24.** $3(7 - 3)^2$

25. $\dfrac{(-3)^2 + 7(1 - 3)}{3 \cdot 2 + 5}$ **26.** $2 + 5 \cdot 3^2 - \dfrac{3}{2} \cdot 2^2$

We now summarize the rules for performing operations on mathematical expressions.

> **ORDER OF OPERATIONS**
>
> **Step 1:** Perform all operations within *grouping symbols* first. When an expression has nested grouping symbols, begin within the innermost pair of grouping symbols and work outward.
>
> **Step 2:** Evaluate expressions containing exponents.
>
> **Step 3:** Perform *multiplication and division* in the order they occur, working from *left to right*.
>
> **Step 4:** Perform *addition and subtraction* in the order they occur, working from *left to right*.

EXAMPLE 10 How to Evaluate an Expression Using Order of Operations

Evaluate: $18 + 7(2^3 - 26) + 5^2$

Step-by-Step Solution

Steps 1 and 2: We evaluate the expression in the parentheses first. In the parentheses, evaluate the expression containing the exponent first.	$18 + 7(2^3 - 26) + 5^2 = 18 + 7(8 - 26) + 25$
Evaluate $8 - 26$ in the parentheses; evaluate 5^2:	$= 18 + 7(-18) + 25$
Step 3: Perform multiplication and division in the order they occur, working from left to right.	Multiply $7(-18)$: $\quad = 18 - 126 + 25$
Step 4: Perform addition and subtraction in the order in which they occur, working from left to right.	$= -108 + 25$ $= -83$

EXAMPLE 11 Evaluating a Numerical Expression Using Order of Operations

Evaluate: $\left(\dfrac{2^3 - 6}{10 - 2 \cdot 3} \right)^2$

Solution

Evaluate the exponential expression inside the parentheses:
$$\left(\frac{2^3 - 6}{10 - 2 \cdot 3} \right)^2 = \left(\frac{8 - 6}{10 - 2 \cdot 3} \right)^2$$

Multiply inside the parentheses:
$$= \left(\frac{8 - 6}{10 - 6} \right)^2$$

Add/subtract inside the parentheses:
$$= \left(\frac{2}{4} \right)^2$$

Divide out common factors:
$$= \left(\frac{1 \cdot 2}{2 \cdot 2} \right)^2$$

$$= \left(\frac{1}{2} \right)^2$$

Evaluate exponential expression:
$$= \frac{1}{4}$$

Work Smart: Study Skills

Selected problems in the exercise sets are identified by a symbol. For extra help, view the worked solutions to these problems on the book's CD Lecture Series.

Quick ✔ *In Problems 27–30, evaluate each expression.*

27. $\dfrac{(4-10)^2}{2^3-5}$

28. $-3[(-4)^2 - 5(8-6)]^2$

29. $\dfrac{(2.9+7.1)^2}{5^2-15}$

30. $\left(\dfrac{4^2-4(-3)(1)}{7\cdot2}\right)^2$

1.7 EXERCISES

MyMathLab

 PRACTICE   WATCH   DOWNLOAD   READ   REVIEW

1–30. *are the* Quick ✔*s that follow each* EXAMPLE

Building Skills

In Problems 31–34, write in exponential form. See Objective 1.

31. $5\cdot5$

32. $4\cdot4\cdot4\cdot4\cdot4$

33. $\dfrac{3}{5}\cdot\dfrac{3}{5}\cdot\dfrac{3}{5}$

34. $(-8)(-8)(-8)$

In Problems 35–54, evaluate each exponential expression. See Objective 1.

35. 8^2

36. 4^3

 37. $(-8)^2$

38. $(-4)^3$

39. 10^3

40. 2^5

41. $\left(\dfrac{3}{4}\right)^3$

42. $\left(\dfrac{5}{2}\right)^4$

43. $(1.5)^2$

44. $(0.04)^2$

45. -3^2

46. -5^4

47. -1^{20}

48. $(-1)^{19}$

49. 0^4

50. 1^6

51. $\left(-\dfrac{1}{2}\right)^6$

52. $\left(-\dfrac{3}{2}\right)^5$

53. $\left(-\dfrac{1}{3}\right)^3$

54. $\left(-\dfrac{3}{4}\right)^2$

In Problems 55–86, evaluate each expression. See Objective 2.

55. $2+3\cdot4$

56. $12+8\cdot3$

57. $-5\cdot3+12$

58. $-3\cdot12+9$

59. $100\div2\cdot50$

60. $50\div5\cdot4$

61. $156-3\cdot2+10$

62. $86-4\cdot3+6$

63. $(2+3)\cdot4$

64. $(7-5)\cdot\dfrac{5}{2}$

65. $8\div4\cdot2$

66. $4\div7\cdot21$

67. $\dfrac{4+2}{2+8}$

68. $\dfrac{5+3}{3+15}$

69. $\dfrac{14-6}{6-14}$

70. $\dfrac{15-7}{7-15}$

 71. $13-[3+(-8)4]$

72. $12-[7+(-6)3]$

73. $(-8.75-1.25)\div(-2)$

74. $(-11.8-15.2)\div(-2)$

75. $4-2^3$

76. $10-4^2$

77. $15+4\cdot5^2$

78. $10+3\cdot2^4$

79. $-2^3+3^2\div(2^2-1)$

80. $-5^2+3^2\div(3^2+9)$

81. $\left(\dfrac{4^2-3}{12-2\cdot5}\right)^2$

82. $\left(\dfrac{7-5^2}{8+4\cdot2}\right)^2$

83. $-2\cdot[5\cdot(9-3)-3\cdot6]$

84. $3\cdot[6\cdot(5-2)-2\cdot5]$

85. $\left(\dfrac{4}{3}+\dfrac{5}{6}\right)\left(\dfrac{2}{5}-\dfrac{9}{10}\right)$

86. $\left(\dfrac{3}{4}+\dfrac{1}{2}\right)\left(\dfrac{2}{3}-\dfrac{1}{2}\right)$

Mixed Practice

In Problems 87–110, evaluate each expression.

87. $-2.5+4.5\div1.5$

88. $7.2-10.4\div5.2$

89. $4+2\cdot(6-2)$

90. $3+6\cdot(9-5)$

91. $\dfrac{12-16\div4+(-24)}{16\cdot2-4\cdot0}$

92. $\dfrac{6+15\div3+16}{6+10\cdot0}$

93. $\left(\dfrac{2-(-4)^3}{5^2-7\cdot2}\right)^2$

94. $\left(\dfrac{9\cdot2-(-2)^3}{4^2+3(-1)^5}\right)^2$

95. $\dfrac{5^2-10}{3^2+6}$

96. $\dfrac{12(2)^3}{4^2+4\cdot5}$

97. $\left|6 \cdot (5 - 3^2)\right|$

98. $-6 \cdot (2 + \left|2 \cdot 3 - 4^2\right|)$

99. $\dfrac{81}{8} + \dfrac{13}{4} \div \dfrac{1}{2}$

100. $\dfrac{5}{12} \div \dfrac{1}{3} - \dfrac{7}{2}$

101. $-\dfrac{7}{20} + \dfrac{3}{8} \div \dfrac{1}{2}$

102. $-\dfrac{4}{5} + \dfrac{3}{10} \div \dfrac{2}{9}$

103. $\dfrac{21 - 3^2}{1 + 3}$

104. $\dfrac{5 + 3^2}{2 + 5}$

105. $\dfrac{3}{4} \cdot \left[\dfrac{5}{4} \div \left(\dfrac{3}{8} - \dfrac{1}{8} \right) - 3 \right]$

106. $\left[\dfrac{9}{10} \div \left(\dfrac{2}{5} + \dfrac{1}{5} \right) + \dfrac{7}{2} \right] \cdot \dfrac{1}{10}$

107. $\left(\dfrac{4}{3} \right)^3 - \left(\dfrac{1}{2} \right)^2 \cdot \left(\dfrac{8}{3} \right) + 2 \div 3$

108. $\dfrac{1}{18} \cdot \dfrac{46}{5} - \left(\dfrac{2}{3} \right)^2$

109. $\dfrac{5^2 - 3^3}{\left|4 - 4^2\right|}$

110. $\dfrac{3 \cdot 2^3 - 2^2 \cdot 12}{3 + 3^2}$

Applying the Concepts

In Problems 111–114, express each number as the product of prime factors. Write the answer in exponential form.

111. 72

112. 675

113. 48

114. 200

In Problems 115–120, insert grouping symbols so that the expression has the desired value.

115. $4 \cdot 3 + 6 \cdot 2$ results in 36

116. $4 \cdot 7 - 4^2$ results in -36

117. $4 + 3 \cdot 4 + 2$ results in 42

118. $6 - 4 + 3 - 1$ results in 0

119. $6 - 4 + 3 - 1$ results in 4

120. $4 + 3 \cdot 2 - 1 \cdot 6$ results in 42

121. Cost of a TV The total amount paid for a flat-screen television that costs $479, plus state tax of 7.5%, is found by evaluating the expression $479 + 0.075(479)$. Evaluate this expression rounded to the nearest cent.

122. Manufacturing Cost Evaluate the expression $3000 + 6(100) - \dfrac{100^2}{1000}$ to find the weekly production cost of manufacturing 100 calculators.

△**123. Surface Area** The surface area of a right circular cylinder whose radius is 6 inches and height is 10 inches is given approximately by $2 \cdot 3.1416 \cdot 6^2 + 2 \cdot 3.1416 \cdot 6 \cdot 10$. Evaluate this expression. Round the answer to two decimal places.

△**124. Volume of a Cone** The volume of a cone whose radius is 3 centimeters and whose height is 12 centimeters is given approximately by $\dfrac{1}{3} \cdot 3.1416 \cdot 3^2 \cdot 12$. Evaluate this expression. Round the answer to two decimal places.

125. Investing If $1000 is invested at 3% annual interest and remains untouched for 2 years, the amount of money that is in the account after 2 years is given by the expression $1000(1 + 0.03)^2$. Evaluate this expression, rounded to the nearest cent.

126. Investing If $5000 is invested at 4.5% annual interest and remains untouched for 5 years, the amount of money that is in the account after 5 years is given by the expression $5000(1 + 0.045)^5$. Evaluate this expression, rounded to the nearest cent.

Extending the Concepts

The Angle Addition Postulate from geometry states that the measure of an angle is equal to the sum of the measures of its parts. Refer to the figure. Use the Angle Addition Postulate to answer Problems 127 and 128.

△**127.** If $\angle XYQ = 46.5°$ and $\angle QYZ = 69.25°$, find the measure of $\angle XYZ$.

△**128.** If $\angle QYZ = 18°$ and $\angle XYZ = 57°$, find the measure of $\angle XYQ$.

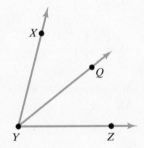

Explaining the Concepts

129. Explain the difference between -3^2 and $(-3)^2$. Identify the distinguishing characteristics of the two problems, and explain how to evaluate each expression.

1.8 Simplifying Algebraic Expressions

Preparing for Simplifying Algebraic Expressions
Before getting started, take this readiness quiz. If you get a problem wrong, go back to the section cited and review the material.

P1. Find the sum: $-3 + 8$ [Section 1.4, pp. 29–32]

P2. Find the difference: $-7 - 8$ [Section 1.4, pp. 32–33]

P3. Find the product: $-\dfrac{4}{3}(27)$ [Section 1.5, pp. 39–40]

What is algebra? The word "algebra" is derived from the Arabic word, *al-jabr,* which means "restoration." Today algebra means more. According to the American Heritage Dictionary, **algebra** is a branch of mathematics in which symbols, usually letters of the alphabet, represent numbers or members of a set. These symbols are used to represent quantities and to express general relationships that hold for all members of the set. In this course (with the exception of Section 9.5), the set of numbers referred to in the definition is the set of real numbers.

1 Evaluate Algebraic Expressions

In arithmetic, we work with numbers. As stated in the definition, in algebra, we use letters such as $x, y, a, b,$ and c to represent numbers.

> **DEFINITION**
>
> When a letter represents any number from a set of numbers, it is called a **variable.**

For most of the text, we use the set of real numbers.

> **DEFINITION**
>
> A **constant** is either a fixed number, such as 5, or a letter or symbol that represents a fixed number.

For example, in Einstein's Theory of Relativity, $E = mc^2$, E and m are variables that represent total energy and mass, respectively, while c is a constant that represents the speed of light (299,792,458 meters per second).

> **DEFINITION**
>
> An **algebraic expression** is any combination of variables, constants, grouping symbols, and mathematical operations such as addition, subtraction, multiplication, division, and exponents.

Some examples of algebraic expressions are

$$x - 5, \quad \frac{1}{2}x, \quad 2y - 7, \quad z^2 + 3 \quad \text{and} \quad \frac{b - 1}{b + 1}$$

Recall that a variable represents a number from a set of numbers. One of the procedures we perform on algebraic expressions is *evaluating an algebraic expression.*

> **DEFINITION**
>
> To **evaluate an algebraic expression,** substitute a numerical value for each variable into the expression and simplify the result.

EXAMPLE 1 Evaluating an Algebraic Expression

Evaluate each expression for the given value of the variable.

(a) $2x + 5$ for $x = 8$ (b) $a^2 - 2a + 4$ for $a = -3$

Solution

(a) We substitute 8 for x in the expression $2x + 5$:

$$2(8) + 5 = 16 + 5$$
$$= 21$$

(b) We substitute -3 for a in $a^2 - 2a + 4$:

$$(-3)^2 - 2(-3) + 4 = 9 + 6 + 4$$
$$= 19$$

EXAMPLE 2 An Algebraic Expression for Revenue

The expression $4.50x + 2.50y$ represents the total amount of money, in dollars, received at a school play where x represents the number of adult tickets sold and y represents the number of student tickets sold. Evaluate $4.50x + 2.50y$ for $x = 50$ and $y = 82$. Interpret the result.

Solution

We substitute 50 for x and 82 for y in the expression $4.50x + 2.50y$.

$$4.50(50) + 2.50(82) = 225 + 205 = 430$$

So $430 was collected by selling 50 adult tickets and 82 student tickets.

Quick ✔

1. Explain what it means to evaluate an algebraic expression.

In Problems 2–5, evaluate each expression for the given value of the variable.

2. $-3k + 5$ for $k = 4$ 3. $\frac{5}{4}t - 6$ for $t = 12$ 4. $-2y^2 - y + 8$ for $y = -2$

5. The Amadeus Coffee Shop wishes to blend two types of coffee to create a breakfast blend. They will mix x pounds of a mild coffee that sells for $7.50 per pound with y pounds of a robust coffee that sells for $10.00 per pound. An algebraic expression that represents the value of the breakfast blend, in dollars, is $7.50x + 10y$. Evaluate this expression for $x = 8$ and $y = 16$.

2 Identify Like Terms and Unlike Terms

Algebraic expressions consist of *terms*.

> **DEFINITION**
>
> A **term** is a constant or the product of a constant and one or more variables raised to a power.

In algebraic expressions, the terms are separated by addition signs.

EXAMPLE 3 Identifying the Terms in an Algebraic Expression

Identify the terms in the following algebraic expressions.

(a) $4a^3 + 5b^2 - 8c + 12$ (b) $\frac{x}{4} - 7y + 8z$

Solution

(a) Rewrite the algebraic expression $4a^3 + 5b^2 - 8c + 12$ so that it contains only addition signs as follows:

$$4a^3 + 5b^2 + (-8c) + 12$$

The four terms are $4a^3$, $5b^2$, $-8c$, and 12.

(b) The algebraic expression $\frac{x}{4} - 7y + 8z$ has three terms: $\frac{x}{4}$, $-7y$, and $8z$. ■

Quick ✔ *In Problems 6–9, identify the terms in each algebraic expression.*

6. $5x^2 + 3xy$ **7.** $9ab - 3bc + 5ac - ac^2$

8. $\dfrac{2mn}{5} - \dfrac{3n}{7}$ **9.** $\dfrac{m^2}{3} - 8$

DEFINITION

The **coefficient** of a term is the numerical factor of the term.

For example, the coefficient of $7x$ is 7; the coefficient of $-2x^2y$ is -2. For terms that have no number as a factor, such as mn, the coefficient is 1 since $mn = 1 \cdot mn$. The coefficient of $-y$ is -1 since $-y = -1 \cdot y$. If a term consists of just a constant, the coefficient is the number itself. We say the coefficient of 14 is 14.

EXAMPLE 4 Determining the Coefficient of a Term

Determine the coefficient of each term:

   (a) $\frac{1}{2}xy^2$ **(b)** $-\frac{t}{12}$

Solution

   (a) The coefficient of $\frac{1}{2}xy^2$ is $\frac{1}{2}$.

   (b) The coefficient of $-\dfrac{t}{12}$ is $-\dfrac{1}{12}$ because $-\dfrac{t}{12}$ can be written as $-\dfrac{1}{12} \cdot t$. ■

EXAMPLE 5 Determining the Coefficient of a Term

Determine the coefficient of each term:

   (a) ab^3 **(b)** 12

Solution

   (a) The coefficient of ab^3 is 1 because ab^3 can be written as $1 \cdot ab^3$.

   (b) The coefficient of 12 is 12 because the coefficient of a constant is the number itself. ■

Quick ✔ *In Problems 10–15, determine the coefficient of each term.*

10. $2z^2$ **11.** xy **12.** $-b$ **13.** 5   **14.** $-\dfrac{2}{3}z$ **15.** $\dfrac{x}{6}$

Sometimes we can simplify algebraic expressions by combining *like terms*.

Work Smart

Like terms can have different coefficients, but they cannot have different variables or different exponents on those variables.

DEFINITION

Terms that have the same variable factor(s) with the same exponent(s) are called **like terms.**

For example, $3x^2$ and $-7x^2$ are like terms because the variable x is raised to the second power, but $3x^2$ and $-7x^3$ are not like terms because the variable x is raised to the second power in $3x^2$ but to the third power in the term $-7x^3$. Constant terms such as -9 and 6 are like terms.

EXAMPLE 6 Classifying Terms as Like or Unlike

Classify the following pairs of terms as *like* or *unlike:*

(a) $2p^3$ and $-5p^3$ (b) $7kr$ and $\frac{1}{4}k^2r$ (c) 5 and 8

Solution

(a) $2p^3$ and $-5p^3$ are *like* terms. They have the same variable p raised to the same power, 3.

(b) $7kr$ and $\frac{1}{4}k^2r$ are *unlike* terms. Although they both have the variables k and r, the variable k is raised to the first power in $7kr$ and to the second power in $\frac{1}{4}k^2r$.

(c) 5 and 8 are *like* terms. They are both constants. ∎

Quick ✔ *In Problems 16–19, tell if the terms are like or unlike.*

16. $-\frac{2}{3}p^2; \frac{4}{5}p^2$ **17.** $\frac{m}{6}; 4m$ **18.** $3a^2b; -2ab^2$ **19.** $8a; 11$

3 Use the Distributive Property

The *Distributive Property* will be used throughout this course and in future courses.

THE DISTRIBUTIVE PROPERTY

If a, b, and c are real numbers, then

$$a \cdot (b + c) = a \cdot b + a \cdot c$$
$$(a + b) \cdot c = a \cdot c + b \cdot c$$

That is, multiply each of the terms inside the parentheses by the factor on the outside.

Because $b - c = b + (-c)$, it is also true that $a(b - c) = a \cdot b - a \cdot c$. One of the uses of the Distributive Property is to remove parentheses from an algebraic expression.

EXAMPLE 7 Using the Distributive Property to Remove Parentheses

Use the Distributive Property to remove the parentheses.

(a) $3(x + 5)$ (b) $-\frac{1}{3}(6x - 12)$

Solution

(a) To use the Distributive Property, we multiply each term in the parentheses by 3:

$$3(x + 5) = 3 \cdot x + 3 \cdot 5$$
$$= 3x + 15$$

Work Smart

The long name for the Distributive Property is The Distributive Property of Multiplication over Addition. This name helps to remind us that we do not distribute across multiplication. For example,

$$6x(5xy) \neq 6x \cdot 5x \cdot 6x \cdot y$$

(b) Multiply each term in the parentheses by $-\frac{1}{3}$:

$$-\frac{1}{3}(6x - 12) = -\frac{1}{3} \cdot 6x - \left(-\frac{1}{3}\right) \cdot 12$$

$$= -2x + 4$$

Quick ✔ *In Problems 20–23, use the Distributive Property to remove the parentheses.*

20. $6(x + 2)$ **21.** $-5(x + 2)$

22. $-2(k - 7)$ **23.** $(8x + 12)\frac{3}{4}$

4 Simplify Algebraic Expressions by Combining Like Terms

An algebraic expression that contains the sum or difference of like terms may be simplified using the Distributive Property "in reverse." When we use the Distributive Property to add coefficients of like terms we say that we are **combining like terms.**

EXAMPLE 8 Using the Distributive Property to Combine Like Terms

Combine like terms:

(a) $2x + 7x$ **(b)** $x^2 - 5x^2$

Solution

(a) $2x + 7x = (2 + 7)x$
$$= 9x$$

(b) $x^2 - 5x^2 = (1 - 5)x^2$
$$= -4x^2$$

Look carefully at the results of Example 8. Notice that when we combine like terms, we add the coefficients of the like terms and keep the variables and exponents the same.

Quick ✔ *In Problems 24–27, combine like terms.*

24. $3x - 8x$ **25.** $-5x^2 + x^2$

26. $-7x - x + 6 - 3$ **27.** $4x - 12x - 3 + 17$

Sometimes we must rearrange the terms in an algebraic expression using the Commutative Property of Addition in order to combine like terms.

EXAMPLE 9 Combining Like Terms Using the Commutative Property

Combine like terms: $4x + 5y + 12x - 7y$

Solution

First, we use the Commutative Property to rearrange the terms.

$$4x + 5y + 12x - 7y = 4x + 12x + 5y - 7y$$

Use the Distributive Property "in reverse": $= (4 + 12)x + (5 - 7)y$

$$= 16x + (-2y)$$

Write the answer in simplest form: $= 16x - 2y$

Quick ✔ *In Problems 28–31, combine like terms.*

28. $3a + 2b - 5a + 7b - 4$

29. $(5ac + 2b) + (7ac - 5a) + (-b)$

30. $5ab^2 + 7a^2b + 3ab^2 - 8a^2b$

31. $\dfrac{4}{3}rs - \dfrac{3}{2}r^2 + \dfrac{2}{3}rs - 5$

Often, we need to first remove parentheses by using the Distributive Property before we can combine like terms. Recall that the rules for order of operations of real numbers place multiplication before addition or subtraction. In this section, the direction **simplify** will mean to remove all parentheses and combine like terms.

EXAMPLE 10 Combining Like Terms Using the Distributive Property

Simplify the algebraic expression: $3 - 4(2x + 3) - (5x + 1)$

Solution

First, we use the Distributive Property to remove parentheses.

$$3 - 4(2x + 3) - (5x + 1) = 3 - 8x - 12 - 5x - 1$$

Rearrange terms using the Commutative Property of Addition: $\quad = -8x - 5x + 3 - 12 - 1$

Combine like terms: $\quad = -13x - 10$ ∎

Work Smart

Remember that multiplication comes before subtraction. In the first step of Example 10, do not compute $3 - 4$ first to obtain $-1(2x + 3)$.

Quick ✔

32. Explain what it means to simplify an algebraic expression.

In Problems 33–36, simplify each expression.

33. $3x + 2(x - 1) - 7x + 1$

34. $m + 2n - 3(m + 2n) - (7 - 3n)$

35. $2(a - 4b) - (a + 4b) + b$

36. $\dfrac{1}{2}(6x + 4) - \dfrac{1}{3}(12 - 9x)$

We summarize the steps for simplifying an algebraic expression below.

Work Smart: Study Skills

Selected problems in the exercise sets are identified by a 🌐 symbol. For extra help, view the worked solutions to these problems on the book's CD Lecture Series.

SUMMARY SIMPLIFYING AN ALGEBRAIC EXPRESSION

Step 1: Remove any parentheses using the Distributive Property.

Step 2: Combine any like terms.

1.8 EXERCISES

PRACTICE   WATCH   DOWNLOAD   READ   REVIEW

1–36. are the Quick ✔*s that follow each* EXAMPLE

Building Skills

In Problems 37–50, evaluate each expression using the given values of the variables. See Objective 1.

37. $2x + 5$ for $x = 4$

38. $3x + 7$ for $x = 2$

39. $x^2 + 3x - 1$ for $x = 3$

40. $n^2 - 4n + 3$ for $n = 2$

🌐 **41.** $4 - k^2$ for $k = -5$

42. $-2p^2 + 5p + 1$ for $p = -3$

43. $\dfrac{5x}{y} + y^2$ for $x = 8$, $y = 10$

44. $m^2 - \dfrac{3n}{m}$ for $m = 2$, $n = 4$

45. $\dfrac{9x - 5y}{x + y}$ for $x = 3$, $y = 2$

46. $\dfrac{3y + 2z}{y - z}$ for $y = 4$, $z = -3$

47. $(x + 3y)^2$ for $x = 3$, $y = 4$

48. $(a - 2b)^2$ for $a = 1$, $b = -2$

49. $x^2 + 9y^2$ for $x = 3$, $y = 4$

50. $a^2 - 4b^2$ for $a = 1$, $b = -2$

In Problems 51–54, for each expression, identify the terms and then name the coefficient of each term. See Objective 2.

51. $2x^3 + 3x^2 - x + 6$ **52.** $3m^4 - m^3n^2 + 4n - 1$

53. $z^2 + \dfrac{2y}{3}$ **54.** $t^3 - \dfrac{t}{4}$

In Problems 55–62, determine if the terms are like or unlike. See Objective 2.

55. $8x$ and 8 **56.** $11p$ and 11

57. 54 and -21 **58.** -13 and 38

59. $12b$ and $-b$ **60.** $6a^2$ and $-3a^2$

61. r^2s and rs^2 **62.** x^2y^3 and y^2x^3

In Problems 63–70, use the Distributive Property to remove the parentheses. See Objective 3.

63. $3(m + 2)$ **64.** $3(4s + 2)$

65. $(3n^2 + 2n - 1)6$ **66.** $(6a^4 - 4a^2 + 2)3$

67. $-(x - y)$ **68.** $-5(k - n)$

69. $(8x - 6y)(-0.5)$ **70.** $(16a + 12b)(-0.4)$

In Problems 71–100, simplify each expression by using the Distributive Property to remove parentheses and combining like terms. See Objective 4.

71. $5x - 2x$ **72.** $14k - 11k$

73. $4z - 6z + 8z$ **74.** $9m - 8m + 2m$

75. $2m + 3n + 8m + 7n$ **76.** $x + 2y + 5x + 7y$

77. $0.3x^7 + x^7 + 0.9x^7$ **78.** $1.7n^4 - n^2 + 2.1n^4$

79. $-3y^6 + 13y^6$ **80.** $-7p^5 + 2p^5$

81. $-(6w + 12y - 13z)$ **82.** $-(-6m + 9n - 8p)$

83. $5(k + 3) - 8k$ **84.** $3(7 - z) - z$

85. $7n - (3n + 8)$ **86.** $18m - (6 + 9m)$

87. $(7 - 2x) - (x + 4)$ **88.** $(3k + 1) - (4 - k)$

89. $(7n - 8) - (3n - 6)$ **90.** $(5y - 6) - (11y + 8)$

91. $-6(n - 3) + 2(n + 1)$ **92.** $-9(7r - 6) + 9(10r + 3)$

93. $\dfrac{2}{3}x + \dfrac{1}{6}x$ **94.** $\dfrac{3}{5}y + \dfrac{7}{10}y$

95. $\dfrac{1}{2}(8x + 5) - \dfrac{2}{3}(6x + 12)$

96. $\dfrac{1}{5}(60 - 15x) + \dfrac{3}{4}(12 - 24x)$

97. $2(0.5x + 9) - 3(1.5x + 8)$

98. $3(0.2x + 6) - 5(1.6x + 1)$

99. $3.2(x + 1.6) + 1.4(2x - 3.7)$

100. $1.8(x + 2.5) + 1.1(3x - 2.8)$

Mixed Practice

In Problems 101–112, (a) evaluate the expression for the given value(s) of the variable(s) before combining like terms, (b) simplify the expression by combining like terms and then evaluate the expression for the given value(s) of the variable(s). Compare your results.

101. $5x + 3x$; $x = 4$ **102.** $8y + 2y$; $y = -3$

103. $-2a^2 + 5a^2$; $a = -3$ **104.** $4b^2 - 7b^2$; $b = 5$

105. $4z - 3(z + 2)$; $z = 6$ **106.** $8p - 3(p - 4)$; $p = 3$

107. $5y^2 + 6y - 2y^2 + 5y - 3$; $y = -2$

108. $3x^2 + 8x - x^2 - 6x$; $x = 5$

109. $\dfrac{1}{2}(4x - 2) - \dfrac{2}{3}(3x + 9)$; $x = 3$

110. $\dfrac{1}{5}(5x - 10) - \dfrac{1}{6}(6x + 12)$; $x = -2$

111. $3a + 4b - 7a + 3(a - 2b)$; $a = 2$, $b = 5$

112. $-4x - y + 2(x - 3y)$; $x = 3$, $y = -2$

Applying the Concepts

In Problems 113–118, evaluate each expression using the given values of the variables.

113. $\frac{1}{2}h(b + B)$; $h = 4$, $b = 5$, $B = 17$

114. $\frac{1}{2}h(b + B)$; $h = 9$, $b = 3$, $B = 12$

115. $\frac{a - b}{c - d}$; $a = 6$, $b = 3$, $c = -4$, $d = -2$

116. $\frac{a - b}{c - d}$; $a = -5$, $b = -2$, $c = 7$, $d = 1$

117. $b^2 - 4ac$; $a = 7$, $b = 8$, $c = 1$

118. $b^2 - 4ac$; $a = 2$, $b = 5$, $c = 3$

119. Renting a Truck The cost of renting a truck from Hamilton Truck Rental is $59.95 per day plus $0.15 per mile. The expression $59.95 + 0.15m$ represents the cost of renting a truck for one day and driving it m miles. Evaluate $59.95 + 0.15m$ for $m = 125$.

120. Renting a Car The cost of renting a compact car for one day from CMH Auto is $29.95 plus $0.17 per mile. The expression $29.95 + 0.17m$ represents the total daily cost. Evaluate the expression $29.95 + 0.17m$ for $m = 245$.

121. Ticket Sales The Center for Science and Industry sells adult tickets for $12 and children's tickets for $7. The expression $12a + 7c$ represents the total revenue from selling a adult tickets and c children's tickets. Evaluate the algebraic expression $12a + 7c$ for $a = 156$ and $c = 421$.

122. Ticket Sales A community college theatre group sold tickets to a recent production. Student tickets cost $5 and nonstudent tickets cost $8. The algebraic expression $5s + 8n$ represents the total revenue from selling s student tickets and n nonstudent tickets. Evaluate $5s + 8n$ for $s = 76$ and $n = 63$.

△**123. Rectangle** The width of a rectangle is w yards and the length of the rectangle is $(3w - 4)$ yards. The perimeter of the rectangle is given by the algebraic expression $2w + 2(3w - 4)$.

(a) Simplify the algebraic expression $2w + 2(3w - 4)$.

(b) Determine the perimeter of a rectangle whose width w is 5 yards.

△**124. Rectangle** The length of a rectangle is l meters and the width of the rectangle is $(l - 11)$ meters. The perimeter of the rectangle is given by the algebraic expression $2l + 2(l - 11)$.

(a) Simplify the expression $2l + 2(l - 11)$.

(b) Determine the perimeter of a rectangle whose length l is 15 meters.

125. Finance Novella invested some money in two investment funds. She placed s dollars in stocks that yield 5.5% annual interest and b dollars in bonds that yield 3.25% annual interest. Evaluate the expression $0.055s + 0.0325b$ for $s = \$2950$ and $b = \$2050$. Round your answer to the nearest cent.

126. Finance Jonathan received an inheritance from his grandparents. He invested x dollars in a Certificate of Deposit that pays 2.95% and y dollars in an off-shore oil drilling venture that is expected to pay 12.8%. Evaluate the algebraic expression $0.0295x + 0.128y$ for $x = \$2500$ and $y = \$1000$.

Extending the Concepts

127. Simplify the algebraic expression (cleverly!!) using the Distributive Property—in reverse!

$2.75(-3x^2 + 7x - 3) - 1.75(-3x^2 + 7x - 3)$

128. Simplify the algebraic expression using the Distributive Property in reverse.

$11.23(7.695x + 81.34) + 8.77(7.695x + 81.34)$

Explaining the Concepts

129. Explain why the sum $2x^2 + 4x^2$ is *not* equivalent to $6x^4$. What is the correct answer?

130. Use $x = 4$ and $y = 5$ to answer parts (a), (b), and (c).

(a) Evaluate $x^2 + y^2$.

(b) Evaluate $(x + y)^2$.

(c) Are the results the same? Is $(x + y)^2$ equal to $x^2 + y^2$? Explain your response.

CHAPTER 1 Activity: The Math Game

Focus: Performing order of operations and simplifying expressions
Time: 10 minutes
Group size: 2–4

- The instructor will announce when the groups may begin solving the problems to the right.

- When your group has completed all of the problems, ask the instructor to check the answers. The instructor will tell you how many answers are correct, but not which ones.

- The first group to complete all of the problems correctly will win a prize, as determined by the instructor.

1. Evaluate: $-8 \div 2^2 \cdot 6 + (-2)^3$

2. Evaluate: $\dfrac{6(-3) + 4^2}{25 + 4(-9 + 4)}$

3. Evaluate: $x^3 - x^2$ for $x = -3$

4. Evaluate: $\dfrac{(x + 2y)^2}{xy}$ for $x = 1$, $y = -2$

5. Simplify: $-2(4x + 3) - (5x - 1)$

6. Simplify: $\dfrac{3}{4}(8x^2 + 16) - 2x^2 + 3x$

CHAPTER 1 Review

Section 1.2   Fractions, Decimals, and Percents

KEY CONCEPTS	KEY TERMS
• To find the LCM of two numbers, (1) factor each number as the product of prime factors; (2) write the factor(s) that the numbers share, if any; (3) write down the remaining factors the greatest number of times that the factors appear in any number. The product of the factors is the LCM. • To write a fraction in lowest terms, find the common factors between the numerator and denominator and use the fact that $\dfrac{a \cdot c}{b \cdot c} = \dfrac{a}{b}$ to divide out the common factors. • To round a decimal, identify the specified place value in the decimal. If the digit to the right is 5 or more, add 1 to the digit; if the digit to the right is 4 or less, leave the digit as it is. Then drop the digits to the right of the specified place value. • To convert a fraction to a decimal, divide the numerator of the fraction by the denominator of the fraction until the remainder is 0 or the remainder repeats. • To convert a decimal to a fraction, identify the place value of the denominator, write the decimal as a fraction using the given denominator, and write in lowest terms. • To convert a percent to a decimal, move the decimal point two places to the left and drop the % symbol. • To convert a decimal to a percent, move the decimal point two places to the right and add the % symbol.	Factor Product Prime Composite Prime factorization Multiple Least Common Multiple (LCM) Numerator Denominator Equivalent fractions Least Common Denominator (LCD) Terminating decimal Repeating decimal Percent

YOU SHOULD BE ABLE TO...	EXAMPLE	REVIEW EXERCISES
1 Factor a number as a product of prime factors (p. 9)	Example 1	1–5
2 Find the least common multiple of two or more numbers (p. 9)	Examples 2 and 3	6, 7
3 Write equivalent fractions (p. 11)	Examples 4 and 5	8–11
4 Write a fraction in lowest terms (p. 13)	Example 6	12–14
5 Round decimals (p. 13)	Examples 7 and 8	15, 16
6 Convert a fraction to a decimal and a decimal to a fraction (p. 14)	Examples 9 through 11	17–23
7 Convert a percent to a decimal and a decimal to a percent (p. 16)	Examples 12 and 13	24–32

In Problems 1–5, factor each number as a product of primes, if possible.

1. 24   **2.** 87   **3.** 81

4. 124   **5.** 17

In Problems 6 and 7, find the LCM of the numbers.

6. 18 and 24   **7.** 4, 8, and 18

In Problems 8 and 9, write each number with the given denominator.

8. Write $\dfrac{7}{15}$ with the denominator 30.

9. Write 3 with the denominator 4.

In Problems 10 and 11, write equivalent fractions with the least common denominator.

10. $\dfrac{1}{6}$ and $\dfrac{3}{8}$.   **11.** $\dfrac{9}{16}$ and $\dfrac{7}{24}$

In Problems 12–14, write each fraction in lowest terms.

12. $\dfrac{25}{60}$ **13.** $\dfrac{125}{250}$ **14.** $\dfrac{96}{120}$

In Problems 15 and 16, round each number to the given place.

15. 21.7648 to the neared hundredth

16. 14.91 to the nearest one (unit)

17. Write $\dfrac{8}{9}$ as a repeating decimal.

18. Write $\dfrac{9}{32}$ as a terminating decimal.

In Problems 19 and 20, write each fraction as a decimal rounded to the indicated place.

19. $\dfrac{11}{6}$ to the nearest hundredth.

20. $\dfrac{19}{8}$ to the nearest tenth.

In Problems 21–23, write each decimal as a fraction in lowest terms.

21. 0.6   **22.** 0.375   **23.** 0.864

In Problems 24–27, write each percent as a decimal.

24. 41%   **25.** 760%

26. 9.03%   **27.** 0.35%

In Problems 28–31, write each decimal as a percent.

28. 0.23   **29.** 1.17

30. 0.045   **31.** 3

32. A student earns 12 points out of a total of 20 points on a quiz.

    (a) Express this score as a fraction in lowest terms.

    (b) Express this score as a percentage.

Section 1.3   The Number Systems and the Real Number Line

KEY CONCEPTS

- $a < b$ means a is to the left of b on a real number line
- $a = b$ means a and b are in the same position on a real number line
- $a > b$ means a is to the right of b on a real number line
- $|a|$ is the distance from 0 to a on a real number line

KEY TERMS

Set	Real number line
Elements	Origin
Empty set	Scale
Natural numbers	Coordinate
Counting numbers	Negative real numbers
Whole numbers	Zero
Integers	Positive real numbers
Rational number	Sign
Irrational number	Inequality symbols
Real numbers	Absolute value

YOU SHOULD BE ABLE TO...	EXAMPLE	REVIEW EXERCISES
1 Classify numbers (p. 20)	Example 2	33–42, 59, 60
2 Plot points on a real number line (p. 24)	Example 3	43, 44
3 Use inequalities to order real numbers (p. 25)	Example 4	45–48, 53–58
4 Compute the absolute value of a real number (p. 26)	Example 5	49–52, 57, 58

In Problems 33–36, write each set.

33. A is the set of whole numbers less than 7.

34. B is the set of natural numbers less than or equal to 3.

35. C is the set of integers greater than -3 and less than or equal to 5.

36. D is the set of integers greater than or equal to -2 and less than 4.

*In Problems 37–42, use the set $\left\{-6, -3.25, 0,\right.$
$5.030030003\ldots, \dfrac{9}{3}, 11, \dfrac{5}{7}\Big\}$. List all the elements that are*

37. natural numbers

38. whole numbers

39. integers

40. rational numbers

41. irrational numbers

42. real numbers

43. Plot the points $\left\{-3, -\dfrac{4}{3}, 0, \dfrac{4}{2}, 3.5\right\}$ on a real number line.

44. Plot the points $\left\{-4, -\dfrac{5}{2}, \dfrac{6}{2}, 5.5\right\}$ on a real number line.

In Problems 45–48, determine whether the statement is True or False.

45. $-3 > -1$

46. $5 \le 5$

47. $-5 \le -3$

48. $\dfrac{1}{2} = 0.5$

In Problems 49–52, evaluate each expression.

49. $-\left|\dfrac{1}{2}\right|$

50. $|-7|$

51. $-|-6|$

52. $-|-8.2|$

In Problems 53–58, replace the ? with the correct symbol:
$>, <, =.$

53. $\dfrac{1}{4}$? 0.25

54. -6 ? 0

55. 0.83 ? $\dfrac{3}{4}$

56. -2 ? -10

57. $|-4|$? $|-3|$

58. $\dfrac{4}{5}$? $\left|-\dfrac{5}{6}\right|$

59. Explain the difference between a rational number and an irrational number. Be sure that your explanation includes a discussion of terminating decimals and non-terminating decimals.

60. What do we call the set of positive integers?

Section 1.4 Adding, Subtracting, Multiplying, and Dividing Integers

KEY CONCEPTS	KEY TERMS

• **Rules of Signs for Multiplying Two Integers**
  1. If we multiply two positive integers, the product is positive.
  2. If we multiply one positive integer and one negative integer, the product is negative.
  3. If we multiply two negative integers, the product is positive.
• **Rules of Signs for Dividing Two Integers**
  1. If we divide two positive integers, the quotient is positive. That is,
 	
$$\dfrac{+a}{+b} = \dfrac{a}{b}$$
 	
  2. If we divide one positive integer and one negative integer, the quotient is negative. That is,
 	
$$\dfrac{-a}{b} = \dfrac{a}{-b} = -\dfrac{a}{b}$$
 	
  3. If we divide two negative integers, the quotient is positive. That is,
 	
$$\dfrac{-a}{-b} = \dfrac{a}{b}$$
	Operations
	Sum
	Difference
	Product
	Quotient
	Mixed number
	Additive inverse
	Opposite
	Evaluate
	Factors
	Dividend
	Divisor
	Multiplicative inverse
	Reciprocal
	Ratio
	Golden ratio

YOU SHOULD BE ABLE TO...	EXAMPLE	REVIEW EXERCISES
1 Add integers (p. 29)	Examples 1 through 6	61–68, 73, 74, 91, 92, 95, 101, 102, 104
2 Determine the additive inverse of a number (p. 32)	Example 7	89, 90
3 Subtract integers (p. 32)	Examples 8 through 10	69–74, 93, 94, 96, 101–103
4 Multiply integers (p. 34)	Examples 11 through 13	75–80, 97, 98, 104
5 Divide integers (p. 35)	Example 15	81–88, 99, 100

In Problems 61–88, perform the indicated operation.

61. $-2 + 9$

62. $6 + (-10)$

63. $-23 + (-11)$

64. $-120 + 25$

65. $-|-2 + 6|$

66. $-|-15| + |-62|$

67. $-110 + 50 + (-18) + 25$

68. $-28 + (-35) + (-52)$

69. $-10 - 12$

70. $18 - 25$

71. $-11 - (-32)$

72. $0 - (-67)$

73. $34 - 18 + 10$

74. $-49 - 8 + 21$

75. $-6(-2)$

76. $4(-10)$

77. $13(-86)$

78. $-19(423)$

79. $(11)(13)(-5)$

80. $(-53)(-21)(-10)$

81. $\dfrac{-20}{-4}$

82. $\dfrac{60}{-5}$

83. $\dfrac{|-55|}{11}$

84. $-\left|\dfrac{-100}{4}\right|$

85. $\dfrac{120}{-15}$

86. $\dfrac{64}{-20}$

87. $\dfrac{-180}{54}$

88. $\dfrac{-450}{105}$

In Problems 89 and 90, determine the additive inverse of each number.

89. 13

90. -45

In Problems 91–100, write the expression using mathematical symbols, and then evaluate the expression.

91. -43 plus 101

92. 45 plus -28

93. -10 minus -116

94. 74 minus 56

95. the sum of 13 and -8

96. the difference between -60 and -10

97. -21 multiplied by -3

98. 54 multiplied by -18

99. -34 divided by -2

100. -49 divided by 14

101. Football Clinton Portis had three possessions of the football within the first few minutes of the game. On his first possession he gained 20 yards, on his second possession he lost 6 yards, and on his third possession he gained 12 yards. What was his total yardage?

102. Temperature On a winter day in Detroit, Michigan, the temperature was 10°F in the morning. The temperature rose 12°F in the afternoon, and then fell 25°F by midnight. What was the temperature at midnight in Detroit?

103. Temperature One day in Bismarck, North Dakota, the high temperature was 6°F above zero and the low temperature was 18°F below zero. What was the difference between the high and the low temperature on that day in Bismarck?

104. Test Score Ms. Rosen awards 5 points for each correct multiple-choice question and awards 8 points for each correct free-response question. On one of Ms. Rosen's tests, Sarah got 11 multiple-choice questions correct and 4 free-response questions correct. What was Sarah's test score?

Section 1.5 Adding, Subtracting, Multiplying, and Dividing Rational Numbers Expressed as Fractions and Decimals

KEY CONCEPTS	KEY TERM
• **Multiplying Fractions** $$\frac{a}{b} \cdot \frac{c}{d} = \frac{a \cdot c}{b \cdot d}, \text{ where } b \text{ and } d \neq 0$$ • **Dividing Fractions** $$\frac{a}{b} \div \frac{c}{d} = \frac{a}{b} \cdot \frac{d}{c} = \frac{a \cdot d}{b \cdot c}, \text{ where } b, c, d \neq 0$$ • **Adding or Subtracting Fractions with the Same Denominator** $$\frac{a}{c} + \frac{b}{c} = \frac{a + b}{c}, \text{ where } c \neq 0$$ $$\frac{a}{c} - \frac{b}{c} = \frac{a - b}{c} = \frac{a + (-b)}{c}, \text{ where } c \neq 0$$ • **Adding or Subtracting Fractions with Unlike Denominators** **Step 1:** Find the LCD of the fractions. **Step 2:** Find equivalent fractions with the LCD by multiplying by a factor of 1. **Step 3:** Add or subtract the numerators and write the result over the common denominator. **Step 4:** Simplify the result.	Least common denominator

YOU SHOULD BE ABLE TO...	EXAMPLE	REVIEW EXERCISES
1 Multiply rational numbers expressed as fractions (p. 39)	Example 1	109–112, 142
2 Divide rational numbers expressed as fractions (p. 40)	Example 2	113–116
3 Add and subtract rational numbers expressed as fractions (p. 41)	Examples 3 through 7	117–128, 143
4 Add, subtract, multiply, and divide rational numbers expressed as decimals (p. 45)	Examples 8 through 11	129–141, 144

In Problems 105–108, write each rational number in lowest terms.

105. $\dfrac{32}{64}$

106. $-\dfrac{27}{81}$

107. $-\dfrac{100}{150}$

108. $-\dfrac{35}{25}$

In Problems 109–128, perform the indicated operation. Write in lowest terms.

109. $\dfrac{2}{3} \cdot \dfrac{15}{8}$

110. $-\dfrac{3}{8} \cdot \dfrac{10}{21}$

111. $\dfrac{5}{8} \cdot \left(-\dfrac{2}{25}\right)$

112. $5 \cdot \left(-\dfrac{3}{10}\right)$

113. $\dfrac{24}{17} \div \dfrac{18}{3}$

114. $-\dfrac{5}{12} \div \dfrac{10}{16}$

115. $-\dfrac{27}{10} \div 9$

116. $20 \div \left(-\dfrac{5}{8}\right)$

117. $\dfrac{2}{9} + \dfrac{1}{9}$

118. $-\dfrac{6}{5} + \dfrac{4}{5}$

119. $\dfrac{5}{7} - \dfrac{2}{7}$

120. $\dfrac{7}{5} - \left(-\dfrac{8}{5}\right)$

121. $\dfrac{3}{10} + \dfrac{1}{20}$

122. $\dfrac{5}{12} + \dfrac{4}{9}$

123. $-\dfrac{7}{35} - \dfrac{2}{49}$

124. $\dfrac{5}{6} - \left(-\dfrac{1}{4}\right)$

125. $-2 - \left(-\dfrac{5}{12}\right)$

126. $-5 + \dfrac{9}{4}$

127. $-\dfrac{1}{10} + \left(-\dfrac{2}{5}\right) + \dfrac{1}{2}$

128. $-\dfrac{5}{6} - \dfrac{1}{4} + \dfrac{3}{24}$

In Problems 129–140, perform the indicated operation.

129. $30.3 + 18.2$

130. $-43.02 + 18.36$

131. $201.37 - 118.39$

132. $-35.1 - 18.64$

133. $(-0.04)(-2.01)$

134. $(87.3)(-2.98)$

135. $\dfrac{69.92}{3.8}$

136. $-\dfrac{1.08318}{0.042}$

137. $12.5 - 18.6 + 8.4$

138. $-13.5 + 10.8 - 20.2$

139. $(12.9)(1.4)(-0.3)$

140. $(2.4)(6.1)(-0.05)$

141. **Checking Account** Lee had a balance of $256.75 in her checking account. Lee wrote a check for $175.68 on Wednesday and wrote a check for $180.00 on Thursday. What is her checking account balance now? Is Lee's account overdrawn?

142. **Super Bowl Party** Jarred had 36 friends at his Super Bowl party. Two-thirds of his friends wanted the NFC team to win. How many of Jarred's friends wanted the NFC team to win the Super Bowl?

143. **Ribbon Cutting** Tara has a piece of ribbon that is 15 inches long. If she cuts off a $3\frac{1}{2}$-inch piece of the ribbon, what is the length of the piece that remains?

144. **Buying Clothes** While shopping at her favorite store, Sierra bought 5 sweaters. If the sweaters cost $35 each and sales tax is 6.75% of the net price (net price = price × quantity), how much did Sierra spend on the clothes?

Section 1.6   Properties of Real Numbers

KEY CONCEPTS	KEY TERMS
• **Identity Property of Addition** For any real number a, $0 + a = a + 0 = a$. • **Commutative Property of Addition** If a and b are real numbers, then $a + b = b + a$. • **Additive Inverse Property** For any real number a, $a + (-a) = -a + a = 0$. • **Associative Property of Addition** If a, b, and c are real numbers, then $a + (b + c) = (a + b) + c$. • **Commutative Property of Multiplication** If a and b are real numbers, then $a \cdot b = b \cdot a$. • **Multiplication Property of Zero** For any real number a, the product of a and 0 is always 0; that is, $a \cdot 0 = 0 \cdot a = 0$. • **Multiplicative Identity** $a \cdot 1 = 1 \cdot a = a$ for any real number a. • **Associative Property of Multiplication** If a, b, and c are real numbers, then $a \cdot (b \cdot c) = (a \cdot b) \cdot c$. • **Multiplicative Inverse Property** $a \cdot \dfrac{1}{a} = \dfrac{1}{a} \cdot a = 1$ provided that $a \neq 0$ • **Division Properties of Zero** For any nonzero number a, 1. The quotient of 0 and a is 0. That is, $\dfrac{0}{a} = 0$. 2. The quotient of a and 0 is undefined. That is, $\dfrac{a}{0}$ is undefined.	Additive Identity Multiplicative Identity Conversion Commutative Property Grouping symbols Associative Property Undefined

YOU SHOULD BE ABLE TO...	EXAMPLE	REVIEW EXERCISES
1 Understand and use the Identity Properties of Addition and Multiplication (p. 51)	Example 1	146, 147, 150–152, 154, 157–162, 170–172
2 Understand and use the Commutative Properties of Addition and Multiplication (p. 53)	Examples 2 through 4	148, 149, 153, 157–160, 163, 164, 167, 168, 173, 174
3 Understand and use the Associative Properties of Addition and Multiplication (p. 54)	Examples 5 through 7	145, 156, 161, 162
4 Understand the Multiplication and Division Properties of 0 (p. 56)	Example 8	155, 165, 166, 169

In Problems 145–156, state the property of real numbers that is being illustrated.

145. $(5 \cdot 12) \cdot 10 = 5 \cdot (12 \cdot 10)$

146. $20 \cdot \frac{1}{20} = 1$

147. $\frac{8}{3} \cdot \frac{3}{8} = 1$

148. $\frac{5}{3} \cdot \left(-\frac{18}{61}\right) \cdot \frac{3}{5} = \frac{5}{3} \cdot \frac{3}{5} \cdot \left(-\frac{18}{61}\right)$

149. $9 \cdot 73 \cdot \frac{1}{9} = 9 \cdot \frac{1}{9} \cdot 73$

150. $23.9 + (-23.9) = 0$

151. $36 + 0 = 36$

152. $-49 + 0 = -49$

153. $23 + 5 + (-23)$ is equivalent to $23 + (-23) + 5$

154. $\frac{7}{8}$ is equivalent to $\frac{7}{8} \cdot \frac{3}{3}$

155. $14 \cdot 0 = 0$

156. $-5.3 + (5.3 + 2.8) = (-5.3 + 5.3) + 2.8$

In Problems 157–174, evaluate each expression, if possible, by using the properties of real numbers.

157. $144 + 29 + (-144)$

158. $76 + 99 + (-76)$

159. $\frac{19}{3} \cdot 18 \cdot \frac{3}{19}$

160. $\frac{14}{9} \cdot 121 \cdot \frac{9}{14}$

161. $3.4 + 42.56 + (-42.56)$

162. $5.3 + 3.6 + (-3.6)$

163. $\frac{9}{7} \cdot \left(-\frac{11}{3}\right) \cdot 7$

164. $\frac{13}{5} \cdot \frac{18}{39} \cdot 5$

165. $\frac{7}{0}$

166. $\frac{0}{100}$

167. $1000(-334)(0.001)$

168. $400(0.5)(0.01)$

169. $43{,}569{,}003 \cdot 0$

170. $154 \cdot \frac{1}{154}$

171. $\frac{3445}{302} + \left(-\frac{3445}{302}\right)$

172. $130 \cdot \frac{42}{42}$

173. $-\frac{7}{48} \cdot \frac{20}{3} \cdot \frac{12}{7}$

174. $\frac{9}{8} \cdot \left(-\frac{25}{13}\right) \cdot \frac{48}{9}$

Section 1.7 Exponents and the Order of Operations

KEY CONCEPTS

- **Exponential Notation**
  If n is a natural number and a is a real number, then

  $$a^n = \underbrace{a \cdot a \cdot a \cdot \ldots \cdot a}_{n \text{ factors}}$$

  where a is called the base and the natural number n is called the exponent or power.

- **Rules for Order of Operations**

  Step 1: Perform all operations within *grouping symbols* first. When an expression has multiple grouping symbols, begin with the innermost pair of grouping symbols and work outward.

  Step 2: Evaluate expressions containing *exponents*.

  Step 3: Perform *multiplication and division* in the order in which they occur, working from *left to right*.

  Step 4: Perform *addition and subtraction* in the order in which they occur, working from *left to right*.

KEY TERMS

Exponential notation
Base
Exponent
Power
Exponential form
Expanded form

YOU SHOULD BE ABLE TO...	EXAMPLE	REVIEW EXERCISES
1 Evaluate exponential expressions (p. 59)	Examples 1 through 4	175–184
2 Apply the rules for order of operations (p. 60)	Examples 5 through 11	185–192

In Problems 175–178, write in exponential form.

175. $3 \cdot 3 \cdot 3 \cdot 3$

176. $\frac{2}{3} \cdot \frac{2}{3} \cdot \frac{2}{3}$

177. $(-4)(-4)$

178. $(-3)(-3)(-3)$

In Problems 179–184, evaluate each expression.

179. 5^3

180. 2^5

181. $(-3)^4$

182. $(-4)^3$

183. -3^4

184. $\left(\frac{1}{2}\right)^6$

In Problems 185–192, evaluate each expression.

185. $-2 + 16 \div 4 \cdot 2 - 10$

186. $-4 + 3[2^3 + 4(2 - 10)]$

187. $(12 - 7)^3 + (19 - 10)^2$

188. $5 - (-12 \div 2 \cdot 3) + (-3)^2$

189. $\dfrac{2 \cdot (4 + 8)}{3 + 3^2}$

190. $\dfrac{3 \cdot (5 + 2^2)}{2 \cdot 3^3}$

191. $\dfrac{6 \cdot [12 - 3 \cdot (5 - 2)]}{5 \cdot [21 - 2 \cdot (4 + 5)]}$

192. $\dfrac{4 \cdot [3 + 2 \cdot (8 - 6)]}{5 \cdot [14 - 2 \cdot (2 + 3)]}$

Section 1.8   Simplifying Algebraic Expressions

KEY CONCEPT	KEY TERMS	
• **Distributive Property** If a, b, and c are real numbers, then $a \cdot (b + c) = a \cdot b + a \cdot c$ and $(a + b) \cdot c = a \cdot c + b \cdot c$	Algebra Variable Constant Algebraic expression Evaluate an algebraic expression	Term Coefficient Like terms Combining like terms Simplify

YOU SHOULD BE ABLE TO...	EXAMPLE	REVIEW EXERCISES
1️⃣ Evaluate algebraic expressions (p. 67)	Examples 1 and 2	193–196, 211
2️⃣ Identify like terms and unlike terms (p. 68)	Examples 3 through 6	197–202
3️⃣ Use the Distributive Property (p. 70)	Example 7	206–210
4️⃣ Simplify algebraic expressions by combining like terms (p. 71)	Examples 8 through 10	203–210

In Problems 193–196, evaluate each expression using the given values of the variables.

193. $x^2 - y^2$ for $x = 5$, $y = -2$

194. $x^2 - 3y^2$ for $x = 3$, $y = -3$

195. $(x + 2y)^3$ for $x = -1$, $y = -4$

196. $\dfrac{a - b}{x - y}$ for $a = 5$, $b = -10$, $x = -3$, $y = 2$

In Problems 197 and 198, identify the terms and then name the coefficient of each term.

197. $3x^2 - x + 6$

198. $2x^2y^3 - \dfrac{y}{5}$

In Problems 199–202, determine if the terms are like or unlike.

199. $4xy^2$, $-6xy^2$

200. $-3x$, $4x^2$

201. $-6y$, -6

202. -10, 4

In Problems 203–210, simplify each algebraic expression.

203. $4x - 6x - x$

204. $6x - 10 - 10x - 5$

205. $0.2x^4 + 0.3x^3 - 4.3x^4$

206. $-3(x^4 - 2x^2 - 4)$

207. $20 - (x + 2)$

208. $-6(2x + 5) + 4(4x + 3)$

209. $5 - (3x - 1) + 2(6x - 5)$

210. $\dfrac{1}{6}(12x + 18) - \dfrac{2}{5}(5x + 10)$

211. Moving Van The cost of renting a moving van for one day is \$19.95 plus \$0.25 per mile. The expression $19.95 + 0.25m$ represents the total cost of renting the truck for one day and driving m miles. Evaluate the expression $19.95 + 0.25m$ for $m = 315$.

CHAPTER 1 TEST

Remember to use your Chapter Test Prep Video CD to see fully worked-out solutions to any of these problems you would like to review.

1. Find the LCM of 2, 6, and 14.

2. Write $\dfrac{21}{66}$ in lowest terms.

3. Write $\dfrac{13}{9}$ as a decimal rounded to the nearest hundredth.

4. Write 0.425 as a fraction in lowest terms.

5. Write 0.6% as a decimal.

6. Write 0.183 as a percent.

In Problems 7–15, perform the indicated operation. Write in lowest terms.

7. $\dfrac{4}{15} - \left(-\dfrac{2}{30}\right)$

8. $\dfrac{21}{4} \cdot \dfrac{3}{7}$

9. $-16 \div \dfrac{3}{20}$

10. $14 - 110 - (-15) + (-21)$

11. $-14.5 + 2.34$

12. $(-4)(-1)(-5)$

13. $16 \div 0$

14. -6 subtracted from -20

15. -110 divided by -2

16. Use the set $\left\{-2, -\dfrac{1}{2}, 0, 2.5, 6\right\}$. List all of the elements that are:

   (a) natural numbers   **(b)** whole numbers

   (c) integers   **(d)** rational numbers

   (e) irrational numbers   **(f)** real numbers

In Problems 17 and 18, replace the ? with the correct symbol >, <, or =.

17. $-|-14|$? -12

18. $\left|-\dfrac{2}{5}\right|$? 0.4

In Problems 19–21, evaluate each expression.

19. $-16 \div 2^2 \cdot 4 + (-3)^2$

20. $\dfrac{4(-9) - 3^2}{25 + 4(-6 - 1)}$

21. $8 - 10[6^2 - 5(2 + 3)]$

22. Evaluate $(x - 2y)^3$ for $x = -1$ and $y = 3$.

In Problems 23 and 24, simplify each algebraic expression.

23. $-6(2x + 5) - (4x - 2)$

24. $\dfrac{1}{2}(4x^2 + 8) - 6x^2 + 5x$

25. Bank Account Latoya started with $675.15 in her bank account. She wrote a check for $175.50, withdrew $78.00 in cash, and made a deposit of $110.20. How much money does Latoya have in her bank account now?

26. Perimeter The length of a rectangle is 5 feet more than its width. The algebraic expression $2(x + 5) + 2x$ represents the perimeter of the rectangle. Simplify the expression $2(x + 5) + 2x$.

2 Equations and Inequalities in One Variable

You and your friends are planning to purchase pizza to eat while watching the Super Bowl. You go shopping at your local grocery store and find that the store carries medium (12") frozen pizzas for $9.99 and small (8") frozen pizzas that are on special for $4.49 each. Which should you choose to get the best deal?

Understanding mathematical formulas and models allows you to solve everyday problems such as this one. See Problem 83 in Section 2.4.

OUTLINE

The Big Picture: Putting It Together

In Chapter 1, we reviewed arithmetic skills that will be needed throughout the course. We also introduced algebraic expressions and discussed how to simplify and evaluate algebraic expressions.

In this chapter we dive into the discussion of algebra. The word "algebra" is derived from the Arabic word, *al-jabr*. The word *al-jabr* means "restoration." This is a reference to the fact that, if a number is added to one side of an equation, then it must also be added to the other side in order to "restore" the equality. While algebra now means a whole lot more than "restoration," we will concentrate on the "restoration" part of algebra in this chapter.

2.1 Linear Equations: The Addition and Multiplication Properties of Equality

OBJECTIVES

1. Determine If a Number Is a Solution of an Equation
2. Use the Addition Property of Equality to Solve Linear Equations
3. Use the Multiplication Property of Equality to Solve Linear Equations

Preparing for Linear Equations: The Addition and Multiplication Properties of Equality
Before getting started, take this readiness quiz. If you get a problem wrong, go back to the section cited and review the material.

P1. Determine the additive inverse of 3. [Section 1.4, p. 32]

P2. Determine the multiplicative inverse of $-\dfrac{4}{3}$. [Section 1.4, pp. 35–36]

P3. Evaluate: $\dfrac{2}{3}\left(\dfrac{3}{2}\right)$ [Section 1.5, pp. 39–40]

P4. Use the Distributive Property to simplify: $-4(2x + 3)$ [Section 1.8, pp. 70–71]

P5. Simplify: $11 - (x + 6)$ [Section 1.8, pp. 71–72]

1   Determine If a Number Is a Solution of an Equation

We begin with a definition.

DEFINITION

A **linear equation in one variable** is an equation that can be written in the form $ax + b = c$, where $a, b,$ and c are real numbers and a does not equal 0.

Examples of linear equations (in the variable x) are

$$x - 5 = 8 \qquad \frac{1}{2}x - 7 = \frac{3}{2}x + 8 \qquad 0.2(x + 5) - 1.5 = 4.25 - (x + 3)$$

The algebraic expressions in the equation are called the **sides** of the equation. For example, in the equation $\dfrac{1}{2}x - 7 = \dfrac{3}{2}x + 8$, the algebraic expression $\dfrac{1}{2}x - 7$ is the **left side** of the equation and the algebraic expression $\dfrac{3}{2}x + 8$ is the **right side** of the equation.

An equation may be true or false. For example, the equation $x - 5 = 8$ is true if the variable x is replaced by the number 13, but the equation $x - 5 = 8$ is false if the variable x is replaced by the number 2.

Because replacing x by 13 in the equation $x - 5 = 8$ results in a true statement, we say that 13 is a *solution* of the equation $x - 5 = 8$. We also say that $x = 13$ *satisfies* the equation.

DEFINITION

The **solution** of a linear equation is the value or values of the variable that make the equation a true statement. The set of all solutions of an equation is called the **solution set.** We sometimes say that the solution **satisfies** the equation.

We use set notation to indicate the solution set of an equation. For example, because $x = 13$ satisfies the equation $x - 5 = 8$, we say that the solution set is $\{13\}$.

To determine whether a number satisfies an equation, we replace the variable with the number and find out whether the left side of the equation equals the right side of the equation. If it does, we have a true statement and the replacement value is a solution of the equation.

Preparing for...Answers **P1.** -3

P2. $-\dfrac{3}{4}$ **P3.** 1   **P4.** $-8x - 12$

P5. $-x + 5$

EXAMPLE 1 **Determine Whether a Number Is a Solution of an Equation**

Determine if the given value of the variable is a solution of the equation
$4x + 7 = 19$.

(a) $x = -2$ (b) $x = 3$

Solution

(a)
$$4x + 7 = 19$$

Replace x with -2: $4(-2) + 7 \overset{?}{=} 19$

Simplify: $-8 + 7 \overset{?}{=} 19$

$$-1 = 19 \quad \text{False}$$

Since the left side of the equation does not equal the right side of the equation when we replace x by -2, $x = -2$ is *not* a solution of the equation.

(b)
$$4x + 7 = 19$$

Replace x with 3: $4(3) + 7 \overset{?}{=} 19$

Simplify: $12 + 7 \overset{?}{=} 19$

$$19 = 19 \quad \text{True}$$

Since the left side of the equation equals the right side of the equation when we replace x by 3, $x = 3$ is a solution of the equation. ∎

Quick ✔

1. The values of the variable that result in a true statement are called _____.

In Problems 2–5, determine if the given number is a solution of the equation.

2. $a - 4 = -7; a = -3$ **3.** $\frac{1}{2} + x = 10; x = \frac{21}{2}$

4. $3x - (x + 4) = 8; x = 6$ **5.** $-9b + 3 + 7b = -3b + 8; b = -3$

⌐2 Use the Addition Property of Equality to Solve Linear Equations

We solve linear equations by writing a series of steps that result in the equation

$$x = a\ number$$

One method for solving equations algebraically requires that a series of *equivalent equations* be developed from the original equation until a solution results.

We form **equivalent equations** using mathematical properties that transform the original equation into a new equation that has the same solution. The first property is called the *Addition Property of Equality*.

In Words

The Addition Property of Equality says that whatever you add to one side of the equation, you must also add to the other side.

ADDITION PROPERTY OF EQUALITY

The **Addition Property of Equality** states that for real numbers a, b, and c,

$$\text{if } a = b, \text{ then } a + c = b + c$$

Also, because $a - b$ is equivalent to $a + (-b)$, the Addition Property of Equality can be used to add a real number to each side of the equation, or to subtract a real number from each side of the equation.

Because the goal in solving a linear equation is to get the variable by itself with a coefficient of 1, we say that we want to **isolate the variable.**

EXAMPLE 2 How to Use the Addition Property of Equality to Solve a Linear Equation

Solve the linear equation: $x - 6 = 11$

Step-by-Step Solution

Since the coefficient of the variable x in this equation is 1, we just need to "get x by itself."

Step 1: Isolate the variable x on the left side of the equation.		$x - 6 = 11$
	Add 6 to each side of the equation:	$x - 6 + 6 = 11 + 6$
Step 2: Simplify the left and right sides of the equation.	Apply the Additive Inverse Property, $a + (-a) = 0$:	$x + 0 = 17$
	Apply the Additive Identity Property, $a + 0 = a$:	$x = 17$
Step 3: Check Verify that x = 17 is the solution.		$x - 6 = 11$
	Replace x by 17 in the original equation to see if a true statement results:	$17 - 6 \stackrel{?}{=} 11$
		$11 = 11 \quad$ True

Because $x = 17$ satisfies the original equation, the solution is 17, or the solution set is $\{17\}$. ■

EXAMPLE 3 Using the Addition Property of Equality to Solve a Linear Equation

Solve the linear equation: $x + \dfrac{5}{2} = \dfrac{1}{4}$

Solution

$$x + \frac{5}{2} = \frac{1}{4}$$

Subtract $\dfrac{5}{2}$ from each side of the equation: $\quad x + \dfrac{5}{2} - \dfrac{5}{2} = \dfrac{1}{4} - \dfrac{5}{2}$

$a + (-a) = 0$; LCD = 4: $\quad x + 0 = \dfrac{1}{4} - \dfrac{5}{2} \cdot \dfrac{2}{2}$

$a + 0 = a$: $\quad x = \dfrac{1}{4} - \dfrac{10}{4}$

$$x = -\frac{9}{4}$$

Check Verify that $x = -\dfrac{9}{4}$ is the solution.

$$x + \frac{5}{2} = \frac{1}{4}$$

$$-\frac{9}{4} + \frac{5}{2} \stackrel{?}{=} \frac{1}{4}$$

$$-\frac{9}{4} + \frac{10}{4} \stackrel{?}{=} \frac{1}{4}$$

$$\frac{1}{4} = \frac{1}{4} \quad \text{True}$$

Because $x = -\dfrac{9}{4}$ satisfies the original equation, the solution is $-\dfrac{9}{4}$, or the solution set is $\left\{-\dfrac{9}{4}\right\}$. ■

Quick ✔ *In Problems 6–13, solve each equation using the Addition Property of Equality.*

6. $x - 11 = 21$ **7.** $y + 7 = 21$ **8.** $-8 + a = 4$

9. $-3 = 12 + c$ **10.** $z - \dfrac{2}{3} = \dfrac{5}{3}$ **11.** $p + \dfrac{5}{4} = \dfrac{1}{4}$

12. $\dfrac{3}{8} = w - \dfrac{1}{4}$ **13.** $\dfrac{5}{4} + x = \dfrac{1}{6}$

EXAMPLE 4 How Much Is the MP3 Player?

The total cost for purchasing an MP3 player including a sales tax of $3.60 was $63.59. To find the price p of the MP3 player before tax, solve the equation $p + 3.60 = 63.59$ for p.

Solution

$$p + 3.60 = 63.59$$

Subtract 3.60 from each side of the equation: $p + 3.60 - 3.60 = 63.59 - 3.60$

Apply the Additive Inverse Property, $a + (-a) = 0$: $p + 0 = 59.99$

Apply the Additive Identity Property, $a + 0 = a$: $p = 59.99$

Since $p = 59.99$, the MP3 player costs $59.99 before tax. ∎

Quick ✔

14. The total cost for a new car, including tax, title, and dealer preparation charges of $1472.25 is $13,927.25. To find the price p of the car before the extra charges, solve the equation $p + 1472.25 = 13,927.25$ for p.

3 Use the Multiplication Property of Equality to Solve Linear Equations

A second property that allows us to create equivalent equations is called the *Multiplication Property of Equality*.

In Words

The Multiplication Property of Equality says that when you multiply one side of an equation by a nonzero quantity, you must also multiply the other side by the same nonzero quantity.

MULTIPLICATION PROPERTY OF EQUALITY

The **Multiplication Property of Equality** states that for real numbers a, b, and c, where c does not equal 0,

$$\text{if } a = b, \quad \text{then} \quad ac = bc$$

Let's see how to use the Multiplication Property of Equality to solve an equation in the next example.

EXAMPLE 5 How to Solve a Linear Equation Using the Multiplication Property of Equality

Solve the equation: $5x = 30$

Step-by-Step Solution

Step 1: Get the coefficient of the variable x to be 1.

$$5x = 30$$

Apply the Multiplication Property of Equality and multiply each side of the equation by $\dfrac{1}{5}$: $\dfrac{1}{5}(5x) = \dfrac{1}{5}(30)$

Step 2: Simplify the left and right sides of the equation.

Regroup factors using the Associative Property of Multiplication: $\left(\frac{1}{5}\cdot 5\right)x = \frac{1}{5}(30)$

Apply the Multiplicative Inverse Property, $a\cdot\frac{1}{a} = 1$: $1\cdot x = 6$

Apply the Multiplicative Identity, $1\cdot a = a$: $x = 6$

Step 3: Check Verify the solution.

$5x = 30$

Replace x by 6 in the original equation: $5(6) \overset{?}{=} 30$

$30 = 30$ True

Because $x = 6$ satisfies the original equation, the solution is 6, or the solution set is $\{6\}$.

In Step 1 of Example 5, we multiplied both sides of the equation by $\frac{1}{5}$ to get the coefficient of x to equal 1. Instead of multiplying by $\frac{1}{5}$, we could also divide both sides of the equation by 5 because dividing by 5 is the same as multiplying by the reciprocal of 5, $\frac{1}{5}$.

$5x = 30$

Divide each side of the equation by 5: $\frac{5x}{5} = \frac{30}{5}$

Simplify: $x = 6$

Which approach do you prefer?

EXAMPLE 6 Solving a Linear Equation Using the Multiplication Property of Equality

Solve the equation: $-4n = 18$

Solution

$-4n = 18$

Multiply each side of the equation by $-\frac{1}{4}$: $-\frac{1}{4}(-4n) = -\frac{1}{4}\cdot 18$

Use the Associative Property of Multiplication: $\left(-\frac{1}{4}\cdot(-4)\right)n = -\frac{18}{4}$

Apply the Multiplicative Inverse Property, $a\cdot\frac{1}{a} = 1$: $1\cdot n = -\frac{9\cdot 2}{2\cdot 2}$

Apply the Multiplicative Identity, $1\cdot a = a$: $n = -\frac{9}{2}$

Check Verify the solution by replacing $n = -\frac{9}{2}$ in the original equation to see if a true statement results.

$-4n = 18$

$-4\left(-\frac{9}{2}\right) \overset{?}{=} 18$

Divide out the common factor: $\overset{-2}{-4}\left(-\frac{9}{\underset{1}{2}}\right) \overset{?}{=} 18$

$18 = 18$

Because $n = -\frac{9}{2}$ satisfies the original equation, the solution is $-\frac{9}{2}$, or the solution set is $\left\{-\frac{9}{2}\right\}$.

Quick ✔

15. Dividing both sides of an equation by 3 is the same as multiplying both sides

by ___.

In Problems 16–19, solve each equation using the Multiplication Property of Equality.

16. $8p = 16$ **17.** $-7n = 14$ **18.** $6z = 15$ **19.** $-12b = 28$

EXAMPLE 7 **Solving a Linear Equation with a Fraction as a Coefficient**

Solve the equation: $\dfrac{x}{3} = -7$

Solution

The left side of the equation, $\dfrac{x}{3}$, is equivalent to $\dfrac{1}{3}x$. To eliminate the fraction, we will multiply both sides of the equation by 3, the reciprocal of $\dfrac{1}{3}$.

$$\frac{x}{3} = -7$$

$$\frac{1}{3} \cdot x = -7$$

Multiply both sides of the equation by 3, the reciprocal of $\dfrac{1}{3}$: $\quad 3 \cdot \left(\dfrac{1}{3}x\right) = 3 \cdot -7$

Use the Associative Property of Multiplication: $\quad \left(3 \cdot \dfrac{1}{3}\right)x = -21$

Apply the Multiplicative Inverse Property, $a \cdot \dfrac{1}{a} = 1$: $\quad 1 \cdot x = -21$

Apply the Multiplicative Identity, $1 \cdot a = a$: $\quad x = -21$

Check Let $x = -21$ in the original equation to see if a true statement results.

$$\frac{x}{3} = -7$$

Let $x = -21$: $\quad \dfrac{-21}{3} \overset{?}{=} -7$

$$-7 = -7 \quad \text{True}$$

The solution is -21, or the solution set is $\{-21\}$. ■

EXAMPLE 8 **Solving a Linear Equation with a Fraction as a Coefficient**

Solve the equation: $12 = \dfrac{2}{3}x$

Solution

Work Smart

When the variable is on the right side of an equation, we isolate the variable in the same way we did when it was on the left side of the equation.

$$12 = \frac{2}{3}x$$

Multiply both sides of the equation by $\dfrac{3}{2}$, the reciprocal of $\dfrac{2}{3}$: $\quad \dfrac{3}{2}(12) = \dfrac{3}{2}\left(\dfrac{2}{3}x\right)$

Use the Associative Property of Multiplication: $\quad 18 = \left(\dfrac{3}{2} \cdot \dfrac{2}{3}\right)x$

Apply the Multiplicative Inverse Property, $a \cdot \dfrac{1}{a} = 1$: $18 = 1 \cdot x$

Apply the Multiplicative Identity Property, $1 \cdot a = a$: $18 = x$

If $b = a$, then $a = b$: $x = 18$

Check Verify the solution by replacing $x = 18$ in the original equation to see if a true statement results.

$$12 = \frac{2}{3}x$$

Let $x = 18$: $12 \overset{?}{=} \frac{2}{3}(18)$

$$12 \overset{?}{=} \frac{2}{\cancel{3}}(\overset{6}{\cancel{18}})$$

$$12 = 12 \quad \text{True}$$

Because $x = 18$ satisfies the original equation, the solution is 18, or the solution set is $\{18\}$.

Quick ✔

20. *True or False:* To solve $-\dfrac{4}{3}z = 16$, add $\dfrac{4}{3}$ to each side of the equation.

In Problems 21–23, solve each equation using the Multiplication Property of Equality.

21. $\dfrac{4}{3}n = 12$ **22.** $-21 = \dfrac{7}{3}k$ **23.** $15 = -\dfrac{z}{2}$

EXAMPLE 9 Solving a Linear Equation with Fractions

Solve the equation: $\dfrac{4}{5} = -\dfrac{2}{15}p$

Solution

$$\frac{4}{5} = -\frac{2}{15}p$$

Multiply both sides by $-\dfrac{15}{2}$: $-\dfrac{15}{2} \cdot \dfrac{4}{5} = -\dfrac{15}{2} \cdot \left(-\dfrac{2}{15}p\right)$

Simplify; use the Associative Property of Multiplication: $-\dfrac{\overset{3}{\cancel{15}}}{\underset{1}{\cancel{2}}} \cdot \dfrac{\overset{2}{\cancel{4}}}{\underset{1}{\cancel{5}}} = \left(-\dfrac{15}{2} \cdot \left(-\dfrac{2}{15}\right)\right)p$

$$-6 = p$$

Check Let $p = -6$ in the original equation to see if a true statement results.

$$\frac{4}{5} = -\frac{2}{15}p$$

Let $p = -6$: $\dfrac{4}{5} \overset{?}{=} -\dfrac{2}{15}(-6)$

Simplify: $\dfrac{4}{5} \overset{?}{=} -\dfrac{2}{\underset{5}{\cancel{15}}}(\overset{-2}{\cancel{-6}})$

$$\frac{4}{5} = \frac{4}{5} \quad \text{True}$$

The solution is -6, or the solution set is $\{-6\}$.

Working with fractional coefficients can be tricky. The three equations $\dfrac{-x}{3} = 7$, $-\dfrac{1}{3}x = 7$, and $\dfrac{x}{-3} = 7$ are all equivalent. Do you see why?

Work Smart

To solve an equation of the form $ax = b$, where a is an integer, either multiply by the reciprocal of a, or divide by a.

To solve an equation of the form $ax = b$, where a is a noninteger rational number, multiply by the reciprocal of a.

Multiply by the reciprocal of a

$$2x = 7 \qquad\qquad 5x = -\dfrac{15}{2}$$

$$\dfrac{1}{2}(2x) = \dfrac{1}{2}\cdot 7 \qquad \dfrac{1}{5}(5x) = \dfrac{1}{5}\left(-\dfrac{15}{2}\right)$$

$$x = \dfrac{7}{2} \qquad\qquad x = -\dfrac{3}{2}$$

Divide by a

$$-3x = 72$$

$$\dfrac{-3x}{-3} = \dfrac{72}{-3}$$

$$x = -24$$

Multiply by the reciprocal of a

$$\dfrac{4}{5}x = -16$$

$$\dfrac{5}{4}\left(\dfrac{4}{5}x\right) = \dfrac{5}{4}(-16)$$

$$x = \dfrac{5}{4}\cdot\dfrac{\overset{-4}{\cancel{-16}}}{1}$$

$$x = -20$$

Quick ✔

In Problems 24–26, solve each equation using the Multiplication Property of Equality.

24. $\dfrac{3}{8}b = \dfrac{9}{4}$

25. $-\dfrac{4}{9} = \dfrac{-t}{6}$

26. $\dfrac{1}{4} = -\dfrac{7}{10}m$

2.1 EXERCISES

PRACTICE   WATCH   DOWNLOAD   READ   REVIEW

1–26. *are the* Quick ✔*s that follow each* EXAMPLE

Building Skills

In Problems 27–34, determine if the given value is a solution to the equation. Answer Yes or No. See Objective 1.

27. $3x - 1 = 5;\ x = 2$

28. $4t + 2 = 16;\ t = 3$

29. $4 - (m + 2) = 3(2m - 1);\ m = 1$

30. $3(x + 1) - x = 5x - 9;\ x = -3$

31. $8k - 2 = 4;\ k = \dfrac{3}{4}$

32. $-15 = 3x - 16;\ x = \dfrac{1}{3}$

33. $r + 1.6 = 2r + 1;\ r = 0.6$

34. $3s - 6 = 6s - 3.4;\ s = -1.2$

In Problems 35–50, solve the equation using the Addition Property of Equality. Be sure to check your solution. See Objective 2.

35. $x - 9 = 11$

36. $y - 8 = 2$

37. $x + 4 = -8$

38. $r + 3 = -1$

39. $12 = n - 7$

40. $13 = u - 6$

41. $-8 = x + 5$

42. $-2 = y + 13$

43. $x - \dfrac{2}{3} = \dfrac{4}{3}$

44. $x - \dfrac{1}{8} = \dfrac{3}{8}$

45. $z + \dfrac{1}{2} = \dfrac{3}{4}$

46. $n + \dfrac{3}{5} = \dfrac{7}{10}$

47. $\dfrac{5}{12} = x - \dfrac{3}{8}$

48. $\dfrac{3}{8} = y - \dfrac{1}{6}$

49. $w + 3.5 = -2.6$

50. $z + 4.9 = -2.6$

In Problems 51–74, solve the equation using the Multiplication Property of Equality. Be sure to check your solution. See Objective 3.

51. $5c = 25$

52. $8b = 48$

53. $-7n = 28$

54. $-8s = 40$

55. $4k = 14$

56. $4z = 30$

57. $-6w = 15$

58. $-8p = 20$

59. $\frac{5}{3}a = 35$

60. $\frac{4}{3}b = 16$

61. $-\frac{3}{11}p = -33$

62. $-\frac{6}{5}n = -36$

63. $\frac{n}{5} = 8$

64. $-\frac{y}{6} = 3$

65. $\frac{6}{5} = 2x$

66. $\frac{9}{2} = 3b$

67. $5y = -\frac{5}{3}$

68. $4r = -\frac{12}{5}$

69. $\frac{1}{2}m = \frac{9}{2}$

70. $\frac{1}{4}w = \frac{7}{2}$

71. $-\frac{3}{8}t = \frac{1}{6}$

72. $\frac{3}{10}q = -\frac{1}{6}$

73. $\frac{5}{24} = -\frac{y}{8}$

74. $\frac{11}{36} = -\frac{t}{9}$

Mixed Practice

In Problems 75–102, solve the equation. Be sure to check your solution.

75. $n - 4 = -2$

76. $m - 6 = -9$

77. $b + 12 = 9$

78. $c + 4 = 1$

79. $2 = 3x$

80. $9 = 5y$

81. $-4q = 24$

82. $-6m = 54$

83. $-39 = x - 58$

84. $-637 = c - 142$

85. $-18 = -301 + x$

86. $-46 = -51 + q$

87. $\frac{x}{5} = -10$

88. $\frac{z}{3} = -12$

89. $m - 56.3 = -15.2$

90. $p - 26.4 = -471.3$

91. $-40 = -6c$

92. $-45 = 12x$

93. $14 = -\frac{7}{2}c$

94. $12 = -\frac{3}{2}n$

95. $\frac{3}{4} = -\frac{x}{16}$

96. $\frac{5}{9} = -\frac{h}{36}$

97. $x - \frac{5}{16} = \frac{3}{16}$

98. $w - \frac{7}{20} = \frac{9}{20}$

99. $-\frac{3}{16} = -\frac{3}{8} + z$

100. $\frac{5}{2} = -\frac{13}{4} + y$

101. $\frac{5}{6} = -\frac{2}{3}z$

102. $-\frac{4}{9} = \frac{8}{3}b$

Applying the Concepts

103. New Car The total cost for a new car, including tax, title, and dealer preparation charges of $1562.35, is $20,062.15. To find the price of the car without the extra charges, solve the equation $y + 1562.35 = 20,062.15$, where y represents the price of the car without the extra charges.

104. New Kayak The total cost for a new kayak is $862.92, including sales tax of $63.92. To find the cost of the kayak without tax, solve the equation $k + 63.92 = 862.92$, where k represents the cost of the kayak.

105. Discount The cost of a sleeping bag has been discounted by $17, so that the sale price of the bag is $51. Find the original price of the sleeping bag, p, by solving the equation $p - 17 = 51$.

106. Discount The cost of a computer has been discounted by $239, so that the sale price is $1230. Find the original price of the computer, c, by solving the equation $c - 239 = 1230$.

107. Eating Out Rebecca purchased several "Happy Meals" at McDonald's for her child's play group. Each Happy Meal costs $4 and she spent a total of $48 on the food. To determine the number of Happy Meals, h, she purchased, solve the equation $4h = 48$.

108. Paperback Books Anne bought 3 paperback books to read on the flight to Europe. She paid $36 for the books (without sales tax). To find the average price, p, of each book solve the equation $3p = 36$.

109. Interest Suppose you have a credit card debt of $3,000. Last month, the bank charged you $45 interest on the debt. The solution to the equation $45 = \frac{3000}{12} \cdot r$ represents the annual interest rate, r, on the credit card. Find the annual interest rate on the credit card.

110. Interest Suppose you have a credit card debt of $4,000. Last month, the bank charged you $40 interest on the debt. The solution to the equation $40 = \frac{4000}{12} \cdot r$ represents the annual interest rate, r, on the credit card. Find the annual interest rate on the credit card.

Extending the Concepts

111. Let λ represent some real number. Solve the equation $x + \lambda = 48$ for x.

112. Let β represent some real number. Solve the equation $x - \beta = 25$ for x.

113. Let θ represent some real number except 0. Solve the equation $14 = \theta x$ for x.

114. Let ψ represent some real number except 0. Solve the equation $\dfrac{2}{5} = \psi x$ for x.

115. Find the value of λ in the equation $x + \lambda = \dfrac{16}{3}$ so that the solution is $-\dfrac{2}{9}$.

116. Find the value of β in the equation $x - \beta = -13.6$ so that the solution is -4.79.

117. Find the value of θ in the equation $-\dfrac{3}{4} = \theta x$ so that the solution is $\dfrac{7}{8}$.

118. Find the value of ψ in the equation $-11.92 = \psi x$ so that the solution is 2.98.

Explaining the Concepts

119. Explain what is meant by finding the *solution* of an equation.

120. Consider the equation $3z = \dfrac{15}{4}$. You could either multiply both sides of the equation by $\dfrac{1}{3}$ or you could divide both sides by 3. Explain which operation you would choose and why you think it is easier.

121. Explain in your own words the difference between an algebraic expression and an algebraic equation. Write an equation involving the algebraic expression $x - 10$. Then solve the equation.

122. A classmate suggests that to solve the equation $4x = 2$, you must divide by 4 and the result will be $x = 2$. Explain why this reasoning is or is not correct.

2.2 Linear Equations: Using the Properties Together

OBJECTIVES

1. Apply the Addition and the Multiplication Properties of Equality to Solve Linear Equations
2. Combine Like Terms and Apply the Distributive Property to Solve Linear Equations
3. Solve a Linear Equation with the Variable on Both Sides of the Equation
4. Use Linear Equations to Solve Problems

Preparing for Linear Equations: Using the Properties Together

Before getting started, take this readiness quiz. If you get a problem wrong, go back to the section cited and review the material.

P1. Simplify by combining like terms: $6 - (4 + 3x) + 8$ [Section 1.8, pp. 71–72]

P2. Evaluate the expression $2(3x + 4) - 5$ for $x = -1$. [Section 1.8, pp. 67–68]

1 Apply the Addition and the Multiplication Properties of Equality to Solve Linear Equations

In the last section, we solved equations such as $x + 3 = 7$ and $\dfrac{1}{2}z = 8$, which required that we use either the Addition Property or the Multiplication Property of Equality, but not both. We now consider equations such as $2x - 3 = 7$ and $\dfrac{1}{2}z + 6 = 18$, which require using both the Addition and Multiplication Properties of Equality to solve for the variable. For example, the equation $2x + 3 = 7$ can be read as "Two *times* a number x *plus* three equals seven." We must "undo" both the multiplication and addition to find the solution of the equation.

EXAMPLE 1 **How to Solve a Linear Equation Using the Addition and Multiplication Properties of Equality**

Solve the equation: $2z - 3 = 9$

Step-by-Step Solution

Step 1: Isolate the term containing the variable.

$$2z - 3 = 9$$

Apply the Addition Property of Equality and add 3 to each side of the equation: $2z - 3 + 3 = 9 + 3$

$$2z = 12$$

Step 2: Get the coefficient of the variable to be 1.

Apply the Multiplication Property of Equality and divide both sides of the equation by 2 (this is the same as multiplying both sides by $\frac{1}{2}$):

$$\frac{2z}{2} = \frac{12}{2}$$

$$z = 6$$

Step 3: **Check** Verify that $z = 6$ is the solution of the equation.

$$2z - 3 = 9$$

Substitute 6 for z into the original equation: $2(6) - 3 \overset{?}{=} 9$

$$12 - 3 \overset{?}{=} 9$$

$$9 = 9 \quad \text{True}$$

Because $z = 6$ satisfies the equation, the solution is 6, or the solution set is $\{6\}$. ■

EXAMPLE 2 **Solving a Linear Equation Using the Addition and Multiplication Properties of Equality**

Solve the equation: $\frac{3}{2}p + 3 = 12$

Solution

$$\frac{3}{2}p + 3 = 12$$

Subtract 3 from both sides of the equation: $\frac{3}{2}p + 3 - 3 = 12 - 3$

Simplify: $\frac{3}{2}p = 9$

Multiply both sides of the equation by $\frac{2}{3}$: $\frac{2}{3}\left(\frac{3}{2}p\right) = \frac{2}{3}(9)$

Simplify: $p = 6$

Check Let $p = 6$ in the original equation to verify the solution.

$$\frac{3}{2}p + 3 = 12$$

Let $p = 6$: $\frac{3}{2}(6) + 3 \overset{?}{=} 12$

Simplify: $9 + 3 \overset{?}{=} 12$

$$12 = 12 \quad \text{True}$$

Because $p = 6$ satisfies the equation, the solution is $p = 6$, or the solution set is $\{6\}$. ■

Quick ✔

1. To solve the equation $2x - 11 = 40$, the first step is to _____.

In Problems 2–5, solve each equation.

2. $5x - 4 = 11$

3. $8 - 5r = -2$

4. $8 = \frac{2}{3}k - 4$

5. $-\frac{3}{2}n + 2 = -\frac{1}{4}$

2 Combine Like Terms and Apply the Distributive Property to Solve Linear Equations

Often, we must combine like terms before we can use the Addition or Multiplication Property of Equality.

EXAMPLE 3 Combining Like Terms to Solve a Linear Equation

Solve the equation: $2x - 6 + 3x = 14$

Solution

$$2x - 6 + 3x = 14$$

Combine like terms: $\quad 5x - 6 = 14$

Add 6 to each side of the equation: $\quad 5x - 6 + 6 = 14 + 6$

$$5x = 20$$

Divide both sides by 5: $\quad \frac{5x}{5} = \frac{20}{5}$

$$x = 4$$

Check Verify that $x = 4$ is the solution.

$$2x - 6 + 3x = 14$$

Substitute 4 for x in the original equation: $\quad 2(4) - 6 + 3(4) \overset{?}{=} 14$

$$8 - 6 + 12 \overset{?}{=} 14$$

$$14 = 14$$

Since $x = 4$ results in a true statement, the solution of the equation is 4, or the solution set is $\{4\}$. ∎

Quick ✔ *In Problems 6–9, solve each equation.*

6. $7b - 3b + 3 = 11$

7. $-3a + 4 + 4a = 13 - 27$

8. $6c - 2 + 2c = 18$

9. $-12 = 5x - 3x + 4$

When an equation contains parentheses, we use the Distributive Property to remove the parentheses before we use the Addition or Multiplication Property of Equality.

EXAMPLE 4 Solving a Linear Equation Using the Distributive Property

Solve the equation: $4(2x + 3) - 7 = -11$

Solution

$$4(2x + 3) - 7 = -11$$

Apply the Distributive Property to remove parentheses: $\quad 8x + 12 - 7 = -11$

Combine like terms: $\quad 8x + 5 = -11$

Subtract 5 from each side of the equation: $\quad 8x + 5 - 5 = -11 - 5$

$$8x = -16$$

Divide both sides by 8: $\quad \frac{8x}{8} = \frac{-16}{8}$

$$x = -2$$

Check Verify that $x = -2$ is the solution.

$$4(2x + 3) - 7 = -11$$

Substitute -2 for x in the original equation: $\quad 4[2(-2) + 3] - 7 \overset{?}{=} -11$

$$4(-4 + 3) - 7 \overset{?}{=} -11$$

$$4(-1) - 7 \overset{?}{=} -11$$

$$-4 - 7 \overset{?}{=} -11$$

$$-11 = -11 \quad \text{True}$$

Because $x = -2$ results in a true statement, the solution of the equation is -2, or the solution set is $\{-2\}$. ■

Quick ✔ *In Problems 10–14, solve each equation.*

10. $2(y + 5) - 3 = 11$

11. $\dfrac{1}{2}(4 - 6x) + 5 = 3$

12. $4 - (6 - x) = 11$

13. $8 + \dfrac{2}{3}(2n - 9) = 10$

14. $\dfrac{1}{3}(2x + 9) + \dfrac{x}{3} = 5$

3 Solve a Linear Equation with the Variable on Both Sides of the Equation

When solving a linear equation, our goal is to get the terms that contain the variable on one side of the equation and the constant terms on the other side.

EXAMPLE 5 Solving a Linear Equation with the Variable on Both Sides of the Equation

Solve the equation: $9y - 5 = 5y + 9$

Solution

$$9y - 5 = 5y + 9$$

Subtract $5y$ from each side of the equation: $\quad 9y - 5 - 5y = 5y + 9 - 5y$

$$4y - 5 = 9$$

Add 5 to each side of the equation: $\quad 4y - 5 + 5 = 9 + 5$

$$4y = 14$$

Divide both sides by 4: $\quad \dfrac{4y}{4} = \dfrac{14}{4}$

Simplify: $\quad y = \dfrac{7}{2}$

Check Verify that $y = \dfrac{7}{2}$ is the solution.

$$9y - 5 = 5y + 9$$

Substitute $\dfrac{7}{2}$ for y in the original equation: $\quad 9\left(\dfrac{7}{2}\right) - 5 \overset{?}{=} 5\left(\dfrac{7}{2}\right) + 9$

$$\dfrac{63}{2} - 5 \overset{?}{=} \dfrac{35}{2} + 9$$

$$\dfrac{63}{2} - \dfrac{10}{2} \overset{?}{=} \dfrac{35}{2} + \dfrac{18}{2}$$

$$\dfrac{53}{2} = \dfrac{53}{2} \quad \text{True}$$

Because $y = \dfrac{7}{2}$ results in a true statement, the solution of the equation is $\dfrac{7}{2}$, or the solution set is $\left\{\dfrac{7}{2}\right\}$. ■

Quick ✔ *In Problems 15 and 16, solve each equation.*

15. $3x + 4 = 5x - 8$ **16.** $10m + 3 = 6m - 11$

EXAMPLE 6 How to Solve a Linear Equation in One Variable

Solve the equation: $2(z - 4) + 3z = 4 - (z + 2)$

Step-by-Step Solution

Step 1: Remove any parentheses using the Distributive Property.	$2(z - 4) + 3z = 4 - (z + 2)$ $\qquad 2z - 8 + 3z = 4 - z - 2$
Step 2: Combine like terms on each side of the equation.	$5z - 8 = 2 - z$
Step 3: Use the Addition Property of Equality to get the terms with the variable on one side of the equation and the constants on the other side.	Add z to both sides of the equation: $5z - 8 + z = 2 - z + z$ Simplify: $6z - 8 = 2$ Add 8 to both sides of the equation: $6z - 8 + 8 = 2 + 8$ Simplify: $6z = 10$
Step 4: Use the Multiplication Property of Equality to get the coefficient of the variable to be 1.	Divide both sides of the equation by 6: $\dfrac{6z}{6} = \dfrac{10}{6}$ Simplify: $z = \dfrac{5}{3}$
Step 5: Check the solution to verify that it satisfies the original equation.	We leave the check to you.

The solution of the equation is $\dfrac{5}{3}$, or the solution set is $\left\{\dfrac{5}{3}\right\}$. ■

Quick ✔

17. *True or False:* To solve the equation $13 - 2(7x + 1) + 8x = 12$, the first step is to subtract 2 from 13 and get $11(7x + 1) + 8x = 12$.

In Problems 18 and 19, solve each equation.

18. $-9x + 3(2x - 3) = -10 - 2x$ **19.** $3 - 4(p + 5) = 5(p + 2) - 12$

We now summarize the steps that you should follow to solve an equation in one variable. Not all the steps may be necessary to solve every equation, but you should use this summary as a guide.

SUMMARY STEPS FOR SOLVING AN EQUATION IN ONE VARIABLE

Step 1: Remove any parentheses using the Distributive Property.

Step 2: Combine like terms on each side of the equation.

Step 3: Use the Addition Property of Equality to get the terms with the variable on one side of the equation and the constants on the other side.

Step 4: Use the Multiplication Property of Equality to get the coefficient of the variable to be 1.

Step 5: Check the solution to verify that it satisfies the original equation.

4   Use Linear Equations to Solve Problems

We continue to solve problems that are modeled by algebraic equations.

EXAMPLE 7   How Much Does Alejandro Make in an Hour?

Alejandro works as an engineer for a hospital. His contract calls for him to earn double time on all hours worked in excess of 40 hours for any given week. One week, Alejandro worked 46 hours and earned \$1326 before taxes. To determine Alejandro's hourly wage, w, solve the equation $40w + 6(2w) = 1326$.

Solution

$$40w + 6(2w) = 1326$$

Simplify: $40w + 12w = 1326$

Combine like terms: $52w = 1326$

Divide both sides of the equation by 52: $\dfrac{52w}{52} = \dfrac{1326}{52}$

Simplify: $w = 25.5$

Alejandro makes \$25.50 per hour.

Quick ✔

20. Marcella works at a clothing store. Whenever she works more than 40 hours in a week, she gets paid twice her regular hourly wage of \$10 per hour. One week, Marcella earned \$640 before taxes. To determine how many hours, h, Marcella worked, solve the equation $400 + 20(h - 40) = 640$ for h.

2.2 EXERCISES

PRACTICE   WATCH   DOWNLOAD   READ   REVIEW

1–20. *are the* Quick ✔*s that follow each* EXAMPLE

Building Skills

In Problems 21–34, solve the equation. Check your solution. See Objective 1.

21. $3x + 4 = 7$ 22. $5t + 1 = 11$

23. $2y - 1 = -5$ 24. $6z - 2 = -8$

25. $-3p + 1 = 10$ 26. $-4x + 3 = 15$

27. $8y + 3 = 15$ 28. $6z - 7 = 3$

29. $5 - 2z = 11$ 30. $1 - 3k = 4$

31. $\dfrac{2}{3}x + 1 = 9$ 32. $\dfrac{5}{4}a + 3 = 13$

33. $\dfrac{7}{2}y - 1 = 13$ 34. $\dfrac{1}{5}p - 3 = 2$

In Problems 35–46, solve the equation. Check your solution. See Objective 2.

35. $3x - 7 + 2x = -17$ 36. $5r + 2 - 3r = -14$

37. $2k - 7k - 8 = 17$ 38. $2b + 5 - 8b = 23$

39. $2(x + 1) = -14$ 40. $3(t - 4) = -18$

41. $-3(2 + r) = 9$ 42. $-5(6 + z) = -20$

43. $17 = 2 - (n + 6)$ 44. $21 = 5 - (2a - 1)$

45. $-8 = 5 - (7 - z)$ 46. $-9 = 3 - (6 + 4y)$

In Problems 47–60, solve the equation. Check your solution. See Objective 3.

47. $2x + 9 = x + 1$ 48. $7z + 13 = 6z + 8$

49. $2t - 6 = 3 - t$ 50. $3 + 8x = 21 - x$

51. $14 - 2n = -4n + 7$ 52. $6 - 12m = -3m + 3$

53. $-3(5 - 3k) = 6k + 6$ 54. $-4(10 - 7x) = 3x + 10$

55. $2(2x + 3) = 3(x - 4)$ 56. $3(5 + x) = 2(2x + 11)$

57. $3 + 2(x - 1) = 5x$ 58. $-8 + 4(p + 6) = 10p$

59. $9(6 + a) + 33a = 10a$ 60. $5(12 - 3w) + 25w = 2w$

Mixed Practice

In Problems 61–76, solve the equation. Check your solution.

61. $-5x + 11 = 1$ 62. $-6n + 14 = -10$

63. $4m + 5 = 2$ 64. $7x + 1 = -9$

65. $-2(3n - 2) = 2$ 66. $-5(2n - 3) = 10$

67. $4k - (3 + k) = -(2k + 3)$

68. $11w - (2 - 4w) = 13 + 2(w - 1)$

69. $2y + 36 = 6 + 6y$

70. $7a - 26 = 13a + 2$

71. $\frac{1}{2}(-4k + 28) = 6 + 14k$

72. $\frac{2}{3}(9a - 12) = -6a - 11$

73. $-\frac{5}{2}(x + 6) + \frac{3}{2}x = -8$

74. $\frac{4}{3}a - \left(\frac{7}{3}a + 6\right) = -15$

75. $-3(2y + 3) - 1 = -4(y + 6) + 2y$

76. $-5(b + 2) + 3b = -2(1 + 5b) + 6$

Applying the Concepts

77. Burger King A Burger King Tendercrisp Chicken garden salad contains 6 more grams of fat than a McDonald's Southwestern salad with crispy chicken. If there are 38 grams of fat in the two salads, find the number of grams of fat in each salad by solving the equation $x + (x + 6) = 38$, where x represents the number of fat grams in the McDonald's Southwestern salad and $x + 6$ represents the number of fat grams in the Burger King Tendercrisp salad. (SOURCE: *Burger King and McDonald's websites*)

78. Wendy's A Wendy's Mandarin Chicken salad contains 10 grams of fat less than a Taco Bell Zesty Chicken Border Bowl. If there are 60 grams of fat in the two salads, find the number of grams of fat in the Taco Bell Zesty Chicken Border Bowl by solving the equation $x + (x - 10) = 60$, where x represents the number of grams of fat in a Taco Bell Border Bowl and $x - 10$ represents the number of grams of fat in the Wendy's Mandarin Chicken salad. (SOURCE: *Wendy's and Taco Bell websites*)

△ **79. Dog Run** The length of a rectangular dog run is two feet more than twice the width, w, and the perimeter of the dog run is 30 feet. Solve the equation $2w + 2(2w + 2) = 30$ to find the width, w, of the dog run. Then find the length, $2w + 2$, of the dog run.

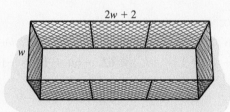

2w + 2

w

△ **80. Garden** The width of a rectangular garden is one yard more than one-half the length, L. The perimeter of the garden is 26 yards. Find the length, L, of the garden by solving the equation $2L + 2\left(\frac{1}{2}L + 1\right) = 26$.

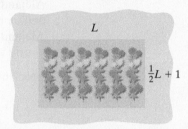

L

$\frac{1}{2}L + 1$

81. Overtime Pay Jennifer worked 44 hours last week, including 4 hours of overtime, and earned $368. She is paid at a rate of 1.5 times her regular hourly rate for overtime hours. Solve the equation $40x + 4(1.5x) = 368$ to find her regular hourly pay rate, x.

82. Overtime Pay Juan worked a total of 50 hours last week and earned $498.75. He earned 1.5 times his regular hourly rate for 6 hours, and double his hourly rate for 4 holiday hours. Solve the equation $40x + 6(1.5x) + 4(2x) = \$498.75$, where x is Juan's regular hourly rate.

△ **83. Hanging Wallpaper** Becky purchased a remnant of 42 feet of a wallpaper border to hang in a rectangular bedroom. She knows that one wall of the bedroom is 5 feet longer than the other wall. Let x represent the length of the shorter wall. Assuming the length of the shorter wall is 8 feet, does Becky have enough wallpaper to hang the border? Use the equation $2x + 2(x + 5) = 42$ to answer the question.

△ **84. Perimeter of a Triangle** The perimeter of a triangle is 210 inches. If the sides are made up of 3 consecutive even integers, find the lengths of each of the 3 sides by solving the equation $x + (x + 2) + (x + 4) = 210$, where x represents the length of the shortest side.

Extending the Concepts

In Problems 85 and 86, solve the equation. Check your solution.

85. $8[4 - 6(x - 1)] + 5[(2x + 3) - 5] = 18x - 338$

86. $3[10 - 4(x - 3)] + 2[(3x + 6) - 2] = 2x + 360$

In Problems 87–90, use a calculator to solve the equation and round your answer to the indicated place.

87. $3(36.7 - 4.3x) - 10 = 4(10 - 2.5x) - 8(3.5 - 4.1x)$
to the nearest hundredth

88. $12(2.3 - 1.5x) - 6 = -3(18.4 - 3.5x) - 6.1(4x + 3)$
to the nearest tenth

89. $3.5\{4 - [6 - (2x + 3)] + 5\} = -18.4$ to the nearest tenth

90. $9\{3 - [4(2.3z - 1)] + 6.5\} = -406.3$ to the nearest hundredth

In Problems 91–94, determine the value of d to make the statement true.

91. In the equation $3d + 2x = 12$, the solution is -4.

92. In the equation $5d - 2x = -2$, the solution is -6.

93. In the equation $\frac{2}{3}x - d = 1$, the solution is $-\frac{3}{8}$.

94. In the equation $\frac{2}{5}x + 3d = 0$, the solution is $\frac{15}{8}$.

Explaining the Concepts

95. Explain the difference between $6x - 2(x + 1)$ and $6x - 2(x + 1) = 6$. In general, what is the difference between an algebraic expression and an algebraic equation?

96. In your own words, explain the Addition and Multiplication Properties of Equality. In the Multiplication Property of Equality, why do you think we cannot multiply both sides of the equation by 0?

97. A classmate begins to solve the equation $7x + 3 - 2x = 9x - 5$ by adding $2x$ in the following manner:

$$7x + 3 - 2x = 9x - 5$$
$$\underline{+2x \quad +2x}$$

Will this lead to the correct solution? Why or why not? Write an explanation telling the steps you would use to solve this equation.

98. A *corollary* is a rule or theorem that is closely related to a previous rule. Write a corollary to the Addition Property of Equality and title it the Subtraction Property of Equality. Write a corollary to the Multiplication Property of Equality, called the Division Property of Equality. What restrictions would you place on the Division Property of Equality? Why do you think these properties were not included in the text?

2.3 Solving Linear Equations Involving Fractions and Decimals; Classifying Equations

OBJECTIVES

1. Use the Least Common Denominator to Solve a Linear Equation Containing Fractions
2. Solve a Linear Equation Containing Decimals
3. Classify a Linear Equation as an Identity, Conditional, or a Contradiction
4. Use Linear Equations to Solve Problems

Work Smart

Although removing fractions is not required to solve an equation, it frequently makes the arithmetic easier.

Preparing for...Answers   **P1.** 20
P2. 24

Preparing for Solving Linear Equations Involving Fractions and Decimals; Classifying Equations

Before getting started, take this readiness quiz. If you get a problem wrong, go back to the section cited and review the material.

P1. Find the LCD of $\frac{3}{5}$ and $\frac{3}{4}$.   [Section 1.2, pp. 11–12]

P2. Find the LCD of $\frac{3}{8}$ and $-\frac{7}{12}$.   [Section 1.2, pp. 11–12]

1   Use the Least Common Denominator to Solve a Linear Equation Containing Fractions

Sometimes equations are easier to solve if they do not contain fractions or decimals. To solve a linear equation containing fractions, we can multiply each side of the equation by the least common denominator (LCD) to rewrite the equation as an equivalent equation without fractions. Recall that the LCD is the smallest number that each denominator has as a common multiple. The Multiplication Property of Equality allows us to multiply both sides of the equation by the LCD.

EXAMPLE 1 How to Solve a Linear Equation That Contains Fractions

Solve the linear equation: $\frac{1}{2}x + \frac{2}{3}x = \frac{14}{3}$

Step-by-Step Solution

Before we follow the steps given in Section 2.2 on page 98, we can rewrite the equation as an equivalent equation by multiplying both sides of the equation by 6, the LCD of 2 and 3.

$$6\left(\frac{1}{2}x + \frac{2}{3}x\right) = 6\left(\frac{14}{3}\right)$$

Now we can follow Steps 1–5 from the summary in Section 2.2 to solve the equation.

Step 1: Apply the Distributive Property to remove parentheses.

$$6\left(\frac{1}{2}x + \frac{2}{3}x\right) = 6\left(\frac{14}{3}\right)$$

Use the Distributive Property: $6\left(\frac{1}{2}x\right) + 6\left(\frac{2}{3}x\right) = 6\left(\frac{14}{3}\right)$

$$3x + 4x = 28$$

Step 2: Combine like terms.

$$7x = 28$$

Step 3: Use the Addition Property of Equality to get the terms with the variable on one side of the equation and the constants on the other side.

This step is not necessary because the only variable term is already on one side of the equation and the constant is on the other side of the equation in this problem.

Step 4: Get the coefficient of the variable to be 1.

Divide both sides of the equation by 7:

$$\frac{7x}{7} = \frac{28}{7}$$

$$x = 4$$

Step 5: Verify that x = 4 is the solution of the equation.

$$\frac{1}{2}x + \frac{2}{3}x = \frac{14}{3}$$

Substitute 4 for x in the original equation:

$$\frac{1}{2}(4) + \frac{2}{3}(4) \stackrel{?}{=} \frac{14}{3}$$

$$2 + \frac{8}{3} \stackrel{?}{=} \frac{14}{3}$$

$$\frac{6}{3} + \frac{8}{3} \stackrel{?}{=} \frac{14}{3}$$

$$\frac{14}{3} = \frac{14}{3} \quad \text{True}$$

The solution of the equation is 4, or the solution set is {4}.

Quick ✔

1. The ___ _____ _____ is the smallest number that each denominator has as a common multiple.

In Problems 2 and 3, solve each equation by multiplying by the LCD.

2. $\dfrac{2x}{5} - \dfrac{x}{4} = \dfrac{3}{2}$

3. $\dfrac{5}{6}x + \dfrac{1}{9} = -\dfrac{1}{6}x - \dfrac{1}{6}$

EXAMPLE 2 Solving a Linear Equation Using the LCD

Solve the linear equation: $\dfrac{7n + 5}{8} = 2 + \dfrac{3n + 15}{10}$

Solution

Because the equation contains fractions, we multiply both sides of the equation by 40, the LCD of 8 and 10.

$$\dfrac{7n + 5}{8} = 2 + \dfrac{3n + 15}{10}$$

Multiply both sides by the LCD, 40: $\quad 40\left(\dfrac{7n + 5}{8}\right) = 40\left(2 + \dfrac{3n + 15}{10}\right)$

Use the Distributive Property to multiply all terms of the equation by the LCD: $\quad 40\left(\dfrac{7n + 5}{8}\right) = 40(2) + 40\left(\dfrac{3n + 15}{10}\right)$

Divide out common factors: $\quad \overset{5}{40}\left(\dfrac{7n + 5}{8}\right) = 40(2) + \overset{4}{40}\left(\dfrac{3n + 15}{10}\right)$

$$5(7n + 5) = 40(2) + 4(3n + 15)$$

Use Distributive Property to remove parentheses: $\quad 35n + 25 = 80 + 12n + 60$

Combine like terms: $\quad 35n + 25 = 140 + 12n$

Isolate terms containing n: $\quad 35n + 25 - 12n = 140 + 12n - 12n$

$$23n + 25 = 140$$

Isolate the constants: $\quad 23n + 25 - 25 = 140 - 25$

$$23n = 115$$

Divide both sides by 23: $\quad \dfrac{23n}{23} = \dfrac{115}{23}$

$$n = 5$$

Does $n = 5$ satisfy the original equation? Let's see.

Check

$$\dfrac{7n + 5}{8} = 2 + \dfrac{3n + 15}{10}$$

Let $n = 5$: $\quad \dfrac{7(5) + 5}{8} \overset{?}{=} 2 + \dfrac{3(5) + 15}{10}$

$$\dfrac{35 + 5}{8} \overset{?}{=} 2 + \dfrac{15 + 15}{10}$$

$$\dfrac{40}{8} \overset{?}{=} 2 + \dfrac{30}{10}$$

$$5 \overset{?}{=} 2 + 3$$

$$5 = 5 \quad \text{True}$$

The solution $n = 5$ checks, so the solution is 5, or the solution set is $\{5\}$.

Quick ✔

4. The result of multiplying the equation $\dfrac{1}{5}x + 7 = \dfrac{3}{10}$ by 10, the LCD of 5 and 10, is $2x + \underline{\quad} = 3$

In Problems 5 and 6, solve each equation by multiplying by the LCD.

5. $\dfrac{a}{3} - \dfrac{1}{3} = -5$

6. $\dfrac{3x - 3}{4} - 1 = \dfrac{3}{5}x$

⌈2⌉ Solve a Linear Equation Containing Decimals

When decimals occur in a linear equation, we can rewrite the equation as an equivalent equation without decimals using the same techniques that we used to clear an equation of fractions. That is, we multiply both sides of the equation by a power of 10 so that the decimal is cleared. For example, $0.8x$ is equivalent to $\frac{8}{10}x$, so we multiply by 10 to clear the decimal from the equation. Because 0.34 is equivalent to $\frac{34}{100}$, we multiply by 100 to clear the decimal from the equation.

⌈EXAMPLE 3⌉ Solving a Linear Equation with a Decimal Coefficient

Solve the equation: $0.3x - 4 = 11$

Solution

We want to rewrite the equation as an equivalent equation without decimals. We can do this by multiplying both sides of the equation by 10. Do you see why? $0.3 = \frac{3}{10}$, so multiplying by 10 will clear the decimal.

$$0.3x - 4 = 11$$

Multiply both sides of the equation by 10: $\quad 10 \cdot (0.3x - 4) = 10 \cdot 11$

Distribute: $\quad 10 \cdot 0.3x - 10 \cdot 4 = 110$

$$3x - 40 = 110$$

Add 40 to both sides of the equation: $\quad 3x = 150$

Divide both sides of the equation by 3: $\quad x = 50$

Check We verify our solution by replacing $x = 50$ in the original equation to see if a true statement results.

$$0.3x - 4 = 11$$
$$0.3(50) - 4 \overset{?}{=} 11$$
$$15 - 4 \overset{?}{=} 11$$
$$11 = 11 \quad \text{True}$$

The solution of the equation $0.3x - 4 = 11$ is 50, or the solution set is $\{50\}$. ∎

It's not a requirement to clear fractions or decimals before solving an equation. Here is another way to solve $0.3x - 4 = 11$.

$$0.3x - 4 = 11$$

Add 4 to each side: $\quad 0.3x - 4 + 4 = 11 + 4$

$$0.3x = 15$$

Divide each side by 0.3: $\quad \dfrac{0.3x}{0.3} = \dfrac{15}{0.3}$

$$x = 50$$

Which method do you prefer?

Quick ✔

7. To clear the decimals in the equation $0.25x + 5 = 7 - 0.3x$, multiply both sides of the equation by ___.

In Problems 8 and 9, solve each equation.

8. $0.2z = 20$

9. $0.15p - 2.5 = 5$

EXAMPLE 4   Solving a Linear Equation Containing Decimals

Solve the equation: $p + 0.08p = 129.6$

Solution

We can clear the decimals by multiplying both sides of the equation by 100. Do you see why? Because $0.08 = \dfrac{8}{100}$ and $129.6 = \dfrac{1296}{10}$, multiplying by the LCD = 100 will clear the decimals. However, before we multiply both sides of the equation by 100, we will first combine like terms on the left-hand side of the equation.

$$p + 0.08p = 129.6$$

$p = 1 \cdot p$:
$$1p + 0.08p = 129.6$$

Combine like terms:
$$1.08p = 129.6$$

Multiply both sides of the equation by 100:
$$100 \cdot 1.08p = 100 \cdot 129.6$$

Simplify:
$$108p = 12{,}960$$

Divide both sides of the equation by 108:
$$\dfrac{108p}{108} = \dfrac{12{,}960}{108}$$

Simplify:
$$p = 120$$

We leave the check to you. The solution of the equation $p + 0.08p = 129.6$ is 120, or the solution set is $\{120\}$. ∎

Quick ✔

10. The coefficient of the first term of the equation $n + 0.25n = 50$ is ___.

In Problems 11 and 12, solve each equation.

11. $p + 0.05p = 52.5$ **12.** $c - 0.25c = 120$

EXAMPLE 5   Solving a Linear Equation That Contains Decimals

Solve the equation: $0.05x + 0.08(10{,}000 - x) = 680$

Solution

Before we clear the equation of decimals, we will distribute the 0.08 and combine like terms.

$$0.05x + 0.08(10{,}000 - x) = 680$$
$$0.05x + 800 - 0.08x = 680$$

Combine like terms:
$$-0.03x + 800 = 680$$

Subtract 800 from both sides:
$$-0.03x = -120$$

Multiply both sides of the equation by 100 to eliminate the decimal:
$$100(-0.03x) = 100(-120)$$
$$-3x = -12{,}000$$

Divide both sides by -3:
$$x = 4000$$

We leave the check to you. The solution of the equation is 4000, or the solution set is $\{4000\}$. ∎

Quick ✔   *In Problems 13 and 14, solve each equation.*

13. $0.36y - 0.5 = 0.16y + 0.3$ **14.** $0.12x + 0.05(5000 - x) = 460$

3   Classify a Linear Equation as an Identity, Conditional, or a Contradiction

All of the linear equations we have solved so far have had a single solution. This one value of the variable made the equation a true statement, while all other values of the variable make the equation false. We give these types of equations a special name.

DEFINITION

A **conditional equation** is an equation that is true for some values of the variable and false for other values of the variable.

For example, the equation

$$x + 5 = 11$$

is a conditional equation because it is true when $x = 6$ and false for every other real number x. The solution set of $x + 5 = 11$ is {6}. All the equations that we have studied to this point have been conditional equations.

There are equations that are false for all values of the variable.

DEFINITION

A **contradiction** is an equation that is false for every value of the variable.

For example, the equation

$$2x + 3 = 7 + 2x$$

Work Smart

Do not write the empty set as {∅}.

is a contradiction because it is false for any replacement value for x. Contradictions are identified through the process of creating equivalent equations. For example, if we subtract $2x$ from both sides of $2x + 3 = 7 + 2x$, we obtain $3 = 7$, which is clearly false. **Contradictions have no solution, so the solution set is the empty set, written as { } or ∅.**

EXAMPLE 6 Solving a Linear Equation That Is a Contradiction

Solve the equation: $3y - (5y + 4) = 12y - 7(2y - 1)$

Solution

$$3y - (5y + 4) = 12y - 7(2y - 1)$$

Use the Distributive Property to remove parentheses: $3y - 5y - 4 = 12y - 14y + 7$

Combine like terms: $-2y - 4 = -2y + 7$

Isolate terms containing y: $-2y + 2y - 4 = -2y + 2y + 7$

$$-4 = 7$$

Work Smart

The term "contradiction" describes this type of equation. The solution set is ∅ or { }.

The statement $-4 = 7$ is false, so the equation is a contradiction. The solution set is ∅ or { }. ∎

Some equations are true for all real numbers for which the equation is defined.

DEFINITION

An **identity** is an equation that is satisfied for all values of the variable for which both sides of the equation are defined.

An example of an identity is the equation

$$2(x - 5) + 1 = 5x - (9 + 3x)$$

This equation is an identity because any real number x makes the equation a true statement. Just as with contradictions, identities are recognized through the process of creating equivalent equations. For example, if we use the Distributive Property and combine like terms in the equation $2(x - 5) + 1 = 5x - (9 + 3x)$, we obtain $2x - 9 = 2x - 9$, which is true for all replacement values for x. **The solution set of a linear equation that is an identity is the set of all real numbers.**

EXAMPLE 7 Solving a Linear Equation That Is an Identity

Solve the equation: $2(x + 5) = 4x - (2x - 10)$

Solution

$$2(x + 5) = 4x - (2x - 10)$$

Use the Distributive Property to remove parentheses: $2x + 10 = 4x - 2x + 10$

Combine like terms: $2x + 10 = 2x + 10$

Isolate terms containing x: $2x - 2x + 10 = 2x - 2x + 10$

$$10 = 10$$

The statement $10 = 10$ is true for all real numbers x. Therefore, the solution set is the set of all real numbers, and the equation is an identity. ∎

Quick ✔

15. *True or False:* The solution of the equation $4x + 1 = 4x + 7$ is the empty set.

In Problems 16–19, solve each equation and state the solution set.

16. $3(x + 4) = 4 + 3x + 18$ **17.** $\frac{1}{3}(6x - 9) - 1 = 6x - [4x - (-4)]$

18. $-5 - (9x + 8) + 23 = 7 + x - (10x - 3)$

19. $\frac{3}{2}x - 8 = x + 7 + \frac{1}{2}x$

SUMMARY

- A *conditional* equation is true for some values of the variable and false for others.
- A *contradiction* is false for all values of the variable.
- An *identity* is true for all of the permitted values of the variable.

EXAMPLE 8 Classifying a Linear Equation

Solve the equation $2(2 + a) - 12a = -a + 5 - 9a$. State whether the equation is a contradiction, an identity, or a conditional equation.

Solution

$$2(2 + a) - 12a = -a + 5 - 9a$$

Use the Distributive Property to remove parentheses: $4 + 2a - 12a = -a + 5 - 9a$

Combine like terms: $4 - 10a = 5 - 10a$

Isolate terms containing a: $4 - 10a + 10a = 5 - 10a + 10a$

$$4 = 5$$

The statement $4 = 5$ is false, so the equation is a contradiction. The solution set is $\varnothing$ or $\{\ \}$. ∎

Quick ✔

20. When the variable is eliminated and a true statement results, the solution set is _____ _____ _____.

21. When the variable is eliminated and a false statement results, the solution set is _____ _____ _____.

In Problems 22–25, solve each equation and state whether each equation is a contradiction, an identity, or a conditional equation.

22. $2(x - 7) + 8 = 6x - (4x + 2) - 4$ **23.** $\frac{4(7 - x)}{3} = x$

24. $\frac{1}{2}(4x - 6) = 6\left(\frac{1}{3}x - \frac{1}{2}\right) + 4$ **25.** $4(5x - 4) + 1 = -2 + 20x$

⌐4⌐ Use Linear Equations to Solve Problems

We continue to solve problems that are modeled by algebraic equations.

⌐EXAMPLE 9⌐ Solving a Problem from Finance

You have $5000 to invest, and your financial advisor advises you to put part of the money in a Certificate of Deposit (CD) that earns 2% simple interest compounded annually, and the rest in bonds that earn 4% simple interest compounded annually. To determine the amount x you should invest in the CD to earn $170 interest at the end of one year, solve the equation $0.02x + 0.04(5000 - x) = 170$.

Solution

We want to solve the equation for x, the amount of money invested in the CD.

$$0.02x + 0.04(5000 - x) = 170$$

Use the Distributive Property to remove parentheses: $\quad 0.02x + 200 - 0.04x = 170$

Combine like terms: $\quad -0.02x + 200 = 170$

Isolate terms containing x: $\quad -0.02x + 200 - 200 = 170 - 200$

$$-0.02x = -30$$

Multiply both sides by 100 to eliminate the decimal: $\quad -2x = -3000$

Divide both sides by -2: $\quad x = 1500$

Because $x = 1500$, you must invest $1500 in Certificates of Deposit to earn $170 in interest at the end of one year. ∎

Quick ✔

26. Janet Majors invested part of her lottery winnings in a savings account that pays 4% annual interest, and $250 more than that in a mutual fund that pays 6% annual interest. Her total interest was $65. To determine the amount x she invested in the savings account, solve the equation $0.04x + 0.06(x + 250) = 65$.

2.3 EXERCISES

PRACTICE   WATCH   DOWNLOAD   READ   REVIEW

1–26. *are the* Quick ✔*s that follow each* EXAMPLE

Building Skills

In Problems 27–42, solve the equation. Check your solution. See Objective 1.

27. $\dfrac{2k - 1}{4} = 2$

28. $\dfrac{3a + 2}{5} = -1$

29. $\dfrac{3x + 2}{4} = \dfrac{x}{2}$

30. $\dfrac{2x - 3}{5} = \dfrac{3x}{10}$

31. $\dfrac{1}{5}x + \dfrac{3}{2} = \dfrac{3}{10}$

32. $\dfrac{3}{2}n - \dfrac{4}{11} = \dfrac{91}{22}$

33. $-\dfrac{2x}{3} + 1 = \dfrac{5}{9}$

34. $\dfrac{3m}{8} - 1 = \dfrac{5}{6}$

35. $\dfrac{a}{4} - \dfrac{a}{3} = -\dfrac{1}{2}$

36. $\dfrac{3}{2}b - \dfrac{4}{5}b = \dfrac{28}{5}$

37. $\dfrac{5}{4}(2a - 10) = -\dfrac{3}{2}a$

38. $\dfrac{2}{3}(6 - x) = \dfrac{5x}{6}$

39. $\dfrac{y}{10} + 3 = \dfrac{y}{4} + 6$

40. $\dfrac{p}{8} - 1 = \dfrac{7p}{6} + 2$

41. $\dfrac{4x - 9}{3} + \dfrac{x}{6} = \dfrac{x}{2} - 2$

42. $\dfrac{3x + 2}{4} - \dfrac{x}{12} = \dfrac{x}{3} - 1$

In Problems 43–62, solve the equation. Check your solution. See Objective 2.

43. $0.4w = 12$

44. $0.3z = 6$

45. $-1.3c = 5.2$

46. $-1.7q = -8.5$

47. $1.05p = 52.5$

48. $1.06z = 31.8$

49. $p + 1.5p = 12$

50. $2.5a + a = 7$

51. $p + 0.05p = 157.5$

52. $p + 0.04p = 260$

53. $0.3x + 2.3 = 0.2x + 1.1$

54. $0.7y - 4.6 = 0.4y - 2.2$

55. $0.65x + 0.3x = x - 3$

56. $0.5n - 0.35n = 2.5n + 9.4$

57. $3 + 1.5(z + 2) = 3.5z - 4$

58. $5 - 0.2(m - 2) = 3.6m + 1.6$

59. $0.02(2c - 24) = -0.4(c - 1)$

60. $0.3(6a - 4) = -0.10(2a - 8)$

61. $0.15x + 0.10(250 - x) = 28.75$

62. $0.03t + 0.025(1000 - t) = 27.25$

In Problems 63–74, solve the equation. State whether the equation is a contradiction, an identity, or a conditional equation See Objective 3.

63. $4z - 3(z + 1) = 2(z - 3) - z$

64. $4(y - 2) = 5y - (y + 1)$

65. $6q - (q - 3) = 2q + 3(q + 1)$

66. $-3x + 2 + 5x = 2(x + 1)$

67. $9a - 5(a + 1) = 2(a - 3)$

68. $7b + 2(b - 4) = 8b - (3b + 2)$

69. $\dfrac{4x - 9}{6} - \dfrac{x}{2} = \dfrac{x}{6} + 3$

70. $\dfrac{2m + 1}{4} - \dfrac{m}{6} = \dfrac{m}{3} - 1$

71. $\dfrac{5z + 1}{5} = \dfrac{2z - 3}{2}$

72. $\dfrac{2y - 7}{4} = \dfrac{3y - 13}{6}$

73. $\dfrac{q}{3} + \dfrac{4}{5} = \dfrac{5q + 12}{15}$

74. $\dfrac{2x}{3} + \dfrac{x + 3}{12} = \dfrac{3x + 1}{4}$

Mixed Practice

In Problems 75–100, solve the equation.

75. $-3(2n + 4) = 10n$

76. $-15(z - 3) = 25z$

77. $-2x + 5x = 4(x + 2) - (x + 8)$

78. $5m - 3(m + 1) = 2(m + 1) - 5$

79. $-6(x - 2) + 8x = -x + 10 - 3x$

80. $3 - (x + 10) = 3x + 7$

81. $\dfrac{3}{4}x = \dfrac{1}{2}x - 5$

82. $\dfrac{1}{3}x = 2 + \dfrac{5}{6}x$

83. $\dfrac{1}{2}x + 2 = \dfrac{4x + 1}{4}$

84. $\dfrac{x}{2} + 4 = \dfrac{x + 7}{3}$

85. $0.3p + 2 = 0.1(p + 5) + 0.2(p + 1)$

86. $1.6z - 4 = 2(z - 1) - 0.4z$

87. $-0.7x = 1.4$

88. $0.2a = -6$

89. $\dfrac{3(2y - 1)}{5} = 2y - 3$

90. $\dfrac{4(2n + 1)}{3} = 2n - 6$

91. $0.6x - 0.2(x - 4) = 0.4(x - 2)$

92. $0.3x - 1 = 0.5(x + 2) - 0.2x$

93. $\dfrac{3x - 2}{4} = \dfrac{5x - 1}{6}$

94. $\dfrac{x - 1}{4} = \dfrac{x - 4}{6}$

95. $0.3x + 2.6x = 5.7 - 1.8 + 2.8x$

96. $0.3(z - 10) - 0.5z = -6$

97. $\dfrac{3}{2}x - 6 = \dfrac{2(x - 9)}{3} + \dfrac{1}{6}x$

98. $\dfrac{2x - 3}{4} + 5 = \dfrac{3(x + 3)}{4} - \dfrac{x}{2} + 2$

99. $\dfrac{2}{3}\left[4 - \left(\dfrac{x}{2} + 6\right) - 2x\right] + 3 = \dfrac{5x}{6}$

100. $\dfrac{1}{2}\left[3 - \left(\dfrac{2x}{3} - 1\right) + 3x\right] = \dfrac{-4x + 1}{3} + 1$

In Problems 101–104, solve the equation and round to the indicated place.

101. $2.8x + 13.754 = 4 - 2.95x$ to the nearest hundredth

102. $-4.88x - 5.7 = 2(-3.41x) + 1.2$ to the nearest whole number

103. $x - \{1.5x - 2[x - 3.1(x + 10)]\} = 0$ to the nearest tenth

104. $-3x - 2\{4 + 3[x - (1 + x)]\} = 12$ to the nearest hundredth

Applying the Concepts

105. Sales Tax The price of a pair of jeans including sales tax of 6% is $53. To find the price p of the jeans, solve the equation $1.06p = 53$.

106. Gardening Bob Adams rented a rototiller for x hours at a cost of $7.50 per hour. Bob paid a bill of $37.50. Find the number of hours he rented the tiller by solving the equation $7.50x = 37.50$.

107. Purchasing a Car The total cost (including 6% sales tax) for the purchase of an automobile was $19,080. To determine the cost of the auto before the sales tax was added, solve the equation $x + 0.06x = 19,080$, where x represents the cost of the car before taxes.

108. Purchasing a Kayak The total cost, including 5.5% sales tax, for the purchase of a kayak was $1266. Find the price of the kayak, k, before sales tax, by solving the equation $k + 0.055k = 1266$.

109. Hourly Pay Bob recently received a 4% pay increase. His hourly wage is now $8.84. To determine his hourly wage, w, before the 4% pay raise, solve the equation $w + 0.04w = 8.84$ for w.

110. Hourly Pay A union representing airline employees recently agreed to a 6% cut in hourly wage in order to help the airline avoid filing for bankruptcy. A baggage handler will now earn $26.32 per hour. To find the baggage handler's hourly wage, w, before the pay cut solve the equation $w - 0.06w = 26.32$.

111. MP3 Player Tamara purchased an MP3 player at a "25% off" sale for $60.00. To determine the original price, p, of the MP3 player, solve the equation $p - 0.25p = 60$.

112. Team Sweatshirt Your favorite college has logo sweatshirts on sale for $33.60. The sweatshirt has been marked down by 30%. To find the original price of the sweatshirt, x, solve the equation $x - 0.30x = 33.60$.

113. Piggy Bank Celeste saves dimes and quarters in a piggy bank. She opened the bank and discovered that she had $7.05 and the number of dimes was 3 more than twice the number of quarters. To find the number of quarters, q, solve the equation $0.25q + 0.10(2q + 3) = 7.05$.

114. Clean Car Pablo cleaned out his car and found nickels and quarters in the car seats. He found $4.25 in change and noticed that the number of quarters was 5 less than twice the number of nickels. Solve the equation $0.05n + 0.25(2n - 5) = 4.25$ to find n, the number of nickels Pablo found.

△ **115. Comparing Perimeters** The two rectangles shown in the figure have the same perimeter. Solve the equation

$$2x + 2(x + 3) = 2\left(\frac{1}{2}x\right) + 2(x + 6) \text{ for } x, \text{ the}$$

width of the first rectangle.

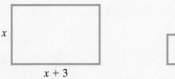
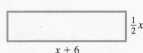

△ **116. Comparing Perimeters** The square and the rectangle shown have the same perimeter. Solve the equation

$$4x = 2\left(\frac{1}{2}x\right) + 2(x + 5) \text{ for } x, \text{ the length of the}$$

side of the square.

117. Paying Your Taxes You are single and just determined that you paid $1442.50 in federal income taxes for 2008. The solution to the equation $1442.50 = 0.15(x - 7300) + 730$ represents your adjusted gross income in 2008. Determine your adjusted gross income in 2008. (SOURCE: *Internal Revenue Service*)

118. Paying Your Taxes You are married and just determined that you paid $12,200 in federal income taxes in 2008. The solution to the equation $12,200 = 0.15(x - 14,600) + 1460$ represents the adjusted gross income of you and your spouse in 2008. Determine the adjusted gross income of you and your spouse in 2008. (SOURCE: *Internal Revenue Service*)

Explaining the Concepts

119. Make up a linear equation that has one solution. Make up a linear equation that has no solution. Make up a linear equation that is an identity. Discuss the differences and similarities in making up each equation.

120. A student solved the equation $3(x + 8) = \frac{1}{2}(6x + 4)$ and wrote the answer $24 = 2$. The instructor did not give full credit for this answer. Explain the student's error and determine the correct solution.

121. When solving the equation $\frac{2}{3}x - 5 = \frac{1}{2}x$, a student decided to multiply both sides by the LCD and wrote $6 \cdot \frac{2}{3}x - 5 = \frac{1}{2}x \cdot 6$. This resulted in the next line $4x - 5 = 3x$. Is this correct? Explain the steps necessary to finish by this technique and then suggest another list of steps that would arrive at the correct solution.

122. Explain how you can tell from the last step of the solution process whether the solution of an equation is the set of all real numbers or the empty set. For example, if the last line of the solution of an equation is $-6 = 8$, is the solution the set of all real numbers or the empty set? If the last line of the solution of an equation is $9 = 9$, is the solution the set of all real numbers or the empty set?

2.4 Evaluating Formulas and Solving Formulas for a Variable

Preparing for Evaluating Formulas and Solving Formulas for a Variable
Before getting started, take this readiness quiz. If you get a problem wrong, go back to the section cited and review the material.

P1. Evaluate the expression $2L + 2W$ for $L = 7$ and $W = 5$. [Section 1.8, pp. 67–68]

P2. Round the expression 0.5873 to hundredths place. [Section 1.2, pp. 13–14]

[1] Evaluate a Formula

In this section, we use *formulas* to solve mathematical problems.

> **DEFINITION**
>
> A mathematical **formula** is an equation that describes how two or more variables are related.

For example, a formula for the area of a rectangle is *area* = *length* · *width*, or $A = l \cdot w$. You use mathematical formulas every day, many times without even realizing it. For instance, if you plan to paint your apartment, you must find the surface area of the walls to compute the amount of paint you will purchase. To determine the number of gallons of gasoline you can afford to put in your car, you may also use a formula, as illustrated in the next example.

EXAMPLE 1 Evaluating a Formula

The number of gallons of gasoline that you put in your car is found by using the formula $\dfrac{C}{p} = n$, where C is the total cost, p is the price per gallon, and n is the number of gallons. How many gallons of gasoline can you purchase for $51.00 if gas costs $4.25 per gallon?

Solution

$$\frac{C}{p} = n$$

Replace *C* with cost, $51, and *p* with price per gallon, $4.25:
$$\frac{\$51}{\$4.25} = n$$

Evaluate the numerical expression:
$$12 = n$$

You can purchase 12 gallons for $51. ∎

Quick ✔

1. A _____ is an equation that describes how two or more variables are related.

2. Your best friend, who is on spring break in Europe, e-mailed you that the temperature in Paris today is 15° Celsius. Use the formula $F = \dfrac{9}{5}C + 32$, where F is degrees Fahrenheit and C is degrees Celsius, to find the approximate temperature in degrees Fahrenheit.

3. The size of a dress purchased in Europe is different from one purchased in the United States. The equation $c = a + 30$ gives the European (Continental) dress size c in terms of the size in the United States, a. Find the Continental dress size that corresponds to a size 10 dress in the United States.

EXAMPLE 2 Evaluating a Formula Containing a Percent

The formula $S = P - 0.25P$ gives the sale price S of an item which originally cost P dollars that was reduced by 25%. Find the sale price of a pair of jeans that originally cost $40.00.

Solution

$$S = P - 0.25P$$

Replace P with the original price of the jeans, $40: $\quad S = 40 - 0.25(40)$

Evaluate the numerical expression: $\quad S = 40 - 10$

$$S = 30$$

The sale price of the jeans is $30. ∎

Quick ✔

4. The formula $E = 250 + 0.05S$ is a formula for the earnings, E, of a salesman who receives $250 per week plus 5% commission on all weekly sales, S. Find the earnings of a salesman who had weekly sales of $1250.

5. The formula $N = p + 0.06p$ models the new population, N, of a town with current population p if the town is expecting population growth of 6% next year. Find the new population of a town whose current population is 5600 persons.

The Simple Interest Formula

Interest is money paid for the use of money. The total amount borrowed is called the **principal.** The principal can be in the form of a loan (an individual borrows from the bank) or a deposit (the bank borrows from the individual). The **rate of interest,** expressed as a percent, is the amount charged for the use of the principal for a given period of time, usually on a yearly basis.

SIMPLE INTEREST FORMULA

If an amount of money, P, called the **principal** is invested for a period of t years at an annual interest rate r, expressed as a decimal, the amount of interest I earned is

$$I = Prt$$

Interest earned according to this formula is called **simple interest.**

EXAMPLE 3 Evaluating Using the Simple Interest Formula

Janice invested $500 in a two-year Certificate of Deposit (CD) at the simple interest rate of 4% per annum (annually). Find the amount of interest Janice will earn in 6 months. Also find the total amount of money Janice will have at the end of 6 months.

Solution

Work Smart

Be sure to express t in years when using the simple interest formula.

We see that the amount of money Janice invested, P, is $500. The interest rate r is 4% = 0.04. Because 6 months is $\frac{1}{2}$ a year, we have that $t = \frac{1}{2}$.

$$I = Prt$$

Let $p = \$500$, $r = 0.04$, and $t = \frac{1}{2}$: $\quad I = 500 \cdot 0.04 \cdot \frac{1}{2}$

Evaluate the numerical expression: $\quad I = 10$

Janice earned $10 on her investment. At the end of 6 months, Janet will have $500 + $10 = $510. ∎

Quick ✔

6. The total amount borrowed in a loan is called _____. _____ is money paid for the use of money.

7. Bill invested his $2500 Virginia Lottery winnings in an 8-month Certificate of Deposit that earns 3% simple interest per annum. Find the amount of interest Bill's investment will earn at the end of 8 months. Also find the total amount of money Bill will have at the end of 8 months.

Geometry Formulas

Let's review a few common terms from geometry.

DEFINITIONS

The **perimeter** is the sum of the lengths of all the sides of a figure.

The **area** is the amount of space enclosed by a two-dimensional figure measured in square units.

The **surface area** of a solid is the sum of the areas of the surfaces of a three-dimensional figure.

The **volume** is the amount of space occupied by a three-dimensional figure measured in units cubed.

The **radius** r of a circle is the line segment that extends from the center of the circle to any point on the circle.

The **diameter** of a circle is any line segment that extends from one point on the circle through the center to a second point on the circle. The length of a diameter is two times the length of the radius, $d = 2r$.

In circles, we use the term **circumference** to mean the perimeter.

Formulas from geometry are useful in solving many types of problems. We list some of these formulas in Table 1.

Table 1			
Plane Figures	**Formulas**	**Plane Figures**	**Formulas**
Square	**Area:** $A = s^2$ **Perimeter:** $P = 4s$	Trapezoid	**Area:** $A = \frac{1}{2}h(B + b)$ **Perimeter:** $P = a + b + c + B$
Rectangle	**Area:** $A = lw$ **Perimeter:** $P = 2l + 2w$	Parallelogram	**Area:** $A = bh$ **Perimeter:** $P = 2a + 2b$
Triangle	**Area:** $A = \frac{1}{2}bh$ **Perimeter:** $P = a + b + c$	Circle	**Area:** $A = \pi r^2$ **Circumference:** $C = 2\pi r = \pi d$

(continued)

Table 1 (continued)

Solids	Formulas	Solids	Formulas
Cube 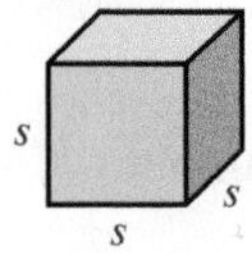	**Volume:** $V = s^3$ **Surface Area:** $S = 6s^2$	Right Circular Cylinder 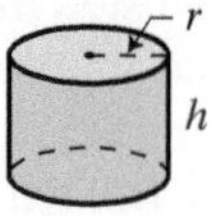	**Volume:** $V = \pi r^2 h$ **Surface Area:** $S = 2\pi r^2 + 2\pi rh$
Rectangular Solid 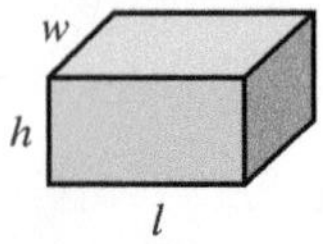	**Volume:** $V = lwh$ **Surface Area:** $S = 2lw + 2lh + 2wh$	Cone 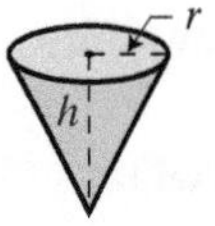	**Volume:** $V = \dfrac{1}{3}\pi r^2 h$
Sphere 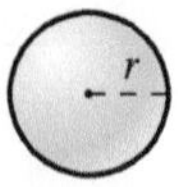	**Volume:** $V = \dfrac{4}{3}\pi r^3$ **Surface Area:** $S = 4\pi r^2$		

EXAMPLE 4 Evaluating a Formula for the Perimeter of a Rectangle

Find the number of yards of fencing that must be purchased to enclose a garden that is 10.5 yards long and 4.25 yards wide as illustrated in Figure 1.

Solution

We are enclosing a rectangular garden, so we use the formula for the perimeter of a rectangle, $P = 2l + 2w$, where $l = 10.5$ yards and $w = 4.25$ yards.

Figure 1

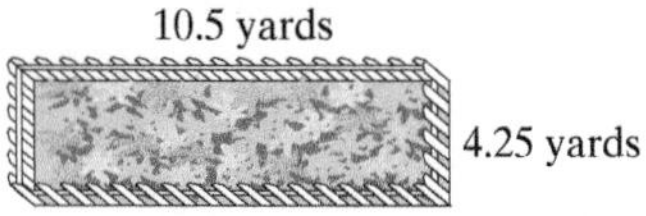

10.5 yards

4.25 yards

$$P = 2l + 2w$$

Replace l with 10.5 and w with 4.25: $\quad P = 2(10.5) + 2(4.25)$

Evaluate the numerical expression: $\quad P = 21 + 8.5$

$$P = 29.5$$

We find that 29.5 yards of fencing must be purchased.

Quick ✔

8. Find the area of a trapezoid with $h = 4.5$ inches, $B = 9$ inches, and $b = 7$ inches.

Sometimes we need to use more than one geometry formula in order to solve a problem.

EXAMPLE 5 Finding the Area of a Lawn and the Cost of Sod

A circular swimming pool whose diameter is 30 feet is to be installed in a rectangular yard that is 100 feet by 60 feet. Once the pool is installed, grass is to be installed on the remaining land. See Figure 2.

(a) Determine the area of land that is to receive grass.

(b) If sod costs $0.25 per square foot installed, what will be the cost of the lawn?

Figure 2

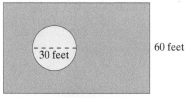

60 feet

100 feet

Solution

(a) The area of a rectangle is $A = lw$ and the area of a circle is $A = \pi r^2$. We find the area of the remaining lawn by subtracting the area of the circular swimming pool from the area of the lawn.

$$\text{Area of remaining lawn} = \text{Area of rectangle} - \text{Area of circle}$$
$$= lw - \pi r^2$$

The length l of the lawn is 100 feet and the width is 60 feet. The radius of the circle is one-half its diameter, so the radius is 15 feet. Substituting into the formulas, we obtain

$$\text{Area of remaining lawn} = (100 \text{ feet})(60 \text{ feet}) - \pi(15 \text{ feet})^2$$
$$= 6000 \text{ feet}^2 - 225\pi \text{ feet}^2$$
$$\pi \approx 3.14159: \quad \approx 5293 \text{ feet}^2$$

Approximately 5293 square feet of sod is needed.

(b) We determine the cost of the sod by multiplying the square footage by the cost per square foot.

$$\text{Cost for sod} = 5293 \text{ square feet} \cdot \frac{\$0.25}{1 \text{ square foot}}$$
$$= \$1323.25$$

The sod will cost $1323.25. ∎

It is worth noting in Example 5(b) that the units "square feet" divided out, so that the answer is measured in dollars. Because the answer is in the appropriate units, we have more confidence that our answer is correct.

Quick ✔

9. The area of a circle is found using the formula _____.

10. A circular water feature whose diameter is 4 feet is to be installed in a rectangular garden that is 20 feet by 10 feet. Once the water feature is installed, grass is to be installed on the remaining land.

   (a) Determine the area, to the nearest square foot, of land that is to receive grass.

   (b) If sod costs $0.25 per square foot installed, what will be the cost of the lawn?

Geometry formulas can even be used to make us savvy consumers.

 EXAMPLE 6 Determining the Better Buy

At Mamma da Vinci's Pizza Parlor, a 16″ pizza costs $14.99 and a 12″ pizza costs $9.99. Which is the "better" buy?

Solution

The "better" buy will be the pizza that costs less per square inch. Our plan is: (1) find the area of each pizza and then (2) find the price per square inch of each pizza. We must consider, too, that a 16″ pizza has a *diameter* of 16 inches so that the radius is 8″ and a 12″ pizza has a *diameter* of 12 inches so that the radius is 6″.

1. Find the area of each pizza.

Since pizzas are circular, we compute the area of the pizza using the formula for the area of a circle.

	Area of the 16″ pizza:	Area of the 12″ pizza:
	$A = \pi r^2$	$A = \pi r^2$
Replace r with its given value:	$A = \pi \cdot 8^2$	$A = \pi \cdot 6^2$
Evaluate the numerical expression:	$A \approx 201.06 \text{ in.}^2$	$A \approx 113.10 \text{ in.}^2$

2. Find the price per square inch of each pizza.

The price per square inch can be found by dividing the price of the pizza by the number of square inches of area.

price per square inch of large pizza: $\dfrac{\$14.99}{201.06 \text{ in.}^2} \approx \$0.075$ per square inch

price per square inch of medium pizza: $\dfrac{\$9.99}{113.10 \text{ in.}^2} \approx \$0.088$ per square inch

The price per square inch of the large pizza is about 7.5¢, while the price per square inch of the medium pizza is about 8.8¢. The large pizza is the "better" buy. ∎

Quick ✔

11. A homeowner plans to construct a circular brick pad for his barbeque grill. The diameter of the brick pad is to be 6 feet. Find, to the nearest hundredth of a square foot, the area of the barbeque pad.

12. An extra large (18″) pizza at Dante's Pizza costs $16.99 and a small (9″) pizza costs $8.99. Which is the better buy?

2 Solve a Formula for a Variable

The expression "solve for a variable" means to isolate the variable with a coefficient of 1 on one side of the equation and all other variables and constants, if any, on the other side by forming equivalent equations. For example, in the formula for the area of a rectangle, $A = lw$, the formula is solved for A because A is by itself with a coefficient of 1 on one side of the equation while all other variables are on the other side.

The steps that we follow when solving formulas for a certain variable are identical to those that we followed when solving equations.

Solve for x:	$15 = \dfrac{3}{2}x$	**Solve for h:**	$A = \dfrac{1}{2}bh$
Multiply both sides of the equation by 2 to clear the fraction.	$2(15) = 2\left(\dfrac{3}{2}x\right)$	Multiply both sides of the equation by 2 to clear the fraction.	$2(A) = 2\left(\dfrac{1}{2}bh\right)$
	$30 = 3x$		$2A = bh$
Divide by 3 to isolate the variable x.	$\dfrac{30}{3} = \dfrac{3x}{3}$	Divide by b to isolate the variable h.	$\dfrac{2A}{b} = \dfrac{bh}{b}$
	$10 = x$		$\dfrac{2A}{b} = h$

EXAMPLE 7 How to Solve a Formula for a Variable

Solve the formula $P = 2l + 2w$ for w. *Note: $P = 2l + 2w$ is the formula for the perimeter of a rectangle.*

Step-by-Step Solution

Step 1: Isolate the term containing the variable.

Subtract $2l$ from both sides of the equation to isolate the term $2w$:

$$P = 2l + 2w$$
$$P - 2l = 2l + 2w - 2l$$
$$P - 2l = 2w$$

Step 2: Get the coefficient of the variable to be 1.   Divide both sides of the equation by 2: $\dfrac{P - 2l}{2} = \dfrac{2w}{2}$

$$\dfrac{P - 2l}{2} = w$$

Work Smart

The Symmetric Property states that if $a = b$, then $b = a$.

We can write $\dfrac{P - 2l}{2} = w$ as $w = \dfrac{P - 2l}{2}$ using the *Symmetric Property*. We have solved the equation $P = 2l + 2w$ for w because w is isolated with a coefficient of 1 on one side of the equation and all other terms are on the other side of the equation. ∎

Quick ✔

13. To convert from degrees Celsius to degrees Fahrenheit, we use the formula $F = \dfrac{9}{5}C + 32$. Solve this formula for C.

14. The formula $S = 2\pi rh + 2\pi r^2$ represents the surface area S of a right circular cylinder whose radius is r and height is h. Solve the formula for h.

This next example illustrates a skill that will be extremely important when we study graphing lines in Chapter 3.

EXAMPLE 8 Solving for a Variable in a Formula

Solve the equation $3x + 2y = 6$ for y.

Solution

We wish to solve for y. That is, we want to get y isolated on one side of the equation and the variable x and constants on the other side. We begin by isolating the term containing y on the left side of the equation.

$$3x + 2y = 6$$

Subtract $3x$ from both sides of the equation to isolate the term containing y: $3x + 2y - 3x = 6 - 3x$

Simplify both sides of the equation: $2y = 6 - 3x$

Divide both sides by 2: $\dfrac{2y}{2} = \dfrac{6 - 3x}{2}$

Simplify: $y = \dfrac{6 - 3x}{2}$

Work Smart

$\dfrac{A + B}{C} = \dfrac{A}{C} + \dfrac{B}{C}$, so

$\dfrac{6 - 3x}{2} = \dfrac{6}{2} - \dfrac{3x}{2}$.

The equation $y = \dfrac{6 - 3x}{2}$ may also be written in the form $y = 3 - \dfrac{3}{2}x$ or $y = -\dfrac{3}{2}x + 3$ by dividing 2 into each term in the numerator. Do you see why these three equations are equivalent? ∎

Quick ✔

15. *True or False:* Solving $x - y = 6$ for y results in $y = -x + 6$

In Problems 16–19, solve each equation for the indicated variable.

16. $x + 2y = 7$; for y

17. $5x - 3y = 15$; for y

18. $\frac{3}{4}a + 2b = 7$; for b

19. $3rs + \frac{1}{2}t = 12$ for t.

EXAMPLE 9 Solving a Formula for a Specified Variable and Evaluating the Formula

The amount of profit, P, earned by a manufacturer is given by the formula $P = R - C$, where R represents the manufacturer's revenue and C represents the manufacturer's costs.

(a) Solve the equation for R, the manufacturer's revenue.

(b) Find the amount of revenue if a manufacturer has a $12,500 profit and $6000 in costs.

Solution

(a) We wish to solve the equation for R, so we must isolate R on one side of the equation.

$$P = R - C$$

Add C to both sides of the equation: $\quad P + C = R - C + C$

Simplify: $\quad P + C = R$

Thus, $R = P + C$.

(b) Evaluate $R = P + C$ if $P = \$12,500$ and $C = \$6000$.

$$R = P + C$$

Replace P with 12,500 and C with 6000: $\quad R = 12,500 + 6000$

Evaluate: $\quad R = 18,500$

The manufacturer has revenue of $18,500 when it has $12,500 profit and $6000 in costs. ∎

Quick ✔

20. (a) Solve the formula $d = rt$ for t, where d represents distance, r represents an average speed, and t represents time.

(b) Suppose that a family drives from Columbus, Ohio, to Raleigh, North Carolina, a distance of 550 miles. Their average speed for the trip is 60 mph. How long will it take the family to reach their destination?

21. (a) Solve the simple interest formula $I = Prt$ for t.

(b) Find the number of years that $1000 must be invested at 7% annual interest to earn $35 interest. *Hint:* Convert the percent to a decimal.

22. (a) Solve the formula $R = pq$ for p, where R represents revenue, p represents price, and q represents quantity.

(b) Find the price of a designer tote if the revenue from selling 125 totes is $5000.

2.4 EXERCISES

PRACTICE   WATCH   DOWNLOAD   READ   REVIEW

1–22. are the Quick ✔s that follow each EXAMPLE

Building Skills

In Problems 23–32, substitute the given values into the formula and then evaluate to find the unknown quantity. Label units in the answer. If the answer is not exact, round your answer to the nearest hundredth. See Objective 1.

23. Height of a Dam The formula $f = 3.281m$ converts a length in meters m to feet f. The world's highest dams, the Rogun and the Nurek, are both in Tajikistan. The Rogun is 335 meters high and the Nurek is 300 meters high. Convert these heights to feet.

24. Length of a Bridge The formula $m = 0.3048f$ converts length in feet f to length in meters m. The George Washington Bridge in New York City is 3500 feet long. How long is the George Washington Bridge in meters?

25. Buying a Digital Media Player The formula $S = P - 0.20P$ gives the sale price S of an item whose original cost P dollars was reduced by 20%. Find the sale price of a digital media player that originally cost $130.00.

26. Buying a Computer The formula $S = P - 0.35P$ gives the sale price S of an item whose original cost P dollars was reduced by 35%. Find the sale price of a computer that originally cost $950.00.

27. Salesperson's Earnings The formula $E = 500 + 0.15S$ is a formula for the earnings, E, of a salesperson who receives $500 per week plus 15% commission on all sales, S. Find the earnings of a salesperson who had weekly sales of $1000.

28. Salesperson's Earnings The formula $E = 750 + 0.07S$ is a formula for the earnings, E, of a salesperson who receives $750 per week plus 7% commission on all sales, S. Find the earnings of a salesperson who had weekly sales of $1200.

29. Planning a Trip A businessperson is planning a trip from Tokyo to San Diego, California, in March. She learns that the average high temperature in San Diego in March is 68°. Use the formula $C = \dfrac{5}{9}(F - 32)$ to convert 68° Fahrenheit to degrees Celsius.

30. Planning a Trip An English Literature professor plans to take twenty students on a study-abroad trip to London in March. He learns that the average daytime temperature in London in March is 10 degrees Celsius. Use the formula $F = \dfrac{9}{5}C + 32$ to convert 10 degrees Celsius to degrees Fahrenheit.

31. Lottery Earnings Therese invested her $200 West Virginia Lottery winnings in a 6-month Certificate of Deposit (CD) that earns 3% simple interest per annum. Use the formula $I = Prt$ to find the amount of interest Therese's investment will earn.

32. Investing an Inheritance Christopher invested his $5000 inheritance from his grandmother in a 9-month Certificate of Deposit that earns 4% simple interest per annum. Use the formula $I = Prt$ to find the amount of interest Christopher's investment will earn.

△ **33.** Find
  (a) the perimeter and
  (b) the area of the rectangle.

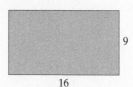

9

16

△ **34.** Find
  (a) the perimeter and
  (b) the area of the rectangle.

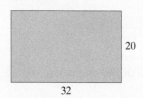

20

32

△ **35.** Find
  (a) the perimeter and
  (b) the area of the rectangle.

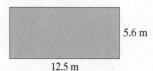

5.6 m

12.5 m

△ **36.** Find
  (a) the perimeter and
  (b) the area of the rectangle.

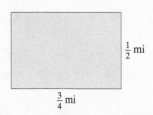

$\dfrac{1}{2}$ mi

$\dfrac{3}{4}$ mi

△ **37.** Find
  (a) the perimeter and
  (b) the area of the square.

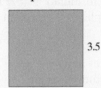

9

△ **38.** Find
  (a) the perimeter and
  (b) the area of the square.

3.5

△ **39.** Find
  (a) the circumference and
  (b) the area of the circle. Use $\pi \approx 3.14$.

$r = 5$ cm

△ **40.** Find
  (a) the circumference and
  (b) the area of the circle. Use $\pi \approx 3.14$.

$r = 2.8$ yards

△ **41. Area of a Circle** Find the area of a circle A when $\pi \approx \dfrac{22}{7}$ and $r = \dfrac{14}{3}$ inches.

△ **42. Area of a Circle** Find the area of a circle A when $\pi \approx 3.14$ and $r = 2.5$ km.

In Problems 43–56, solve each formula for the stated variable. See Objective 2.

43. $d = rt$; solve for r

44. $A = lw$; solve for w

45. $C = \pi d$; solve for d

46. $F = mv^2$; solve for m

47. $I = Prt$; solve for t

48. $V = LWH$; solve for W

49. $A = \dfrac{1}{2}bh$; solve for b

50. $V = \dfrac{1}{3}Bh$; solve for B

51. $P = a + b + c$; solve for a

52. $S = a + b + c$; solve for b

53. $A = P + Prt$; solve for r

54. $P = 2l + 2w$: solve for l

55. $A = \dfrac{1}{2}h(B + b)$; solve for b

56. $S = 2\pi r(r + h)$; solve for h

In Problems 57–64, solve for y. See Objective 2.

57. $3x + y = 12$

58. $-2x + y = 18$

59. $10x - 5y = 25$

60. $12x - 6y = 18$

61. $4x + 3y = 13$

62. $5x + 6y = 18$

63. $\dfrac{1}{2}x - \dfrac{1}{6}y = 2$

64. $\dfrac{2}{3}x - \dfrac{5}{2}y = 5$

Applying the Concepts

In Problems 65–78, (a) solve for the indicated variable, and then (b) find the value of the unknown quantity. When given, label units in the answer.

65. Profit = Revenue − Cost: $P = R - C$
  (a) Solve for C.
  (b) Find C when $P = \$1200$ and $R = \$1650$.

66. Profit = Revenue − Cost: $P = R - C$
  (a) Solve for R.
  (b) Find R when $P = \$4525$ and $C = \$1475$.

67. Simple Interest: $I = Prt$
  (a) Solve for r.
  (b) Find r when $I = \$225$, $P = \$5000$, and $t = 1.5$ years.

68. Simple Interest: $I = Prt$
  (a) Solve for t.
  (b) Find t when $I = \$42$, $P = \$525$, and $r = 4\%$.

69. Statistics Formula: $Z = \dfrac{x - \mu}{\sigma}$
  (a) Solve for x.
  (b) Find x when $Z = 2$, $\mu = 100$, and $\sigma = 15$.

70. Physics Formula: $P = mgh$
  (a) Solve for m.
  (b) Find m when $P = 8192$, $g = 32$, and $h = 1$.

71. Algebra: $y = mx + 5$
  (a) Solve for m.
  (b) Find m when $x = 3$ and $y = -1$.

72. Fahrenheit/Celsius Temperature Conversion:
  $F = \dfrac{9}{5}C + 32$
  (a) Solve for C.
  (b) Find C when $F = 59°$.

73. Finance: $A = P + Prt$
  (a) Solve for r.
  (b) Find r when $A = \$540$, $P = \$500$, and $t = 2$.

74. Finance: $A = P + Prt$

(a) Solve for t.

(b) Find t when $A = \$249$, $P = \$240$, and $r = 2.5\% = 0.025$.

△ **75. Volume of a Right Circular Cylinder:** $V = \pi r^2 h$

(a) Solve for h.

(b) Find h when $V = 320\pi$ mm^3 and $r = 8$ mm.

△ **76. Volume of a Cone:** $V = \dfrac{1}{3}\pi r^2 h$

(a) Solve for h.

(b) Find h when $V = 75\pi$ in.^{3} and $r = 5$ in.

△ **77. Area of a Triangle:** $A = \dfrac{1}{2}bh$

(a) Solve for b.

(b) Find b when $A = 45$ ft and $h = 5$ ft

△ **78. Area of a Trapezoid:** $A = \dfrac{1}{2}h(b + B)$

(a) Solve for h.

(b) Find h when $A = 99$ cm^2, $b = 19$ cm, and $B = 3$ cm.

79. Energy Expenditure Basal energy expenditure (E) is the amount of energy required to maintain the body's normal metabolic activity such as respiration, maintenance of body temperature, and so on. For males, the Basal energy expenditure is given by the formula

$$E = 66.67 + 13.75W + 5H - 6.76A$$

where W is the weight of the male (in kilograms), H is the height of the male (in centimeters), and A is the age of the male. Determine the Basal energy expenditure of a 37-year-old male who is 178 cm (5 feet, 10 inches) tall and weighs 82 kg (180 pounds).

80. Energy Expenditure See Problem 79. The Basal energy expenditure for females is given by

$$E = 665.1 + 9.56W + 1.85H - 4.68A$$

Compute the Basal energy expenditure of a 40-year-old female who is 168 cm tall (5 feet, 6 inches) and weighs 57 kg (125 pounds).

△ **81. Cylinders** The volume V of a right circular cylinder is given by the formula $V = \pi r^2 h$, where r is the radius and h is the height.

(a) Solve the formula for h.

(b) Find the height of a right circular cylinder whose volume is 90π cubic inches and whose radius is 3 inches.

△ **82. Soup Can** The formula $S = 2\pi rh + 2\pi r^2$ gives the surface area S of a right circular cylinder whose radius is r and height is h.

(a) Solve the formula for h.

(b) Find the height of a right circular cylinder whose surface area is 8.25π square inches and radius is 1.5 inches.

△ **83. Grocery Store** You are standing at the freezer case at your local grocery store trying to decide which is the "better" buy: a medium $(12'')$ pizza for $9.99 or 2 small pizzas $(8'')$ that are on special for $4.49 each. Which should you choose to get the best deal?

△ **84. Pizza for Dinner** Mama Mimi's Take and Bake Pizzeria is running a special on southwestern-style pizzas: a large $16''$ pizza for $13.99 or two small $8''$ pizzas for $12.99. Which should you choose to get the best deal?

85. Taking a Trip Jason drives a truck as an independent contractor. He bills himself out at $28 per hour. Suppose Jason has a contract that calls for him to leave a dock at 9:00 A.M. and travel 600 miles to a warehouse. Jason has driven this route many times and figures that he can travel at an average speed of 50 miles per hour.

(a) Using the formula $d = rt$, where d is the distance traveled, r is the average speed, and t is the time spent traveling, determine how long Jason expects the trip to take.

(b) How much money does Jason expect to earn from this contract?

86. Taking a Trip Messai drives a truck as an independent contractor. He bills himself out at $32 per hour. Messai has a contract that calls for him to leave a dock at 8:00 A.M. and travel 145 miles to a warehouse. At the warehouse, he will wait while the truck is loaded (this takes 2 hours) and then return to his original dock. Messai has driven this route many times and figures that he can travel at an average speed of 58 miles per hour.

(a) Using the formula $d = rt$, where d is the distance traveled, r is the average speed, and t is the time spent traveling, determine how long Messai expects the round-trip to take. Exclude the time Messai waits for the truck to be loaded.

(b) How much money does Messai expect to earn from this contract driving his truck?

△ **87. Area of a Region** Find the area of the figure below.

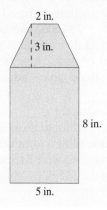

2 in.

3 in.

8 in.

5 in.

△ **88. Area of a Region** Find the area of the figure below.

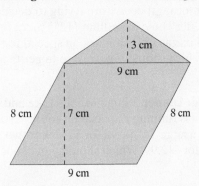

△ **89. Ice Cream Cone** Find the amount of ice cream in a cone if the radius of the cone is 4 cm and its height is 10 cm. The ice cream fully fills the cone and the hemisphere of ice cream on the top has a radius of 4 cm.

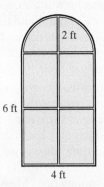

△ **90. Window** Find the area of the window given that the upper portion is a semicircle:

91. Federal Taxes According to the tax code in 2007, a married couple that earns over $234,600 per year filing a joint income tax return is subject to having their itemized deductions reduced. The formula $P = D - 0.02(I - 234,600)$ can be used to determine the permitted deductions P, where D represents the amount of deductions from Schedule A and I represents the couple's adjusted gross income.

(a) Solve the formula for I.

(b) Determine the adjusted gross income of a married couple filing a joint return whose allowed deductions were $15,500 and Schedule A deductions were $15,821.

92. Computing a Grade Jose's art history instructor uses the formula $G = \dfrac{a + b + 2c + 2d}{6}$ to compute her students' semester grade. The variables a and b represent the grades on two tests, c represents the grade on a research paper, d represents the final exam grade, and G represents the student's average.

(a) Solve the equation for d, Jose's final exam grade.

(b) A final average of 84 will earn Jose a B in the course. Compute the grade Jose must make on his final exam in order to earn a B for the semester, if he scored 78 and 74 on his tests, and 84 on his research paper.

△ **93. Remodel a Bathroom** You plan to remodel your bathroom and you've chosen 1-foot-by-1-foot ceramic tiles for the floor. The bathroom is 7 feet 6 inches long and 8 feet 2 inches wide.

(a) How many tiles do you need to cover the floor of your bathroom?

(b) Each tile costs $6. How much will it cost to tile your floor?

(c) The store from which you purchase the tile offers a discount of 10% on orders over $350. Does your order qualify for the discount?

△ **94. Painting a Room** A gallon of paint can cover about 500 square feet. Find the number of gallon containers of paint that must be purchased to paint two coats on each wall of a rectangular room measuring 8 feet by 12 feet, with a 10-foot ceiling. *Note:* You cannot purchase a partial can of paint!

△ **95. Landscaping a Back Yard** A circular swimming pool whose diameter is 24 feet is to be installed in a rectangular yard that is 60 feet by 90 feet. Once the pool is installed, grass is to be installed on the remaining land.

(a) Determine the area of land that is to receive grass. Round your answer to the nearest foot. Use $\pi \approx 3.14159$.

(b) If sod costs $0.25 per square foot installed, what will be the cost of the lawn?

△ **96. Landscaping a Back Yard** A rectangular swimming pool whose dimensions are 12 feet by 24 feet is to be installed in a rectangular yard that is 80 feet by 40 feet. Once the pool is installed, grass is to be installed on the remaining land.

(a) Determine the area of land that is to receive grass. Round your answer to the nearest foot.

(b) A pallet of sod covers 500 square feet. How many pallets of sod are required?

(c) Each pallet of sod costs $96. What is the cost of the sod?

Extending the Concepts

△ **97. Conversion** A rectangle has length 5 feet and width 18 inches.

   (a) What is the area in square inches?
   (b) What is the area in square feet?

△ **98. Conversion** A rectangle has length 9 yards and width 8 feet.

   (a) What is the area in square feet?
   (b) What is the area in square yards?

△ **99. Conversion** Determine a formula for converting square inches to square feet.

△ **100. Conversion** Determine a formula for converting square yards to square feet.

Explaining the Concepts

101. A student solved the equation $x + 2y = 6$ for y and obtained the result $y = \dfrac{-x + 6}{2}$. Another student solved the same equation for y and obtained the result $y = -\dfrac{1}{2}x + 3$. Are both solutions correct? Explain why or why not.

102. Make up an example of a linear equation whose coefficients are integers. Make up a similar example where the coefficients are constants (letters). Solve both and then explain which steps in the solution are alike and which are different.

PUTTING THE CONCEPTS TOGETHER (Sections 2.1–2.4)

These problems cover important concepts from Sections 2.1 through 2.4. We designed these problems so that you can review the chapter so far and show your mastery of the concepts. Take time to work these problems before proceeding with the next section. The answers to these problems are located at the back of the text on page AN-5.

1. Determine if the given value of the variable is a solution of the equation

$$4 - (6 - x) = 5x - 8$$

   (a) $x = \dfrac{3}{2}$ **(b)** $x = -\dfrac{5}{2}$

2. Determine if the given value of the variable is a solution of the equation

$$\dfrac{1}{2}(x - 4) + 3x = x + \dfrac{1}{2}$$

   (a) $x = -4$ **(b)** $x = 1$

In Problems 3–14, solve the equation and check the solution.

3. $x + \dfrac{1}{2} = -\dfrac{1}{6}$ **4.** $-0.4m = 16$

5. $14 = -\dfrac{7}{3}p$ **6.** $8n - 11 = 13$

7. $\dfrac{5}{2}n - 4 = -19$ **8.** $-(5 - x) = 2(5x + 8)$

9. $7(x + 6) = 2x + 3x - 15$

10. $-7a + 5 + 8a = 2a + 8 - 28$

11. $-\dfrac{1}{2}(x - 6) + \dfrac{1}{6}(x + 6) = 2$

12. $0.3x - 1.4 = -0.2x + 6$

13. $5 + 3(2x + 1) = 5x + x - 10$

14. $3 - 2(x + 5) = -2(x + 2) - 3$

15. Investment You have $7500 to invest and your financial advisor suggests that you put part of the money in a Certificate of Deposit that earns 2.4% simple interest and the remainder in bonds that earn 4% simple interest. To determine the amount you should invest in the CD to earn $220 interest at the end of one year, solve the equation $0.024x + 0.04(7500 - x) = 220$, where x represents the amount of money invested in CDs.

16. Area of a trapezoid: $A = \dfrac{1}{2}h(B + b)$

   (a) Solve for b.
   (b) Find b when $A = 76$ in.^{2}, $h = 8$ in., and $B = 13$ in.

17. Volume of a right circular cylinder: $V = \pi r^2 h$
   (a) Solve for h.
   (b) Find h when $V = 117\pi$ in.^{2} and $r = 3$ in.

18. Solve the equation $3x + 2y = 14$ for y.

2.5 Introduction to Problem Solving: Direct Translation Problems

OBJECTIVES

1. Translate English Phrases to Algebraic Expressions
2. Translate English Sentences to Equations
3. Build Models for Solving Direct Translation Problems

Preparing for Introduction to Problem Solving: Direct Translation Problems

Before getting started, take this readiness quiz. If you get a problem wrong, go back to the section cited and review the material.

P1. Solve the equation: $x + 34.95 = 60.03$ [Section 2.1, pp. 86–88]

P2. Solve the equation: $x + 0.25x = 60$ [Section 2.2, p. 96]

1 Translate English Phrases to Algebraic Expressions

One of the neat features of mathematics is that the symbols we use allow us to express English phrases briefly and consistently. An algebraic expression is similar to an English phrase. For example, the English phrase "5 more than a number x" is represented algebraically as $x + 5$.

There are certain words or phrases in English that easily translate into mathematical symbols. Table 2 lists various English words or phrases and their corresponding math symbols.

Table 2 Math Symbols and the Words They Represent			
Add (+)	Subtract (−)	Multiply (·)	Divide (/)
sum	difference	product	quotient
plus	minus	times	divided by
greater than	subtracted from	of	per
more than	less	twice	ratio
exceeds by	less than	double	
in excess of	decreased by	half	
added to	fewer		
increased by			
combined			
altogether			

EXAMPLE 1 Writing English Phrases Using Math Symbols

Express each English phrase using mathematical symbols.

(a) The sum of 2 and 5

(b) The difference of 12 and 7

(c) The product of −3 and 8

(d) The quotient of 10 and 2

(e) 9 less than 15

(f) A number z decreased by 11

(g) Three times the sum of a number x and 8

Solution

(a) Because we are talking about a sum, we know to use the + symbol, so "The sum of 2 and 5" is represented mathematically as $2 + 5$.

(b) Because we are talking about a difference, we know to use the − symbol, so "The difference of 12 and 7" is represented mathematically as $12 - 7$.

(c) "The product of -3 and 8" is represented as $-3 \cdot 8$.

(d) "The quotient of 10 and 2" is represented mathematically as $\dfrac{10}{2}$.

(e) "9 less than 15" is represented mathematically as $15 - 9$.

(f) "A number z decreased by 11" is represented algebraically as $z - 11$.

(g) "Three times the sum of a number x and 8" is represented as an algebraic expression as $3(x + 8)$. ∎

In Example 1(g), we know the mathematical representation of the phrase is $3(x + 8)$ rather than $3x + 8$ because the phrase "three times the sum" means to multiply the sum of the two numbers by 3. The English phrase that would result in $3x + 8$ might be "the sum of three times a number and 8." Do you see the difference?

Work Smart

When translating from English to math, try some specific examples. For example, to translate "a number z decreased by 11," pick specific values of z, as in "16 decreased by 11," which would be $16 - 11$ or 5. So "z decreased by 11" is $z - 11$.

Quick ✔ *In Problems 1–6, express each English phrase using mathematical symbols.*

1. The sum of 5 and 17

2. The product of -2 and 6

3. The quotient of 25 and 3

4. The difference of 7 and 4

5. Twice a less 2

6. Three plus the quotient of z and 4

EXAMPLE 2 Translating from an English Phrase to an Algebraic Expression

Write an algebraic expression for each problem.

(a) The Raiders scored p points in a football game. The Packers scored 12 more points than the Raiders. Write an algebraic expression for the number of points the Packers scored.

(b) A lumberman cuts a 50-foot log into 2 pieces. One piece is t feet long. Express the length of the second piece as an algebraic expression in t.

(c) The number of quarters in a drink machine is two less than the number of dimes, d, in the machine. Write an expression for the number of quarters as an algebraic expression in d.

Solution

(a) The phrase "more than" implies addition. The Packers scored $p + 12$ points in the football game.

(b) The log is 50 feet long. If the lumberman cuts one piece 20 feet long, then the other piece must be $50 - 20 = 30$ feet long. In general, if the lumberman cuts one piece that is t feet long, then the remaining piece must be $(50 - t)$ feet long.

(c) The phrase "less than" implies subtraction. Two less than the number of dimes is represented algebraically as $d - 2$. ∎

Quick ✔ *In Problems 7–9, translate each phrase to an algebraic expression.*

7. Terry earned z dollars last week. Anne earned $50 more than Terry last week. Write an algebraic expression for Anne's earnings in terms of z.

8. Melissa paid x dollars for her college math book and $15 less than that for her college sociology book. Express the cost of her sociology book in terms of x.

9. Tim raided his piggy bank and found he had 75 dimes and quarters. Tim has d dimes. Express the number of quarters in his piggy bank as an algebraic expression in d.

EXAMPLE 3 Translating from an English Phrase to an Algebraic Expression

Write an algebraic expression for each problem.

(a) The number of student tickets sold for a play is five fewer than four times the number n of nonstudent tickets sold. Write an algebraic expression for the number of student tickets sold in terms of n.

(b) The height of a full-grown maple tree is ten feet more than three times the height h of a sapling. Write an algebraic expression for the height of the full-grown tree in terms of h.

(c) A pedestrian bridge over a river is f feet long. Further downstream, another pedestrian bridge over the same river is three feet less than twice the length of the first bridge. Write an algebraic expression for the length of the second bridge in terms of f.

Solution

(a) The phrase "fewer than" implies subtraction. The number of student tickets sold is five fewer than four times the number of nonstudent tickets sold. So the algebraic expression representing the number of student tickets sold is 4 times the number of nonstudent tickets sold minus 5, or $4n - 5$.

(b) The full-grown tree is ten feet more than three times the height of the sapling, so $(3h + 10)$ feet represents the height of the full-grown tree.

(c) The second bridge is three feet less than twice the length of the first bridge, so $(2f - 3)$ feet represents the length of the second bridge. ∎

Quick ✔ *In Problems 10–12, translate each phrase to an algebraic expression.*

10. The width of a platform is 2 feet less than three times the length, l. Express the width of the platform as an algebraic expression in terms of l.

11. T.J. has quarters and dimes in his piggy bank. The number of dimes is three more than twice the number of quarters. T.J. has q quarters. Express the number of dimes as an algebraic expression in terms of q.

12. The number of red M&Ms in a bowl is five less than three times the number of brown M&Ms, b, in the bowl. Express the number of red M&Ms in the bowl as an expression in terms of b.

⌐2⌐ Translate English Sentences to Equations

In Words

English phrase is to algebraic expression as English sentence is to algebraic equation.

Nearly every word problem that we do in algebra requires some type of translation. Learning to speak the language of math is the same as learning to speak any language. Now that we have the ability to translate English phrases to algebraic expressions, we will extend the idea to translating English sentences to algebraic equations.

In English, a complete sentence must contain a subject and a verb, so expressions or "phrases" are not complete sentences. For example "Beats me!" is an expression, but it is not a complete sentence because it does not contain a subject. The expression "5 more than a number x" does not contain a verb and therefore is not a complete sentence either. The statement "5 more than a number x is 18" is a complete sentence because it contains a subject and a verb. Because this is a complete sentence, we can translate it into a mathematical statement. In mathematics, statements can be represented symbolically as equations.

Work Smart

We learned in Section 2.1 that an equation is a statement in which two algebraic expressions are equal.

In English, statements can be true or false. For example, "The moon is made of green cheese" is a false statement, while "The sky is blue" is a true statement. Mathematical statements can be true or false as well—we call them conditional equations.

Table 3 provides a summary of words that typically translate into an equal sign.

Table 3 Words That Translate into an Equal Sign			
is	yields	are	equals
was	gives	results in	is equal to
is equivalent to			

Notice that the words that translate into an equal sign are all verbs. So, the equal sign in an equation acts like a verb in a sentence.

Let's look at some examples where we translate English sentences into equations.

EXAMPLE 4   Translating English Sentences into Equations

Translate each of the following sentences into an equation. Do not solve the equation.

(a) Five more than a number x is 20.

(b) Four times the sum of a number z and 3 is 15.

(c) The difference of x and 5 equals the quotient of x and 2.

Solution

(a) 5 more than a number x is 20
$$x + 5 \qquad = \quad 20$$

(b) Because the expression reads "Four times the sum," we first need to determine the sum and then multiply this result by 4.

Four times the sum of a number z and 3 is 15
$$4(z + 3) \qquad = \quad 15$$

(c) The difference of x and 5 equals the quotient of x and 2
$$x - 5 \qquad = \qquad \frac{x}{2}$$

Quick ✔

13. To translate an English sentence into a mathematical statement we use algebraic _____.

In Problems 14–17, translate each English statement into an equation. Do not solve the equation.

14. The product of 3 and y is equal to 21.

15. The sum of 3 and x is equivalent to the product of 5 and x.

16. The difference of x and 10 equals the quotient of x and 2.

17. Three less than a number y is five times y.

Work Smart

5 more than a number x can be written as $5 + x$ or $x + 5$. Be careful! $5 - x$ is not the same as $x - 5$. Can you explain why?

Work Smart

The English sentence "The sum of four times a number z and 3 is 15" would be expressed mathematically as $4z + 3 = 15$. Do you see how this differs from Example 4(b)?

An Introduction to Problem Solving and Mathematical Models

Every day we encounter various types of problems that must be solved. **Problem solving** is the ability to use information, tools, and our own skills to achieve a goal. For example, suppose 4-year-old Kevin wants a glass of water, but he is too short to reach the sink. Kevin has a problem. To solve the problem, he finds a step stool and pulls it over to the sink. He uses the step stool to climb on the counter, opens the kitchen cabinet, and pulls out a cup. He then crawls along the counter top, turns on the faucet, fills the cup, and proceeds to drink the water. Problem solved!

Of course, this is not the only way that Kevin could solve the problem. Can you think of any other solutions? Just as there are various approaches to solving life's everyday problems, there are many ways to solve problems using mathematics. However, regardless of the approach, there are always some common aspects in solving any problem. For example, regardless of how Kevin ultimately ends up with his cup of water, someone must get a cup from the cabinet and someone must turn on the faucet.

One of the purposes of learning algebra is to be able to solve certain types of problems. To solve these problems, we will need techniques that can help us translate the verbal descriptions in the problems into equations that can be solved. The process of taking a verbal description in a problem and developing a mathematical equation that can be used to solve the problem is **mathematical modeling.**

Mathematical modeling begins with a problem. The problem is summarized as a verbal description. The verbal description is then translated into the language of mathematics. This translation results in an equation that can be solved (the mathematical problem). The solution must be checked against the mathematical problem (the equation) and the verbal description. This entire process is called the **modeling process.** We call the equation that is developed the **mathematical model.** See Figure 3.

Figure 3

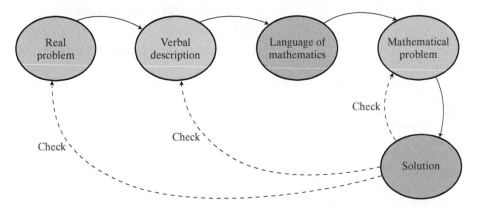

Not all models are mathematical. In general, a **model** is a way of using graphs, pictures, small-scale reproductions, equations, or even verbal descriptions to represent a real-life situation. Because the world is an extremely complex place, we often need to simplify information when we develop a model. For example, a map is a model of our road system. Maps don't show all the details of the system such as trees, buildings, or potholes, but they do a good job of describing how to get from point A to point B. Mathematical models are similar in that we often make assumptions regarding our world in order to make the mathematics more manageable.

It is difficult to give a step-by-step approach for solving problems because each problem is unique in some way. However, because there are common links to many types of problems, we can categorize problems. In this text, we will present five categories of problems.

Five Categories of Problems

1. **Direct Translation**—problems in which we must translate from English into the language of mathematics by using key words in the verbal description.

2. **Geometry**—problems in which the unknown quantities are related through geometric formulas.

3. **Mixtures**—problems in which two or more quantities are combined in some fashion.

4. **Uniform Motion**—problems in which an object travels at a constant speed.

5. **Work Problems**—problems in which two or more entities join forces to complete a job.

We will present strategies for solving categories of problems throughout the text. In this section, we will concentrate on direct translation problems.

Regardless of the type of problem we solve, there are certain steps that should always be followed to assist in solving the problem. On the following page we provide you with a series of steps that should be followed when developing any mathematical model. As we proceed through this course, and in future courses, you will use the techniques that you have studied in this course to solve more complicated problems, but the approach remains the same.

STEPS FOR SOLVING PROBLEMS WITH MATHEMATICAL MODELS

Step 1: Identify What You Are Looking For Read the problem very carefully, perhaps two or three times. Identify the type of problem. Identify the information that is given, and the information that we wish to learn from the problem. It is fairly typical that the last sentence in the problem indicates what it is we wish to solve for in the problem.

Step 2: Give Names to the Unknowns Assign variables to the unknown quantities in the problem. Choose a variable that is representative of the unknown quantity it represents. For example, use t for time.

Step 3: Translate the Problem into the Language of Mathematics Read the problem again. This time, after each sentence is read, determine if the sentence can be translated into a mathematical statement or expression in terms of the variables identified in Step 2. It is often helpful to create a table, chart, or figure. When you have finished reading the problem, if necessary, combine the mathematical statements or expressions into an equation that can be solved.

Step 4: Solve the Equation(s) Found in Step 3 Solve the equation for the variable.

Step 5: Check the Reasonableness of Your Answer Check your answer to be sure that it makes sense. If it does not, go back and try again.

Step 6: Answer the Question Write your answer in a complete sentence.

Let's review each of these steps, one at a time.

- **Identify** Carefully read the problem. Reading a verbal description of a problem is not like reading a spy novel. You may need to read the problem three or four times. You may not know how to solve the problem while reading it, but you should get a sense of which of the five categories the problem falls into, what information you are given, and what you are being asked to do.

- **Name** Reread the problem and assign variables to the unknowns. You should write the name of each variable and what it represents. You will use this to check your final answer.

- **Translate** In this step, you develop a model (equation) that mathematically describes the problem. Be sure to use the guidelines presented in each category of problem. We will present these guidelines shortly.

- **Solve the equation** This is generally the easy part. Most students say, "I could solve the problem, if I could find the right equation."

- **Check** Checking your answer can be difficult because you can make two types of errors while setting up or solving the problem. One type of error occurs if you correctly translate the problem into a model but then make an error solving the equation. A second type of error occurs if you misinterpret the problem and develop an incorrect model. The solution you obtain may still satisfy your model, but it probably will not be the solution to the original problem. We can check for this type of error by determining whether the solution is reasonable. Does your answer make sense?

- **Answer the question** Always be sure that you are answering the question that is being asked. Write your answer to the problem in words.

Work Smart

Remember that you can use any letter to represent the unknown(s) when you make your model. Choose a letter that reminds you what it represents. For example, use t for time.

Quick ✔

18. Letting variables represent unknown quantities and then expressing relationships among the variables in the form of equations is called _____ _____ .

⌐3 Build Models for Solving Direct Translation Problems

Let's look at a "direct translation" problem. Remember, these are problems that can be set up by reading the problem and using everyday language to translate the verbal description into a mathematical equation.

EXAMPLE 5 Solving a Direct Translation Problem

The price of a "premium" ticket for a performance of a popular Broadway show in New York is $69 more than twice the price of a premium ticket for a performance of that same Broadway show in Chicago. If you purchase a ticket for this show in Chicago, and your friend purchases a ticket for the same show in New York, and the total cost of the two tickets is $436.50, what is the cost of each ticket?

Solution

Step 1: Identify This is a direct translation problem. We can obtain an equation from the words of the problem. We want to know the price of a premium ticket for a performance of a popular Broadway show in New York and the price of a premium ticket for a performance of that same show in Chicago.

Work Smart

It is helpful to assign the variable to the quantity that you know **least** about.

Step 2: Name We know that the price of a ticket to the Broadway show in New York is $69 more than twice the price of a ticket for that show in Chicago. We will let c represent the price of a ticket to the show in Chicago. Then $2c + 69$ represents the price of a ticket to the show in New York.

Step 3: Translate Because we know that the total cost for the tickets to both performances is $436.50, we use the equation

$$\underbrace{c}_{\text{price of ticket in Chicago}} + \underbrace{2c + 69}_{\text{plus price of ticket in New York}} = \underbrace{436.50}_{\text{equals total cost}} \qquad \text{The Model}$$

Step 4: Solve We now solve the equation

$$c + (2c + 69) = 436.50$$

Combine like terms: $\qquad 3c + 69 = 436.50$

Subtract 69 from each side of the equation: $3c + 69 - 69 = 436.50 - 69$

$$3c = 367.50$$

Divide each side by 3: $\qquad \dfrac{3c}{3} = \dfrac{369.50}{3}$

$$c = 122.50$$

We have found $c = 122.50$. Recall that c represents the price of a ticket for the Broadway show in Chicago. The price of a ticket for the same Broadway show in New York is $69 more than twice the price of a ticket for the show in Chicago. So $2c + 69 = 2(122.50) + 69 = 314$. It costs $314 for a ticket to a performance of the Broadway show in New York.

Step 5: Check Is the total cost of a ticket to the show in Chicago and a ticket to the show in New York $436.50? Since $122.50 + $314 = $436.50, our answers are correct.

Step 6: Answer The price of a premium ticket to a performance of a popular Broadway show in Chicago is $122.50 and the price of a premium ticket to a performance of the same Broadway show in New York is $314. ∎

Quick ✔ *Translate the problem to an algebraic equation and solve the equation for the unknowns.*

19. Sean and Connor decide to buy a pizza. The pizza costs $15 and they decide to split the cost based upon how much pizza each eats. Connor eats two-thirds of the amount that Sean eats, so Connor pays two-thirds of the amount that Sean pays. How much does each pay?

Examples of consecutive even integers are

16, 18, 20
78, 80, 82
752, 754, 756

Examples of consecutive odd integers are

9, 11, 13
31, 33, 35
623, 625, 627

Consecutive Integer Problems

Recall that an *integer* is a member of the set $\{\ldots, -3, -2, -1, 0, 1, 2, 3, \ldots\}$. An *even integer* is an integer that is divisible by two. For example, 16 and 124 are even integers. An *odd integer* is an integer that is not even. For example, 9 and 17 are odd integers. Consecutive integers differ by one, so if n represents the first integer, $n + 1$ represents the second integer, $n + 2$ represents the third integer, and so on. Consecutive *even* integers, such as 14 and 16, differ by two so if n represents the first even integer, $n + 2$ represents the second even integer and $n + 4$ represents the third even integer. Consecutive *odd* integers also differ by 2 (41 and 43, for example), so if n represents the first odd integer, $n + 2$ represents the second odd integer, and $n + 4$ represents the third odd integer. See Figure 4.

Figure 4

Consecutive integers

Consecutive **even** integers, if n is even

Consecutive **odd** integers, if n is odd

EXAMPLE 6   Solving a Direct Translation Problem: Consecutive Integers

The sum of three consecutive even integers is 324. Find the integers.

Solution

Step 1: Identify This is a direct translation problem. We are looking for three consecutive even integers, and we know that their sum is 324. Examples of consecutive even integers are $6, 8, 10, \ldots$.

Step 2: Name We will let n represent the first even integer, so $n + 2$ is the next even integer, and $n + 4$ is the third even integer.

Step 3: Translate We know that the sum of the three consecutive even integers is 324. We also know that the word "sum" translates to "addition" and the word "is" translates to "equals." So our equation is

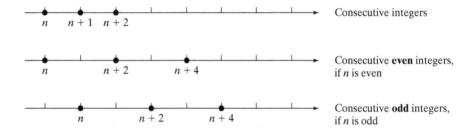

$$\underbrace{n}_{\text{first even integer}} + \underbrace{n + 2}_{\text{second even integer}} + \underbrace{n + 4}_{\text{third even integer}} = \underbrace{324}_{\text{sum}} \quad \text{The Model}$$

Step 4: Solve We solve the equation.

$$n + (n + 2) + (n + 4) = 324$$

Combine like terms: $\quad 3n + 6 = 324$

Subtract 6 from each side of the equation: $\quad 3n + 6 - 6 = 324 - 6$

$$3n = 318$$

Divide each side by 3: $\quad \dfrac{3n}{3} = \dfrac{318}{3}$

$$n = 106$$

Since $n = 106$, is the first even integer, the remaining even integers are 108 and 110.

Step 5: Check These numbers are all even integers, so we know that they are possible solutions. Does $106 + 108 + 110 = 324$? Yes! We know we have the correct answer.

Step 6: Answer The three consecutive even integers are 106, 108, and 110. ∎

Quick ✔

20. *True or False:* If *n* represents the first of three consecutive odd integers, then *n* + 1 and *n* + 3 represent the next two odd integers.

In Problems 21 and 22, translate the problem to an algebraic equation and solve the equation for the unknowns.

21. The sum of three consecutive even integers is 270. Find the integers.

22. The sum of 4 consecutive odd integers is 72. Find the integers.

EXAMPLE 7 Solving a Direct Translation Problem: Piece Lengths

A carpenter is building a shelving system and cuts a 14-foot length of cherry shelving into three pieces. The second piece is twice as long as the first, and the third piece is 2 feet longer than the first. Find the length of each piece of cherry shelving.

Solution

Step 1: Identify This is a direct translation problem. We are looking for the length of each piece of shelving. We know that the board is 14 feet long.

Step 2: Name Because the length of the second and third pieces are described in terms of the length of the first piece, we will let *x* represent the length of the first piece of shelving. The second piece is twice as long as the first piece, so 2*x* represents the length of the second piece. Because the third piece is 2 feet longer than the first piece, its length is *x* + 2. See Figure 5.

Step 3: Translate We know that the lengths of the three pieces must total 14 feet, so our equation is

$\underbrace{\text{length of}}_{\text{first piece}}$	$\underbrace{\text{length of}}_{\text{second piece}}$	$\underbrace{\text{length of}}_{\text{third piece}}$	$\underbrace{\text{total}}_{\text{length}}$	
x	$+\quad 2x$	$+\quad x+2$	$=\quad 14$	The Model

Step 4: Solve We solve the equation.

$$x + 2x + (x + 2) = 14$$

Combine like terms: $\quad 4x + 2 = 14$

Subtract 2 from each side of the equation: $\quad 4x + 2 - 2 = 14 - 2$

$$4x = 12$$

Divide each side by 4: $\quad \dfrac{4x}{4} = \dfrac{12}{4}$

$$x = 3$$

Since *x* = 3 feet is the length of the first piece, the second piece of shelving is 2*x* = 2 · 3 = 6 feet and the third piece is *x* + 2 = 3 + 2 = 5 feet long.

Step 5: Check Is the sum of the three pieces of cherry shelving equal to 14 feet? Does 3 + 6 + 5 = 14? Yes! We know we have the correct answer.

Step 6: Answer The three pieces of shelving are 3 feet, 6 feet, and 5 feet long. ∎

Work Smart

Sometimes these problems are called "the whole equals the sum of the parts" problems because the values of the "parts" must sum to the value of the "whole."

Figure 5

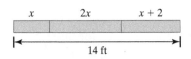

Quick ✔ *In Problem 23, translate the problem to an algebraic equation and solve.*

23. A 76-inch length of ribbon is to be cut into three pieces. The longest piece is to be 24 inches longer than the shortest piece, and the third piece is to be half the length of the longest piece. Find the length of each piece of ribbon.

EXAMPLE 8   Investment Decisions

A total of $25,000 is to be invested, some in bonds and some in certificates of deposit (CDs). The amount invested in CDs is to be $8000 less than the amount invested in bonds. How much is to be invested in each type of investment?

Solution

Step 1: Identify We want to know the amount invested in each type of investment.

Step 2: Name Let b represent the amount invested in bonds.

Step 3: Translate The equation that we will use is

   Amount invested in bonds + Amount invested in CDs = Total investment

Suppose we invested $18,000 in bonds; then the amount in CDs will be $8000 less than this amount, or $10,000. In general, if b is the amount invested in bonds, then $b - 8000$ represents the amount invested in CDs. Our total investment is $25,000. Substituting into the above equation, we have

$$\underbrace{b}_{\text{Amount invested in bonds}} + \underbrace{b - 8000}_{\text{Amount invested in CDs}} = \underbrace{25{,}000}_{\text{Total investment}} \quad \text{The Model}$$

Step 4: Solve We now solve the equation.

$$b + (b - 8000) = 25{,}000$$

Combine like terms: $\qquad\qquad\qquad 2b - 8000 = 25{,}000$

Add 8000 to each side of the equation: $\qquad\qquad 2b = 33{,}000$

Divide both sides by 2: $\qquad\qquad\qquad\qquad b = 16{,}500$

Step 5: Check If we invest $16,500 in bonds, then the amount invested in CDs should be $8000 less than this amount or $8500. The total investment should then be $25,000. Since the amount invested in bonds plus the amount invested in CDs is $16,500 + $8500 = $25,000, the answer checks.

Step 6: Answer Invest $16,500 in bonds and $8500 in CDs. ■

Quick ✔ *In Problem 24, translate the problem to an algebraic equation and solve.*

24. A total of $18,000 is to be invested, some in stocks and some in bonds. If the amount invested in bonds is twice that invested in stocks, how much is invested in each category?

EXAMPLE 9   Choosing a Long-Distance Carrier

MCI has a long-distance phone plan that charges $6.99 a month plus $0.04 per minute of usage. Sprint has a long-distance phone plan that charges $5.95 a month plus $0.05 per minute of usage. For how many minutes of long-distance calls will the monthly costs for the two plans be the same? (SOURCE: *MCI and Sprint*)

Solution

Step 1: Identify This is a direct translation problem. We are looking for the number of minutes for which the two plans cost the same.

Step 2: Name Let m represent the number of long-distance minutes used in the month.

Step 3: Translate The monthly fee for MCI is $6.99 plus $0.04 for each minute used. So, if one minute is used, the fee is $6.99 + 0.04(1) = 7.03$ dollars. If two minutes are used, the fee is $6.99 + 0.08(2) = 7.07$ dollars. In general, if m minutes are used, the monthly fee is $(6.99 + 0.04m)$ dollars. Similar logic results in the monthly fee for Sprint being $(5.95 + 0.05m)$ dollars. We want to know the number of minutes for which the cost for the two plans will be the same, which means we need to solve

$$\underbrace{6.99 + 0.04m}_{\text{Cost for MCI}} = \underbrace{5.95 + 0.05m}_{\text{Cost for Sprint}} \qquad \text{The Model}$$

Step 4: Solve

$$6.99 + 0.04m = 5.95 + 0.05m$$

Subtract 5.95 from both sides: $\quad 1.04 + 0.04m = 0.05m$

Subtract 0.04m from both sides: $\quad 1.04 = 0.01m$

Multiply both sides by 100: $\quad 104 = m$

Step 5: Check We believe the cost of the two plans will be the same if 104 minutes are used. The cost of MCI's plan will be $6.99 + 0.04(104) = \$11.15$. The cost of Sprint's plan will be $5.95 + 0.05(104) = \$11.15$. They are the same!

Step 6: Answer the Question The cost of the two plans will be the same if 104 minutes are used. ∎

Quick ✔

25. You need to rent a moving truck. You have identified two companies that rent trucks. EZ-Rental charges $30 per day plus $0.15 per mile. Do It Yourself Rental charges $15 per day plus $0.25 per mile. For how many miles will the daily cost of renting be the same?

26. Your grandmother wants a cell phone for emergency use only. You have researched cell phone plans and have found that Company A charges $15 per month plus $0.05 per minute, while Company B charges $0.20 per minute with no monthly charge. For how many minutes will the monthly cost be the same?

2.5 EXERCISES

PRACTICE   WATCH   DOWNLOAD   READ   REVIEW

1–26. are the Quick ✔s that follow each EXAMPLE

Building Skills

In Problems 27–44, translate each phrase to an algebraic expression. Let x represent the unknown number. See Objective 1.

27. the sum of −5 and a number

28. a number increased by 32.3

29. the product of a number and $\dfrac{2}{3}$

30. the product of −2 and a number

31. half of a number

32. double a number

33. a number less −25

34. 8 less than a number

35. the quotient of a number and 3

36. the quotient of −14 and a number

37. $\dfrac{1}{2}$ more than a number

38. $\dfrac{4}{5}$ of a number

39. 9 more than 6 times a number

40. 21 more than 4 times a number

41. twice the sum of 13.7 and a number

42. 50 less than half of a number

43. the sum of twice a number and 31

44. the sum of twice a number and 45

In Problems 45–52, choose a variable to represent one quantity. State what that quantity represents and then express the second quantity in terms of the first. See Objective 1.

45 The Columbus Clippers scored 5 more runs than the Richmond Braves.

46. The Toronto Blue Jays scored 3 fewer runs than the Cleveland Indians.

47. Jan has $0.55 more in her piggy bank than Bill.

48. Beryl has $0.25 more than 3 times the amount Ralph has.

49. Janet and Kathy will share the $200 grant.

50. Juan and Emilio will share the $1500 lottery winnings.

51. There were 1433 visitors to the Arts Center Spring show. Some were adults and some were children.

52. There were 12,765 fans at a recent NBA game. Some held paid admission tickets and some held special promotion tickets.

In Problems 53–60, translate each statement into an equation. Let x represent the unknown number. DO NOT SOLVE. See Objective 2.

53. The sum of a number and 15 is −34.

54. The sum of 43 and a number is −72.

55. 35 is 7 less than triple a number.

56. 49 is 3 less than twice a number.

57. The quotient of a number and −4, increased by 5, is 36.

58. The quotient of a number and −6, decreased by 15, is 30.

59. Twice the sum of a number and 6 is the same as 3 more than the number.

60. Twice the sum of a number and 5 is the same as 7 more than the number.

Applying the Concepts

61. **Number Sense** The sum of a number and −12 is 71. Find the number.

62. **Number Sense** The difference between a number and 13 is −29. Find the number.

63. **Number Sense** 25 less than twice a number is −53. Find the number.

64. **Number Sense** The sum of 13 and twice a number is −19. Find the number.

65. **Consecutive Integers** The sum of three consecutive integers is 165. Find the numbers.

66. **Consecutive Integers** The sum of three consecutive odd integers is 81. Find the numbers.

67. **Bridges** The longest bridge in the United States is the Verrazano-Narrows Bridge. The second-longest bridge in the United States is the Golden Gate Bridge, which is 60 feet shorter than the Verrazano-Narrows Bridge. The combined length of the two bridges is 8460 feet. Find the length of each bridge.

68. **Towers** The tallest buildings in the world (those having the most stories) are the Sears Tower in Chicago, Illinois, and the Ryugyong Hotel in Pyongyang, North Korea. The Ryugyong Hotel has 5 fewer stories than the Sears Tower. The two buildings together have 215 stories. Find the number of stories in each building.

69. **Buying a Motorcycle** The total price for a new motorcycle is $11,894.79. The tax, title, and dealer preparation charges amount to $679.79. Find the price of the motorcycle before the extra charges.

70. **Buying a Desk** The total price for a new desk is $285.14, including sales tax of $16.14. Find the original cost of the desk.

71. **Finance** A total of $20,000 is to be invested, some in bonds and some in certificates of deposit (CDs). The amount invested in bonds is to be $3000 greater than the amount invested in CDs. How much is to be invested in each type of investment?

72. **Finance** A total of $10,000 is to be divided between Sean and George. George is to receive $3000 less than Sean. How much will each receive?

73. **Investments** Suppose that your Aunt May has left you an unexpected inheritance of $32,000. You have decided to invest the money rather than blow it on frivolous purchases. Your financial advisor has recommended that you diversify by placing some of the money in stocks and some in bonds. Based upon current market conditions, she has recommended that the amount in bonds should equal three-fifths of the amount invested in stocks. How much should be invested in stocks? How much should be invested in bonds?

74. **Investments** Jack and Diane have $40,000 to invest. Their financial advisor has recommended that they diversify by placing some of the money in stocks and some in bonds. Based upon current market conditions, he has recommended that the amount in bonds should equal two-thirds of the amount invested in stocks. How much should be invested in stocks? How much should be invested in bonds?

75. **Cereal** A serving of Kashi Go Lean Crunch cereal contains 4 times the amount of fiber as a serving of Kellogg's Smart Start Cereal. If you eat a serving of each cereal, you will consume 10 g of dietary fiber. Find the amount of dietary fiber in each cereal.

76. **Books** A paperback edition of a book costs $12.50 less than the hardback edition of the book. If you purchase one of each version, you will pay $37.40. Find the cost of the paperback edition of the book.

77. **Income** On a joint income tax return, Elizabeth Morrell's adjusted gross income was $2549 more than her husband Dan's adjusted gross income. Their combined adjusted gross income was $55,731. Find Elizabeth Morrell's adjusted gross income.

78. **Spring Break** Allison went shopping to prepare for her Spring Break trip. Her bathing suit cost $8 more than a pair of shorts, and a T-shirt cost $2 less than the shorts. Find the cost of the bathing suit if Allison spent $60 on the items, before sales tax.

79. **Truck Rentals** You need to rent a moving truck. You have identified two companies that rent trucks. EZ-Rental charges $35 per day plus $0.15 per mile. Do It Yourself Rental charges $20 per day plus $0.25 per mile. For how many miles will the daily cost of renting be the same?

80. **Cellular Telephones** You need a new cell phone for emergencies only. Company A charges $12 per month plus $0.10 per minute, while Company B charges $0.15 per minute with no monthly service charge. For how many minutes will the monthly cost be the same?

81. **Comparing Printers** Samuel is trying to decide between two laser printers, one manufactured by Hewlett-Packard, the other by Brother. Both have similar features and warranties, so price is the determining factor. The Hewlett-Packard costs $200 and printing costs are approximately $0.03 per page. The Brother costs $240 and printing costs are approximately $0.01 per page. How many pages need to be printed for the cost of the two printers to be the same?

82. **Comparing Job Offers** Hans has just been offered two sales jobs selling vacuums. The first job offer is a base monthly salary of $2000 plus a commission of $50 for each vacuum sold. The second job offer is a base monthly salary of $1200 plus a commission of $60 for each vacuum sold. How many vacuums must be sold for the two jobs to pay the same salary?

83. **Adjusted Gross Income** On a joint income tax return, Jensen Beck's adjusted gross income was $249 more than his wife Maureen's adjusted gross income. Their combined adjusted gross income was $72,193. Find Jensen and Maureen Beck's adjusted gross income.

84. **Camping Trip** Jaime Juarez purchased some new camping equipment. He spent $199 on a cookware set, a lantern, and a cook stove. The cookware set cost $30 more than the lantern, and the cook stove cost $34 more than the lantern. Find the cost of each item.

85. **Baseball Games** The Columbus Comets played a double-header and won both games. The number of

runs they scored in the two games are consecutive even integers, and the score of each game was a pair of consecutive integers. A total of 26 runs were scored. Find the number of runs scored in each of the two baseball games.

86. **Computing Grades** Going into the final exam, which will count as two tests, Brooke has test scores of 80, 83, 71, 61, and 95. What score does Brooke need on the final exam in order to have an average score of 80?

Extending the Concepts

In Problems 87–90, write a problem that would translate into the given equation.

87. $10x = 370$

88. $5n + 10 = 170$

89. $\dfrac{x + 74}{2} = 80$

90. $n + n + 2 = 98$

△ 91. **Angles** The sum of the measures of the three angles in a triangle is 180 degrees. The measure of the smallest angle of a triangle is half the measure of the second angle. The measure of the largest angle is 40° more than 4 times the measure of the smallest. Find the measure of each angle.

△ 92. **Angles** The sum of the measures of the three angles in a triangle is 180 degrees. The measure of one angle of a triangle is one degree more than three times the measure of the smallest angle. The measure of the third angle is 13° less than twice the measure of the second angle. Find the measure of each angle.

Explaining the Concepts

93. How is mathematical modeling related to problem solving? Why do we make assumptions when creating mathematical models?

94. What is the difference between an algebraic expression and an equation? How is each related to English phrases and English statements?

95. Two students write an equation to solve a word problem with consecutive odd integers. One student assigns the variables as $n - 1, n + 1, n + 3$, where n is an even integer. A second student uses $n, n + 2, n + 4$, where n is an odd integer. Which student is correct? Will the value for n be the same for both? Make up a problem that can be solved in more than one way and explain how the variables were assigned.

96. Using the algebraic expression $3x + 5$, make up a problem that uses the direction "evaluate." Using the same algebraic expression, make up a problem that uses the direction "solve."

2.6 Problem Solving: Direct Translation Problems Involving Percent

OBJECTIVES

1. Solve Direct Translation Problems Involving Percent
2. Model and Solve Direct Translation Problems from Business That Involve Percent

Preparing for Problem Solving: Direct Translation Problems Involving Percent

Before getting started, take the following readiness quiz. If you get a problem wrong, go back to the section cited and review the material.

P1. Write 45% as a decimal.   [Section 1.2, p. 16]

P2. Write 0.2875 as a percent.   [Section 1.2, p. 17]

1 Solve Direct Translation Problems Involving Percent

Percent means "divided by 100" or "per hundred." We use the symbol % to denote percent, so 45% means 45 out of 100 or $\frac{45}{100}$ or 0.45. In applications involving percents, we often encounter the word "of," as in 20% of 100. The word "of" translates into multiplication in mathematics, so 20% of 100 means $0.20 \cdot 100 = 20$.

EXAMPLE 1 Solving an Equation Involving Percent

A number is 35% of 40. Find the number.

Solution

Step 1: Identify We want to know the unknown number.

Step 2: Name Let n represent the number.

Step 3: Translate We translate the words of the problem:

$$\underbrace{\text{a number}}_{n} \quad \underbrace{\text{is}}_{=} \quad \underbrace{35\%}_{0.35} \quad \underbrace{\text{of}}_{\cdot} \quad \underbrace{40}_{40}$$

The equation we want to solve is $n = 0.35(40)$.

Step 4: Solve We now solve the equation.

$$n = 0.35(40)$$
$$\text{Multiply:} \quad n = 14$$

Step 5: Check Check the multiplication: $0.35(40) = 14$.

Step 6: Answer 14 is 35% of 40.

Quick ✔

1. Percent means "divided by _____."

2. The word "of" translates into _____ in mathematics so 40% of 120 means 0.40 _____ 120.

3. A number is 89% of 900. Find the number.

4. A number is 3.5% of 72. Find the number.

5. A number is 150% of 24. Find the number.

6. A number is $8\frac{3}{4}$% of 40. Find the number.

EXAMPLE 2 Solving an Equation Involving Percent

The number 240 is what percent of 800?

Solution

Step 1: Identify We want to know the percent.

Step 2: Name Let x represent the percent.

Step 3: Translate We translate the words of the problem:

$$\underbrace{240}_{240} \quad \underbrace{is}_{=} \quad \underbrace{what\ percent}_{x} \quad \underbrace{of}_{\cdot} \quad \underbrace{800?}_{800}$$

The equation we will solve is $240 = 800x$.

Step 4: Solve We now solve the equation.

$$240 = 800x$$

Divide each side by 800: $\dfrac{240}{800} = \dfrac{800x}{800}$

$$0.3 = x$$

Since we are finding a percent and our answer is a decimal, we must change 0.3 to a percent by moving the decimal point two places to the right: $0.30 = 30\%$.

Step 5: Check Is 240 equal to 30% of 800? Does $(0.30)(800) = 240$? Yes!

Step 6: Answer The number 240 is 30% of 800. ■

Quick ✔

7. The number 8 is what percent of 20?

8. The number 15 is what percent of 40?

9. The number 12.3 is what percent of 60?

10. The number 44 is what percent of 40?

EXAMPLE 3 Solving an Equation Involving Percent

42 is 35% of what number?

Solution

Step 1: Identify We want to know the number.

Step 2: Name Let x represent the number.

Step 3: Translate We translate the words of the problem:

$$\underbrace{42}_{42} \quad \underbrace{is}_{=} \quad \underbrace{35\%}_{0.35} \quad \underbrace{of}_{\cdot} \quad \underbrace{what\ number?}_{x}$$

The equation we will solve is $42 = 0.35x$.

Step 4: Solve We now solve the equation.

$$42 = 0.35x$$

Divide each side by 0.35: $\dfrac{42}{0.35} = \dfrac{0.35x}{0.35}$

$$120 = x$$

Step 5: Check Is 35% of 120 equal to 42? Because $(0.35)(120) = 42$, the answer is correct.

Step 6: Answer 42 is 35% of 120. ■

11. 14 is 28% of what number? **12.** 111 is 74% of what number?

13. 14.8 is 18.5% of what number? **14.** 102 is 136% of what number?

EXAMPLE 4 Educational Attainment of U.S. Residents

In 2007, the number of U.S. residents 25 years of age or older was approximately 195,000,000. If 30% of all U.S. residents 25 years of age or older are high school graduates, determine the number of U.S. residents 25 years of age or older in 2007 who were high school graduates. (SOURCE: *U.S. Census Bureau*)

Solution

Step 1: Identify We want to know the number of U.S. residents 25 years of age or older in 2007 who are high school graduates.

Step 2: Name Let x represent the number of high school graduates.

Step 3: Translate We know that 30% of U.S. residents 25 years of age or older are high school graduates. We also know that in the year 2007 there were approximately 195,000,000 U.S. residents 25 years of age or older. We translate the words of the problem:

$$\underbrace{30\%}_{} \ \underbrace{\text{of}}_{} \ \underbrace{\text{U.S. residents}}_{} \ \underbrace{\text{are}}_{} \ \underbrace{\text{high school graduates}}_{}$$
$$0.30 \quad \cdot \quad 195{,}000{,}000 \quad = \quad\quad x \qquad \text{The Model}$$

Our equation is $(0.30)(195{,}000{,}000) = x$.

Step 4: Solve We solve the equation.

$$(0.30)(195{,}000{,}000) = x$$
$$\text{Multiply:} \qquad 58{,}500{,}000 = x$$

Step 5: Check We can recheck our arithmetic. Because $0.30 \cdot 195{,}000{,}000 = 58{,}500{,}000$, the answer is correct.

Step 6: Answer In the year 2007, the number of U.S. residents 25 years of age or older who were high school graduates was 58,500,000. ■

15. In 2007, the number of U.S. residents 25 years of age or older was approximately 195,000,000. If 17% of all U.S. residents 25 years of age or older have bachelor's degrees, determine the number of U.S. residents 25 years of age or older in 2007 who have bachelor's degrees.

2 Model and Solve Direct Translation Problems from Business That Involve Percent

Now let's look at direct translation problems that involve percents. Typically, "percent problems" involve discounts or mark-ups that businesses use in determining their prices. They may also include finding the cost of an item excluding sales tax, as shown in Example 5.

EXAMPLE 5 Finding the Cost of an Item Excluding Sales Tax

You just purchased a new pair of jeans. The price of the jeans, including sales tax of 6%, was $41.34. How much did the jeans cost before sales tax?

Solution

Step 1: Identify We want to know the price of the jeans before sales tax.

Step 2: Name Let p represent the price of the jeans before sales tax.

Work Smart

To change a percent to a decimal, move the decimal point two places to the left.

Step 3: Translate The algebraic expression for total cost is computed by adding the price of the jeans before sales tax p and the amount of tax. The amount of tax is 6% of the price of jeans before sales tax.

$$\underbrace{\text{original price}}_{p} + \underbrace{\text{amount of tax}}_{0.06p}$$

So the final cost of the jeans is represented by the algebraic expression $p + 0.06p$. We can now construct our equation.

$$\underbrace{\text{original price}}_{p} + \underbrace{\text{amount of tax}}_{0.06p} = \underbrace{\text{total price}}_{41.34} \qquad \text{The Model}$$

Step 4: Solve We solve the equation.

$$p + 0.06p = 41.34$$

The coefficient of p is 1: $\quad 1p + 0.06p = 41.34$

Combine like terms: $\quad 1.06p = 41.34$

Divide each side of the equation by 1.06: $\quad \dfrac{1.06p}{1.06} = \dfrac{41.34}{1.06}$

$$p = 39$$

The jeans cost $39.

Step 5: Check If the jeans cost $39, then the jeans plus the 6% sales tax on $39 amounts to $39 + (0.06)($39) = $39 + $2.34 = $41.34, so our answer is correct.

Step 6: Answer The jeans cost $39 before the sales tax. ■

Quick ✔

16. As a reward for being named "Teacher of the Year," Janet will receive a 2.5% pay raise. If Janet's current salary is $39,000, determine Janet's new salary.

17. Suppose that you just purchased a used car. The price of the car including 7% sales tax was $7811. What was the price of the car before sales tax?

Another type of percent problem involves the discounts or mark-ups that businesses use in determining their prices. When dealing with percents and the price of goods, it is helpful to remember the following:

$$\text{Original Price} - \text{Discount} = \text{Sale Price}$$

$$\text{Wholesale Price} + \text{Markup} = \text{Selling Price}$$

EXAMPLE 6 Markdown

Suppose you just learned that a local clothing store is going out of business and that all merchandise is marked down by 40%. The sale price of a jacket is $108. What was the original price?

Solution

Step 1: Identify This is a direct translation problem. We are looking for the original price of a jacket that was marked down by 40%, and we know that the sale price is $108.

Step 2: Name Let p represent the original price of the jacket.

Step 3: Translate We know that the original price minus the amount of discount will give us the sale price. We also know that the sale price was $108, so

$$p - \text{discount} = 108$$

"Marked down by 40%" means that the discount is 40% of the original price, so discount is represented by the expression $0.40p$. Substituting into the equation $p -$ discount $= 108$, we obtain the equation

$$p - 0.40p = 108 \quad \text{The Model}$$

Step 4: Solve

$$p - 0.40p = 108$$
$$1p - 0.40p = 108$$

Combine like terms: $0.60p = 108$

Divide each side by 0.60: $\dfrac{0.60p}{0.60} = \dfrac{108}{0.60}$

$$p = 180$$

Remember, p represents the original price, so the original price of the jacket was $180.

Step 5: Check If the original price of the jacket was $180, then the discount would be $0.40(\$180) = \$72$. Subtracting $72 from the original price of $180 results in a sale price of $108. This answer agrees with the information in the problem.

Step 6: Answer The original price of the jacket was $180.

Quick ✔

18. Suppose that a gas station marks its gasoline up 80%. If the gas station charges $4.50 per gallon of 87 octane gasoline, what does it pay for the gasoline?

19. A furniture store marks recliners down by 25%. The sale price, excluding the sales tax, is $494.25. Find the original price of each recliner.

20. Albert's house lost 2% of its value last year. The value of the house is now $148,000. To the nearest dollar, what was the value of the house one year ago?

2.6 EXERCISES

PRACTICE   WATCH   DOWNLOAD   READ   REVIEW

1–20. are the Quick ✔*s that follow each* EXAMPLE

Building Skills

In Problems 21–38, find the unknown in each percent question. See Objective 1.

21. What is 50% of 160?

22. What is 85% of 50?

23. 7% of 200 is what number?

24. 75% of 20 is what number?

25. What number is 16% of 30?

26. What number is 150% of 9?

27. 31.5 is 15% of what number?

28. 40% of what number is 122?

29. 60% of 120 is what number?

30. 45% of what number is 900?

31. 24 is 120% of what number?

32. 11 is 5.5% of what number?

33. What percent of 60 is 24?

34. 15 is what percent of 75?

35. 1.5 is what percent of 20?

36. 4 is what percent of 25?

37. What percent of 300 is 600?

38. What percent of 16 is 12?

Applying the Concepts

39. Sales Tax The sales tax in Delaware County, Ohio, is 6%. The total cost of purchasing a tennis racket, including tax, is $57.24. Find the cost of the tennis racket before sales tax.

40. Sales Tax The sales tax in Franklin County, Ohio, is 5.75%. The total cost of purchasing a used Honda Civic, including sales tax, is $8460. Find the cost of the car before sales tax.

41. Pay Cut Todd works for a computer firm, and in 2008 he earned a salary of $120,000. Recently, Todd was required to take a 15% pay cut. Find Todd's salary after the pay cut.

42. Pay Raise MaryBeth works from home as a graphic designer. Recently she raised her hourly rate by 5% to cover increased costs. Her new hourly rate is $23.70. Find MaryBeth's previous hourly rate.

43. Bad Investment After Mrs. Fisher lost 9% of her investment, she had $22,750. What was Mrs. Fisher's original investment?

44. Good Investment Perry just learned that his house increased in value by 4% over the past year. The value of the house is now $208,000. What was the value of the home one year ago?

45. Bookstore Purchase The bookstore at Marietta College had a one-day-only 25%-off sale on all merchandise, except for computer software and textbooks. You purchased pens, notebooks, and a sweatshirt for $51. What was the price of the merchandise before the discount?

46. Hailstorm Toyota Town had a 15%-off sale on cars that had been damaged in a hailstorm. A new Toyota truck is on sale for $13,217.50. What was the price of the truck before the hailstorm discount?

47. Business: Discount Pricing A wool suit, discounted by 30% for a clearance sale, has a price tag of $399. What was the suit's original price?

48. Business: Marking up the Price of Books A college bookstore marks up the price that it pays the publisher for a book by 35%. If the selling price of a book is $56.00, how much did the bookstore pay for the book?

49. Furniture Sale A furniture store discounted a dining room table by 40%. The discounted price of the dining room table was $240. Determine the original price of the dining room table.

50. Vacation Package The Liberty Travel Agency advertised a 5-night vacation package in Jamaica for 30% off the regular price. The sale price of the package is $1139. To the nearest dollar, how much was the vacation package before the 30% off sale? (SOURCE: *New York Times*, 2/10/08)

51. Voting In an election for school president, the loser received 60% of the winner's votes. If 848 votes were cast, how many did each receive?

52. Voting On a committee consisting of Republicans and Democrats, there are twice as many Republicans as Democrats. If 30% of the Republicans and 20% of the Democrats voted in favor of a bill and there were 8 yes votes, how many people are on the committee?

53. Commission Melanie receives a 3% commission on every house she sells. If she received a commission of $8571, what was the value of the house she sold?

54. Commission Mario collects a commission for bringing in advertisers to his magazine company. He receives 8% on $450 full-page ads and 5% for $300 half-page ads. If he sells twice as many half-page as full-page ads and his commission was $5610, how many of each type did he bring in?

55. Voting In the 2006 Ohio 15th District U.S. Congressional race, Deborah Pryce received 50.24% of the votes cast, and her opponent, attorney Mary Jo Kilroy, received 49.76% of the votes. If 220,369 votes were cast in the contest, how many votes separated the two candidates?

56. Grades If 15% of Grant's astronomy class received an A, how many students were in his astronomy class if 6 students earned A's this term?

57. Bachelors Based on data obtained from the U.S. Census Bureau, 29% of the 106 million males aged 18 years or older have never married. How many males aged 18 years or older have never married?

58. Census Data Based on data obtained from the U.S. Census Bureau, 22% of the 113 million females aged 18 years or older have never married. How many females aged 18 years or older have never married?

According to the U.S. Census Bureau, the level of education of the U.S. population is changing. The table below shows the number of persons aged 25 years and older and their educational attainment in 2004 and 2006. In Problems 59–62, use the information in the table to answer each question.

	2004		2006	
	Number	Percent	Number	Percent
Population 25 years and older	186,534,177	100.0	196,932,824	100.0
Associate's degree	13,243,927		14,573,029	
Bachelor's degree	32,083,878		33,675,513	

SOURCE: *United States Census Bureau, Census 2006*

59. Find, to the nearest tenth of a percent, the percent of the U.S. population aged 25 years and older that held an associate's degree in 2004.

60. Find, to the nearest tenth of a percent, the percent of the U.S. population aged 25 years and older that held an associate's degree in 2006.

61. Find, to the nearest tenth of a percent, the percent of the U.S. population aged 25 years and older that held a bachelor's degree in 2004.

62. Find, to the nearest tenth of a percent, the percent of the U.S. population aged 25 years and older that held a bachelor's degree in 2006.

Extending the Concepts

63. Discount Pricing Suppose that you are the manager of a clothing store and have just purchased 100 shirts for $12 each. After 1 month of selling the shirts at the regular price, you plan to have a sale giving 25% off the original selling price. However, you still want to make a profit of $6 on each shirt at the sale price. What should you price the shirts at initially to ensure this?

In Problems 64–69, find the percent increase or decrease. The percent increase or percent decrease is defined as $\dfrac{\text{amount of change}}{\text{original amount}} \times 100\%$.

64. Population Growth The population in a small fishing town grew from 2500 to 2825. Find the percent increase.

65. Gas Mileage The gas mileage on your van decreases due to the heavy weight of extra passengers and gear. With the extra weight your van gets 15 mpg and without the passengers and gear it gets 21 mpg. To the nearest tenth, what is your percent decrease in gas mileage with extra passengers and gear?

66. Teaching Salaries The highest average teaching salary in 2004–2005 was $57,760 in Connecticut. You

decided to move from Connecticut to Oregon where the average teaching salary was $48,320. After the move, to the nearest tenth, what percent decrease in salary do you expect to take?

67. Car Depreciation A new car decreases in value by 25% each year. At *www.bmwusa.com* Misha priced his 335i convertible at $55,670.

(a) After two years, what will the car be worth?
(b) To the nearest tenth of a percent, after 2 years, what is the overall decrease in the value of the car?

68. Gas Prices Suppose gas prices went from $4.05 to $4.29 per gallon. To the nearest hundredth, what was the percent increase?

69. Gas Prices Last week Danivan bought gas for $3.89 per gallon. This week gas is selling for $4.39 per gallon. To the nearest tenth, what is the percent increase in gas prices?

Explaining the Concepts

70. The sales tax rate is 6%. Explain why 1.06*x* will correctly calculate the total purchase price of any item that sells for *x* dollars.

71. A problem on a quiz stated: Write an equation to solve the following problem. "Jack received a 5% raise in hourly wage, effective on his birthday. Jack's new hourly wage will be $12.81. Find Jack's current hourly wage." You wrote the equation $x + 0.05 = 12.81$, and your instructor counted your answer wrong. Explain why your equation is incorrect, and then write the correct equation and solve it for Jack's current hourly wage.

72. An item is reduced by 10% and then this is reduced by another 20%. Is this the same as reducing the item by 30%? Explain why or why not.

2.7 Problem Solving: Geometry and Uniform Motion

OBJECTIVES

1. Set Up and Solve Complementary and Supplementary Angle Problems
2. Set Up and Solve Angles of Triangle Problems
3. Use Geometry Formulas to Solve Problems
4. Set Up and Solve Uniform Motion Problems

Preparing for Problem Solving: Geometry and Uniform Motion
Before getting started, take the following readiness quiz. If you get a problem wrong, go back to the section cited and review the material.

P1. Solve: $q + 2q - 30 = 180$ [Section 2.2, p. 96]
P2. Solve: $30w + 20(w + 5) = 300$ [Section 2.2, pp. 96–97]

In this section we continue to solve problems using the six-step method introduced in Section 2.5.

1 Set Up and Solve Complementary and Supplementary Angle Problems

We begin by defining *complementary* and *supplementary angles*.

Figure 6

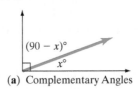

(a) Complementary Angles

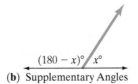

(b) Supplementary Angles

DEFINITION

Two angles whose measures sum to 90° are called **complementary angles.** Each angle is called the *complement* of the other.

For example, the angles shown in Figure 6(a) are complements because their sum is 90°. Notice the use of the symbol ⌐ to show the 90° angle.

DEFINITION

Two angles whose measures sum to 180° are called **supplementary angles**. Each angle is called the *supplement* of the other.

The angles shown in Figure 6(b) are supplementary because their sum is 180°.

EXAMPLE 1 Solving a Complementary Angle Problem

Find the measure of two complementary angles such that the measure of the larger angle is 6° greater than twice the measure of the smaller angle.

Solution

Step 1: Identify This is a complementary angle problem. We are looking for the measure of two angles whose sum is 90°.

Step 2: Name We know least about the measure of the smaller angle so we let x represent the measure of the smaller angle.

Step 3: Translate The measure of the larger angle is 6° more than twice the measure of the smaller angle, so $(2x + 6)$ represents the measure of the larger angle.
    Because the angles are complementary, we use the fact that the sum of the measures of the two angles must equal 90°.

$$\underbrace{x}_{\text{measure of smaller angle}} + \underbrace{(2x + 6)}_{\text{measure of larger angle}} = 90 \quad \text{The Model}$$

Step 4: Solve

$$x + (2x + 6) = 90$$

Combine like terms: $3x + 6 = 90$

Subtract 6 from each side of the equation: $3x = 84$

Divide each side by 3: $x = 28$

Step 5: Check The measure of the smaller angle is 28°. The measure of the larger angle is $(2x + 6)$ degrees $= 2(28) + 6 = 56 + 6 = 62°$. Is the sum of the measures of these angles 90°? Because $28° + 62° = 90°$, our answer is correct.

Step 6: Answer The two complementary angles measure 28° and 62°.   ■

Quick ✔

1. Complementary angles are angles whose measures sum to __ degrees.
2. Find two complementary angles such that the measure of the larger angle is 12° more than the measure of the smaller angle.
3. Find two supplementary angles such that the measure of the larger angle is 30° less than twice the measure of the smaller angle.

Figure 7

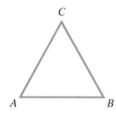

⌐2 Set Up and Solve Angles of Triangle Problems

The sum of the measures of the interior angles of a triangle is 180°. In the triangle in Figure 7, we have three angles, $A, B,$ and $C,$ and the sum of the measures of these three angles must equal 180°.

EXAMPLE 2 Solving Sum of Angles of a Triangle Problem

The measure of the largest angle of a triangle is 20° more than twice the measure of the smallest angle, and the measure of the second angle is 10° more than twice the measure of the smallest angle. Find the measure of each angle of the triangle.

Solution

Step 1: Identify This is an "angles of a triangle" problem. We know that the sum of the measures of the interior angles of a triangle is 180°.

Step 2: Name We know least about the measure of the smallest angle so we let x represent the measure of the smallest angle. We will call this $\angle A$.

Step 3: Translate The measure of the largest angle is 20° more than twice the measure of the smallest angle, so $(2x + 20)$ represents the measure of the largest angle. The measure of the second angle is 10° more than twice the measure of the smallest angle so $(2x + 10)$ represents the measure of the second angle. We will call the largest angle, $\angle C,$ and the second angle, $\angle B$. The sum of the measures of the interior angles in a triangle is 180°, so we have

$$\underbrace{x}_{\text{measure of angle } A} + \underbrace{(2x + 10)}_{\text{measure of angle } B} + \underbrace{(2x + 20)}_{\text{measure of angle } C} = 180 \quad \text{The Model}$$

Step 4: Solve

$$x + (2x + 10) + (2x + 20) = 180$$

Combine like terms: $5x + 30 = 180$

Subtract 30 from each side of the equation: $5x = 150$

Divide each side by 5: $x = 30$

Step 5: Check 30 degrees is the measure of the smallest angle, $\angle A$. The largest angle, $\angle C,$ has a measure of $(2x + 20)$ degrees $= 2(30) + 20 = 60 + 20 = 80$ degrees. The second angle, $\angle B,$ has a measure of $(2x + 10)$ degrees $= 2(30) + 10 = 60 + 10 = 70$ degrees.

Is the sum of the measures of these angles 180°? Because $30° + 70° + 80° = 180°$, our answer is correct.

Step 6: Answer The measures of the angles of the triangle are 30°, 70°, and 80°. ∎

Quick ✔

4. The sum of the measures of the angles of a triangle is ___ degrees.

5. The measure of the smallest angle of a triangle is one-third the measure of the largest angle. The measure of the second angle is 65° less than the measure of the largest angle. Find the measure of the angles of the triangle.

⌐3⌐ Use Geometry Formulas to Solve Problems

Recall from Section 2.4, that the perimeter of a figure is the sum of the lengths of its sides.

EXAMPLE 3 Solving a Perimeter Problem

The perimeter of the rectangular swimming pool shown in Figure 8 is 80 feet. If the length is 10 feet more than the width, find the length and the width of the pool.

Figure 8

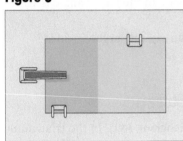

Solution

Step 1: Identify This is a perimeter problem. We want to find the length and the width of the pool, given the perimeter. We know that the perimeter of a rectangle is the sum of the measures of the sides.

Step 2: Name Because we know the length in terms of the width, we let w represent the width of the pool.

Step 3: Translate The length of the pool is 10 feet more than the width, so the length of the pool is $w + 10$. The formula for perimeter of a rectangle is $P = 2l + 2w$, where l represents the length of the rectangle and w represents the width. So we have

$$\underbrace{2l}_{2 \cdot \text{length}} + \underbrace{2w}_{2 \cdot \text{width}} = \underbrace{P}_{\text{perimeter}}$$

$$2(w + 10) + 2(w) = 80 \qquad \text{The Model}$$

Step 4: Solve

$$2(w + 10) + 2(w) = 80$$

$$\text{Use the Distributive Property:} \qquad 2w + 20 + 2w = 80$$

$$\text{Combine like terms:} \qquad 4w + 20 = 80$$

$$\text{Subtract 20 from each side of the equation:} \qquad 4w = 60$$

$$\text{Divide each side by 4:} \qquad w = 15$$

Step 5: Check The width of the pool is $w = 15$ feet, so the length is $w + 10 = 15 + 10 = 25$ feet. We need to see if the perimeter of the pool is 80 feet. Does $15 + 15 + 25 + 25 = 80$? Yes! Our answer is correct.

Step 6: Answer The length of the rectangular pool is 25 feet and the width of the pool is 15 feet. ∎

Work Smart

In solving problems dealing with geometric figures, it is helpful to draw a picture.

Quick ✔

6. *True or False:* The perimeter of a square is 4s, where s is the length of a side of the square.

7. *True or False:* The perimeter of a rectangle can be found by multiplying the length of a rectangle by the width of the rectangle.

8. The perimeter of a small rectangular garden is 9 feet. If the length is twice the width, find the width and length of the garden.

Recall, the area of a plane (two-dimensional) figure is the number of square units that the figure contains, such as square feet, square inches or square yards.

EXAMPLE 4   Solving an Area Problem

A garden in the shape of a trapezoid between a sidewalk and curb has an area of 18 square feet. The height is 3 feet and the length of the shorter base is 2 feet less than the length of the longer base. Find the length of each base of the trapezoid. See Figure 9.

Figure 9

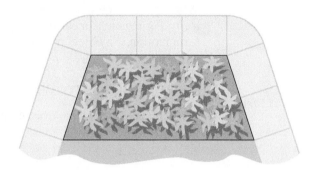

Solution

Step 1: Identify This problem is about the area of a trapezoid. The formula for the area of a trapezoid is $A = \frac{1}{2}h(B + b)$, where h is the height, B is the length of the longer base, and b is the length of the shorter base. We are given the area and the height of the trapezoid.

Step 2: Name We know that one base is 2 feet shorter than the other. Let B represent the length of the longer base.

Step 3: Translate Since one base is 2 feet shorter than the other base, and B represents the length of the longer base, then $B - 2$ represents the length of the shorter base. Using the area of a trapezoid formula, we replace the values we know for $A, h, B,$ and b.

$$A = \frac{1}{2}h(B + b)$$

$$\underbrace{18}_{\text{area}} = \frac{1}{2} \cdot \underbrace{3}_{\text{height}} \; (\underbrace{B}_{B} + \underbrace{B - 2}_{b}) \qquad \text{The Model}$$

Step 4: Solve

$$18 = \frac{1}{2} \cdot 3(B + B - 2)$$

Combine like terms in the parentheses: $18 = \frac{1}{2} \cdot 3(2B - 2)$

Multiply by 2 to clear fractions: $2[18] = 2\left[\frac{1}{2} \cdot 3(2B - 2)\right]$

$$36 = 3(2B - 2)$$

Use the Distributive Property: $36 = 6B - 6$

Add 6 to each side of the equation: $42 = 6B$

Divide each side by 6: $7 = B$

Work Smart

Instead of distributing the 3 in

$$36 = 3(2B - 2)$$

we could divide both sides by 3. Try it! Which approach do you prefer?

Step 5: Check The longer base is 7 feet long. The smaller base is $B - 2 = 7 - 2 = 5$ feet long. Is the area of the trapezoidal garden 18 square feet? Because $\frac{1}{2} \cdot 3(7 + 5) = \frac{1}{2} \cdot 3(12) = 18$, the answers 7 feet and 5 feet are correct.

Step 6: Answer The lengths of the two bases are 5 feet and 7 feet. ∎

Quick ✔

9. The surface area of a rectangular box is 62 square feet. If the length of the box is 3 feet and the width is 2 feet, find the height of the box.

⌐4⌐ Set Up and Solve Uniform Motion Problems

Objects that move at a constant velocity (speed) are said to be in **uniform motion.** When the average speed of an object is known, it can be interpreted as its constant velocity. For example, a car traveling at an average speed of 45 miles per hour is in uniform motion. An object traveling down an assembly line at a constant speed is also in uniform motion.

In Words

The uniform motion formula states that distance equals rate times time.

UNIFORM MOTION FORMULA

If an object moves at an average speed r, the distance d covered in time t is given by the formula

$$d = r \cdot t$$

When solving uniform motion problems, we often write $d = rt$ as $rt = d$. We will use a chart to set up uniform motion problems as shown in Table 4.

Table 4				
	Rate	•	Time	=	Distance
Object #1					distance 1
Object #2					distance 2

Rate, time, and distance must be expressed in corresponding units. For example, if rate (speed) is stated in miles per hour, then distance must be in miles and time must be in hours. If rate is measured in kilometers per minute, then distance is kilometers and time is minutes.

⌐EXAMPLE 5 Solving a Uniform Motion Problem for Time

Bob and Karen drove from Atlanta, Georgia, to Durham, North Carolina, a distance of 390 miles, to attend a family reunion. Their average speed for the first part of the trip was 60 miles per hour. Due to road construction, their average speed for the remainder of the trip was 45 miles per hour. How long did they travel at 45 miles per hour (mph) if they drove 3 hours longer at 60 mph than at 45 mph?

Solution

Step 1: Identify This is a uniform motion problem. We wish to know the number of hours Bob and Karen drove at 45 mph.

Step 2: Name Let t represent the number of hours Bob and Karen drove at 45 miles per hour. Since they traveled 3 hours longer at 60 mph, $t + 3$ represents the number of hours driven at 60 mph.

Step 3: Translate We will set up Table 5, listing the information that we know.

Table 5				
	Rate (in mph)	•	Time	=	Distance
First part of trip	60		$t + 3$		$60(t + 3)$
Second part of trip	45		t		$45t$
Total					390

We summarize the information from Table 5. We know that the total distance that Bob and Karen traveled is 390 miles, so we state that

$$\underbrace{60(t + 3)}_{\substack{\text{distance traveled} \\ \text{at 60 mph}}} + \underbrace{45t}_{\substack{\text{distance traveled} \\ \text{at 45 mph}}} = \underbrace{390}_{\substack{\text{total} \\ \text{distance}}} \qquad \text{The Model}$$

Step 4: Solve

$$60(t + 3) + 45t = 390$$

Use the Distributive Property: $\qquad 60t + 180 + 45t = 390$

Combine like terms: $\qquad 105t + 180 = 390$

Subtract 180 from both sides: $\quad 105t + 180 - 180 = 390 - 180$

$$105t = 210$$

Divide both sides by 105: $\qquad \dfrac{105t}{105} = \dfrac{210}{105}$

$$t = 2$$

Step 5: Check It appears that Bob and Karen drove for 2 hours at 45 mph. So they drove $t + 3 = 2 + 3 = 5$ hours at 60 miles per hour. Let's see if 2 hours driven at 45 mph plus 5 hours driven at 60 mph equals a distance of 390 miles. Because $2 \text{ hrs} \cdot 45 \text{ mi/hr} + 5 \text{ hrs} \cdot 60 \text{ mi/hr} = 90 \text{ miles} + 300 \text{ miles} = 390 \text{ miles}$, our answer checks!

Step 6: Answer the Question Bob and Karen drove for 2 hours at 45 mph. ∎

EXAMPLE 6 Solving a Uniform Motion Problem for Rate

Two groups of friends took a canoe trip down Big Darby Creek. The first group left Dan's Canoe Livery at 12 noon. One-half hour later, the second group left Dan's Canoe Livery, paddling at an average speed that was 0.75 miles per hour faster than the first group. At 2:30 P.M. the second group caught up to the first group. How fast was each group paddling?

Solution

Step 1: Identify This is a uniform motion problem. We wish to know the rate at which each group is paddling.

Step 2: Name Let r represent the rate at which the first group paddled. The second group's paddling rate was 0.75 miles per hour greater than the first group, so we let $r + 0.75$ represent the rate of the second group.

Step 3: Translate Notice that we are given a specific time that the first group left, 12 noon. The second group left $\dfrac{1}{2}$ hour later than the first group. The variable time in our formula represents number of hours traveled. So the first group traveled for two-and-a-half (or 2.5) hours (12 noon until 2:30 P.M.), but the second group only traveled for two hours. We're now ready to fill in the chart as shown in Table 6.

Table 6				
	Rate (in mph)	•	Time	= Distance
First group	r		2.5	2.5r
Second group	$r + 0.75$		2	$2(r + 0.75)$

We summarize the information from the chart. We know that the second group caught up to the first group, so the total distance the two groups traveled was the same.

$$\underbrace{2.5r}_{\text{distance traveled by first group}} = \underbrace{2(r + 0.75)}_{\text{distance traveled by second group}} \qquad \text{The Model}$$

Step 4: Solve

$$2.5r = 2(r + 0.75)$$

Use the Distributive Property: $\qquad 2.5r = 2r + 1.5$

Subtract $2r$ from both sides: $\quad 2.5r - 2r = 2r - 2r + 1.5$

$$0.5r = 1.5$$

Divide both sides by 0.5: $\qquad \dfrac{0.5r}{0.5} = \dfrac{1.5}{0.5}$

$$r = 3$$

Step 5: Check It appears that the first group paddled at 3 miles per hour and the second group paddled at $r + 0.75 = 3 + 0.75 = 3.75$ miles per hour. Let's see if the distance traveled by each group is the same. Does 3 miles per hour $\cdot$ 2.5 hours $=$ 2 hours $\cdot$ 3.75 miles per hour? Because $(3)(2.5) = 7.5$ miles and $(2)(3.75)$ also equals 7.5 miles, our answers are correct.

Step 6: Answer the Question The first group paddled at 3 miles per hour and the second group paddled at 3.75 miles per hour.

Quick ✔

10. *True or False:* When using $d = rt$ to calculate the distance traveled, it is not necessary to assume that the object travels at a constant speed.

11. Two bikers, José and Luis, start at the same point at the same time and travel in opposite directions. José's average speed is 5 miles per hour more than that of Luis, and after 3 hours the bikers are 63 miles apart. Find the average speed of each biker.

12. Tanya, a long-distance runner, runs at an average speed of 8 miles per hour. Two hours after Tanya leaves your house you leave in your car and follow the same route. If your average speed is 40 miles per hour, how long will it be before you catch up to Tanya? How far will each of you be from your home?

2.7 EXERCISES

MyMathLab Powered by CourseCompass™ and MathXL®

PRACTICE | WATCH | DOWNLOAD | READ | REVIEW

1–12. *are the* Quick ✔*s that follow each* EXAMPLE

Building Skills

In Problems 13–16, find the value of x and then identify the measure of each of the angles. See Objective 1.

△ **13.** Find two supplementary angles such that the measure of the first angle is 10° less than three times the measure of the second.

△ **14.** Find two supplementary angles such that the measure of the first angle is four times the measure of the second.

△ **15.** The measures of two complementary angles are consecutive even integers. Find the measure of each angle.

△ **16.** Find two complementary angles such that the measure of the first angle is 25° less than the measure of the second.

In Problems 17–20, find the measures of the angles of the triangle. See Objective 2.

△ **17.**

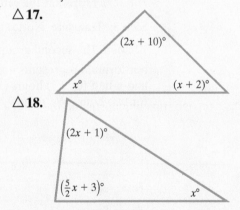

△ **18.**

△ **19.** The measures of the angles of a triangle are consecutive even integers. Find the measure of each angle.

△ **20.** In a triangle, the second angle measures four times the first. The measure of the third angle is 18° more than the second. Find the measures of the three angles.

In Problems 21–26, use a formula from geometry to solve for the unknown quantity. See Objective 3.

△ **21.** The length of a rectangle is 8 ft longer than twice the width. If the perimeter is 88 ft, find the length and width of the rectangle.

△ **22.** The width of a rectangle is 10 m less than half of the length. If the perimeter is 52 meters, find the length of each side of the rectangle.

△ **23.** A rectangular field is divided into 2 squares of the same size and shape. If it takes 294 yards of fencing to enclose the field and divide the field into the two parcels, find the dimensions of the field. See the figure.

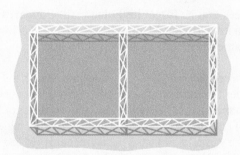

△ **24.** A rectangular field has been divided so that the length of one of the parcels is twice the other. The smaller parcel is a square and the larger parcel is a rectangle. If it takes 279 m of fencing to enclose the field and divide the two parcels, find the dimensions of the field.

△ **25.** An **isosceles triangle** has exactly two sides that are equal in length (*congruent*). If the base (the third side) measures 45 inches and the perimeter is 98 inches, find the length of the two congruent sides, called *legs*.

△ **26.** An isosceles triangle has a base of 17 cm. See Problem 25. If the perimeter is 95 cm, find the length of each of the legs.

In Problems 27 and 28, set up the model to solve the uniform motion problems by answering parts (a)–(d). See Objective 4.

27. Two cars leave Chicago, one traveling north and the other south. The car going north is traveling at 62 mph and the car going south is traveling at 68 mph. How long before they are 585 miles apart?

  (a) Write an algebraic expression for the distance traveled by the car going north.

  (b) Write an algebraic expression for the distance traveled by the car going south.

  (c) Write an algebraic expression for the total distance traveled by the two cars.

  (d) Write an equation to answer the question.

28. Two trains leave Albuquerque, traveling the same direction on parallel tracks. One train is traveling at

72 mph and the other is traveling at 66 mph. How long before they are 45 miles apart?

  (a) Write an algebraic expression for the distance traveled by the faster train.

  (b) Write an algebraic expression for the distance traveled by the slower train.

  (c) Write an algebraic expression for the difference in distance between the two.

  (d) Write an equation to answer the question.

In Problems 29 and 30, fill in the table from the information given. Then write the equation that will solve the problem. DO NOT SOLVE. See Objective 4.

29. Martha is running in her first marathon. She can run at a rate of 528 ft per min. Ten minutes later her mom starts the same course, running at a rate of 880 ft per min. How long before Mom catches up to Martha?

	Rate	·	Time	=	Distance
Martha	?		?		?
Mom	?		?		?

30. A 580-mile trip in a small plane took a total of 5 hours. The first two hours were flown at one rate and then the plane encountered a headwind and was slowed by 10 mph. Find the rate for each portion of the trip.

	Rate	·	Time	=	Distance
Beginning of trip	?		?		?
Rest of the trip	?		?		?
Total			?		?

Applying the Concepts

△ **31.** **Rectangle** The width of a rectangle is 3 inches less than one-half the length. Find the length and the width of the rectangle if the perimeter of the rectangle is 36 inches.

△ **32.** **Garden** The length of a rectangular garden is 9 feet. If 26 feet of fencing are required to fence the garden, find the width of the garden.

△ **33.** **Billboard** A billboard along a highway has a perimeter of 110 feet. Find the length of the billboard if its height is 15 feet.

△ **34.** **Buying Wallpaper** Erika is buying wallpaper for her bedroom. She remembers that the perimeter of the room is 54 ft and that the room is twice as long as it is wide.

  (a) Find the dimensions of the room.

  (b) If the walls are 8 ft high, how many square feet of wallpaper does she need to buy?

  (c) Erika arrives at the decorating store and finds that wallpaper is sold by the square yard. How many square yards of wallpaper does Erika need to buy?

△ 35. **Back Yard** Bob's backyard is in the shape of a trapezoid with height of 60 feet. The shorter base is 8 feet shorter than the longer base, and the area of the backyard is 2160 square feet. Find the length of each base of the trapezoidal yard.

△ 36. **Buying Fertilizer** Melinda has to buy fertilizer for a flower garden in the shape of a right triangle. If the area of the garden is 54 square feet and the base of the garden measures 9 feet, find the height of the triangular garden.

△ 37. **Garden** The perimeter of a rectangular garden is 60 yards. The width of the garden is three yards less than twice the length.

(a) Find the length and width of the garden.

(b) What is the area of the garden?

△ 38. **Table** The Jacksons are having a custom rectangular table made for a small dining area. The length of the table is 18 inches more than the width, and the perimeter is 180 inches. Find the length and the width of the table.

39. **Boats** Two boats leave a port at the same time, one going north and the other traveling south. The northbound boat travels 16 mph faster than the southbound boat. If the southbound boat is traveling at 47 mph, how long will it be before they are 1430 miles apart?

40. **Cyclists** Two cyclists leave a city at the same time, one going east and the other going west. The west-bound cyclist bikes at 4 mph faster than the east-bound cyclist. After 5 hours they are 200 miles apart. How fast is the east-bound cyclist riding?

41. **Road Trip** Two cars leave a city on the same road, one driving 12 mph faster than the other. After 4 hours, the car traveling faster stops for lunch. After 4 hours and 30 minutes, the car traveling slower stops for lunch. Assuming that the person in the faster car is still eating lunch, the cars are now 24 miles apart. How fast is each car driving?

42. **Passenger and Freight Trains** Two trains leave a city on parallel tracks, traveling the same direction. The passenger train is going twice as fast as the freight train. After 45 minutes, the trains are 30 miles apart. Find the speed of each train.

43. **Down the Highway** A 360-mile trip began on a freeway in a car traveling at 62 mph. Once the road became a 2-lane highway, the car slowed to 54 mph. If the total trip took 6 hours, find the time spent on each type of road.

44. **River Trip** Max lives on a river, 30 miles from town. Max travels downstream (with the current) at 20 mph. Returning upstream (against the current) his rate is 12 mph. If the total trip to town and back took 4 hours, how long did he spend returning from town?

45. **Walking and Jogging** Carol knows that when she jogs along her neighborhood greenway, she can complete the route in 10 minutes. It takes 30 minutes to cover the same distance when she walks. If her jogging rate is 4 mph faster than her walking rate, find the speed at which she jogs.

46. **Trip to School** Dien drives to school at 40 mph. Five minutes $\left(\dfrac{1}{12}\text{hour}\right)$ after he leaves home, his mother sees that he forgot his homework and leaves to take it to him, driving 48 mph. If they arrive at school at the same time, how far away is the school?

△ 47. **Isosceles Triangle** In an isosceles triangle, the base angles (angles opposite the two congruent legs) are equal in measure (*congruent*). Find the measures of the angles of an isosceles triangle in which the third angle (called the *vertex angle*) has a measure that is 16° less than twice the measures of the base angles.

△ 48. **Isosceles Triangle** See Problem 47. In an isosceles triangle, the measure of the third angle is 4 degrees less than twice the measures of the base angles. Find the measure of each of the angles of the triangle.

Extending the Concepts

Parallel lines are lines in the same plane that never intersect (think of railroad tracks going infinitely far out into space). A line that cuts two parallel lines is called a *transversal*. The transversal forms 8 different angles that are related in following ways:

Corresponding angles are equal in measure.

Alternate interior angles are equal in measure.

Interior angles on the same side of the transversal are supplementary.

In the figure shown, lines L_1 and L_2 are parallel ($L_1 \| L_2$) and the transversal is labeled t. In this figure, there are 4 pairs of corresponding angles:

$\angle 1$ and $\angle 5$, $\angle 2$ and $\angle 6$, $\angle 3$ and $\angle 7$, $\angle 4$ and $\angle 8$

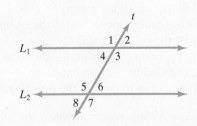

There are 2 pairs of alternate interior angles:
$\angle 3$ and $\angle 5$, $\angle 4$ and $\angle 6$.

There are 2 pairs of interior angles on the same side of the transversal: $\angle 3$ and $\angle 6$, $\angle 4$ and $\angle 5$.

In Problems 49–54, given $L_1 \| L_2$, use the appropriate properties from geometry to solve for x.

△ **49.**

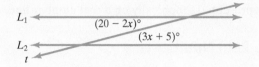

△ **50.**

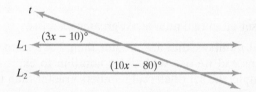

△ **51.**   △ **52.**

△ **53.**

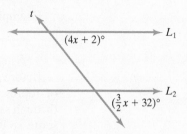

△ **54.**

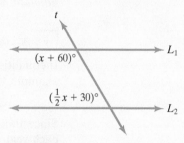

Explaining the Concepts

55. Explain the difference between complementary angles and supplementary angles.

56. Explain the difference between the area of a rectangle and the perimeter of a rectangle.

57. When setting up a uniform motion problem, you wrote $65t + 40t = 115$. Your classmate wrote $65t - 40t = 115$. Write a word problem for each of these equations, and explain the keys to recognizing the difference between the two types.

2.8 Solving Linear Inequalities in One Variable

OBJECTIVES

1. Graph Inequalities on a Real Number Line
2. Use Interval Notation
3. Solve Linear Inequalities Using Properties of Inequalities
4. Model Inequality Problems

Preparing for Solving Linear Inequalities in One Variable
Before getting started, take this readiness quiz. If you get a problem wrong, go back to the section cited and review the material.

In Problems P1–P4, replace the question mark by $<$, $>$, or $=$ to make the statement true.

P1. $4 \, ? \, 19$ **P2.** $-11 \, ? \, -24$ **P3.** $\frac{1}{4} \, ? \, 0.25$ **P4.** $\frac{5}{6} \, ? \, \frac{4}{5}$ [Section 1.3, p. 25]

The goal of this section is to solve *linear inequalities in one variable*.

DEFINITION

A **linear inequality in one variable** is an inequality that can be written in the form
$$ax + b < c \quad \text{or} \quad ax + b \le c \quad \text{or} \quad ax + b > c \quad \text{or} \quad ax + b \ge c$$
where $a, b,$ and c are real numbers and $a \ne 0$.

Examples of linear inequalities in one variable, x, are

$$x + 2 > 7 \qquad \frac{1}{2}x + 4 \le 9 \qquad 5x > 0 \qquad 3x + 7 \ge 8x - 3$$

Before we discuss methods for solving linear inequalities, we will present three ways of representing inequalities. One of the methods for representing an inequality is through set-builder notation. However, set-builder notation can be somewhat cumbersome, so we present a more streamlined way to represent an inequality using *interval notation*. Inequalities can also be represented graphically on a real number line.

1 Graph Inequalities on a Real Number Line

Inequalities that contain one inequality symbol are called **simple inequalities.** For example, the simple inequality

$$x > 2 \qquad \text{means} \qquad \text{the set of all real numbers } x \text{ greater than two}$$

Since there are infinitely many real numbers that are greater than 2, we cannot list each real number greater than 2. Instead we use **set-builder notation** to express the inequality in written form. For example, the set of all real numbers greater than two is represented in set-builder notation as

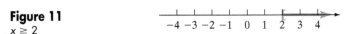

The set of all x such that x is greater than 2

Representing an inequality on a number line is called graphing the inequality, and the picture is called the **graph of the inequality.** For example, we graph $\{x \mid x > 2\}$ on a real number line by shading the portion of the number line that is to the right of 2. The number 2 is called an **endpoint.** We use a parenthesis to indicate that the number 2 is *not* included in the solution set. See Figure 10.

Figure 10
$x > 2$

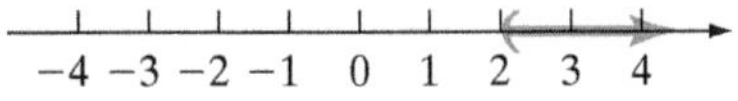

To graph the inequality $x \ge 2$, we also shade the number line to the right of 2, but this time we use a bracket on the endpoint (to indicate that 2 is included in the solution set). See Figure 11.

Figure 11
$x \ge 2$

In a similar way, we graph the inequality $x < 4$ in Figure 12 and $x \le 4$ in Figure 13.

Figure 12
$x < 4$

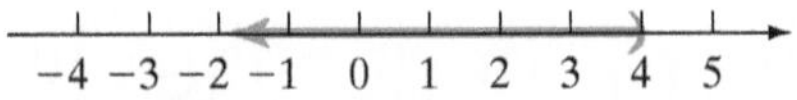

Figure 13
$x \le 4$

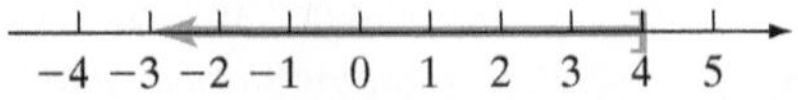

EXAMPLE 1 Graphing Simple Inequalities on a Real Number Line

Graph each inequality on a real number line.

(a) $x > 5$ (b) $x \le -4$

Solution

(a) The inequality $x > 5$ represents all real numbers greater than 5. Because the number 5 is not included in this set, we draw a parenthesis on the 5 and shade to the right. See Figure 14.

Figure 14
$x > 5$

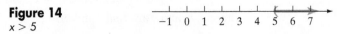

(b) The inequality $x \leq -4$ is all real numbers less than or equal to negative four. Because -4 is included in the set, we place a bracket on the number -4 and shade to the left. See Figure 15.

Work Smart

The inequalities $x > 5$ and $5 < x$ have the same graph. Do you see why?

Figure 15
$x \leq -4$

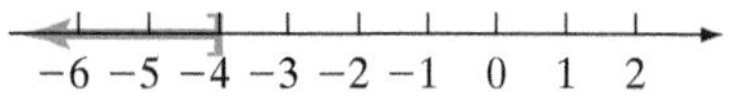

Quick ✔

1. *True or False:* When graphing an inequality that contains a $>$ or a $<$ symbol, we use a parenthesis.

In Problems 2–5, graph each inequality on a real number line.

2. $n \geq 8$ **3.** $a < -6$ **4.** $x > -1$ **5.** $p \leq 0$

⎡2⎤ Use Interval Notation

In addition to using set-builder notation to represent inequalities, we can use *interval notation*. To use interval notation, we need to introduce a new symbol.

The symbol ∞ (read "infinity") is not a real number; it is used to indicate that there is no right endpoint on an inequality. The symbol $-\infty$ (read as "minus infinity" or "negative infinity") also is not a real number and means that there is no left endpoint on an inequality. Using the symbols ∞ and $-\infty$, we can define five intervals for simple inequalities:

Work Smart

The symbols ∞ and $-\infty$ are never included as endpoints because they are not real numbers. So, we use parentheses when $-\infty$ or ∞ are endpoints.

INTERVALS INVOLVING ∞

$[a, \infty)$	consists of all real numbers x for which $x \geq a$
(a, ∞)	consists of all real numbers x for which $x > a$
$(-\infty, a]$	consists of all real numbers x for which $x \leq a$
$(-\infty, a)$	consists of all real numbers x for which $x < a$
$(-\infty, \infty)$	consists of all real numbers x (or $-\infty < x < \infty$)

For example, we now have three ways to represent all real numbers greater than 2.

SET-BUILDER NOTATION	NUMBER LINE GRAPH	INTERVAL NOTATION
$\{x \mid x > 2\}$	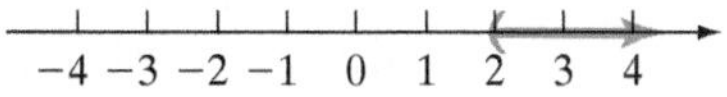	$(2, \infty)$

We represent inequalities involving $\leq$ and $\geq$ graphically using brackets, [and], so the interval notation for $x \leq 1$ is $(-\infty, 1]$.

Table 7 summarizes interval notation, inequality notation, and the graphs.

Work Smart

Intervals are always read from left to right. For example $(5, \infty)$ represents all real numbers greater than 5 because 5 is the left endpoint. So $(5, \infty)$ as an inequality can be represented as $x > 5$ or $5 < x$.

Table 7		
Set-Builder Notation	Interval Notation	Graph
$\{x \mid x \geq a\}$	$[a, \infty)$	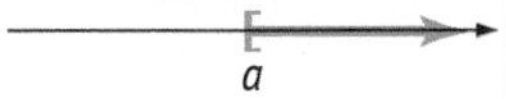
$\{x \mid x > a\}$	(a, ∞)	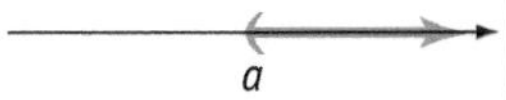
$\{x \mid x \leq a\}$	$(-\infty, a]$	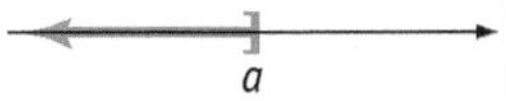
$\{x \mid x < a\}$	$(-\infty, a)$	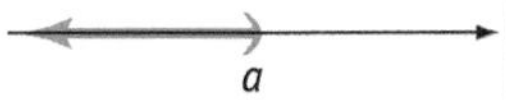
$\{x \mid x \text{ is a real number}\}$	$(-\infty, \infty)$	

EXAMPLE 2 Writing an Inequality in Interval Notation

Write each inequality using interval notation.

(a) $x > -4$ **(b)** $x \leq 8$

(c) 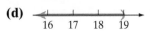 **(d)**

Solution

Remember, if the inequality contains $<$ or $>$, use a parenthesis, (or). If the inequality contains $\leq$ or $\geq$, use a bracket, [or].

(a) $(-4, \infty)$ **(b)** $(-\infty, 8]$ **(c)** $[1.75, \infty)$ **(d)** $(-\infty, 19)$ ∎

Quick ✔

6. *True or False:* The inequality $x \geq 3$ is written $[3, \infty)$.

7. *True or False:* The inequality $x < -4$ is written in interval notation as $(-4, -\infty)$.

In Problems 8–11, write the inequality in interval notation.

8. $x \geq -3$ **9.** $x < 12$

10. **11.**

⌐3⌐ Solve Linear Inequalities Using Properties of Inequalities

To **solve an inequality** means to find all values of the variable for which the statement is true. These values are called **solutions** of the inequality. The set of all solutions is called the **solution set.** As with equations, one method for solving a linear inequality is to replace it by a series of equivalent inequalities until an inequality with an obvious solution, such as $x > 2$, is obtained.

Two inequalities that have exactly the same solution set are called **equivalent inequalities.** We obtain equivalent inequalities by applying some of the same operations as those used to find equivalent equations.

Consider the inequality $3 < 8$. If we add 2 to both sides of the inequality, the left side becomes 5 and the right side becomes 10. Since $5 < 10$, we see that adding the same quantity to both sides of an inequality does not change the sense, or direction, of the inequality. This result is called the **Addition Property of Inequality.**

In Words

The Addition Property of Inequality states that the direction of the inequality does not change when the same quantity is added to each side of the inequality.

ADDITION PROPERTY OF INEQUALITY

For real numbers $a, b,$ and c

$$\text{If} \quad a < b, \quad \text{then} \quad a + c < b + c$$
$$\text{If} \quad a > b, \quad \text{then} \quad a + c > b + c$$

The Addition Property of Inequality also holds true for subtracting a real number from both sides of an inequality, since $a - b$ is equivalent to $a + (-b)$. In other words, subtracting a quantity from both sides of an inequality does not change the sense of the inequality.

EXAMPLE 3   How to Solve an Inequality Using the Addition Property of Inequality

Solve the linear inequality $3y + 5 \leq 2y + 8$ and express the solution set using set-builder notation and interval notation. Graph the solution set.

Step-by-Step Solution

Step 1: Get the expressions containing variables on the left side of the inequality.	Apply the Addition Property of Inequality and subtract $2y$ from both sides:	$3y + 5 \leq 2y + 8$ $3y + 5 - 2y \leq 2y + 8 - 2y$ $y + 5 \leq 8$
Step 2: Isolate the variable y on the left side.	Apply the Addition Property of Inequality and subtract 5 from both sides:	$y + 5 - 5 \leq 8 - 5$ $y \leq 3$

Figure 16

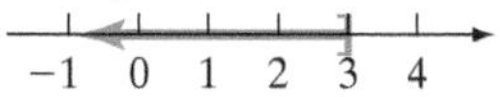

The solution set using set-builder notation is $\{y \mid y \leq 3\}$. The solution set using interval notation is $(-\infty, 3]$. The solution set is graphed in Figure 16. ■

Quick ✔

12. To ____ an inequality means to find the set of all replacement values of the variable for which the statement is true.

13. The _____ _____ __ _____ states that the direction, or sense, of each inequality remains the same when the same quantity is added to each side of the inequality.

In Problems 14–17, find the solution of the linear inequality and express the solution set in set-builder notation and interval notation. Graph the solution set.

14. $5n - 3 > 4n$

15. $-2x + 3 < 7 - 3x$

16. $5n + 8 \leq 4n + 4$

17. $3(4x - 8) + 12 > 11x - 13$

We've seen what happens when we add a real number to both sides of an inequality. Let's look at two examples from arithmetic to see if we can figure out what happens when we multiply or divide both sides of an inequality by a nonzero constant.

EXAMPLE 4   Multiplying or Dividing an Inequality by a Positive Number

(a) Express the inequality that results by multiplying both sides of the inequality $-2 < 5$ by 3.

(b) Express the inequality that results by dividing both sides of the inequality $18 > 14$ by 2.

Solution

(a) We begin with

$$-2 < 5$$

Multiplying both sides by 3 results in the numbers -6 and 15 on each side of the inequality, so we have

$$-6 < 15$$

(b) We begin with

$$18 > 14$$

Dividing both sides by 2 results in the numbers 9 and 7 on each side of the inequality, so we have

$$9 > 7$$ ■

Based on the results of Example 4, we see that multiplying (or dividing) both sides of an inequality by a positive real number does not affect the sense, or direction, of the inequality.

EXAMPLE 5 Multiplying or Dividing an Inequality by a Negative Number

(a) Express the inequality that results by multiplying both sides of the inequality $-2 < 5$ by -3.

(b) Express the inequality that results by dividing both sides of the inequality $18 > 14$ by -2.

Solution

(a) We begin with

$$-2 < 5$$

Multiplying both sides by -3 results in the numbers 6 and -15 on each side of the inequality, so we have

$$6 > -15$$

(b) We begin with

$$18 > 14$$

Dividing both sides by -2 results in the numbers -9 and -7 on each side of the inequality, so we have

$$-9 < -7$$

In Example 5, we see that multiplying (or dividing) both sides of an inequality by a negative real number produces an inequality that has the opposite sense, or direction, of the original inequality. The results of Examples 4 and 5 lead us to the **Multiplication Properties of Inequality.**

In Words

The Multiplication Properties of Inequality state that if you multiply both sides of an inequality by a positive number, the inequality symbol remains the same, but if you multiply both sides by a negative number, the inequality symbol reverses.

MULTIPLICATION PROPERTIES OF INEQUALITY

Let a, b, and c be real numbers.

If $a < b$, and if $c > 0$, then $ac < bc$.
If $a > b$, and if $c > 0$, then $ac > bc$.
If $a < b$, and if $c < 0$, then $ac > bc$.
If $a > b$, and if $c < 0$, then $ac < bc$.

EXAMPLE 6 Solving a Linear Inequality Using the Multiplication Properties of Inequality

Solve each linear inequality and state the solution set using set-builder notation and interval notation. Graph the solution set.

(a) $7x > -35$ **(b)** $-4x \geq 24$

Solution

(a)

$$7x > -35$$

Divide both sides of the inequality by 7: $\dfrac{7x}{7} > \dfrac{-35}{7}$

$$x > -5$$

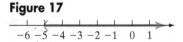

The solution set using set-builder notation is $\{x|x > -5\}$. The solution set using interval notation is $(-5, \infty)$. The graph of the solution set is shown in Figure 17.

Figure 17

(b) $$-4x \geq 24$$

Divide both sides of the inequality by -4. $$\frac{-4x}{-4} \leq \frac{24}{-4}$$
Remember to reverse the inequality symbol!

$$x \leq -6$$

The solution set using set-builder notation is $\{x | x \leq -6\}$. The solution set using interval notation is $(-\infty, -6]$. The graph of the solution set is shown in Figure 18.

Figure 18

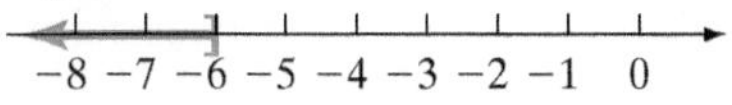

Quick ✔

18. When solving an inequality, we reverse the direction of the inequality symbol when we multiply or divide by a _____ number.

19. *True or False:* The solution to the inequality $-\frac{1}{2}x > 9$ is $\{x | x < -18\}$. This solution is written in interval notation as $(-18, -\infty)$.

In Problems 20–23, find the solution of the linear inequality and express the solution set in set-builder notation and interval notation. Graph the solution set.

20. $6k < -36$ **21.** $2n \geq -5$

22. $-\frac{3}{2}k > 12$ **23.** $-\frac{4}{3}p \leq -\frac{4}{5}$

We are now ready to solve inequalities using both the Addition and Multiplication Properties of Inequality. In each solution, we isolate the variable on the left side of the inequality, so the inequality is easier to read. Just remember that

$$a < x \text{ is equivalent to } x > a$$
$$\text{and} \quad a > x \text{ is equivalent to } x < a$$

In general, if the two sides of the inequality are interchanged, the direction of the inequality reverses.

EXAMPLE 7 How to Solve an Inequality Using Both the Addition and Multiplication Properties of Inequality

Solve the inequality $4(x + 1) - 2x < 8x - 26$. State the solution set using set-builder notation and interval notation. Graph the solution set.

Step-by-Step Solution

Step 1: Remove parentheses. $$4(x + 1) - 2x < 8x - 26$$

Use the Distributive Property: $$4x + 4 - 2x < 8x - 26$$

Step 2: Combine like terms on each side of the inequality. $$2x + 4 < 8x - 26$$

Step 3: Get the variable expressions on the left side of the inequality and the constants on the right side.

Subtract $8x$ from both sides: $$2x + 4 - 8x < 8x - 26 - 8x$$
$$-6x + 4 < -26$$
Subtract 4 from both sides: $$-6x + 4 - 4 < -26 - 4$$
$$-6x < -30$$

Step 4: Get the coefficient of the variable term to be one.

Divide both sides by -6: $$\frac{-6x}{-6} > \frac{-30}{-6}$$
Remember to reverse the inequality symbol!

$$x > 5$$

Figure 19

The solution set using set-builder notation is $\{x \mid x > 5\}$, or using interval notation, $(5, \infty)$. The graph of the solution is shown in Figure 19.

  ■

We can gather evidence to support that our solution to an inequality is correct in the same way we check the solution of an equation. We substitute a value for the variable that is in the solution set into the original inequality and see if we obtain a true statement. If we obtain a true statement, then we have evidence our solution is correct. Be warned, however, this does not prove that your solution is correct. The check for Example 7 is shown below.

Check Since the solution of the inequality $4(x + 1) - 2x < 8x - 26$ is any real number greater than 5, let's replace x by 10.

$$4(x + 1) - 2x < 8x - 26$$

Replace x with 10: $4(10 + 1) - 2(10) \overset{?}{<} 8(10) - 26$

$$4(11) - 20 \overset{?}{<} 80 - 26$$

Perform the arithmetic: $24 < 54$ True

$24 < 54$ is a true statement, so $x = 10$ is in the solution set. We have some evidence that our solution set, $(5, \infty)$, is correct.

Quick ✔ *In Problems 24–27, find the solution of the linear inequality and express the solution set using set-builder notation and interval notation. Graph the solution set.*

24. $3x - 7 > 14$

25. $-4n - 3 < 9$

26. $2x - 6 < 3(x + 1) - 5$

27. $-4(x + 6) + 18 \geq -2x + 6$

EXAMPLE 8 Solving a Linear Inequality Containing Fractions

Solve the inequality $\dfrac{1}{2}(x - 4) \geq \dfrac{3}{4}(2x + 1)$. Express the solution using set-builder notation and interval notation. Graph the solution set.

Solution

To rewrite the inequality as an equivalent inequality without fractions, we multiply both sides of the inequality by 4, the least common denominator of $\dfrac{1}{2}$ and $\dfrac{3}{4}$.

$$\frac{1}{2}(x - 4) \geq \frac{3}{4}(2x + 1)$$

$$4 \cdot \frac{1}{2}(x - 4) \geq 4 \cdot \frac{3}{4}(2x + 1)$$

$$2(x - 4) \geq 3(2x + 1)$$

Use the Distributive Property: $2x - 8 \geq 6x + 3$

Subtract 6x from both sides: $2x - 8 - 6x \geq 6x + 3 - 6x$

$$-4x - 8 \geq 3$$

Add 8 to both sides: $-4x - 8 + 8 \geq 3 + 8$

$$-4x \geq 11$$

Divide both sides by -4 and remember
to reverse the inequality symbol! $\dfrac{-4x}{-4} \leq \dfrac{11}{-4}$

$$x \leq -\frac{11}{4}$$

The solution of the inequality $\frac{1}{2}(x - 4) \geq \frac{3}{4}(2x + 1)$ is $\left\{ x \mid x \leq -\frac{11}{4} \right\}$, or using interval notation, $\left(-\infty, -\frac{11}{4} \right]$. The graph of the solution is given in Figure 20.

Figure 20

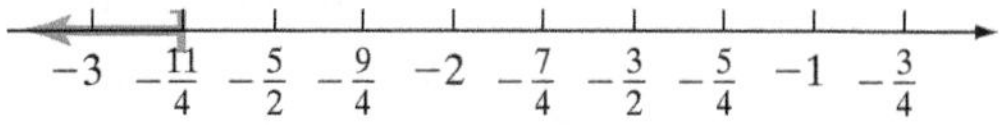

Quick ✔

In Problems 28 and 29, find the solution of the linear inequality and express the solution set using set-builder notation and interval notation. Graph the solution set.

28. $\frac{1}{2}(x + 2) > \frac{1}{5}(x + 17)$ **29.** $\frac{4}{3}x - \frac{2}{3} \leq \frac{4}{5}x + \frac{3}{5}$

There are inequalities that are true for all values of the variable and inequalities that are false for all values of the variable. We present these special cases now.

EXAMPLE 9   Solving an Inequality for Which the Solution Set Is All Real Numbers

Solve the inequality $3(x + 4) - 5 > 7x - (4x + 2)$. Express the solution using set-builder notation and interval notation. Graph the solution set.

Solution

$$3(x + 4) - 5 > 7x - (4x + 2)$$

Use the Distributive Property: $3x + 12 - 5 > 7x - 4x - 2$

$$3x + 7 > 3x - 2$$

Subtract 3x from each side: $3x + 7 - 3x > 3x - 2 - 3x$

$$7 > -2$$

Figure 21

Since 7 is greater than -2, the solution to this inequality is all real numbers. The solution set is $\{x \mid x$ is any real number$\}$. In interval notation, the solution is $(-\infty, \infty)$. Figure 21 shows the graph of the solution set.

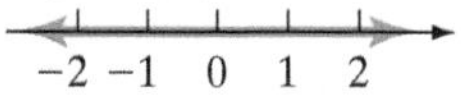

EXAMPLE 10   Solving an Inequality for Which the Solution Set Is the Empty Set

Solve the inequality $8\left(\frac{1}{2}x - 1 \right) + 2x \leq 6x - 10$. Express the solution using set-builder notation and interval notation, if possible. Graph the solution set.

Solution

$$8\left(\frac{1}{2}x - 1 \right) + 2x \leq 6x - 10$$

Use the Distributive Property: $4x - 8 + 2x \leq 6x - 10$

$$6x - 8 \leq 6x - 10$$

Subtract 6x from each side: $6x - 8 - 6x \leq 6x - 10 - 6x$

$$-8 \leq -10$$

The statement $-8 \leq -10$ is false. Therefore, there is no solution to this inequality. The solution set is the empty set, $\varnothing$ or $\{\ \}$. Figure 22 shows the graph of the solution set on a real number line.

Figure 22

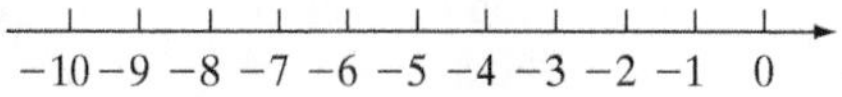

Quick ✔

30. When solving an inequality, if the variable is eliminated and the result is a true statement, the solution is __ ____ _____.

31. When solving an inequality, if the variable is eliminated and the result is a false statement, the solution is ___ _____ _____.

In Problems 32–35, find the solution of the linear inequality and express the solution set using set-builder notation and interval notation, if possible. Graph the solution set.

32. $-2x + 7(x - 5) \le 6x + 32$ **33.** $-x + 7 - 8x \ge 2(8 - 5x) + x$

34. $\dfrac{3}{2}x + 5 - \dfrac{5}{2}x < 4x - 3(x + 1)$ **35.** $0.8x + 3.2(x + 4) \ge 2x + 12.8 + 3x - x$

Work Smart

The context of the words "less than" is important! 3 **less than** x is $x - 3$, but 3 is **less than** x is $3 < x$.

4 Model Inequality Problems

When solving word problems that are modeled by inequalities, you need to look for key words that indicate the type of inequality symbol that should be used. Some key words and phrases are listed in Table 8.

Table 8

Word or Phrase	Inequality Symbol	Word or Phrase	Inequality Symbol
at least	$\ge$	no more than	$\le$
no less than	$\ge$	at most	$\le$
more than	$>$	fewer than	$<$
greater than	$>$	less than	$<$

When we solve applications involving linear inequalities, we use the same steps for setting up applied problems that we introduced in Section 2.5, on page 129.

EXAMPLE 11 A Handyman's Fee

A handyman charges a flat fee of \$60 plus \$22 per hour for a job. How many hours does this handyman need to work to make more than \$500?

Solution

Step 1: Identify This is a direct translation problem. We want to know the number of hours the handyman must work to make more than \$500.

Step 2: Name Let h represent the number of hours that the handyman must work.

Step 3: Translate We know that the sum of the flat fee that the handyman charges plus the hourly charge must exceed \$500. So

$$\underbrace{60}_{\text{flat fee}} \; \underbrace{+}_{\text{plus}} \; \underbrace{22}_{\text{hourly wage}} \; \underbrace{\cdot}_{\text{times}} \; \underbrace{h}_{\text{no. hours worked}} \; \underbrace{>}_{\text{more than}} \; \underbrace{500}_{500} \quad \text{The Model}$$

Step 4: Solve

$$60 + 22h > 500$$

Subtract 60 from each side and simplify: $60 - 60 + 22h > 500 - 60$

$$22h > 440$$

Divide both sides by 22: $\dfrac{22h}{22} > \dfrac{440}{22}$

$$h > 20$$

Step 5: Check If the handyman works 23 hours (for example), will he earn more than \$500? Since $60 + 22(23) = 566$ is greater than 500, we have evidence that our answer is correct.

Step 6: Answer The handyman must work more than 20 hours to earn more than \$500.

Quick ✔

36. A worker in a large apartment complex uses an elevator to move supplies. The elevator has a weight limit of 2000 pounds. The worker weighs 180 pounds and each box of supplies weighs 91 pounds. Find the maximum number of boxes of supplies the worker can move on one trip in the elevator.

2.8 EXERCISES

PRACTICE   WATCH   DOWNLOAD   READ   REVIEW

1–36. are the Quick ✔s that follow each EXAMPLE

Building Skills

In Problems 37–44, graph each inequality on a number line, and write each inequality in interval notation. See Objectives 1 and 2.

37. $x > 2$

38. $n > 5$

39. $x \le -1$

40. $x \le 6$

41. $z \ge -3$

42. $x \ge -2$

43. $x < 4$

44. $y < -3$

In Problems 45–50, use interval notation to express the inequality shown in each graph. See Objective 2.

45.

46.

47.

48.

49.

50.

In Problems 51–58, fill in the blank with the correct symbol. State which property of inequality is being utilized. See Objective 3.

51. If $x - 7 < 11$, then x____18

52. If $3x - 2 > 7$, then $3x$____9

53. If $\frac{1}{3}x > -2$, then x____-6

54. If $\frac{5}{3}x \ge -10$, then x____-6

55. If $3x + 2 \le 13$, then $3x$___11

56. If $\frac{3}{4}x + 1 \le 9$, then $\frac{3}{4}x$___8

57. If $-3x \ge 15$, then x___-5

58. If $-4x < 28$, then x___-7

In Problems 59–88, solve the inequality and express the solution set in set-builder notation and interval notation. Graph the solution set on a real number line. See Objective 3.

59. $x + 1 < 5$

60. $x + 4 \le 3$

61. $x - 6 \ge -4$

62. $x - 2 < 1$

63. $3x \le 15$

64. $4x > 12$

65. $-5x < 35$

66. $-7x \ge 28$

67. $3x - 7 > 2$

68. $2x + 5 > 1$

69. $3x - 1 \ge 3 + x$

70. $2x - 2 \ge 3 + x$

71. $1 - 2x \le 3$

72. $2 - 3x \le 5$

73. $-2(x + 3) < 8$

74. $-3(1 - x) > x + 8$

75. $4 - 3(1 - x) \le 3$

76. $8 - 4(2 - x) \le -2x$

77. $\frac{1}{2}(x - 4) > x + 8$

78. $3x + 4 > \frac{1}{3}(x - 2)$

79. $4(x - 1) > 3(x - 1) + x$

80. $2y - 5 + y < 3(y - 2)$

81. $5(n + 2) - 2n \le 3(n + 4)$

82. $3(p + 1) - p \ge 2(p + 1)$

83. $2n - 3(n - 2) < n - 4$

84. $4x - 5(x + 1) \le x - 3$

85. $4(2w - 1) \ge 3(w + 2) + 5(w - 2)$

86. $3q - (q + 2) > 2(q - 1)$

87. $3y - (5y + 2) > 4(y + 1) - 2y$

88. $8x - 3(x - 2) \geq x + 4(x + 1)$

In Problems 89–98, write the given statement using inequality symbols. Let x represent the unknown quantity. See Objective 4.

89. Karen's salary this year will be at least $16,000.

90. Bob's salary this year will be at most $120,000.

91. There will be at most 20,000 fans at the Cleveland Indians game today.

92. The cost of a new lawnmower is at least $250.

93. The cost to remodel a kitchen is more than $12,000.

94. There are fewer than 25 students in your math class on any given day.

95. x is a positive number

96. x is a nonnegative number

97. x is a nonpositive number

98. x is a negative number

Mixed Practice

In Problems 99–116, solve the inequality and express the solution set in set-builder notation and interval notation, if possible. Graph the solution set on a real number line.

99. $-1 < x - 5$

100. $6 \geq x + 15$

101. $-\dfrac{3}{4}x > -\dfrac{9}{16}$

102. $-\dfrac{5}{8}x > \dfrac{25}{48}$

103. $3(x + 1) > 2(x + 1) + x$

104. $5(x - 2) < 3(x + 1) + 2x$

105. $-4a + 1 > 9 + 3(2a + 1) + a$

106. $-5b + 2(b - 1) \leq 6 - (3b - 1) + 2b$

107. $n + 3(2n + 3) > 7n - 3$

108. $2k - (k - 4) \geq 3k + 10 - 2k$

109. $\dfrac{x}{2} \geq 1 - \dfrac{x}{4}$

110. $\dfrac{x}{3} \geq 2 + \dfrac{x}{6}$

111. $\dfrac{x + 5}{2} + 4 > \dfrac{2x + 1}{3} + 2$

112. $\dfrac{3z - 1}{4} + 1 \leq \dfrac{6z + 5}{2} + 2$

113. $-5z - (3 + 2z) > 3 - 7z$

114. $2(4a - 3) \leq 5a - (2 - 3a)$

115. $1.3x + 3.1 < 4.5x - 15.9$

116. $4.9 + 2.6x < 4.2x - 4.7$

Applying the Concepts

117. Auto Rental A car can be rented from Certified Auto Rental for $55 per week plus $0.18 per mile. How many miles can be driven if you have at most $280 to spend for weekly transportation?

118. Truck Rental A truck can be rented from Acme Truck Rental for $80 per week plus $0.28 per mile. How many miles can be driven if you have at most $100 to spend on truck rental?

119. Final Grade Yvette has scores of 72, 78, 66, and 81 on her algebra tests. Find the score she can make on the final exam in order to pass the course with at least 360 points. The final exam counts as two test grades.

120. Final Grade To earn an A in Mrs. Smith's elementary statistics class, Elizabeth must earn at least 540 points. Thus far, Elizabeth has earned scores of 85, 83, 90, and 96. The final exam counts as two test grades. How many points does Elizabeth have to score on the final exam to earn an A?

121. Calling Plan Imperial Telephone has a long-distance calling plan that has a monthly fee of $10 and a charge of $0.03 per minute used. Mayflower Communications has a monthly fee of $6 and a fee of $0.04 per minute. For how many minutes is Imperial Telephone the cheaper plan?

122. Commission A recent college graduate had an offer of a sales position that pays $15,000 per year plus 1% of all sales.

(a) Write an expression for the total annual salary based on sales of S dollars.

(b) For what total sales amount will the college graduate earn in excess of $150,000 annually?

123. Borrowing Money The amount of money that a lending institution will allow you to borrow mainly depends on the interest rate and your annual income. The equation $L = 2.98I - 76.11$ describes the amount of money, L, that a bank will lend at an interest rate of 7.5% for 30 years, based upon annual income, I. For what annual income, I, will a bank lend at least $150,000? (SOURCE: *Information Please Almanac*)

124. Advertising A marketing firm found that the equation $S = 2.1A + 224$ describes the amount of sales S of a product depends on A, the amount spent on advertising the product. Both S and A are measured in thousands of dollars. For what amount, A, is the sales of a product at least 350 thousand dollars?

Extending the Concepts

125. Grades In your Economics 101 class, you have scores of 68, 82, 87, and 89 on the first four of five tests. To earn a grade of B or higher, the average of the first five test scores must be greater than or equal to 80. Find the minimum score that you need on the last test to earn a B.

126. Delivery Service A messenger service charges $10 to make a delivery to an address. In addition, each letter delivered costs $3 and each package delivered costs $8. If there are 15 more letters than packages delivered to this address, what is the maximum number of items that can be delivered for $85?

Compound inequalities are solved using the properties of inequality. Study the example below and then solve Problems 127–134. State the solution in set-builder notation.

$$-15 \quad \le 2x - 1 \quad < 37$$
$$-15 + 1 \le 2x - 1 + 1 \quad < 37 + 1$$
$$\frac{-14}{2} \le \frac{2x}{2} \qquad < \frac{38}{2}$$
$$-7 \le \quad x \qquad < 19$$

127. $-3 < x + 30 < 16$

128. $-41 \le x - 37 \le 26$

129. $-6 \le \dfrac{3x}{2} \le 9$

130. $-4 < \dfrac{8x}{9} < 12$

131. $-7 \le 2x - 3 < 15$

132. $4 < 3x + 7 \le 28$

133. $4 < 6 - \dfrac{x}{2} \le 10$

134. $-1 \le 5 - \dfrac{x}{3} < 1$

Explaining the Concepts

135. When graphing an inequality, when is a left parenthesis used? When is a left bracket used?

136. Explain the circumstances in which the direction of the inequality symbol is reversed when solving a simple inequality.

137. Explain how you recognize when the solution of an inequality is all real numbers. Explain how you recognize when the solution of an inequality is the empty set.

138. Why is the interval notation $[-7, -\infty)$ for $x > -7$ incorrect? What is the correct notation?

CHAPTER 2 Activity: Pass to the Right

Focus: Solving linear equations and inequalities as a group.
Time: 20–30 minutes
Group size: 3–4

1. Each member of the group should choose one of the following four equations and write it down on a piece of paper. Do not begin to solve.

(a) $\dfrac{x + 2}{2} - \dfrac{5x - 12}{6} = 1$

(b) $-\dfrac{1}{9}(x + 27) + \dfrac{1}{3}(x + 3) = x + 6$

(c) $\dfrac{x + 3}{3} - \dfrac{2x - 12}{9} = 1$

(d) $-\dfrac{1}{2}(x + 6) + \dfrac{1}{7}(x + 7) = x + 3$

2. Each member of the group should pass their equation to the person on their right. This member should perform the first step in solving the equation. When you are done, pass your paper to the next group member on your right.

3. Upon receipt of the equation, each group member should check the previous member's work and then perform the next step. If an error is found, discuss and correct the error.

4. Continue passing the problems until all equations have been solved.

5. As a group, discuss the results.

6. If time permits, repeat this activity except choose one of the following inequalities. Express your final answer using interval notation.

(a) $\frac{1}{4}(2x + 12) > \frac{3}{8}(x - 1)$

(b) $\frac{3x + 1}{10} - \frac{1 + 6x}{5} \le -\frac{1}{2}$

(c) $\frac{1}{2}(2x + 14) > \frac{3}{4}(x - 1)$

(d) $\frac{3x + 1}{21} - \frac{1 + 4x}{7} \le -\frac{1}{3}$

CHAPTER 2 Review

Section 2.1 Linear Equations: The Addition and Multiplication Properties of Equality

KEY CONCEPTS	KEY TERMS
• **Linear Equation in One Variable** An equation equivalent to one of the form $ax + b = c$, where a, b, and c are real numbers and $a \ne 0$. • **Addition Property of Equality** For real numbers a, b, and c, if $a = b$, then $a + c = b + c$. • **Multiplication Property of Equality** For real numbers a, b, and c where $c \ne 0$, if $a = b$, then $ac = bc$.	Linear equation Sides Left side Right side Solution Solution set Satisfies Equivalent equations

YOU SHOULD BE ABLE TO...	EXAMPLE	REVIEW EXERCISES
1 Determine if a number is a solution of an equation (p. 85)	Example 1	1–4
2 Use the Addition Property of Equality to solve linear equations (p. 86)	Examples 2 through 4	5–10, 15, 16, 19
3 Use the Multiplication Property of Equality to solve linear equations (p. 88)	Examples 5 through 9	11–14, 17, 18, 20

In Problems 1–4, determine if the given value is the solution to the equation. Answer Yes or No.

1. $3x + 2 = 7$; $x = 5$

2. $5m - 1 = 17$; $m = 4$

3. $6x + 6 = 12$; $x = \frac{1}{2}$

4. $9k + 3 = 9$; $k = \frac{2}{3}$

In Problems 5–18, solve the equation. Check your solution.

5. $n - 6 = 10$

6. $n - 8 = 12$

7. $x + 6 = -10$

8. $x + 2 = -5$

9. $-100 = m - 5$

10. $-26 = m - 76$

11. $\frac{2}{3}y = 16$

12. $\frac{x}{4} = 20$

13. $-6x = 36$

14. $-4x = -20$

15. $z + \frac{5}{6} = \frac{1}{2}$

16. $m - \frac{1}{8} = \frac{1}{4}$

17. $1.6x = 6.4$

18. $1.8m = 9$

19. Discount The cost of a new Honda Accord has been discounted by $1200, so that the sale price is $18,900. Find the original price of the Honda Accord, p, by solving the equation $p - 1200 = 18,900$.

20. Coffee While studying for an exam, Randi drank coffee at a local coffeehouse. She bought 3 cups of coffee for a total of $7.65. Find the cost of each cup of coffee, c, by solving the equation $3c = 7.65$.

Section 2.2 Linear Equations: Using the Properties Together

KEY CONCEPT	KEY TERM
• The steps for solving an equation in one variable are given on page 98.	Distributive Property

YOU SHOULD BE ABLE TO...	EXAMPLE	REVIEW EXERCISES
1 Apply the Addition and Multiplication Properties of Equality to solve linear equations (p. 94)	Examples 1 and 2	21–24
2 Combine like terms and apply the Distributive Property to solve linear equations (p. 96)	Examples 3 and 4	25–30
3 Solve a linear equation with the variable on both sides of the equation (p. 97)	Examples 5 and 6	31–34
4 Use linear equations to solve problems (p. 99)	Example 7	35, 36

In Problems 21–34, solve the equation. Check your solution.

21. $5x - 1 = -21$

22. $-3x + 7 = -5$

23. $\frac{2}{3}x + 5 = 11$

24. $\frac{5}{7}x - 2 = -17$

25. $-2x + 5 + 6x = -11$

26. $3x - 5x + 6 = 18$

27. $2m + 0.5m = 10$

28. $1.4m + m = -12$

29. $-2(x + 5) = -22$

30. $3(2x + 5) = -21$

31. $5x + 4 = -7x + 20$

32. $-3x + 5 = x - 15$

33. $4(x - 5) = -3x + 5x - 16$

34. $4(m + 1) = m + 5m - 10$

35. Ages Skye is 4 years older than Beth. The sum of their ages is 24. Find Skye's age by solving the equation $x + x + 4 = 24$, where x represents Beth's age and $x + 4$ represents Skye's age.

36. Parking Lot The length of a rectangular parking lot is 10 yards longer than the width, w, and the perimeter of the parking lot is 96 yards. Solve the equation $2w + 2(w + 10) = 96$ to find the width, w, of the parking lot. Then find the length of the parking lot, $w + 10$.

Section 2.3 Solving Linear Equations Involving Fractions and Decimals; Classifying Equations

KEY CONCEPTS	KEY TERMS
• A **conditional equation** is an equation that is true for some values of the variable and false for other values of the variable. • An equation that is false for every replacement value of the variable is called a **contradiction.** • An equation that is satisfied for every choice of the variable for which both sides of the equation are defined is called an **identity.**	Least common denominator (LCD) Identity Conditional equation Contradiction

YOU SHOULD BE ABLE TO...	EXAMPLE	REVIEW EXERCISES
1 Use the least common denominator to solve a linear equation containing fractions (p. 101)	Examples 1 and 2	37–40, 45, 46
2 Solve a linear equation containing decimals (p. 104)	Examples 3 through 5	41–44, 47, 48
3 Classify a linear equation as an identity, conditional, or a contradiction (p. 105)	Examples 6 through 8	49–54
4 Use linear equations to solve problems (p. 108)	Example 9	55, 56

In Problems 37–48, solve the equation. Check your solution.

37. $\frac{6}{7}x + 3 = \frac{1}{2}$ **38.** $\frac{1}{4}x + 6 = \frac{5}{6}$

39. $\frac{n}{2} + \frac{2}{3} = \frac{n}{6}$ **40.** $\frac{m}{8} + \frac{m}{2} = \frac{3}{4}$

41. $1.2r = -1 + 2.8$ **42.** $0.2x + 0.5x = 2.1$

43. $1.2m - 3.2 = 0.8m - 1.6$

44. $0.3m + 0.8 = 0.5m + 1$

45. $\frac{1}{2}(x + 5) = \frac{3}{4}$

46. $-\frac{1}{6}(x - 1) = \frac{2}{3}$

47. $0.1(x + 80) = -0.2 + 14$

48. $0.35(x + 6) = 0.45(x + 7)$

In Problems 49–54, solve each equation. State whether the equation is a contradiction, an identity, or a conditional equation.

49. $4x + 2x - 10 = 6x + 5$

50. $-2(x + 5) = -5x + 3x + 2$

51. $-5(2n + 10) = 6n - 50$

52. $8m + 10 = -2(7m - 5)$

53. $10x - 2x + 18 = 2(4x + 9)$

54. $-3(2x - 8) = -3x - 3x + 24$

55. T-Shirt Al purchased a tie-dyed T-shirt at a "20% off" sale for $12.60. What was the original price, p, of the shirt? Solve the equation $p - 0.20p = 12.60$.

56. Couch Cushions Juanita was cleaning under her couch cushions and found some nickels and dimes. She found $0.55 in change, with the number of nickels one less than twice the number of dimes. Solve the equation $0.10x + 0.05(2x - 1) = 0.55$ to find x, the number of dimes Juanita found.

Section 2.4 Evaluating Formulas and Solving Formulas for a Variable

KEY CONCEPTS	KEY TERMS
• **Simple interest formula** $I = Prt$, I represents the amount of interest, P is the principal, r is the rate of interest (expressed as a decimal), and t is time (expressed in years). • **Geometry Formulas (pages 113–114)**	Formula Interest Principal Rate of interest

YOU SHOULD BE ABLE TO...	EXAMPLE	REVIEW EXERCISES
1 Evaluate a formula (p. 111)	Examples 1 through 6	57–60, 67–70
2 Solve a formula for a variable (p. 116)	Examples 7 through 9	61–66, 67, 68

In Problems 57–60, substitute the given values into the formula and then simplify to find the unknown quantity. Label units in the answer.

57. area of a rectangle: $A = lw$; Find A when $l = 8$ inches and $w = 6$ inches.

58. perimeter of a square: $P = 4s$; Find P when $s = 16$ cm.

59. perimeter of a rectangle: $P = 2l + 2w$; Find w when $P = 16$ yards and $l = \frac{13}{2}$ yards.

60. circumference of a circle: $C = \pi d$; Find C when $d = \frac{15}{\pi}$ mm.

In Problems 61–66, solve each formula for the stated variable.

61. $V = LWH$; solve for H.

62. $I = Prt$; solve for P.

63. $S = 2LW + 2LH + 2WH$; solve for W.

64. $\rho = mv + MV$; solve for M.

65. $2x + 3y = 10$; solve for y.

66. $6x - 7y = 14$; solve for x.

67. Finance The formula $A = P(1 + r)^t$ can be used to find the future value A of a deposit of P dollars in an account that earns an annual interest rate r (expressed as a decimal) after t years.

(a) Solve the formula for P.

(b) How much would you have to deposit today in order to have $3000 in 6 years in a bank account that pays 5% annual interest? Round your answer to the nearest cent.

68. Cylinders The surface area A of a right circular cylinder is given by the formula $A = 2\pi rh + 2\pi r^2$, where r is the radius and h is the height.

(a) Solve the formula for h.

(b) Determine the height of a right circular cylinder whose surface area is 72π square centimeters and whose radius is 4 centimeters.

69. Christmas Bonus Samuel invested his $500 Christmas bonus in a 9-month Certificate of Deposit that earns 3% simple interest. Use the formula $I = Prt$ to find the amount of interest Samuel's investment will earn.

70. Coffee Table Find the area of a circular coffee table top with a diameter of 3 feet.

Section 2.5 Introduction to Problem Solving: Direct Translation Problems

KEY CONCEPTS	KEY TERMS
• **Six steps for solving problems with mathematical models** **Identify** what you are looking for **Name** the unknown(s) **Translate** to a mathematical equation **Solve** the equation **Check** the answer **Answer** the question in a complete sentence	Problem solving Mathematical modeling Modeling process Mathematical model Model Direct translation

YOU SHOULD BE ABLE TO...	EXAMPLE	REVIEW EXERCISES
1 Translate English phrases to algebraic expressions (p. 124)	Examples 1 through 3	71–76; 83–86
2 Translate English sentences to equations (p. 126)	Example 4	77–82
3 Build models for solving direct translation problems (p. 130)	Examples 5 through 9	87–90

In Problems 71–76, translate each phrase to an algebraic expression. Let x represent the unknown number.

71. the difference between a number and 6

72. eight subtracted from a number

73. the product of -8 and a number

74. the quotient of a number and 10

75. twice the sum of 6 and a number

76. four times the difference of 5 and a number

In Problems 77–82, translate each statement into an equation. Let x represent the unknown number. DO NOT SOLVE.

77. The sum of 6 and a number is equal to twice the number increased by 5.

78. The product of 6 and a number decreased by 10 is one more than double the number.

79. Eight less than a number is the same as half of the number.

80. The ratio of 6 to a number is the same as the number added to 10.

81. Four times the sum of twice a number and 8 is 16.

82. Five times the difference between double a number and 8 is -24.

In Problems 83–86, choose a variable to represent one quantity. State what the quantity represents, and then express the second quantity in terms of the first.

83. Jacob is seven years older than Sarah.

84. José runs twice as fast as Consuelo.

85. Irene has $6 less than Max.

86. Victor and Larry will share $350.

87. Losing Weight Over the past year Lee Lai lost 28 pounds. Find Lee Lai's weight one year ago if her current weight is 125 pounds.

88. Consecutive Integers The sum of three consecutive integers is 39. Find the integers.

89. Finance A total of $20,000 is to be divided between Roberto and Juan, with Roberto to receive $2000 less than Juan. How much will each receive?

90. Truck Rentals You need to rent a moving truck. You identified two companies that rent trucks. ABC-Rental charges $30 per day plus $0.15 per mile. U-Do-It Rental charges $15 per day plus $0.30 per mile. For how many miles will the daily cost of renting be the same?

Section 2.6 Problem Solving: Direct Translation Problems Involving Percent

KEY CONCEPTS

- Percent means divided by 100 or per hundred.
- Total Cost = Original Cost + Sales Tax
- Original Price − Discount = Sale Price
- Wholesale Price + Markup = Selling Price

YOU SHOULD BE ABLE TO...	EXAMPLE	REVIEW EXERCISES
1 Solve direct translation problems involving percent (p. 137)	Examples 1 through 4	91–94
2 Model and solve direct translation problems from business that involve percent (p. 139)	Examples 5 and 6	95–100

In Problems 91–94, find the unknown in each percent question.

91. What is 6.5% of 80?

92. 18 is 30% of what number?

93. 15.6 is what percent of 120?

94. 110% of what number is 55?

95. Sales Tax The sales tax in Florida is 6%. The total cost of purchasing a leotard, including tax, was $19.61. Find the cost of the leotard before sales tax.

96. Tutoring Mei Ling is a private tutor. She raised her hourly fee by 8.5% to cover her traveling expenses. Her new hourly rate is $32.55. Find Mei Ling's previous hourly fee.

97. Business: Discount Pricing A sweater, discounted by 70% for an end of the year clearance sale, has a price tag of $12. What was the sweater's original price?

98. Business: Mark-Up A clothing store marks up the price that it pays for a suit 80%. If the selling price of a suit is $360, how much did the store pay for the suit?

99. Salary Tanya earns $500 each week plus 2% of the value of the computers she sells each week. If Tanya wishes to earn $3000 this week, what must be the total value of the computers she sells?

100. Voting In an election for school president, the loser received 80% of the winner's votes. If 900 votes were cast, how many did each receive?

Section 2.7 Problem Solving: Geometry and Uniform Motion

KEY CONCEPTS	KEY TERMS
- Complementary angles are two angles whose measures sum to 90°. - Supplementary angles are two angles whose measures sum to 180°. - The sum of the measures of the angles of a triangle is 180°. - **Uniform Motion** If an object moves at an average speed r, the distance d covered in time t is given by the formula $d = rt$.	Complementary angles Supplementary angles Uniform motion

YOU SHOULD BE ABLE TO...	EXAMPLE	REVIEW EXERCISES
1 Set up and solve complementary and supplementary angle problems (p. 144)	Example 1	101, 102
2 Set up and solve angles of triangle problems (p. 145)	Example 2	103, 104
3 Use geometry formulas to solve problems (p. 146)	Examples 3 and 4	105–108
4 Set up and solve uniform motion problems (p. 148)	Examples 5 and 6	109, 110

△ **101. Complementary Angles** Find two complementary angles such that the measure of the first angle is 20° more than six times the second.

△ **102. Supplementary Angles** Find two supplementary angles such that the measure of the first angle is 60° less than twice the second.

△ **103. Triangles** In a triangle, the measure of the second angle is twice the first. The measure of the third angle is 30° more than the second. Find the measures of the three angles.

△ **104. Triangles** In a triangle, the measure of the second angle is 5° less than the first. The measure of the third angle is 5° less than twice the second. Find the measures of the three angles.

△ **105. Rectangle** The length of a rectangle is 15 inches longer than twice its width. If the perimeter is 78 inches, find the length and width of the rectangle.

△ **106. Rectangle** The length of a rectangle is four times its width. If the perimeter is 70 cm, find the length and width of the rectangle.

△ **107. Garden** The perimeter of a rectangular garden is 120 feet. The width of the garden is twice the length.

(a) Find the length and width of the garden.

(b) What is the area of the garden?

△ **108. Back Yard** Yvonne's back yard is in the shape of a trapezoid with height of 80 feet. The shorter base is 10 feet shorter than the longer base, and the area of the back yard is 3600 square feet. Find the length of each base of the trapezoidal yard.

109. Boating Two motorboats leave the same dock at the same time traveling in the same direction. One boat travels at 18 miles per hour and the other travels at 25 miles per hour. In how many hours will the motorboats be 35 miles apart?

110. Train Station Two trains leave a station at the same time. One train is traveling east at 10 miles per hour faster than the other train, which is traveling west. After 6 hours, the two trains are 720 miles apart. At what speed did the faster train travel?

Section 2.8 Solving Linear Inequalities in One Variable

KEY CONCEPTS

- A linear inequality is of the form $ax + b < c$, $ax + b \le c$, $ax + b > c$ or $ax + b \ge c$, where $a, b,$ and c are real numbers and $a \ne 0$.

- **Addition Property of Inequality**
  For real numbers $a, b,$ and c
  If $a < b$, then $a + c < b + c$.
  If $a > b$, then $a + c > b + c$.

- **Multiplication Properties of Inequality**
  For real numbers $a, b,$ and c
  If $a < b$, and if $c > 0$, then $ac < bc$.
  If $a > b$, and if $c > 0$, then $ac > bc$.
  If $a < b$, and if $c < 0$, then $ac > bc$.
  If $a > b$, and if $c < 0$, then $ac < bc$.

KEY TERMS

Linear inequality
Simple inequality
Set-builder notation
Graph of an inequality
Endpoint
Interval
Solve an inequality
Equivalent inequalities

SET-BUILDER NOTATION	INTERVAL NOTATION	GRAPH
$\{x \mid x \ge a\}$	$[a, \infty)$	
$\{x \mid x > a\}$	(a, ∞)	
$\{x \mid x \le a\}$	$(-\infty, a]$	
$\{x \mid x < a\}$	$(-\infty, a)$	
$\{x \mid x \text{ is a real number}\}$	$(-\infty, \infty)$	

YOU SHOULD BE ABLE TO...	EXAMPLE	REVIEW EXERCISES
1 Graph inequalities on a real number line (p. 154)	Example 1	111–116
2 Use interval notation (p. 155)	Example 2	117–120
3 Solve linear inequalities using properties of inequalities (p. 156)	Examples 3 through 10	121–128
4 Model inequality problems (p. 162)	Example 11	129, 130

In Problems 111–116, graph each inequality on a number line.

111. $x \le -3$ **112.** $x > 4$

113. $m < 2$ **114.** $m \ge -5$

115. $0 < n$ **116.** $-3 \le n$

In Problems 117–120, write the inequality in interval notation.

117. $x < -4$ **118.** $x \ge 7$

119.

$$\begin{array}{cccccccc} & | & | & | & [& | & \rightarrow & | \\ -1 & 0 & 1 & 2 & 3 & 4 & 5 \end{array}$$

120.

$$\begin{array}{cccccccc} | & \leftarrow & | & | & | & | & \rightarrow & | \\ -3 & -2 & -1 & 0 & 1 & 2 & 3 & 4 \end{array}$$

In Problems 121–128, solve the inequality and express the solution in set-builder notation and interval notation if possible. Graph the solution set on a real number line.

121. $4x + 3 < 2x - 10$

122. $3x - 5 \ge -12$

123. $-4(x - 1) \le x + 8$

124. $6x - 10 < 7x + 2$

125. $-3(x + 7) > -x - 2x$

126. $4x + 10 \le 2(2x + 7)$

127. $\dfrac{1}{2}(3x - 1) > \dfrac{2}{3}(x + 3)$

128. $\dfrac{5}{4}x + 2 < \dfrac{5}{6}x - \dfrac{7}{6}$

129. Moving The Rent-A-Moving-Van Company charges a flat rate of $19.95 per day plus $0.20 for each mile driven. How many miles can be driven if a customer can afford to spend at most only $32.95 for one day?

130. Bowling Travis is bowling three games in a tournament. In the first game, his score was 148. In the second game, his score was 155. What score must Travis get in the third game for his tournament average to be greater than 151?

CHAPTER 2 TEST

Remember to use your Chapter Test Prep Video CD to see fully worked-out solutions to any of these problems you would like to review.

In Problems 1–8, solve the equation. Check your solution.

1. $x + 3 = -14$

2. $-\dfrac{2}{3}m = \dfrac{8}{27}$

3. $5(2x - 4) = 5x$

4. $-2(x - 5) = 5(-3x + 4)$

5. $-\dfrac{2}{3}x + \dfrac{3}{4} = \dfrac{1}{3}$

6. $-0.6 + 0.4y = 1.4$

7. $8x + 3(2 - x) = 5(x + 2)$

8. $2(x + 7) = 2x - 2 + 16$

In Problems 9 and 10, (a) solve for the indicated variable, and then (b) find the value of the unknown quantity. Label units in the answer.

9. Volume of a rectangular solid: $V = lwh$

  (a) Solve for l.

  (b) Find l when $V = 540$ in.^{3}, $w = 6$ in., and $h = 10$ in.

10. Equation of a line: $2x + 3y = 12$

  (a) Solve for y.

  (b) Find y when $x = 8$.

11. Translate the following statement into an equation: Six times the difference between a number and 8 is equal to 5 less than twice the number. DO NOT SOLVE.

12. 18 is 30% of a number. Find the number.

13. Consecutive Integers The sum of three consecutive integers is 48. Find the integers.

14. Trading Spaces On the show *Trading Spaces*, designer Vern Yip constructs a triangular art piece for a bedroom. The length of the longest side is two inches longer than the length of the middle side. The shortest side is 14 inches shorter than the middle side. If the perimeter of the art piece is 60 inches, what is the length of each side?

15. Buses Kimberly and Clay leave a concert hall at the same time traveling in buses going in opposite directions. Kimberly's bus travels at 40 mph and Clay's bus travels at 60 mph. In how many hours will Kimberly and Clay be 350 miles apart?

16. Construction A carpenter cuts an oak board 21 feet long into two pieces. The longer board is 1 foot longer than three times the shorter one. Find the length of each board.

17. New Backpack Sherry purchased a new backpack for her daughter. The backpack was on sale for 20% off the regular price. If Sherry paid $28.80 for the backpack without sales tax, what was the original price?

In Problems 18 and 19, solve the inequality and express the solution in set-builder notation and interval notation. Graph the solution set on a real number line.

18. $3(2x - 5) \leq x + 15$

19. $-6x - 4 < 2(x - 7)$

20. Cell Phone Danielle's cell phone plan has a $30 monthly fee and an extra charge of $0.35 a minute. For how many minutes can Danielle use her cell phone so that the monthly bill is at most $100?

3

Introduction to Graphing and Equations of Lines

Your legs feel like they are on fire. Exactly how steep is this hill anyhow? We can use mathematics to describe the steepness of a hill. See Example 7 and Problems 71 and 72 in Section 3.3.

The Big Picture: Putting It Together

It is now time to switch gears. In Chapter 2, we solved linear equations and inequalities involving one unknown. We are now going to focus our attention on linear equations and inequalities involving two unknowns.

When we dealt with a single unknown, we could represent solutions to equations or inequalities graphically using real number lines. In that case, we only needed one dimension to represent the solution. When we have two unknowns, we need to work in two dimensions. This is accomplished through the *rectangular coordinate system*.

3.1 The Rectangular Coordinate System and Equations in Two Variables

OBJECTIVES

1 Plot Points in the Rectangular Coordinate System

2 Determine If an Ordered Pair Satisfies an Equation

3 Create a Table of Values That Satisfy an Equation

Preparing for the Rectangular Coordinate System and Equations in Two Variables

Before getting started, take the following readiness quiz. If you get a problem wrong, go back to the section cited and review the material.

P1. Plot the following points on a real number line: [Section 1.3, pp. 24–25]

$$4, -3, \frac{1}{2}, 5.5$$

P2. Evaluate $3x + 5$ for **(a)** $x = 4$ **(b)** $x = -1$ [Section 1.8, pp. 67–68]

P3. Evaluate $2x - 5y$ for **(a)** $x = 3$, $y = 2$ [Section 1.8, pp. 67–68]
   (b) $x = 1$, $y = -4$

P4. Solve: $3x + 5 = 14$ [Section 2.2, pp. 94–96]

P5. Solve: $5(x - 3) - 2x = 3x + 12$ [Section 2.2, pp. 94–98]

Figure 1

1 Plot Points in the Rectangular Coordinate System

We have all heard the saying, "A picture is worth a thousand words." Because pictures allow individuals to visualize ideas, they are typically more powerful than any other form of printed communication. Consider the picture shown in Figure 1, which shows the results of the Manhattan Project from the test conducted July 16, 1945. It illustrates the power of the atom in a way that words never could.

While the pictures that we use in mathematics might not deliver as powerful a message as the picture in Figure 1, they are powerful nonetheless. To draw pictures of mathematical relationships, we need a "canvas." The "canvas" that we use in this chapter is the *rectangular coordinate system.*

In Section 1.3, we learned how to plot points on a real number line. We locate a point on a real number line by assigning it a single real number, called the *coordinate of the point.* We can think of this as plotting in one dimension. In this chapter, we use the *rectangular coordinate system,* a system that allows us to plot points in two dimensions.

We begin by drawing two real number lines that intersect at right (90°) angles. One of the real number lines is drawn horizontally, while the other is drawn vertically. We call the horizontal real number line the **x-axis,** and the vertical real number line is called the **y-axis.** The point where the x-axis and y-axis intersect is called the **origin, O.** See Figure 2.

Figure 2

The rectangular coordinate system

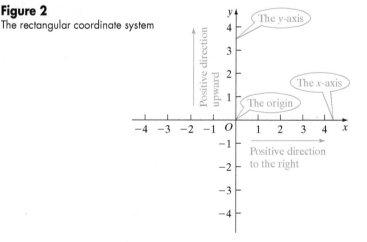

The origin O has a value of 0 on the x-axis and on the y-axis. Points on the x-axis to the right of O represent positive real numbers; points on the x-axis to the left of O represent negative real numbers. Points on the y-axis that are above O represent positive real numbers. Points on the y-axis that are below O represent negative real numbers. Notice in Figure 2 that we label the x-axis "x" and the y-axis "y." An arrow is used at the end of each axis to denote the positive direction.

The coordinate system presented in Figure 2 is called a **rectangular** or **Cartesian coordinate system,** named after René Descartes (1596–1650), a French mathematician, philosopher, and theologian. The plane formed by the x-axis and y-axis is often referred to as the **xy-plane,** and the x-axis and y-axis are called the **coordinate axes.**

We can represent any point P in the rectangular coordinate system by using an **ordered pair (x, y)** of real numbers. We say that x represents the distance that P is from the y-axis. If $x > 0$ (that is, if x is positive), we travel x units to the right of the y-axis. If $x < 0$, we travel $|x|$ units to the left of the y-axis. We say that y represents the distance that P is from the x-axis. If $y > 0$, we travel y units above the x-axis. If $y < 0$, we travel $|y|$ units below the x-axis. The ordered pair (x, y) is also called the **coordinates** of P. For example, to plot the point whose coordinates are $(2, 5)$, from the origin we would travel 2 units to the right along the x-axis and then 5 units up as shown in Figure 3(a).

Figure 3

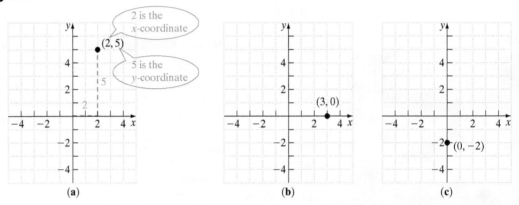

(a)　　　(b)　　　(c)

The origin O has coordinates $(0, 0)$. Any point on the x-axis has coordinates of the form $(x, 0)$, and any point on the y-axis has coordinates of the form $(0, y)$. For example, the point whose coordinates are $(3, 0)$ is 3 units to the right of the y-axis on the x-axis. See Figure 3(b). The point whose coordinates are $(0, -2)$ is 2 units below the x-axis on the y-axis. See Figure 3(c).

If (x, y) are the coordinates of a point P, then x is called the **x-coordinate** of P and y is called the **y-coordinate** of P.

If you look back at Figure 2, you should notice that the x- and y-axes divide the plane into four separate regions or **quadrants.** In quadrant I, both the x-coordinate and y-coordinate are positive. In quadrant II, x is negative and y is positive. In quadrant III, both x and y are negative. In quadrant IV, x is positive and y is negative. Points on the coordinate axes do not belong to a quadrant. See Figure 4.

Work Smart

Be careful: The order in which numbers appear in the ordered pairs matters. For example, (3, 2) represents a different point from (2, 3).

Figure 4

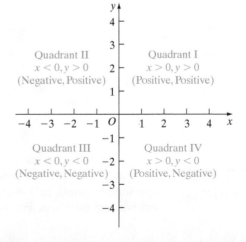

Let's summarize what we've learned so far.

> ## SUMMARY THE RECTANGULAR COORDINATE SYSTEM
>
> - Composed of two real number lines—one horizontal (the x-axis) and one vertical (the y-axis). The x- and y-axes intersect at the origin.
> - Also called the Cartesian coordinate system or xy-plane.
> - Points in the rectangular coordinate system are denoted (x, y) and are called the coordinates of the point. We call x the x-coordinate and y the y-coordinate.
> - If both x and y are positive, the point lies in quadrant I; if x is negative, but y is positive, the point lies in quadrant II; if x is negative and y is negative, the point lies in quadrant III; if x is positive and y is negative, the point lies in quadrant IV.
> - Points on the x-axis have a y-coordinate of 0; points on the y-axis have an x-coordinate of 0. Points on the x- or y-axis do not lie in a quadrant.

EXAMPLE 1 Plotting Points in the Rectangular Coordinate System

Plot the following ordered pairs in the rectangular coordinate system. Tell which quadrant each point lies in or state that the point lies on the x- or y-axis.

(a) $A(3, 1)$ **(b)** $B(-4, 2)$ **(c)** $C(3, -5)$

(d) $D(4, 0)$ **(e)** $E(0, -3)$ **(f)** $F\left(-\dfrac{5}{2}, -\dfrac{7}{2}\right)$

Solution

Before we can plot the points, we draw a rectangular or Cartesian coordinate system. See Figure 5(a). We now plot the points.

Figure 5

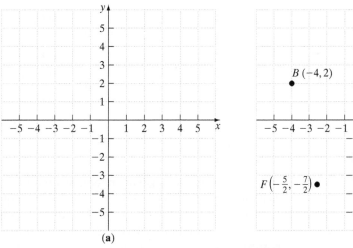

(a)

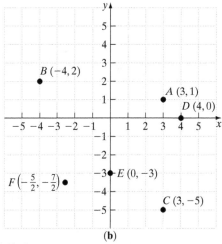

(b)

(a) To plot the point whose coordinates are $A(3, 1)$, from the origin O, we travel 3 units to the right and then 1 unit up. Label the point A. Point A lies in quadrant I because both x and y are positive. See Figure 5(b).

(b) To plot the point whose coordinates are $B(-4, 2)$, from the origin O, we travel 4 units to the left and then 2 units up. Label the point B. See Figure 5(b). Point B lies in quadrant II.

(c) See Figure 5(b). Point C lies in quadrant IV.

(d) See Figure 5(b). Point D does not lie in a quadrant because it lies on the x-axis.

(e) See Figure 5(b). Point E does not lie in a quadrant because it lies on the y-axis.

(f) It is helpful to convert the fractions to decimals, so $F\left(-\dfrac{5}{2}, -\dfrac{7}{2}\right) = F(-2.5, -3.5)$.

We see that the x-coordinate of the point is halfway between -3 and -2; the y-coordinate of the point is halfway between -4 and -3. See Figure 5(b). Point F lies in quadrant III. ∎

Quick ✔

1. In the rectangular coordinate system, we call the horizontal real number line the _____ and we call the vertical real number line the _____. The point where these two axes intersect is called the _____.

2. If (x, y) are the coordinates of a point P, then x is called the _____ of P and y is called the _____ of P.

3. *True or False:* The point whose ordered pair is $(-2, 4)$ is located in quadrant IV.

4. *True or False:* The ordered pairs $(7, 4)$ and $(4, 7)$ represent the same point in the Cartesian plane.

In Problems 5 and 6, plot the ordered pairs in the rectangular coordinate system. Tell which quadrant each point lies in or state that the point lies on the x-axis or y-axis.

5. **(a)** $(5, 2)$ **(b)** $(-4, -3)$ **(c)** $(1, -3)$ **(d)** $(-2, 0)$ **(e)** $(0, 6)$ **(f)** $\left(-\dfrac{3}{2}, \dfrac{5}{2}\right)$

6. **(a)** $(-6, 2)$ **(b)** $(1, 7)$ **(c)** $(-3, -2)$ **(d)** $(4, 0)$ **(e)** $(0, -1)$ **(f)** $\left(\dfrac{3}{2}, -\dfrac{7}{2}\right)$

EXAMPLE 2 Identifying Points in the Rectangular Coordinate System

Identify the coordinates of each point labeled in Figure 6.

Figure 6

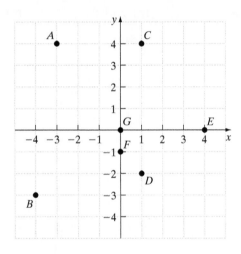

Solution

In an ordered pair (x, y), remember that x represents the position of the point left or right of the y-axis, while y represents the position of the point above or below the x-axis.

Since the point A is 3 units left of the y-axis, it has an x-coordinate of -3; since the point A is 4 units above the x-axis, it has a y-coordinate of 4. The ordered pair corresponding to the point A is $(-3, 4)$. We find the remaining coordinates in a similar fashion.

Point	Position	Ordered Pair
A	3 units left of the y-axis, 4 units above the x-axis	$(-3, 4)$
B	4 units left of the y-axis, 3 units below the x-axis	$(-4, -3)$
C	1 unit right of the y-axis, 4 units above the x-axis	$(1, 4)$
D	1 unit right of the y-axis, 2 units below the x-axis	$(1, -2)$
E	4 units right of the y-axis, on the x-axis	$(4, 0)$
F	On the y-axis, 1 unit below the x-axis	$(0, -1)$
G	On the x-axis; on the y-axis	$(0, 0)$

Quick ✔

7. Identify the coordinates of each point labeled in the figure below.

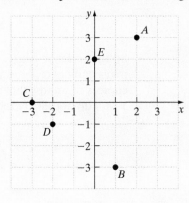

(a) A **(b)** B **(c)** C **(d)** D **(e)** E

2 Determine If an Ordered Pair Satisfies an Equation

In Sections 2.1–2.3, we solved linear equations in one variable. Recall that the solution of a linear equation is either a single value of the variable (conditional equation), the empty set (contradiction), or all real numbers (identity). Table 1 illustrates the three categories of linear equations in one variable.

Table 1		
Conditional Equation	Contradiction	Identity
$3x + 2 = 11$	$4(x - 2) - x = 2(x + 1) + x$	$-2(x + 3) + 4x = 2(x - 3)$
$3x = 9$	$4x - 8 - x = 2x + 2 + x$	$-2x - 6 + 4x = 2x - 6$
$x = 3$	$3x - 8 = 3x + 2$	$2x - 6 = 2x - 6$
	$-8 = 2$	$-6 = -6$
	no solution	solution is all real numbers

We will now look at equations in two variables.

DEFINITION

An **equation in two variables,** x and y, is a statement in which the algebraic expressions involving x and y are equal. The expressions are called **sides** of the equation.

For example, the following are all equations in two variables.

$$x + 2y = 6 \qquad y = -3x + 7 \qquad y = x^2 + 3$$

Since an equation is a statement, it may be true or false, depending upon the values of the variables. Any values of the variable that make the equation a true statement are said to **satisfy** the equation.

The first equation $x + 2y = 6$ is satisfied when $x = 4$ and $y = 1$. Why? If we substitute 4 for x and 1 for y into the equation $x + 2y = 6$, we obtain a true statement.

$$x + 2y = 6$$
$$x = 4, y = 1: \quad 4 + 2(1) \stackrel{?}{=} 6$$
$$6 = 6 \quad \text{True}$$

Rather than saying the equation is satisfied when $x = 4$ and $y = 1$, we can say that the ordered pair (4, 1) satisfies the equation. Does $x = 8$ and $y = -1$ satisfy the equation $x + 2y = 6$?

$$x + 2y = 6$$
$$x = 8, y = -1: \quad 8 + 2(-1) \stackrel{?}{=} 6$$
$$6 = 6 \quad \text{True}$$

So the ordered pair $(8, -1)$ satisfies the equation as well. In fact, there are infinitely many choices of x and y that satisfy the equation $x + 2y = 6$. However, there are some choices of x and y that do not satisfy the equation $x + 2y = 6$. For example, $x = 3$ and $y = 4$ do not satisfy the equation $x + 2y = 6$.

$$x + 2y = 6$$
$$x = 3, y = 4: \quad 3 + 2(4) \stackrel{?}{=} 6$$
$$11 = 6 \quad \text{False}$$

EXAMPLE 3 Determining Whether an Ordered Pair Satisfies an Equation

Determine if the following ordered pairs satisfy the equation $x + 2y = 8$.

(a) $(2, 3)$ (b) $(6, -1)$ (c) $(-2, 5)$

Solution

(a) For the ordered pair $(2, 3)$, we check to see if $x = 2$, $y = 3$ satisfies the equation $x + 2y = 8$.

$$x + 2y = 8$$
$$\text{Let } x = 2, y = 3: \quad 2 + 2(3) \stackrel{?}{=} 8$$
$$2 + 6 \stackrel{?}{=} 8$$
$$8 = 8 \quad \text{True}$$

The statement is true, so $(2, 3)$ satisfies the equation $x + 2y = 8$.

(b) For the ordered pair $(6, -1)$, we have

$$x + 2y = 8$$
$$\text{Let } x = 6, y = -1: \quad 6 + 2(-1) \stackrel{?}{=} 8$$
$$6 - 2 \stackrel{?}{=} 8$$
$$4 = 8 \quad \text{False}$$

The statement $4 = 8$ is false, so $(6, -1)$ does not satisfy the equation $x + 2y = 8$.

(c) For the ordered pair $(-2, 5)$, we have

$$x + 2y = 8$$
$$\text{Let } x = -2, y = 5: \quad -2 + 2(5) \stackrel{?}{=} 8$$
$$-2 + 10 \stackrel{?}{=} 8$$
$$8 = 8 \quad \text{True}$$

The statement is true, so $(-2, 5)$ satisfies the equation $x + 2y = 8$. ∎

Quick ✔

8. *True or False:* An equation in two variables can have more than one solution.

9. Determine if the following ordered pairs satisfy the equation $x + 4y = 12$.

     (a) $(4, 2)$ (b) $(-2, 4)$ (c) $(1, 8)$

10. Determine if the following ordered pairs satisfy the equation $y = 4x + 3$.

     (a) $(1, 3)$ (b) $(-2, -5)$ (c) $\left(-\dfrac{3}{2}, -3\right)$

3 Create a Table of Values That Satisfy an Equation

In Example 3 we learned how to determine whether a given ordered pair satisfies an equation. However, we do not yet know how to find an ordered pair that satisfies an equation.

EXAMPLE 4 How to Find an Ordered Pair That Satisfies an Equation

Find an ordered pair that satisfies the equation $3x + y = 5$.

Step-by-Step Solution

Step1: Choose any value for one of the variables in the equation.	You may choose any value of x or y that you wish. In this example, we will let $x = 2$.
Step 2: Substitute the value of the variable chosen in Step 1 into the equation and then use the techniques learned in Chapter 2 to solve for the remaining variable.	Substitute 2 for x in the equation $3x + y = 5$ and then solve for y.

$$3x + y = 5$$
$$\text{Let } x = 2: \quad 3(2) + y = 5$$
$$\text{Simplify:} \quad 6 + y = 5$$
$$\text{Subtract 6 from both sides:} \quad 6 - 6 + y = 5 - 6$$
$$y = -1$$

One ordered pair that satisfies the equation is $(2, -1)$.

Quick ✔ *In Problems 11–13, determine an ordered pair that satisfies the given equation by substituting the given value of the variable into the equation.*

11. $2x + y = 10; x = 3$ **12.** $-3x + 2y = 11; y = 1$ **13.** $4x + 3y = 0; x = \dfrac{1}{2}$

Look again at Example 3. Did you notice that two different ordered pairs satisfy the equation? In fact, there are an infinite number of ordered pairs that satisfy the equation $x + 2y = 8$ because for any real number y we can find a value of x that makes the equation a true statement. One approach to finding some of the solutions of an equation in two variables is to create a table of values that satisfy the equation. The table is created by choosing values of x and using the equation to find the corresponding value of y (as we did in Example 4) or by choosing a value of y and using the equation to find the corresponding value of x.

EXAMPLE 5 Creating a Table of Values That Satisfy an Equation

Use the equation $y = -2x + 5$ to complete Table 2 and list some of the ordered pairs that satisfy the equation.

Solution

The first entry in the table is $x = -2$. We substitute -2 for x and use the equation $y = -2x + 5$ to find y.

Table 2

x	y	(x, y)
−2		
0		
1		

$$y = -2x + 5$$
$$x = -2: \quad y = -2(-2) + 5$$
$$y = 4 + 5$$
$$y = 9$$

Now substitute 0 for x in the equation $y = -2x + 5$.

$$y = -2x + 5$$
$$x = 0: \quad y = -2(0) + 5$$
$$y = 0 + 5$$
$$y = 5$$

Finally, substitute 1 for x in the equation $y = -2x + 5$.

$$y = -2x + 5$$
$$x = 1: \quad y = -2(1) + 5$$
$$y = -2 + 5$$
$$y = 3$$

The completed table is shown as Table 3.

The ordered pairs that satisfy the equation are $(-2, 9)$, $(0, 5)$, and $(1, 3)$. ■

Table 3

x	y	(x, y)
−2	9	(−2, 9)
0	5	(0, 5)
1	3	(1, 3)

Quick ✔ *In Problems 14 and 15, use the equation to complete the table. Use the table to list some of the ordered pairs that satisfy the equation.*

14. $y = 5x - 2$

x	y	(x, y)
−2		
0		
1		

15. $y = -3x + 4$

x	y	(x, y)
−1		
2		
5		

Table 4

x	y	(x, y)
−3		
	−4	
6		

EXAMPLE 6 Creating a Table of Values That Satisfy an Equation

Use the equation $2x - 3y = 12$ to complete Table 4 and list some of the ordered pairs that satisfy the equation.

Solution

The first entry in the table is $x = -3$. We substitute -3 for x and use the equation $2x - 3y = 12$ to find y.

$$2x - 3y = 12$$
$$x = -3: \quad 2(-3) - 3y = 12$$
$$-6 - 3y = 12$$
$$\text{Add 6 to both sides:} \quad -3y = 18$$
$$\text{Divide both sides by } -3: \quad y = -6$$

Substitute -4 for y in the equation $2x - 3y = 12$.

$$2x - 3y = 12$$
$$y = -4: \quad 2x - 3(-4) = 12$$
$$2x + 12 = 12$$
$$\text{Subtract 12 from both sides:} \quad 2x = 0$$
$$\text{Divide both sides by 2:} \quad x = 0$$

Substitute 6 for x in the equation $2x - 3y = 12$.

$$2x - 3y = 12$$
$$x = 6: \quad 2(6) - 3y = 12$$
$$12 - 3y = 12$$
$$\text{Subtract 12 from both sides:} \quad -3y = 0$$
$$\text{Divide both sides by } -3: \quad y = 0$$

Table 5

x	y	(x, y)
−3	−6	(−3, −6)
0	−4	(0, −4)
6	0	(6, 0)

The completed table is shown in Table 5.

The ordered pairs that satisfy the equation are $(-3, -6)$, $(0, -4)$, and $(6, 0)$. ∎

Quick ✔ *In Problems 16 and 17, use the equation to complete the table. Use the table to list some of the ordered pairs that satisfy the equation.*

16. $2x + y = -8$

x	y	(x, y)
−5		
	−4	
2		

17. $2x - 5y = 18$

x	y	(x, y)
−6		
	−4	
2		

When we are working with equations that model a situation, we often do not use the variables x and y. Instead, we use variables that remind us of what they represent. For example, we might use the equation $C = 1.20m + 3$ to represent the cost of taking a taxi. Here C represents the cost (in dollars) and m represents the number of miles driven.

Recall from Section 1.3 that the scale of a number line refers to the distance between tick marks on the number line. In Figures 2 through 6, we used a scale of 1 on both the x-axis and y-axis. In applications, a different scale is often used to accommodate the ordered pairs that need to be plotted.

EXAMPLE 7 An Electric Bill

In North Carolina, Duke Power determines that the monthly electric bill for a household will be C dollars for using x kilowatt-hours (kWh) of electricity using the formula

$$C = 7.87 + 0.073572x$$

where $x \leq 350$ kWh. (SOURCE: *Duke Power*)

(a) Complete Table 6 and use the table to list ordered pairs that satisfy the equation. Express answers rounded to the nearest penny.

Table 6			
x(kWh)	50 kWh	100 kWh	250 kWh
C($)			

(b) Plot the ordered pairs (x, C) found in part (a) in a rectangular coordinate system.

Solution

(a) The first entry in the table is $x = 50$. We substitute 50 for x and use the equation $C = 7.87 + 0.073572x$ to find C. When we find C we will round our answer to two decimal places because C represents the cost, so our answer is rounded to the nearest penny.

$$C = 7.87 + 0.073572x$$
$$x = 50: \quad C = 7.87 + 0.073572(50)$$
$$\text{Use a calculator:} \quad C = 11.55$$

Now substitute 100 for x and use the equation $C = 7.87 + 0.073572x$ to find C.

$$C = 7.87 + 0.073572x$$
$$x = 100: \quad C = 7.87 + 0.073572(100)$$
$$\text{Use a calculator:} \quad C = 15.23$$

Figure 7

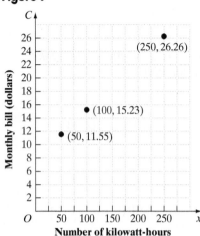

Number of kilowatt-hours

Now substitute 250 for x and use the equation $C = 7.87 + 0.073572x$ to find C.

$$C = 7.87 + 0.073572x$$
$$x = 250: \quad C = 7.87 + 0.073572(250)$$
$$\text{Use a calculator:} \quad C = 26.26$$

Table 7 shows the completed table.

Table 7			
x (kWh)	50 kWh	100 kWh	250 kWh
C($)	$11.55	$15.23	$26.26

The ordered pairs that satisfy the equation are $(50, 11.55)$, $(100, 15.23)$, and $(250, 26.26)$.

(b) Remember that x represents the number of kilowatt-hours used, so we label the horizontal axis x. Also, recall that C represents the bill, so we label the vertical axis C. Figure 7 shows a rectangular coordinate system with the ordered pairs found in part (a) plotted. Notice we use a different scale on the horizontal and vertical axis. ∎

Notice in Figure 7 that we labeled the horizontal and vertical axis so that it is clear what they represent. Labeling the axes is a good practice to follow whenever you are drawing a graph.

Quick ✔

18. Piedmont Natural Gas charges its customers in North Carolina a monthly fee C dollars for using x therms of natural gas using the formula

$$C = 10 + 1.32607x$$

(SOURCE: *Piedmont Natural Gas*)

(a) Complete the table and use the results to list ordered pairs (x, C) that satisfy the equation. Express answers rounded to the nearest penny.

x (therms)	50 therms	100 therms	150 therms

(b) Plot the ordered pairs found in part **(a)** in a rectangular coordinate system. ⌐

3.1 EXERCISES

PRACTICE   WATCH   DOWNLOAD   READ   REVIEW

1–18. *are the* Quick ✔s *that follow each* EXAMPLE

Building Skills

In Problems 19–22, plot the following ordered pairs in the rectangular coordinate system. Tell which quadrant each point lies in or state that the point lies on the x-axis or y-axis. See Objective 1.

19. $A(-3, 2);$ $B(4, 1);$ $C(-2, -4);$ $D(5, -4);$
$E(-1, 3);$ $F(2, -4)$

20. $P(-3, -2);$ $Q(2, -4);$ $R(4, 3);$ $S(-1, 4);$
$T(-2, -4);$ $U(3, -3)$

21. $A\left(\frac{1}{2}, 0\right);$ $B\left(\frac{3}{2}, -\frac{1}{2}\right);$ $C\left(4, \frac{7}{2}\right);$ $D\left(0, -\frac{5}{2}\right);$
$E\left(\frac{9}{2}, 2\right);$ $F\left(-\frac{5}{2}, -\frac{3}{2}\right);$ $G(0, 0)$

22. $P\left(\frac{3}{2}, -2\right);$ $Q\left(0, \frac{5}{2}\right);$ $R\left(-\frac{9}{2}, 0\right);$ $S(0, 0);$
$T\left(-\frac{3}{2}, -\frac{9}{2}\right);$ $U\left(3, \frac{1}{2}\right);$ $V\left(\frac{5}{2}, -\frac{7}{2}\right)$

In Problems 23 and 24, plot the following ordered pairs in the rectangular coordinate system. Tell the location of each point: positive x-axis, negative x-axis, positive y-axis, or negative y-axis. See Objective 1.

23. $A(3,0)$; $B(0,-1)$; $C(0,3)$; $D(-4,0)$

24. $P(0,-1)$; $Q(-2,0)$; $R(0,3)$; $S(1,0)$

In Problems 25 and 26, identify the coordinates of each point labeled in the figure. Name the quadrant in which each point lies or state that the point lies on the x- or y-axis. See Objective 1.

25.

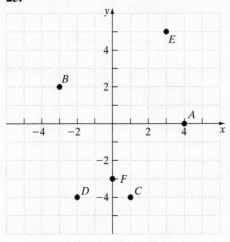

26.

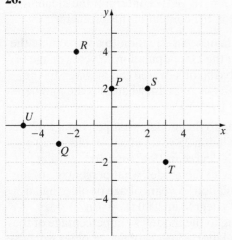

In Problems 27–32, determine whether or not the ordered pair satisfies the equation. See Objective 2.

27. $y = -3x + 5$ $A(-2,-1)$ $B(2,-1)$ $C\left(\dfrac{1}{3},4\right)$

28. $y = 2x - 3$ $A(-1,-5)$ $B(4,-5)$ $C(-2,-7)$

29. $3x + 2y = 4$ $A(0,2)$ $B(1,0)$ $C(4,-4)$

30. $5x - y = 12$ $A(2,0)$ $B(0,12)$ $C(-2,-22)$

31. $\dfrac{4}{3}x + y - 1 = 0$ $A(3,-3)$ $B(-6,-9)$ $C\left(\dfrac{3}{4},0\right)$

32. $\dfrac{3}{4}x + 2y = 0$ $A\left(-4,\dfrac{3}{2}\right)$ $B(0,0)$ $C\left(1,-\dfrac{3}{2}\right)$

For Problems 33–38, see Objective 3.

33. Find an ordered pair that satisfies the equation $x + y = 5$ by letting $x = 4$.

34. Find an ordered pair that satisfies the equation $x + y = 7$ by letting $x = 2$.

35. Find an ordered pair that satisfies the equation $2x + y = 9$ by letting $y = -1$.

36. Find an ordered pair that satisfies the equation $-4x - y = 5$ by letting $y = 7$.

37. Find an ordered pair that satisfies the equation $-3x + 2y = 15$ by letting $x = -3$.

38. Find an ordered pair that satisfies the equation $5x - 3y = 11$ by letting $y = 3$.

In Problems 39–52, use the equation to complete the table. Use the table to list some of the ordered pairs that satisfy the equation. See Objective 3.

39. $y = -x$

x	y	(x, y)
-3		
0		
1		

40. $y = x$

x	y	(x, y)
-4		
0		
2		

41. $y = -3x + 1$

x	y	(x, y)
-2		
-1		
4		

42. $y = 4x - 5$

x	y	(x, y)
-3		
1		
2		

43. $2x + y = 6$

x	y	(x, y)
-1		
2		
3		

44. $3x + 4y = 2$

x	y	(x, y)
-2		
2		
4		

45. $y = 6$

x	y	(x, y)
-4		
1		
12		

46. $x = 2$

x	y	(x, y)
	-4	
	0	
	8	

47. $x - 2y + 6 = 0$

x	y	(x, y)
1		
	1	
-2		

48. $2x + y - 4 = 0$

x	y	(x, y)
-1		
	-4	
	2	

49. $y = 5 + \dfrac{1}{2}x$

x	y	(x, y)
	7	
-4		
	2	

50. $y = 8 - \dfrac{1}{3}x$

x	y	(x, y)
	10	
9		
	27	

51. $\dfrac{x}{2} + \dfrac{y}{3} = -1$

x	y	(x, y)
0		
	0	
	-6	

52. $\dfrac{x}{5} - \dfrac{y}{2} = 1$

x	y	(x, y)
	0	
0		
-5		

In Problem 53–64, for each equation find the missing value in the ordered pair. See Objective 3.

53. $y = -3x - 10$ $A(\underline{\quad}, -16)$ $B(-3, \underline{\quad})$
   $C\left(\underline{\quad}, -9\right)$

54. $y = 5x - 4$ $A(-1, \underline{\quad})$ $B(\underline{\quad}, 31)$
   $C\left(-\dfrac{2}{5}, \underline{\quad}\right)$

55. $x = -\dfrac{1}{3}y$ $A(2, \underline{\quad})$ $B(\underline{\quad}, 0)$ $C\left(\underline{\quad}, -\dfrac{1}{2}\right)$

56. $y = \dfrac{2}{3}x$ $A\left(\underline{\quad}, -\dfrac{8}{3}\right)$ $B(0, \underline{\quad})$ $C\left(-\dfrac{5}{6}, \underline{\quad}\right)$

57. $x = 4$ $A(\underline{\quad}, -8)$ $B(\underline{\quad}, -19)$ $C(\underline{\quad}, 5)$

58. $y = -1$ $A(6, \underline{\quad})$ $B(-1, \underline{\quad})$ $C(0, \underline{\quad})$

59. $y = \dfrac{2}{3}x + 2$ $A(\underline{\quad}, 4)$ $B(-6, \underline{\quad})$ $C\left(\dfrac{1}{2}, \underline{\quad}\right)$

60. $y = -\dfrac{5}{4}x - 1$ $A(\underline{\quad}, -6)$ $B(-8, \underline{\quad})$
   $C\left(\underline{\quad}, -\dfrac{11}{6}\right)$

61. $\dfrac{1}{2}x - 3y = 2$ $A\left(-4, \underline{\quad}\right)$ $B(\underline{\quad}, -1)$
   $C\left(-\dfrac{2}{3}, \underline{\quad}\right)$

62. $\dfrac{1}{3}x + 2y = -1$ $A\left(-4, \underline{\quad}\right)$ $B\left(\underline{\quad}, -\dfrac{3}{4}\right)$
   $C\left(0, \underline{\quad}\right)$

63. $0.5x - 0.3y = 3.1$ $A(20, \underline{\quad})$ $B(\underline{\quad}, -17)$
   $C(2.6, \underline{\quad})$

64. $-1.7x + 0.2y = -5$ $A(\underline{\quad}, -110)$ $B(40, \underline{\quad})$
   $C(2.4, \underline{\quad})$

Applying the Concepts

65. Mail-Order CDs The cost of ordering CDs from a mail-order house is $9.95 per CD plus $4.95 for shipping and handling per order. The equation $C = 9.95n + 4.95$ represents the total cost, C, of ordering n CDs.

   (a) How much will it cost to order 2 CDs?
   (b) How much will it cost to order 5 CDs?
   (c) If you have $64.65 to spend, how many CDs can you order?
   (d) If (n, C) represents any ordered pair that satisfies $C = 9.95n + 4.95$, interpret the meaning of $(3, 34.8)$ in the context of this problem.

66. Taxi Ride The cost to take a taxi is $1.70 plus $2.00 per mile for each mile driven. The total cost, C, is given by the equation $C = 1.7 + 2m$, where m represents the total miles driven.

   (a) How much will it cost to take a taxi 5 miles?
   (b) How much will it cost to take a taxi 20 miles?
   (c) If you spent $32.70 on cab fare, how far was your trip?
   (d) If (m, C) represents any ordered pair that satisfies $C = 1.7 + 2m$, interpret the meaning of $(14, 29.7)$ in the context of this problem.

67. College Graduates An equation to approximate the percentage of the U.S. population 25 years of age or older with a bachelor's degree can be given by the model $P = 0.444n + 21.14$, where n is the number of years after 1990.

   (a) According to the model, what percentage of the U.S. population 25 years of age or older had a bachelor's degree in 1990 ($n = 0$)?
   (b) According to the model, what percentage of the U.S. population 25 years of age or older had a bachelor's degree in 2000 ($n = 10$)?
   (c) According to the model, what percentage of the U.S. population 25 years of age or older will have a bachelor's degree in 2020 ($n = 30$)?
   (d) In which year will 50% of the U.S. population 25 years of age or older have a bachelor's degree?
   (e) According to the model 100% of the U.S. population 25 years of age or older will have a bachelor's degree in 2168. Do you think this is reasonable? Why or why not?

68. Life Expectancy The model $A = 0.183n + 67.895$ is used to estimate the life expectancy A of residents of the United States born n years after 1950.

   (a) According to the model, what is the life expectancy for a person born in 1950?
   (b) According to the model, what is the life expectancy for a person born in 1980 ($n = 30$)?

(c) If the model holds true for future generations, what is the life expectancy for a person born in 2020?

(d) If a person has a life expectancy of 77 years, to the nearest year, when was the person born?

(e) Do you think life expectancy will continue to increase in the future? What could happen that would change this model?

In Problems 69–72, use the equation to complete the table. Use the table to list some of the ordered pairs that satisfy the equation.

69. $4a + 2b = -8$

a	b	(a, b)
2		
	-4	
	6	

70. $2r - 3s = 3$

r	s	(r, s)
	3	
	-1	
-3		

71. $\dfrac{2p}{5} + \dfrac{3q}{10} = 1$

p	q	(p, q)
0		
	0	
-10		

72. $\dfrac{4a}{3} + \dfrac{2b}{5} = -1$

a	b	(a, b)
	0	
	0	
	10	

Extending the Concepts

In Problems 73–78, determine the value of k so that the given ordered pair is a solution to the equation.

73. Find the value of k for which $(1, 2)$ satisfies $y = -2x + k$.

74. Find the value of k for which $(-1, 10)$ satisfies $y = 3x + k$.

75. Find the value of k for which $(2, 9)$ satisfies $7x - ky = -4$.

76. Find the value of k for which $(3, -1)$ satisfies $4x + ky = 9$.

77. Find the value of k for which $\left(-8, -\dfrac{5}{2}\right)$ satisfies $kx - 4y = 6$.

78. Find the value of k for which $\left(-9, \dfrac{1}{2}\right)$ satisfies $kx + 2y = -2$.

In Problems 79 and 80, use the equation to complete the table. Choose any value for x and then solve the resulting equation to find the corresponding value for y. Then plot these ordered pairs in a rectangular coordinate system. Connect the points and describe the figure.

79. $3x - 2y = -6$

x	y	(x, y)

80. $-x + y = 4$

x	y	(x, y)

In Problems 81–84, use the equation to complete the table. Then plot the points in a rectangular coordinate system.

81. $y = x^2 - 4$

x	y	(x, y)
-2		
-1		
0		
1		
2		

82. $y = -x^2 + 3$

x	y	(x, y)
-2		
-1		
0		
1		
2		

83. $y = -x^3 + 2$

x	y	(x, y)
-2		
-1		
0		
1		
2		

84. $y = 2x^3 - 1$

x	y	(x, y)
-2		
-1		
0		
1		
2		

Explaining the Concepts

85. Describe how the quadrants in the rectangular coordinate system are labeled and how you can determine the quadrant in which a point lies. Describe the characteristics of a point that lies on either the *x*- or *y*-axis.

86. Describe how to plot the ordered pair $(3, -5)$.

The Graphing Calculator

Graphing calculators can also create tables of values that satisfy an equation. To do this, we first solve the equation for *y*. For example, to obtain a table of values that satisfy the equation $2x - 3y = 12$ (Example 6), we solve for *y* as follows:

$$2x - 3y = 12$$

Subtract 2x from both sides: $-3y = -2x + 12$

Divide both sides by -3: $y = \dfrac{-2x + 12}{-3}$

Divide -3 into each term in the numerator: $y = \dfrac{-2x}{-3} + \dfrac{12}{-3}$

Simplify: $y = \dfrac{2}{3}x - 4$

We now enter the equation $y = \dfrac{2}{3}x - 4$ into the calculator and create the table shown.

X	Y1
-3	-6
-2	-5.333
-1	-4.667
0	-4
1	-3.333
2	-2.667
3	-2

Y1 ☐ (2/3)X-4

In Problems 87–94, use a graphing calculator to create a table of values that satisfy each equation. Have the table begin at -3 and increase by 1.

87. $y = 2x - 9$ **88.** $y = -3x + 8$ **89.** $y = -x + 8$

90. $y = 2x - 4$ **91.** $y + 2x = 13$ **92.** $y - x = -15$

93. $y = -6x^2 + 1$ **94.** $y = -x^2 + 3x$

3.2 Graphing Equations in Two Variables

Preparing for Graphing Equations in Two Variables

Before getting started, take the following readiness quiz. If you get a problem wrong, go back to the section cited and review the material.

P1. Solve: $4x = 24$ [Section 2.1, pp. 88–90]

P2. Solve: $-3y = 18$ [Section 2.1, pp. 88–90]

P3. Solve: $2x + 5 = 13$ [Section 2.2, pp. 94–96]

1   Graph a Line by Plotting Points

In the previous section, we found values of x and y that satisfy an equation. What does this mean? Well, it means that the ordered pair (x, y) is a point on the graph of the equation.

In Words

The graph of an equation is a geometric way of representing the set of all ordered pairs that make the equation a true statement. Think of the graph as a picture of the solution set.

DEFINITION

The **graph of an equation in two variables** x and y is the set of points whose coordinates, (x, y), in the xy-plane satisfy the equation.

But how do we obtain the graph of an equation? One method for graphing an equation is the **point-plotting method.**

EXAMPLE 1 How to Graph an Equation Using the Point-Plotting Method

Graph the equation $y = 2x - 3$ using the point-plotting method.

Step-by-Step Solution

Step 1: We find ordered pairs that satisfy the equation by choosing some values of x and using the equation to find the corresponding values of y. See Table 8.

Table 8		
x	**y**	**(x, y)**
-2	$y = 2(-2) - 3$ $= -4 - 3$ $= -7$	$(-2, -7)$
-1	$y = 2(-1) - 3$ $= -5$	$(-1, -5)$
0	$y = 2(0) - 3$ $= -3$	$(0, -3)$
1	$y = 2(1) - 3$ $= -1$	$(1, -1)$
2	$y = 2(2) - 3$ $= 1$	$(2, 1)$

Step 2: Plot the points whose coordinates, (x, y), were found in Step 1 in a rectangular coordinate system. See Figure 8.

Figure 8

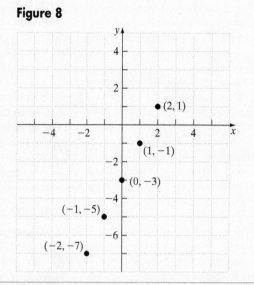

Step 3: Connect the points with a straight line. See Figure 9.

Figure 9

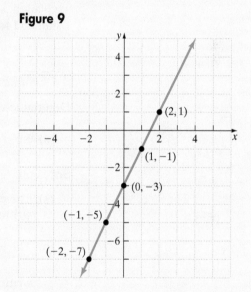

Work Smart

Remember, all coordinates of the points on the graph shown in Figure 9 satisfy the equation $y = 2x - 3$.

The graph of the equation shown in Figure 9 does not show all the points that satisfy the equation. For example, in Figure 9 the point $(5, 7)$ is a part of the graph of $y = 2x - 3$, but it is not shown. Since the graph of $y = 2x - 3$ could be extended as far as we please, we use arrows to indicate that the pattern shown continues. It is important to show enough of the graph so that anyone who is looking at it will "see" the rest of it as an obvious continuation of what is there. This is called a **complete graph.** For the remainder of the text, we will say "the point (x, y)" for short rather than "the point whose coordinates are (x, y)."

We summarize the steps for graphing an equation using the point-plotting method below.

GRAPHING AN EQUATION USING THE POINT-PLOTTING METHOD

Step 1: Find several ordered pairs that satisfy the equation.

Step 2: Plot the points found in Step 1 in a rectangular coordinate system.

Step 3: Connect the points with a smooth curve or line.

Quick ✔ *In Problems 1 and 2, draw a complete graph of each equation using point plotting.*

1. $y = 3x - 2$ **2.** $y = -4x + 8$

A question you may be asking yourself is, "How many points do I need to find before I can be sure that I have a complete graph?" The answer is that it depends on the type of equation you are graphing. In mathematics, we classify equations as different types. For example, the equation that we graphed in Example 1 is called a *linear equation*.

DEFINITION

A **linear equation in two variables** is an equation of the form

$$Ax + By = C$$

where A, B, and C are real numbers. A and B cannot both be 0. When a linear equation is written in the form $Ax + By = C$, we say that the linear equation is in **standard form.**

EXAMPLE 2 Identifying Linear Equations in Two Variables

Determine whether or not the equation is a linear equation in two variables.

(a) $3x - 4y = 9$ **(b)** $\frac{1}{2}x + \frac{2}{3}y = 4$ **(c)** $x^2 + 5y = 10$ **(d)** $-2y = 5$

Solution

(a) The equation $3x - 4y = 9$ is a linear equation in two variables because it is written in the form $Ax + By = C$ with $A = 3$, $B = -4$, and $C = 9$.

(b) The equation $\frac{1}{2}x + \frac{2}{3}y = 4$ is a linear equation in two variables because it is written in the form $Ax + By = C$ with $A = \frac{1}{2}$, $B = \frac{2}{3}$, and $C = 4$.

(c) The equation $x^2 + 5y = 10$ is not a linear equation because x is squared.

(d) The equation $-2y = 5$ is a linear equation in two variables because it is written in the form $Ax + By = C$ with $A = 0$, $B = -2$, and $C = 5$. ∎

Quick ✔

3. A(n) _____ equation is an equation of the form $Ax + By = C$, where A, B, and C are real numbers, and A and B are not both zero. Equations written in this form are said to be in _____ ____.

In Problems 4–6, determine whether or not the equation is a linear equation in two variables.

4. $4x - y = 12$ **5.** $5x - y^2 = 10$ **6.** $5x = 20$

Work Smart

When graphing a line, be sure to find three points—just to be safe!

For the remainder of the text, we will refer to linear equations in two variables as **linear equations.** The graph of a linear equation is a **line.** To graph a linear equation requires only two points; however, we recommend that you find a third point as a check.

EXAMPLE 3   Graphing a Linear Equation Using the Point-Plotting Method

Graph the linear equation $2x + y = 4$.

Solution

We need to find ordered pairs that satisfy the equation. Because the coefficient of y is 1, it is easier to choose values of x and find the corresponding values of y. We will determine the value of y for $x = -2, 0$, and 2. There is nothing magical about these choices. Any three different values of x will give us the results we want.

Work Smart

Choose values of x (or y) that make the algebra easy.

$x = -2$:	$x = 0$:	$x = 2$:
$2x + y = 4$	$2x + y = 4$	$2x + y = 4$
Let $x = -2$: $2(-2) + y = 4$	Let $x = 0$: $2(0) + y = 4$	Let $x = 2$: $2(2) + y = 4$
$-4 + y = 4$	$y = 4$	$4 + y = 4$
Add 4 to both sides: $y = 8$		Subtract 4 from both sides: $y = 0$

Table 9 summarizes the results. The ordered pairs $(-2, 8)$, $(0, 4)$, and $(2, 0)$ represent points that are on the graph of the equation. We plot these points in Figure 10(a). After connecting the points with a straight line we obtain the graph in Figure 10(b).

Table 9

x	y	(x, y)
-2	8	$(-2, 8)$
0	4	$(0, 4)$
2	0	$(2, 0)$

Figure 10

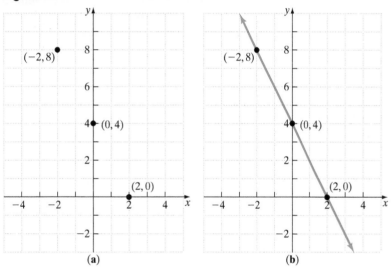

(a)   (b)

Quick ✔ *In Problems 7 and 8, graph each linear equation using the point-plotting method.*

7. $-3x + y = -6$ **8.** $2x + 3y = 12$

EXAMPLE 4   Cost of Renting a Car

Your favorite car-rental agency quotes you the cost of renting a car in Washington, D.C., as \$30 per day plus \$0.20 per mile. The linear equation $C = 0.20m + 30$ models the daily cost, where C represents total cost and m represents the number of miles that were traveled in one day.

(a) Complete Table 10 and use the results to list ordered pairs that satisfy the equation. Express answers rounded to the nearest penny.

(b) Graph the linear equation $C = 0.20m + 30$ using the points obtained in part **(a)**.

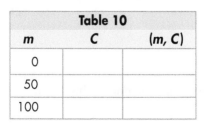

Table 10

m	C	(m, C)
0		
50		
100		

Solution

(a) The first entry in the table is $m = 0$. We substitute 0 for m and use the equation $C = 0.20m + 30$ to find C.

$$C = 0.20m + 30$$
$$m = 0: \quad C = 0.20(0) + 30$$
$$C = 30$$

Now substitute 50 for m and use the equation $C = 0.20m + 30$ to find C.

$$C = 0.20m + 30$$
$$m = 50: \quad C = 0.20(50) + 30$$
$$C = 40$$

Now substitute 100 for m and use the equation $C = 0.20m + 30$ to find C.

$$C = 0.20m + 30$$
$$m = 100: \quad C = 0.20(100) + 30$$
$$C = 50$$

Table 11		
m	C	(m, C)
0	30	$(0, 30)$
50	40	$(50, 40)$
100	50	$(100, 50)$

Table 11 shows the completed table.

The ordered pairs that satisfy the equation are $(0, 30)$, $(50, 40)$, and $(100, 50)$. The ordered pair $(50, 40)$ means if a car is driven 50 miles, the cost of renting the car for one day will be $40.

(b) Remember that m represents the number of miles driven, so we label the horizontal axis m. Also, recall that C represents the cost of renting the car, so we label the vertical axis C. When drawing the horizontal axis, we set the scale to 10, which means each tick mark represents 10 miles. We scale the vertical axis to 5, which means each tick mark represents 5 dollars. Scaling in this way makes it easier to plot the ordered pairs. We plot the points found in part (a) in the rectangular coordinate system and then draw the line. See Figure 11.

Figure 11

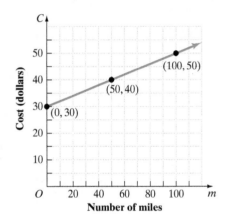

Quick ✔

9. Michelle sells computers. Her monthly salary is $3000 plus 8% of total sales. The linear equation $S = 0.08x + 3000$ models Michelle's monthly salary, S, where x represents her total sales in the month.

(a) Complete the table and use the results to list ordered pairs that satisfy the equation. Express answers rounded to the nearest penny.

x	S	(x, S)
0		
10,000		
25,000		

(b) Graph the linear equation $S = 0.08x + 3000$ using the points obtained in part **(a)**.

Figure 12
$2x + y = 4$

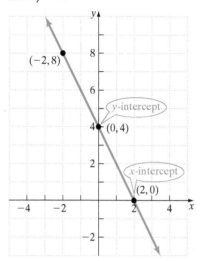

In Words

An x-intercept exists when $y = 0$.
A y-intercept exists when $x = 0$.

☐2 Graph a Line Using Intercepts

Intercepts should always be displayed in a complete graph.

> **DEFINITIONS**
>
> The **intercepts** are the points, if any, where a graph crosses or touches the coordinate axes. The x-coordinate of a point at which the graph crosses or touches the x-axis is an **x-intercept,** and the y-coordinate of a point at which the graph crosses or touches the y-axis is a **y-intercept.**

See Figure 12 for an illustration. The graph in Figure 12 is the graph obtained in Example 3.

EXAMPLE 5 Finding Intercepts from a Graph

Find the intercepts of the graphs shown in Figures 13(a) and 13(b). What are the x-intercepts? What are the y-intercepts?

Figure 13

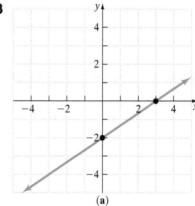
(a)

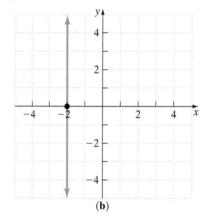
(b)

Solution

(a) The intercepts of the graph in Figure 13(a) are the points $(0, -2)$ and $(3, 0)$. The x-intercept is 3. The y-intercept is -2.

(b) The intercept of the graph in Figure 13(b) is the point $(-2, 0)$. The x-intercept is -2. There are no y-intercepts. ▪

   In Example 5, you should notice the following: If we do not specify the type of intercept (x-intercept versus y-intercept), we report the intercept as an ordered pair. However, if we specify the type of intercept, then we only need report the coordinate of the intercept. For example, we would say $(4, 0)$ is an intercept, while we would say 4 is an x-intercept (since it is understood that the y-coordinate is 0 for an x-intercept).

Quick ✔

10. The _____ are the points, if any, where a graph crosses or touches the coordinate axes.

In Problems 11 and 12, find the intercepts of the graph shown in the figure. What are the x-intercepts? What are the y-intercepts?

11.

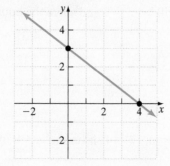

12.

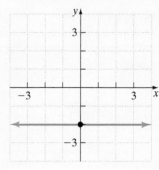

Now we will explain how to find the intercepts algebraically. From Figure 12 it should be clear that an *x*-intercept exists when the value of *y* is 0 and that a *y*-intercept exists when the value of *x* is 0. This leads to the following procedure for finding intercepts.

Work Smart

Every point on the *x*-axis has a *y*-coordinate of 0. That's why we set $y = 0$ to find an *x*-intercept. Likewise, every point on the *y*-axis has an *x*-coordinate of 0. That's why we set $x = 0$ to find a *y*-intercept.

PROCEDURE FOR FINDING INTERCEPTS

1. To find the *x*-intercept(s), if any, of the graph of an equation, let $y = 0$ in the equation and solve for *x*.
2. To find the *y*-intercept(s), if any, of the graph of an equation, let $x = 0$ in the equation and solve for *y*.

We can use the intercepts to graph a line. Because this method for graphing a linear equation results in only two points, we find a third point so that we can check our work.

EXAMPLE 6 How to Graph a Linear Equation by Finding Its Intercepts

Graph the linear equation $4x - 3y = 24$ by finding its intercepts.

Step-by-Step Solution

Step 1: Find the *y*-intercept by letting $x = 0$ and solving the equation for *y*.

$$4x - 3y = 24$$
$$\text{Let } x = 0: \quad 4(0) - 3y = 24$$
$$0 - 3y = 24$$
$$-3y = 24$$
$$\text{Divide both sides by } -3: \quad y = -8$$

The *y*-intercept is -8, so the point $(0, -8)$ is on the graph of the equation.

Step 2: Find the *x*-intercept by letting $y = 0$ and solving the equation for *x*.

$$4x - 3y = 24$$
$$\text{Let } y = 0: \quad 4x - 3(0) = 24$$
$$4x - 0 = 24$$
$$4x = 24$$
$$\text{Divide both sides by } 4: \quad x = 6$$

The *x*-intercept is 6, so the point $(6, 0)$ is on the graph of the equation.

Step 3: Find one additional point on the graph by choosing any value of *x* that is convenient and solving the equation for *y*.

We will let $x = 3$ and solve the equation $4x - 3y = 24$ for *y*.

$$\text{Let } x = 3: \quad 4(3) - 3y = 24$$
$$12 - 3y = 24$$
$$\text{Subtract 12 from both sides:} \quad -3y = 12$$
$$\text{Divide both sides by } -3: \quad y = -4$$

The point $(3, -4)$ is on the graph of the equation.

Step 4: Plot the points found in Steps 1–3 and draw in the line.

We plot the points $(0, -8)$, $(6, 0)$, and $(3, -4)$. Connect the points with a straight line and obtain the graph in Figure 14.

Figure 14
$4x - 3y = 24$

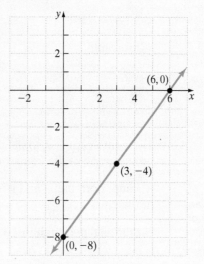

EXAMPLE 7 **Graphing a Linear Equation by Finding Its Intercepts**

Graph the linear equation $\frac{1}{2}x - 2y = 3$ by finding its intercepts.

Solution

x-intercept:

$$\frac{1}{2}x - 2y = 3$$

Let $y = 0$: $\frac{1}{2}x - 2(0) = 3$

$$\frac{1}{2}x = 3$$

Multiply both sides by 2: $x = 6$

y-intercept:

$$\frac{1}{2}x - 2y = 3$$

Let $x = 0$: $\frac{1}{2}(0) - 2y = 3$

$$-2y = 3$$

Divide both sides by -2: $y = -\frac{3}{2}$

Additional point (choose $x = 2$):

$$\frac{1}{2}x - 2y = 3$$

Let $x = 2$: $\frac{1}{2}(2) - 2y = 3$

$$1 - 2y = 3$$

Subtract 1 from both sides: $-2y = 2$
Divide both sides by -2: $y = -1$

Plot the points $(6, 0)$, $\left(0, -\frac{3}{2}\right)$, and $(2, -1)$. Connect the points with a straight line. See Figure 15.

Figure 15
$\frac{1}{2}x - 2y = 3$

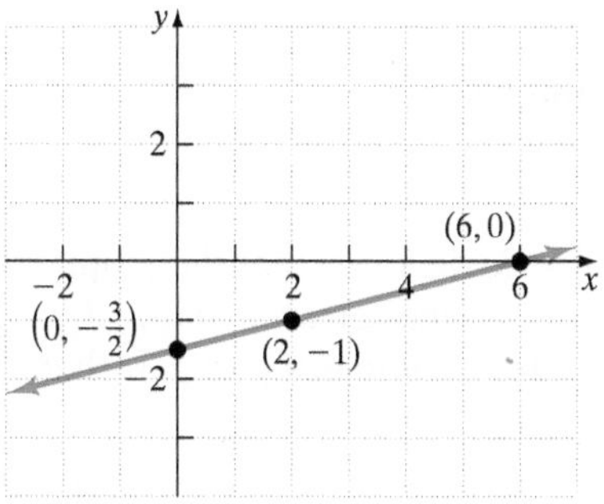

Quick ✔

13. *True or False:* To find the *y*-intercept(s), if any, of the graph of an equation, let $y = 0$ in the equation and solve for *x*.

In Problems 14–16, graph each linear equation by finding its intercepts.

14. $x + y = 3$ **15.** $2x - 5y = 20$ **16.** $\frac{3}{2}x - 2y = 9$

EXAMPLE 8 Graphing a Linear Equation of the Form $Ax + By = 0$

Graph the linear equation $2x + 3y = 0$ by finding its intercepts.

Solution

x-intercept:

$$2x + 3y = 0$$
Let $y = 0$: $\quad 2x + 3(0) = 0$
$$2x + 0 = 0$$
Divide both sides by 2: $\qquad x = 0$

The x-intercept is 0, so the point $(0, 0)$ is on the graph of the equation.

y-intercept:

$$2x + 3y = 0$$
Let $x = 0$: $\quad 2(0) + 3y = 0$
$$3y = 0$$
Divide both sides by 3: $\qquad y = 0$

The y-intercept is 0, so the point $(0, 0)$ is on the graph of the equation.

Because both the x- and y-intercepts are 0, we find *two* additional points on the graph of the equation.

Additional point (choose $x = 3$):

$$2x + 3y = 0$$
Let $x = 3$: $\quad 2(3) + 3y = 0$
$$6 + 3y = 0$$
Subtract 6 from both sides: $\quad 3y = -6$
Divide both sides by 3: $\qquad y = -2$

Additional point (choose $x = -3$):

$$2x + 3y = 0$$
Let $x = -3$: $\quad 2(-3) + 3y = 0$
$$-6 + 3y = 0$$
Add 6 to both sides: $\quad 3y = 6$
Divide both sides by 2: $\qquad y = 2$

The points $(3, -2)$ and $(-3, 2)$ are on the graph of the equation. We plot the points $(0, 0)$, $(-3, 2)$, and $(3, -2)$. Connect the points with a straight line and obtain the graph in Figure 16.

Work Smart

Linear equations of the form $Ax + By = 0$, where $A \neq 0$ and $B \neq 0$ have only one intercept at $(0, 0)$, so two additional points should be plotted to obtain the graph.

Figure 16
$2x + 3y = 0$

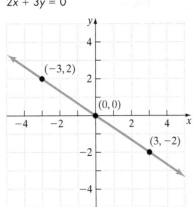

Quick ✔ *In Problems 17 and 18, graph the equation by finding its intercepts.*

17. $y = \dfrac{1}{2}x$

18. $4x + y = 0$

3 Graph Vertical and Horizontal Lines

In the equation of a line, $Ax + By = C$, we said that A and B cannot both be zero. But what if $A = 0$ or $B = 0$? We find that this leads to special types of lines called *vertical lines* (when $B = 0$) and *horizontal lines* (when $A = 0$).

EXAMPLE 9 Graphing a Vertical Line

Graph the equation $x = 3$ using the point-plotting method.

Solution

Because the equation $x = 3$ can be written as $1x + 0y = 3$, we know that the graph is a line. When you look at the equation $x = 3$, notice that no matter what value of y we choose, the corresponding value of x is going to be 3. For example, if $y = -1$, then

$$1x + 0(-1) = 3$$
$$x = 3$$

See Table 12 for other choices for y. We see that the points $(3, -2)$, $(3, -1)$, $(3, 0)$, $(3, 1)$, and $(3, 2)$ are all points on the line. See Figure 17.

	Table 12	
x	**y**	**(x, y)**
3	−2	(3, −2)
3	−1	(3, −1)
3	0	(3, 0)
3	1	(3, 1)
3	2	(3, 2)

Figure 17
$x = 3$

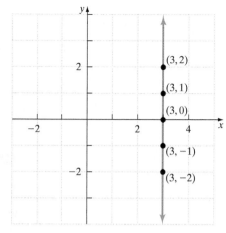

Based on the results of Example 9, we can write a definition of a *vertical line:*

DEFINITION EQUATION OF A VERTICAL LINE

A **vertical line** is given by an equation of the form

$$x = a$$

where a is the x-intercept.

Now let's look at equations that lead to graphs that are horizontal lines.

EXAMPLE 10 Graphing a Horizontal Line

Graph the equation $y = -2$ using the point-plotting method.

Solution

Because the equation $y = -2$ can be written as $0x + 1y = -2$, we know that the graph is a line. In looking at the equation $y = -2$, notice that no matter what value of x we choose, the corresponding value of y is going to be -2. For example, if $x = -2$, then

$$0(-2) + 1y = -2$$
$$y = -2$$

See Table 13 for other choices of x. Therefore, the points $(-2, -2)$, $(-1, -2)$, $(0, -2)$, $(1, -2)$, and $(2, -2)$ are all points on the line. See Figure 18.

	Table 13	
x	**y**	**(x, y)**
−2	−2	(−2, −2)
−1	−2	(−1, −2)
0	−2	(0, −2)
1	−2	(1, −2)
2	−2	(2, −2)

Figure 18
$y = -2$

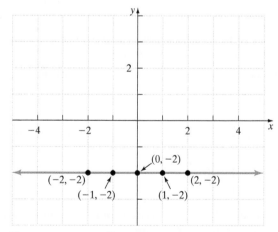

Based on the results of Example 10, we can generalize:

DEFINITION EQUATION OF A HORIZONTAL LINE

A **horizontal line** is given by an equation of the form

$$y = b$$

where b is the y-intercept.

Quick ✔ *In Problems 19 and 20, graph each equation.*

19. $x = -5$

20. $y = -4$

We covered a lot of material in this section. We present a summary below to help you organize the information presented.

SUMMARY INTERCEPTS AND EQUATIONS OF LINES

Topic	Comments
Intercepts: Points where the graph crosses or touches a coordinate axis.	Intercepts need to be shown for a graph to be complete.
x-intercept: Point where the graph crosses or touches the *x*-axis. Found by letting $y = 0$ in the equation.	
y-intercept: Point where the graph crosses or touches the *y*-axis. Found by letting $x = 0$ in the equation.	
Standard Form of an Equation of a Line: $Ax + By = C$, where A and B are not both zero	Can be graphed using point-plotting or intercepts.
Equation of a Vertical Line: $x = a$	Graph is a vertical line whose *x*-intercept is *a*.
Equation of a Horizontal Line: $y = b$	Graph is a horizontal line whose *y*-intercept is *b*.

3.2 EXERCISES

MyMathLab Powered by CourseCompass™ and MathXL®

PRACTICE   WATCH   DOWNLOAD   READ   REVIEW

1–20. *are the* Quick ✔*s that follow each* EXAMPLE

Building Skills

In Problems 21–28, determine whether or not the equation is a linear equation in two variables. See Objective 1.

21. $2x - 5y = 10$

22. $y^2 = 2x + 3$

23. $x^2 + y = 1$

24. $y - 2x = 9$

25. $y = \dfrac{4}{x}$

26. $x - 8 = 0$

27. $y - 1 = 0$

28. $y = -\dfrac{2}{x}$

In Problems 29–46, graph each linear equation using the point-plotting method. See Objective 1.

29. $y = 2x$

30. $y = 3x$

31. $y = 4x - 2$

32. $y = -3x - 1$

33. $y = -2x + 5$

34. $y = x - 6$

35. $x + y = 5$

36. $x - y = 6$

37. $-2x + y = 6$

38. $5x - 2y = -10$

39. $4x - 2y = -8$

40. $x + 3y = 6$

41. $x = -4y$

42. $x = \dfrac{1}{2}y$

43. $y + 7 = 0$

44. $x - 6 = 0$

45. $y - 2 = 3(x + 1)$

46. $y + 3 = -2(x - 2)$

In Problems 47–54, find the intercepts of each graph. See Objective 2.

47.

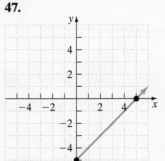

48.

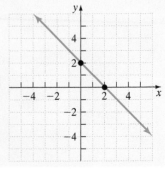

49.
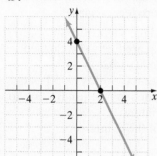

50.
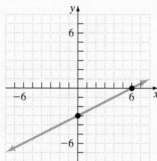

51.
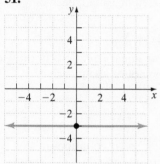

52.
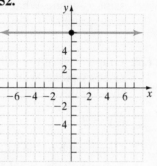

53.
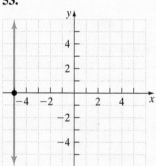

54.
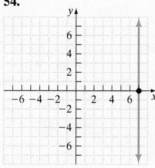

In Problems 55–66, find the intercepts of each equation.
See Objective 2.

 55. $2x + 3y = -12$ **56.** $3x - 5y = 30$

57. $x = -6y$ **58.** $y = 10x$

59. $y = x - 5$ **60.** $y = -x + 7$

61. $\dfrac{x}{6} + \dfrac{y}{8} = 1$ **62.** $\dfrac{x}{2} - \dfrac{y}{8} = 1$

63. $x = 4$ **64.** $y = 6$

65. $y + 2 = 0$ **66.** $x + 8 = 0$

In Problems 67–82, graph each linear equation by finding its inter-
cepts. See Objective 2.

 67. $3x + 6y = 18$ **68.** $3x - 5y = 15$

69. $-x + 5y = 15$ **70.** $-2x + y = 14$

71. $\dfrac{1}{2}x = y + 3$ **72.** $\dfrac{4}{3}x = -y + 1$

73. $9x - 2y = 0$ **74.** $\dfrac{1}{3}x - y = 0$

 75. $y = -\dfrac{1}{2}x + 3$ **76.** $y = \dfrac{2}{3}x - 3$

77. $\dfrac{1}{3}y + 2 = 2x$ **78.** $\dfrac{1}{2}x - 3 = 3y$

79. $\dfrac{x}{2} + \dfrac{y}{3} = 1$ **80.** $\dfrac{y}{4} - \dfrac{x}{3} = 1$

81. $4y - 2x + 1 = 0$ **82.** $2y - 3x + 2 = 0$

In Problems 83–90, graph each horizontal or vertical line.
See Objective 3.

 83. $x = 5$ **84.** $x = -7$

 85. $y = -6$ **86.** $y = 2$

87. $y - 12 = 0$ **88.** $y + 3 = 0$

89. $3x - 5 = 0$ **90.** $2x - 7 = 0$

Mixed Practice

In Problems 91–102, graph each linear equation by the point-
plotting method or by finding intercepts.

91. $y = 2x - 5$ **92.** $y = -3x + 2$

93. $y = -5$ **94.** $x = 2$

95. $2x + 5y = -20$ **96.** $3x - 4y = 12$

97. $2x = -6y + 4$ **98.** $5x = 3y - 10$

99. $x - 3 = 0$ **100.** $y + 4 = 0$

101. $3y - 12 = 0$ **102.** $-4x + 8 = 0$

103. If $(3, y)$ is a point on the graph of $4x + 3y = 18$,
find y.

104. If $(-4, y)$ is a point on the graph of $3x - 2y = 10$,
find y.

105. If $(x, -2)$ is a point on the graph of $3x + 5y = 11$,
find x.

106. If $(x, -3)$ is a point on the graph of $4x - 7y = 19$,
find x.

Applying the Concepts

107. Plot the points $(3, 5)$ and $(-2, 5)$ and draw a line
through the points. What is the equation of this line?

108. Plot the points $(-1, 2)$ and $(5, 2)$ and draw a line
through the points. What is the equation of this line?

109. Plot the points $(-2, -4)$ and $(-2, 1)$ and draw a line
through the points. What is the equation of this line?

110. Plot the points $(3, -1)$ and $(3, 2)$ and draw a line
through the points. What is the equation of this line?

In Problems 111–114, find the equation of each line.

111.

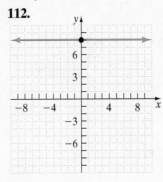

112.

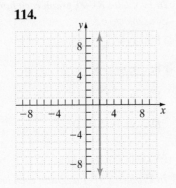

113.

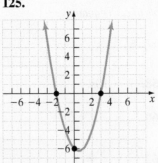

114.

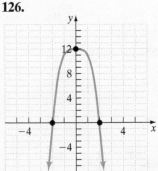

115. Create a set of ordered pairs in which the *x*-coordinate is twice the *y*-coordinate. What is the equation of this line?

116. Create a set of ordered pairs in which the *y*-coordinate is twice the *x*-coordinate. What is the equation of this line?

117. Create a set of ordered pairs in which the *y*-coordinate is 2 more than the *x*-coordinate. What is the equation of this line?

118. Create a set of ordered pairs in which the *x*-coordinate is 3 less than the *y*-coordinate. What is the equation of this line?

119. Calculating Wages Marta earns $500 per week plus $100 in commission for every car she sells. The linear equation that calculates her weekly earnings is $E = 100n + 500$, where *E* represents her weekly earnings in dollars and *n* represents the number of cars she sold during the week.

  (a) Create a set of ordered pairs (n, E) if, in three consecutive weeks, she sold 0 cars, 4 cars, and 10 cars.

  (b) Graph the linear equation $E = 100n + 500$ using the ordered pairs obtained in part **(a)**. Be sure to label the axes appropriately.

  (c) Explain the meaning of the *E*-intercept.

120. Carpet Cleaning Harry's Carpet Cleaning charges a $50 service charge plus $0.10 for each square foot of carpeting to be cleaned. The linear equation that calculates the total cost to clean a carpet is

$C = 0.1f + 50$, where *C* is the total cost in dollars and *f* is the number of square feet of carpet.

  (a) Create a set of ordered pairs (f, C) for the following number of square feet to be cleaned: 1000 sq ft, 2000 sq ft, 2500 sq ft.

  (b) Graph the linear equation $C = 0.1f + 50$ using the ordered pairs obtained in part **(a)**. Be sure to label the axes appropriately.

  (c) Explain the meaning of the *C*-intercept.

Extending the Concepts

121. Graph each of the following linear equations in the same *xy*-plane. What do you notice about each of these graphs?

$$y = 2x - 1 \qquad y = 2x + 3 \qquad 2x - y = 5$$

122. Graph each of the following linear equations in the same *xy*-plane. What do you notice about each of these graphs?

$$y = 3x + 2 \qquad 6x - 2y = -4 \qquad x = \frac{1}{3}y - \frac{2}{3}$$

123. Graph each of the following linear equations in the same *xy*-plane. What statement can you make about the steepness of the line as the coefficient of *x* gets larger?

$$y = x \qquad y = 2x \qquad y = 10x$$

124. Graph each of the following linear equations in the same *xy*-plane. What statement can you make about the steepness of the line as the coefficient of *x* gets smaller?

$$y = x + 2 \qquad y = \frac{1}{2}x + 2 \qquad y = \frac{1}{8}x + 2$$

In Problems 125–128, find the intercepts of each graph.

125.

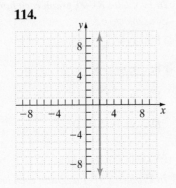

126.

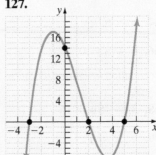

127.

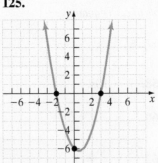

128.

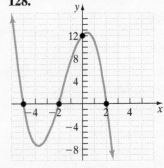

Explaining the Concepts

129. Explain what the graph of an equation represents.

130. What is meant by a complete graph?

131. How many points are required to graph a line? Explain your reasoning and why you might include additional point(s) when graphing a line.

132. Explain how to use the intercepts to graph the equation $Ax + By = C$, where A, B, and C are not equal to zero. Explain how to graph the same equation when C is equal to zero. Can you use the same techniques for both equations? Why or why not?

The Graphing Calculator

Graphing calculators can graph equations. In fact, graphing calculators also use the point-plotting method to obtain the graph by choosing 95 values of x and using the equation to find the corresponding value of y. As with creating tables, we first solve the equation for y. For example, to obtain a table of values that satisfy the equation $2x - 3y = 12$ (Example 6 from Section 3.1), we must

solve for y and we obtain $y = \dfrac{2}{3}x - 4$. We enter the equation $y = \dfrac{2}{3}x - 4$ into the calculator and create the graph shown below.

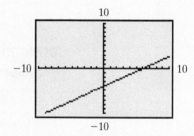

In Problems 133–138, use a graphing calculator to graph each equation.

133. $y = 2x - 9$ **134.** $y = -3x + 8$

135. $y + 2x = 13$ **136.** $y - x = -15$

137. $y = -6x^2 + 1$ **138.** $y = -x^2 + 3x$

3.3 Slope

OBJECTIVES

- 1 Find the Slope of a Line Given Two Points
- 2 Find the Slope of Vertical and Horizontal Lines
- 3 Graph a Line Using Its Slope and a Point on the Line
- 4 Work with Applications of Slope

Preparing for Slope

Before getting started, take the following readiness quiz. If you get a problem wrong, go back to the section cited and review the material.

P1. Evaluate: $\dfrac{5 - 2}{8 - 7}$ [Section 1.7, p. 62]

P2. Evaluate: $\dfrac{3 - 7}{9 - 3}$ [Section 1.7, p. 62]

P3. Evaluate: $\dfrac{-3 - 4}{6 - (-1)}$ [Section 1.7, p. 62]

Figure 19

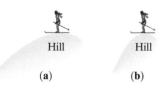

Pretend you are on snow skis for the first time in your life. The ski resort that you are visiting has two hills available to beginning skiers. The profile of each hill is shown in Figure 19. Which hill would you prefer to go down? Why?

It is clear from the figure that the hill in Figure 19(a) is not as steep as the hill in Figure 19(b). One of the things that mathematicians like to do is give numerical descriptions to situations such as the steepness of a hill. Measuring the steepness of each hill allows for them to be compared more easily. The numerical measure that we use to describe the steepness of a hill is its *slope*.

1 Find the Slope of a Line Given Two Points

Consider the staircase drawn in Figure 20(a) on the next page. If we draw a line through the top of each riser on the staircase (in blue), we can see that each step contains exactly the same horizontal change (or **run**) and the same vertical change (or **rise**). We define *slope* in terms of the rise and run.

Preparing for...Answers **P1.** 3 **P2.** $-\dfrac{2}{3}$
P3. -1

Figure 20

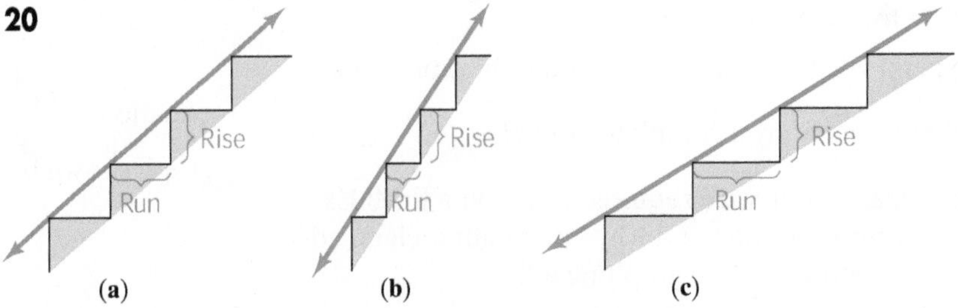

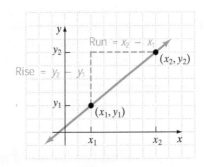

(a)   (b)   (c)

DEFINITION

The **slope** of a line, denoted by the letter m, is the ratio of the rise to the run. That is,

$$\text{Slope} = m = \frac{\text{Rise}}{\text{Run}}$$

The accepted symbol for the slope of a line is m. It comes from the French word *monter*, which means "to go up, ascend, or climb." Slope is a numerical measure of the steepness of the line. For example, if the run is decreased and the rise remains the same, then the staircase becomes steeper. See Figure 20(b). If the run is increased and the rise remains the same, then the staircase becomes less steep. See Figure 20(c).

Suppose that the staircase in Figure 20(a) has a rise of 6 inches and a run of 6 inches. Then the slope of the line is

$$m = \frac{\text{rise}}{\text{run}} = \frac{6 \text{ inches}}{6 \text{ inches}} = 1$$

If the rise of the stair is increased to 9 inches, then the slope of the line is

$$m = \frac{\text{rise}}{\text{run}} = \frac{9 \text{ inches}}{6 \text{ inches}} = \frac{3}{2}$$

The main idea is the steeper the line, the larger the slope. We can define the slope of a line using rectangular coordinates.

Work Smart

The subscripts 1 and 2, on x_1, x_2, y_1, and y_2 do not represent a computation (as superscripts do in x^2). Instead, they are used to indicate that the values of the variable x_1 may be different from x_2, and y_1 may be different from y_2.

DEFINITION

If $x_1 \neq x_2$, the **slope m** of the line containing the points (x_1, y_1) and (x_2, y_2) is defined by the formula

$$m = \frac{y_2 - y_1}{x_2 - x_1} \qquad x_1 \neq x_2$$

Figure 21 provides an illustration of the slope of a line.

Figure 21

From Figure 21 we can see that the slope m of a line may be viewed as

$$m = \frac{\text{rise}}{\text{run}} = \frac{y_2 - y_1}{x_2 - x_1}$$

In Words

Slope is rise over run, or the change in y
divided by the change in x.

We can also write the slope m of a line as

$$m = \frac{y_2 - y_1}{x_2 - x_1} = \frac{\text{change in } y}{\text{change in } x} = \frac{\Delta y}{\Delta x}$$

The symbol Δ is the Greek letter "delta." In mathematics, we read the symbol Δ as "change in." So the notation $\dfrac{\Delta y}{\Delta x}$ is read "change in y divided by change in x." The symbol Δ comes from the first letter of the Greek word *diaphora*, which means "difference."

EXAMPLE 1 How to Find the Slope of a Line

Find the slope of the line drawn in Figure 22.

Figure 22

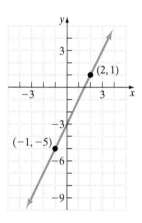

Step-by-Step Solution

Step 1: Let one of the points be (x_1, y_1) and the other point be (x_2, y_2).

Let's say that $(x_1, y_1) = (-1, -5)$ and $(x_2, y_2) = (2, 1)$.

Step 2: Find the slope by evaluating

$$m = \frac{y_2 - y_1}{x_2 - x_1}$$

$$m = \frac{y_2 - y_1}{x_2 - x_1}$$

$$x_1 = -1, y_1 = -5; \qquad = \frac{1 - (-5)}{2 - (-1)}$$
$$x_2 = 2, y_2 = 1:$$

$$= \frac{6}{3}$$

$$m = 2$$

Figure 23

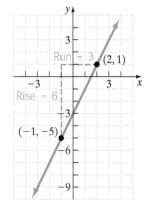

Work Smart

It doesn't matter which point is called (x_1, y_1) and which is called (x_2, y_2). The answer will be the same. In Example 1, if we let $(x_1, y_1) = (2, 1)$ and $(x_2, y_2) = (-1, -5)$, we obtain

$$m = \frac{y_2 - y_1}{x_2 - x_1} = \frac{-5 - 1}{-1 - 2} = \frac{-6}{-3} = 2$$

Remember—we said that the slope of the line can be thought of as "rise divided by run." This description of the slope of a line is illustrated in Figure 23.

We interpret the slope of the line drawn in Figure 23 as follows: "The value of y will increase by 6 units whenever x increases by 3 units." Or because $\dfrac{6}{3} = 2 = \dfrac{2}{1}$ "the value of y will increase by 2 units whenever x increases by 1 unit." Both interpretations are acceptable.

EXAMPLE 2 Finding and Interpreting the Slope of a Line

Plot the points $(-1, 3)$ and $(2, -2)$ in a rectangular coordinate system. Then draw a line through the two points. Find and interpret the slope of the line.

Solution

We plot the points $(x_1, y_1) = (-1, 3)$ and $(x_2, y_2) = (2, -2)$ in the rectangular coordinate system and draw a line through the two points. See Figure 24. The slope of the line drawn in Figure 24 is

$$m = \frac{y_2 - y_1}{x_2 - x_1} = \frac{-2 - 3}{2 - (-1)}$$

$$= \frac{-5}{3}$$

$$= -\frac{5}{3}$$

Figure 24

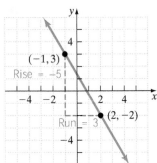

You can interpret a slope of $-\frac{5}{3} = \frac{-5}{3}$ this way: The value of y will go down 5 units whenever x increases by 3 units. Because $-\frac{5}{3} = \frac{5}{-3} = \frac{\text{rise}}{\text{run}}$, a second interpretation is as follows: The value of y will increase by 5 units whenever x decreases by 3 units. ∎

Notice that the line drawn in Figure 23 goes up and to the right and the slope is positive, while the line drawn in Figure 24 goes down and to the right and slope is negative. In general, a line that goes down and to the right will have negative slope and a line that goes up and to the right will have positive slope. We illustrate this idea in Figure 25.

Figure 25

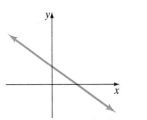

Line goes down and to the right: negative slope

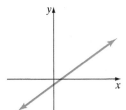

Line goes up and to the right: positive slope

Quick ✔

1. If the run of a line is 10 and its rise is 6, then its slope is __.

2. *True or False:* If $P = (x_1, y_1)$ and $Q = (x_2, y_2)$ are two distinct points with $y_1 \neq y_2$, the slope m of the line that contains points P and Q is defined by the formula $m = \frac{x_2 - x_1}{y_2 - y_1}$.

3. *True or False:* If the slope of a line is $\frac{3}{2}$, then y will increase by 3 units when x increases by 2 units.

4. If the graph of a line goes up as you move to the right, then the slope of this line must be _____.

In Problems 5 and 6, plot the points in a rectangular coordinate system. Then draw a line through the two points. Find and interpret the slope of the line containing the points.

5. $(0, 2)$ and $(2, 10)$ 6. $(-2, 2)$ and $(3, -7)$

2 Find the Slope of Vertical and Horizontal Lines

Did you notice in the definition of slope, $m = \dfrac{y_2 - y_1}{x_2 - x_1}$, we have the restriction that $x_1 \neq x_2$? This means that the formula does not apply if the x-coordinates of the two points are the same. Why? Let's look at the following example.

EXAMPLE 3 The Slope of a Vertical Line

Plot the points $(2, -1)$ and $(2, 3)$ in a rectangular coordinate system. Then draw a line through the two points. Find and interpret the slope of the line.

Solution

We plot the points $(x_1, y_1) = (2, -1)$ and $(x_2, y_2) = (2, 3)$ in the rectangular coordinate system and draw a line through the two points. See Figure 26. The slope of the line drawn in Figure 26 is

$$m = \frac{y_2 - y_1}{x_2 - x_1} = \frac{3 - (-1)}{2 - 2}$$
$$= \frac{4}{0}$$

Because division by 0 is undefined, we say that the slope of the line is undefined. When y increases by 4, there is no change in x. ■

Let's generalize the results of Example 3. Let (x_1, y_1) and (x_2, y_2) be two distinct points. If $x_1 = x_2$, then we have a **vertical line** whose slope m is **undefined** (since this results in division by 0). Figure 27 illustrates a vertical line.

Figure 26

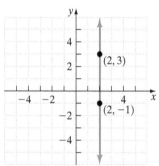

Figure 27

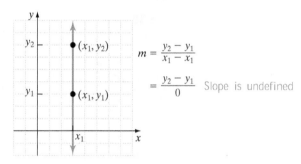

Okay, but what if $y_1 = y_2$?

EXAMPLE 4 The Slope of a Horizontal Line

Plot the points $(-2, 4)$ and $(3, 4)$ in a rectangular coordinate system. Then draw a line through the two points. Find and interpret the slope of the line.

Solution

We plot the points $(x_1, y_1) = (-2, 4)$ and $(x_2, y_2) = (3, 4)$ in the rectangular coordinate system and draw a line through the two points. See Figure 28. The slope of the line drawn in Figure 28 is

$$m = \frac{y_2 - y_1}{x_2 - x_1} = \frac{4 - 4}{3 - (-2)}$$
$$= \frac{0}{5}$$
$$= 0$$

Figure 28

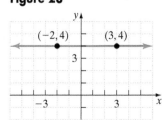

The slope of the line is 0. A slope of 0 can be interpreted as: There is no change in y when x increases by 1 unit. ■

Let's generalize the results of Example 4. Let (x_1, y_1) and (x_2, y_2) be two distinct points. If $y_1 = y_2$, then we have a **horizontal line** whose slope m is 0. Figure 29 illustrates a horizontal line.

Figure 29

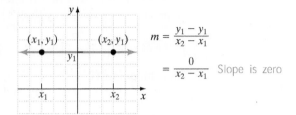

$$m = \frac{y_1 - y_1}{x_2 - x_1}$$

$$= \frac{0}{x_2 - x_1} \quad \text{Slope is zero}$$

Quick ✔

7. The slope of a horizontal line is _____ , while the slope of a vertical line is

_____ .

In Problems 8 and 9, plot the given points in a rectangular coordinate system. Then draw a line through the two points. Find and interpret the slope of the line.

8. $(2, 5)$ and $(2, -1)$ **9.** $(2, 5)$ and $(6, 5)$

SUMMARY THE SLOPE OF A LINE

Figure 30 illustrates the four possibilities for the slope of a line. Remember, just as we read a text from left to right, we also read graphs from left to right.

Figure 30

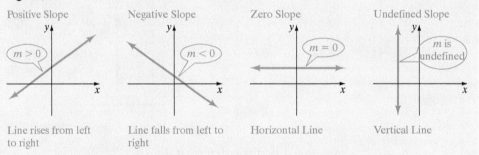

Positive Slope | Negative Slope | Zero Slope | Undefined Slope

$m > 0$ | $m < 0$ | $m = 0$ | m is undefined

Line rises from left to right | Line falls from left to right | Horizontal Line | Vertical Line

⌐3⌐ Graph a Line Using Its Slope and a Point on the Line

We now illustrate how to use the slope of a line to graph lines.

EXAMPLE 5 Graphing a Line Given a Point and Its Slope

Draw a graph of the line that contains the point $(1, 3)$ and has a slope of 2.

Solution

Because slope $= \dfrac{\text{rise}}{\text{run}}$, we have that $2 = \dfrac{2}{1} = \dfrac{\text{rise}}{\text{run}}$. This means that y will increase by 2 units (the rise), when x increases by 1 unit (the run). So if we start at $(1, 3)$ and move 2 units up and then 1 unit to the right, we end up at the point $(2, 5)$. We then draw a line through the points $(1, 3)$ and $(2, 5)$ to obtain the graph of the line. See Figure 31.

Figure 31

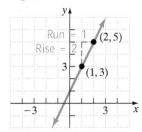

EXAMPLE 6 Graphing a Line Given a Point and Its Slope

Draw a graph of the line that contains the point $(1, 3)$ and has a slope of $-\dfrac{2}{3}$.

Solution

Because slope $= \dfrac{\text{rise}}{\text{run}}$, we have $-\dfrac{2}{3} = \dfrac{-2}{3} = \dfrac{\text{rise}}{\text{run}}$.

Figure 32

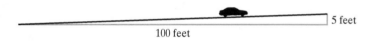

This means that y will decrease by 2 units when x increases by 3 units. If we start at $(1, 3)$ and move 2 units down and then 3 units to the right, we end up at the point $(4, 1)$. We then draw a line through the points $(1, 3)$ and $(4, 1)$ to obtain the graph of the line. See Figure 32.

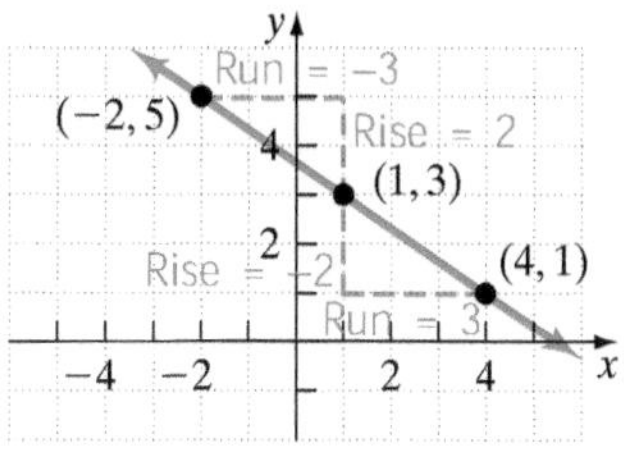

It is perfectly acceptable to set $\dfrac{\text{rise}}{\text{run}} = -\dfrac{2}{3} = \dfrac{2}{-3}$ so

that we move 2 units up from $(1, 3)$ and then 3 units to the left. We would then end up at $(-2, 5)$, which is also on the graph of the line as indicated in Figure 32. ∎

Work Smart

If the "rise" is positive, we go up. If the "rise" is negative, we go down. Similarly, if the "run" is positive, then we go to the right. If the "run" is negative, then we go to the left.

Quick ✔

10. Draw a graph of the line that contains the point $(1, 2)$ and has a slope of

   (a) $\dfrac{1}{2}$ **(b)** -3 **(c)** 0

④ Work with Applications of Slope

In its simplest form, slope is a ratio of rise over run. For example, if we are climbing a hill whose grade is $5\% \left(= 0.05 = \dfrac{5}{100} \right)$, then we go up 5 feet (the rise) for every 100 feet we travel horizontally (the run). See Figure 33.

Figure 33

5 feet

100 feet

Or consider the pitch of a roof. If a roof's pitch is $\dfrac{5}{12}$, then every 5-foot measurement upward will result in a horizontal measurement of 12 feet. See Figure 34.

Figure 34

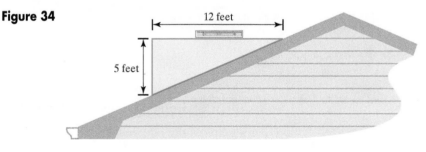

12 feet

5 feet

Work Smart

The pitch of a roof or grade of a road is always represented as a positive number.

EXAMPLE 7 Finding the Grade of a Road

In Heckman Pass, British Columbia, there is a road that rises 9 feet for every 50 feet of horizontal distance covered. What is the grade of the road?

Solution

The grade of the road is given by $\dfrac{\text{rise}}{\text{run}}$. Since a rise of 9 feet is accompanied by a run

of 50 feet, the grade of the road is $\dfrac{9 \text{ feet}}{50 \text{ feet}} = 0.18 = 18\%$. ∎

The slope m of a line measures the amount that y changes as x changes from x_1 to x_2. The slope of a line is also called the **average rate of change** of y with respect to x.

In applications, we are often interested in knowing how the change in one variable might affect some other variable. For example, if your income increases by $1000, how much will your spending (on average) change? Or, if the speed of your car increases by 10 miles per hour, how much (on average) will your car's gas mileage change?

EXAMPLE 8 Slope as an Average Rate of Change

In Naples, Florida, the price of a new three-bedroom house that is 1828 square feet is $280,000. The price of a new three-bedroom home that is 1987 square feet is $296,000. Find and interpret the slope of the line joining the points (1828, 280,000) and (1987, 296,000).

Solution

Let x represent the square footage of the house and y represent the price. Let $(x_1, y_1) = (1828, 280{,}000)$ and $(x_2, y_2) = (1987, 296{,}000)$ and compute the slope as

$$m = \frac{y_2 - y_1}{x_2 - x_1} = \frac{296{,}000 - 280{,}000}{1987 - 1828}$$

$$= \frac{16{,}000}{159}$$

Round to the nearest cent: $= 100.63$

The unit of measure of y is dollars while the unit of measure for x is square feet. So, the slope can be interpreted as follows: Between 1828 and 1987 square feet, the price increases by $100.63 per square foot, on average. ∎

Quick ✔

11. A road rises 4 feet for every 50 feet of horizontal distance covered. What is the grade of the road?

12. The average annual cost of operating a Chevy Cobalt is $1370 when it is driven 10,000 miles. The average annual cost of operating a Chevy Cobalt is $1850 when it is driven 14,000 miles. Find and interpret the slope of the line joining (10,000, 1370) and (14,000, 1850).

3.3 EXERCISES

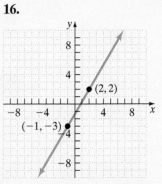

1–12. *are the* Quick ✔*s that follow each* EXAMPLE

Building Skills

In Problems 13–18, find the slope of the line whose graph is given. See Objective 1.

13.

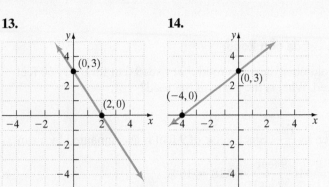

14.

15.

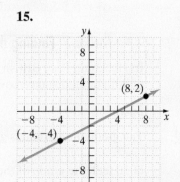

16.

17.

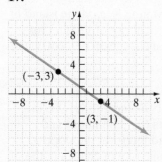

18.

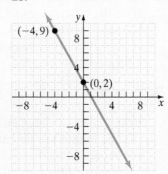

39.

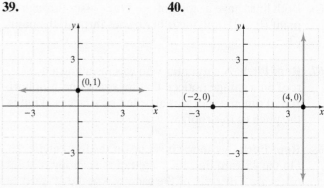

40.

In Problems 19–22, (a) plot the points in a rectangular coordinate system, (b) draw a line through the points, (c) and find and interpret the slope of the line. See Objective 1.

19. $(-3, 2)$ and $(3, 5)$ **20.** $(2, 6)$ and $(-2, -4)$

21. $(2, -9)$ and $(-2, -1)$ **22.** $(4, -5)$ and $(-2, -4)$

In Problems 23–36, find and interpret the slope of the line containing the given points. See Objective 1.

23. $(10, 4)$ and $(6, 12)$ **24.** $(7, 3)$ and $(0, -11)$

25. $(4, -4)$ and $(12, -12)$ **26.** $(-3, 2)$ and $(2, -3)$

27. $(7, -2)$ and $(4, 3)$ **28.** $(-8, -1)$ and $(2, 3)$

29. $(0, 6)$ and $(-4, 0)$ **30.** $(-5, 0)$ and $(0, 3)$

31. $(-4, -1)$ and $(2, 3)$ **32.** $(5, 1)$ and $(-1, -1)$

33. $\left(\frac{1}{2}, \frac{3}{4}\right)$ and $\left(-\frac{5}{2}, -\frac{1}{4}\right)$ **34.** $\left(-\frac{1}{3}, \frac{2}{5}\right)$ and $\left(\frac{2}{3}, -\frac{3}{5}\right)$

35. $\left(\frac{1}{2}, \frac{1}{3}\right)$ and $\left(\frac{3}{4}, \frac{5}{6}\right)$ **36.** $\left(\frac{1}{4}, -\frac{4}{3}\right)$ and $\left(-\frac{5}{4}, \frac{1}{3}\right)$

In Problems 37–40, find the slope of the line whose graph is given. See Objective 2.

37.

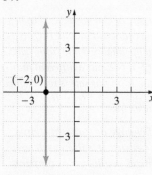

38.

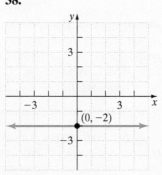

In Problems 41–44, find and interpret the slope of the line containing the given points. See Objective 2.

41. $(4, -6)$ and $(-1, -6)$ **42.** $(-1, -3)$ and $(-1, 2)$

43. $(3, 9)$ and $(3, -2)$ **44.** $(5, 1)$ and $(-2, 1)$

In Problems 45–62, draw a graph of the line that contains the given point and has the given slope. See Objective 3.

45. $(4, 2)$; $m = 1$ **46.** $(3, -1)$; $m = -1$

47. $(0, 6)$; $m = -2$ **48.** $(-1, 3)$; $m = 3$

49. $(-1, 0)$; $m = \dfrac{1}{4}$ **50.** $(5, 2)$; $m = -\dfrac{1}{2}$

51. $(2, -3)$; $m = 0$ **52.** $(1, 4)$; m is undefined

53. $(2, 1)$; $m = \dfrac{2}{3}$ **54.** $(-2, -3)$; $m = \dfrac{5}{2}$

55. $(-1, 4)$; $m = -\dfrac{5}{3}$ **56.** $(0, -2)$; $m = -\dfrac{3}{2}$

57. $(0, 0)$; m is undefined   **58.** $(3, -1)$; $m = 0$

59. $(0, 2)$; $m = -4$ **60.** $(0, 0)$; $m = \dfrac{1}{5}$

61. $(2, -3)$; $m = \dfrac{3}{4}$ **62.** $(-3, 0)$; $m = -3$

Applying the Concepts

In Problems 63–66, draw the graph of the two lines with the given properties on the same rectangular coordinate system.

63. Both lines pass through the point $(2, -1)$. One has slope of 2 and the other has slope of $-\dfrac{1}{2}$.

64. Both lines pass through the point $(3, 0)$. One has slope of $\dfrac{2}{3}$ and the other has slope of $-\dfrac{3}{2}$.

65. Both lines have a slope of $\dfrac{3}{4}$. One passes through the point $(-1, -2)$, and the other passes through the point $(2, 1)$.

66. Both lines have a slope of -1. One passes through the point $(0, -3)$, and the other passes through the point $(2, -1)$.

67. **Roof Pitch** A carpenter who was installing a new roof on a garage noticed that for every one-foot horizontal run, the roof was elevated by 4 inches. What is the pitch of this roof?

68. **Roof Pitch** A canopy is set up on the football field. On the 45-yard line, the height of the canopy is 68 inches. The peak of the canopy is at the 50-yard marker where the height is 84 inches. What is the pitch of the roof of the canopy?

69. **Building a Roof** To build a shed in his backyard, Moises has decided to use a pitch of $\frac{2}{5}$ for his roof. The shed measures 30 in. from the side to the center. How much height should he add to the roof to get the desired pitch?

70. **Building a Roof** The design for the bedroom of a house requires a roof pitch of $\frac{7}{20}$. If the room measures 5 feet from the wall to the center, how high above the ceiling is the peak of the roof?

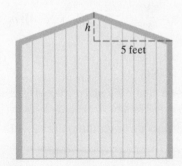

71. **Road Grade** Fall River Road was completed in 1920 and was the first road built through the Rocky Mountains in Colorado. It was so steep that sometimes the early model cars had to drive up the hill in reverse to maximize their weak engines and fuel systems. If the road rises 200 feet for every 1250 feet of horizontal change, what is the grade of this road in percent?

72. **Road Grade** Barbara decided to take a bicycle trip up to the observatory on Mauna Kea on the island of Hawaii. The road has a vertical rise of 120 feet for every 800 feet of horizontal change. In percent, what is the grade of this road?

73. **Population Growth** The population of the United States was 123,202,624 in 1930 and 281,421,906 in 2000. Use the ordered pairs (0, 123 million) and (70, 281 million) to find and interpret the slope of line representing the average rate of change in the population of the United States.

74. **Earning Potential** On average, a person who graduates from high school can expect to have lifetime earnings of 1.2 million dollars. It takes four years to earn a bachelor's degree, but the lifetime earnings will increase to 2.1 million dollars. Use the ordered pairs (0, 1.2 million) and (4, 2.1 million) to find and interpret the slope of the line representing the increase in earnings due to finishing college.

Extending the Concepts

In Problems 75–78, find any two ordered pairs that lie on the given line. Graph the line and then determine the slope of the line.

75. $3x + y = -5$

76. $2x + 5y = 12$

77. $y = 3x + 4$

78. $y = -x - 6$

In Problems 79–84, find the slope of the line containing the given points.

79. $(2a, a)$ and $(3a, -a)$

80. $(4p, 2p)$ and $(-2p, 5p)$

81. $(2p + 1, q - 4)$ and $(3p + 1, 2q - 4)$

82. $(3p + 1, 4q - 7)$ and $(5p + 1, 2q - 7)$

83. $(a + 1, b - 1)$ and $(2a - 5, b + 5)$

84. $(2a - 3, b + 4)$ and $(4a + 7, 5b - 1)$

*In economics, **marginal revenue** is a rate of change defined as the change in total revenue divided by the change in output. If Q_1 represents the number of units sold, then the total revenue from selling these goods is represented by R_1. If Q_2 represents a different number of units sold, then the total revenue from this sale is represented by R_2. We compute marginal revenue as $MR = \dfrac{R_2 - R_1}{Q_2 - Q_1}$.*

So marginal revenue is a rate of change or slope. Marginal revenue is important in economics because it is used to determine the level of output that maximizes profits for a company. Use the marginal revenue formula to solve Problems 85 and 86.

85. Determine and interpret marginal revenue if total revenue is $1000 when 400 hot dogs are sold at a baseball game and total revenue is $1200 when 500 hot dogs are sold.

86. Determine and interpret marginal revenue if total revenue is $300 when 30 compact disks are sold and total revenue is $400 when 50 compact disks are sold.

Explaining the Concepts

87. Describe a line that has one x-intercept but no y-intercept. Give two ordered pairs that could lie on this line and then describe how to find its slope.

88. Describe a line that has one y-intercept but no x-intercept. Give two ordered pairs that could lie on this line and then describe how to find its slope.

3.4 Slope-Intercept Form of a Line

OBJECTIVES

1. Use the Slope-Intercept Form to Identify the Slope and y-Intercept of a Line
2. Graph a Line Whose Equation Is in Slope-Intercept Form
3. Graph a Line Whose Equation Is in the Form $Ax + By = C$
4. Find the Equation of a Line Given Its Slope and y-Intercept
5. Work with Linear Models in Slope-Intercept Form

Preparing for Slope-Intercept Form of a Line
Before getting started, take the following readiness quiz. If you get a problem wrong, go back to the section cited and review the material.

P1. Solve $4x + 2y = 10$ for y.   [Section 2.4, pp. 117–118]

P2. Solve: $10 = 2x - 8$ [Section 2.2, pp. 94–96]

1 Use the Slope-Intercept Form to Identify the Slope and y-Intercept of a Line

We have defined a linear equation as an equation of the form $Ax + By = C$, where A and B are not both zero. So far, we have graphed equations of this form using point plotting or by finding its intercepts. From the previous section, we know the slope can be used to help us graph a line.

In this section, we use the slope and y-intercept to graph a line. This method for graphing will be more efficient than plotting points. Why? Well, suppose we wish to graph the equation $-2x + y = 5$ by plotting points. To do this, we might first solve the equation for y (get y by itself) by adding $2x$ to both sides of the equation.

$$-2x + y = 5$$
Add 2x to both sides: $$y = 2x + 5$$

We now create Table 14, which gives us points on the graph of the equation. Figure 35 shows the graph of the line.

Notice two things about the line in Figure 35. First, the slope is $m = 2$. Second, the y-intercept is 5. If you look back at the form of the equation $-2x + y = 5$ after we solved for y, namely, $y = 2x + 5$, you should notice that the coefficient of the variable x is 2 and the constant is 5. This is no coincidence!

Table 14

x	$y = 2x + 5$	(x, y)
-2	$2(-2) + 5 = 1$	$(-2, 1)$
-1	$2(-1) + 5 = 3$	$(-1, 3)$
0	$2(0) + 5 = 5$	$(0, 5)$

Figure 35
$-2x + y = 5$

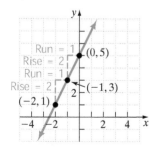

SLOPE-INTERCEPT FORM OF AN EQUATION OF A LINE

An equation of a line with slope m and y-intercept b is

$$y = mx + b$$

Preparing for...Answers
P1. $y = -2x + 5$ **P2.** $\{9\}$

EXAMPLE 1 Finding the Slope and y-Intercept of a Line

Find the slope and y-intercept of the line whose equation is $y = -3x + 1$.

Solution

We compare the equation $y = -3x + 1$ to the slope-intercept form of a line $y = mx + b$ and find that the coefficient of x, -3, is the slope and the constant, 1, is the y-intercept. ∎

EXAMPLE 2 Finding the Slope and y-Intercept of a Line Whose Equation Is in Standard Form

Find the slope and y-intercept of the line whose equation is $3x + 2y = 6$.

Solution

First, we rewrite the equation $3x + 2y = 6$ so that it is of the form $y = mx + b$. That is, we want to solve the equation for y.

$$3x + 2y = 6$$

Subtract 3x from both sides: $\quad 2y = -3x + 6$

Divide both sides by 2: $\quad y = \dfrac{-3x + 6}{2}$

$\dfrac{a + b}{c} = \dfrac{a}{c} + \dfrac{b}{c}$: $\quad y = \dfrac{-3}{2}x + \dfrac{6}{2}$

Simplify: $\quad y = -\dfrac{3}{2}x + 3$

Work Smart

Notice that after we subtracted 3x from both sides, we wrote the equation as $2y = -3x + 6$ rather than $2y = 6 - 3x$. This is because we want to get the equation in the form $y = mx + b$, so the term involving x should be first.

Now we compare the equation $y = -\dfrac{3}{2}x + 3$ to the slope-intercept form of a line $y = mx + b$ and find that the coefficient of x, $-\dfrac{3}{2}$, is the slope and the constant, 3, is the y-intercept. So for the line $3x + 2y = 6$, $m = -\dfrac{3}{2}$, and the y-intercept is $b = 3$. ∎

Any equation of the form $y = b$ can be written $y = 0x + b$. So, the slope of the line whose equation is $y = b$ is 0 and the y-intercept is b.

Any equation of the form $x = a$ cannot be written in the form $y = mx + b$. The line whose equation is $x = a$ has an undefined slope and no y-intercept.

Quick ✔ *In Problems 1–5, find the slope and y-intercept of the line whose equation is given.*

1. $y = 4x - 3$ **2.** $3x + y = 7$ **3.** $2x + 5y = 15$

4. $y = 8$ **5.** $x = 3$

⌐2 Graph a Line Whose Equation Is in Slope-Intercept Form

In the previous section, we graphed an equation of a line using a point on the line and its slope. If an equation is in slope-intercept form, we can graph the line by plotting the y-intercept and using the slope to find another point on the line.

EXAMPLE 3 How to Graph a Line Whose Equation Is in Slope-Intercept Form

Graph the line $y = 3x - 1$ using the slope and y-intercept.

Step-by-Step Solution

Step 1: Identify the slope and y-intercept of the line.

$$y = 3x - 1$$
$$y = 3x + (-1)$$

$m = 3$ $b = -1$

The slope is $m = 3$ and the y-intercept is $b = -1$.

Step 2: Plot the y-intercept and then use the slope to find a second point on the graph. Draw a line through the points.

Plot the y-intercept at $(0, -1)$. Use the slope $m = \dfrac{3}{1} = \dfrac{\text{rise}}{\text{run}}$ to find a second point on the graph. See Figure 36.

Figure 36
$y = 3x - 1$

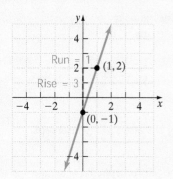

Quick ✔ *In Problems 6 and 7, graph the line using the slope and y-intercept.*

6. $y = 2x - 5$ **7.** $y = \dfrac{1}{2}x - 5$

EXAMPLE 4 Graphing a Linear Equation Whose Equation Is in Slope-Intercept Form

Graph the line $y = -\dfrac{4}{3}x + 2$ using the slope and y-intercept.

Solution

First, we determine the slope and y-intercept.

$$y = -\frac{4}{3}x + 2$$

$b = 2$

$m = -\dfrac{4}{3}$

The slope is $m = -\dfrac{4}{3}$ and the y-intercept is $b = 2$. We plot the point $(0, 2)$. Now use the slope $m = -\dfrac{4}{3} = \dfrac{-4}{3} = \dfrac{\text{rise}}{\text{run}}$ to find a second point on the graph. We then draw a line through these two points. See Figure 37.

Figure 37
$y = -\dfrac{4}{3}x + 2$

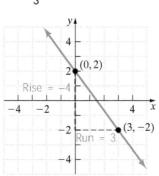

Quick ✔ *In Problems 8 and 9, graph the line using the slope and y-intercept.*

8. $y = -3x + 1$ **9.** $y = -\dfrac{3}{2}x + 4$

3 Graph a Line Whose Equation Is in the Form Ax + By = C

If a linear equation is written in standard form $Ax + By = C$, we can still use the slope and y-intercept to obtain the graph of the equation. Let's see how.

EXAMPLE 5 How to Graph a Line Whose Equation Is in the Form Ax + By = C

Graph the line $8x + 2y = 10$ using the slope and y-intercept.

Step-by-Step Solution

Step 1: Solve the equation for y to put it in the form $y = mx + b$.	$8x + 2y = 10$ Subtract 8x from both sides: $2y = -8x + 10$ Divide both sides by 2: $y = \dfrac{-8x + 10}{2}$ Simplify: $y = -4x + 5$
Step 2: Identify the slope and y-intercept of the line.	The slope is $m = -4$ and the y-intercept is $b = 5$.
Step 3: Plot the y-intercept and then use the slope to find a second point on the graph. Draw a line through the points.	Plot the point $(0, 5)$ and use the slope $m = -4 = \dfrac{-4}{1} = \dfrac{\text{rise}}{\text{run}}$ to find a second point on the graph. See Figure 38.

Figure 38

$8x + 2y = 10$

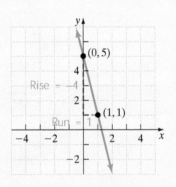

Work Smart

An alternative to graphing the equation in Example 5 using the slope and y-intercept would be to graph the line using intercepts.

Quick ✔ *In Problems 10–12, graph each line using the slope and y-intercept.*

10. $-2x + y = -3$ **11.** $6x - 2y = 2$ **12.** $3x + 5y = 0$

13. List three techniques that can be used to graph a line.

4 Find the Equation of a Line Given Its Slope and y-Intercept

Up to now, we have identified the slope and y-intercept of a line from an equation. We will now reverse the process and find the equation of a line whose slope and y-intercept are given. This is a fairly straightforward process—replace m with the given slope and b with the y-intercept.

EXAMPLE 6 **Finding the Equation of a Line Given Its Slope and *y*-Intercept**

Find the equation of a line whose slope is $\dfrac{3}{8}$ and whose *y*-intercept is -4. Graph the line.

Solution

The slope is $m = \dfrac{3}{8}$ and the *y*-intercept is $b = -4$. Substitute $\dfrac{3}{8}$ for m and -4 for b in the slope-intercept form of a line $y = mx + b$ to obtain

$$y = \frac{3}{8}x - 4$$

Figure 39 shows the graph of the equation.

Figure 39

$y = \dfrac{3}{8}x - 4$

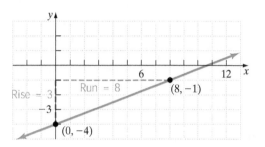

Quick ✔ *In Problems 14–16, find the equation of the line whose slope and y-intercept are given. Graph the line.*

14. $m = 3, b = -2$ **15.** $m = -\dfrac{1}{4}, b = 3$ **16.** $m = 0, b = -1$

⌐5⌐ Work with Linear Models in Slope-Intercept Form

There are many situations where we can use a linear equation to describe the relationship that exists between two variables. For example, your long-distance phone bill depends linearly upon the number of minutes used, or the cost of renting a moving truck depends linearly on the number of miles driven. Let's look at a couple of examples.

EXAMPLE 7 **A Model for Total Cholesterol**

When you have a physical exam, your doctor draws blood for your cholesterol test. Your total cholesterol count is measured in milligrams per deciliter (mg/dL). It is the sum of low-density lipoprotein cholesterol (LDL)—sometimes called "bad cholesterol"—and high-density lipoprotein cholesterol (HDL)—sometimes called your "good cholesterol." Based on data from the National Center for Health Statistics, a woman's total cholesterol y is related to her age x by the following linear equation:

$$y = 1.1x + 157$$

   (a) Use the equation to predict the total cholesterol of a woman who is 40 years old.

   (b) Determine and interpret the slope of the equation.

   (c) Determine and interpret the *y*-intercept of the equation.

   (d) Graph the equation in a rectangular coordinate system.

Solution

(a) Because *x* represents the woman's age, we substitute 40 for *x* in the equation $y = 1.1x + 157$ to find the total cholesterol *y*.

$$y = 1.1x + 157$$
$$x = 40: \quad y = 1.1(40) + 157$$
$$= 201$$

We predict that a 40-year-old woman will have a total cholesterol of 201 mg/dL.

(b) The slope of the equation $y = 1.1x + 157$ is 1.1. Because slope equals $\dfrac{\text{rise}}{\text{run}} = \dfrac{1.1 \text{ mg/dL}}{1 \text{ year}}$, we interpret the slope as follows: "The total cholesterol of a female increases by 1.1 mg/dL as age increases by 1 year."

(c) The *y*-intercept of the equation $y = 1.1x + 157$ is 157. The *y*-intercept is the value of total cholesterol, *y*, when $x = 0$. Since *x* represents age, we interpret the *y*-intercept as follows: "The total cholesterol of a newborn girl is 157 mg/dL."

(d) Figure 40 shows the graph of the equation. Because it does not make sense for *x* to be less than 0, we only graph the equation in quadrant I.

Work Smart

Notice that we did not use the slope to obtain an additional point on the graph of the equation. It would be difficult to find an additional point with a slope of 1.1. For example, from the *y*-intercept, we would go up 1.1 mg/dL and right 1 year and end up at (1, 158.1). It would be hard to draw the line through these two points!

Figure 40
$y = 1.1x + 157$

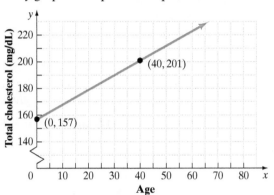

In Figure 40, notice the "broken line" (⚡) on the *y*-axis near the origin. We include this in the graph to indicate that a portion of the graph has been removed. This is done so that we do not have to start the *y*-axis at 0 and work our way higher. This avoids a lot of white space in the graph. Whenever you are reading a graph, always look carefully at how the axes are labeled and the units on each axis.

Quick ✔

17. Based on data obtained from the National Center for Health Statistics, the birth weight *y* of a baby, measured in grams, is linearly related to gestation period *x* (in weeks) according to the equation

$$y = 143x - 2215$$

(a) Use the equation to predict the birth weight of a baby if the gestation period is 30 weeks.

(b) Use the equation to predict the birth weight of a baby if the gestation period is 36 weeks.

(c) Determine and interpret the slope of the equation.

(d) Explain why it does not make sense to interpret the *y*-intercept of the equation.

(e) Graph the equation in a rectangular coordinate system for $28 \le x \le 43$.

We know that the slope can be interpreted as a rate of change. For this reason, when information in a problem is given as a rate of change as in miles per gallon or dollars per pound, the rate of change will represent the slope in a linear model.

EXAMPLE 8 Cost of Owning and Operating a Car

There are many costs that factor into owning a car including gas, maintenance, and insurance. Some of these costs are affected by the number of miles that are driven (gas and maintenance), while others are not (comprehensive insurance, license plates, depreciation). Suppose the annual cost of operating a Chevy Cobalt is $0.25 per mile plus $3000.

(a) Write a linear equation that relates the annual cost of operating the car y to the number of miles driven in a year x.

(b) What is the annual cost of driving 11,000 miles?

(c) Graph the equation in a rectangular coordinate system.

Solution

(a) The rate of change in the problem is $0.25 per mile. We can express this as $\frac{\$0.25}{1\ \text{mile}}$, which is the slope m of the linear equation. The cost of $3000 is a cost that does not change with the number of miles driven. Put another way, if we drive 0 miles, the cost will be $3000, so this value represents the y-intercept, b. The linear equation that relates cost y to the number of miles driven x is

$$y = 0.25x + 3000$$

(b) Let $x = 11,000$ in the equation $y = 0.25x + 3000$.

$$y = 0.25(11,000) + 3000$$
$$= 2750 + 3000$$
$$= \$5750$$

The cost of driving 11,000 miles in a year is $5750. Remember, this cost includes gas, insurance, maintenance, and depreciation in the value of the vehicle!

(c) See Figure 41.

Figure 41
$y = 0.25x + 3000$

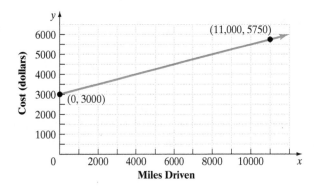

Quick ✔

18. The daily cost, y, of renting a 16-foot moving truck for a day is $50 plus $0.38 per mile driven, x.

(a) Write a linear equation relating the daily cost y to the number of miles driven, x.

(b) Determine the cost of renting the truck if the truck is driven 75 miles.

(c) If the cost of renting the truck is $84.20, how many miles were driven?

(d) Graph the linear equation.

3.4 EXERCISES

PRACTICE   WATCH   DOWNLOAD   READ   REVIEW

1–18. are the Quick ✔s that follow each EXAMPLE

Building Skills

In Problems 19–38, find the slope and y-intercept of the line whose equation is given. See Objective 1.

19. $y = 5x + 2$ **20.** $y = 7x + 1$

21. $y = x - 9$ **22.** $y = x - 7$

23. $y = -10x + 7$ **24.** $y = -6x + 2$

25. $y = -x - 9$ **26.** $y = -x - 12$

27. $2x + y = 4$ **28.** $3x + y = 9$

29. $2x + 3y = 24$ **30.** $6x - 8y = -24$

31. $5x - 3y = 9$ **32.** $10x + 6y = 24$

33. $x - 2y = 5$ **34.** $-x - 5y = 3$

35. $y = -5$ **36.** $y = 3$

37. $x = 6$ **38.** $x = -2$

In Problems 39–46, use the slope and y-intercept to graph each line whose equation is given. See Objective 2.

39. $y = x + 3$ **40.** $y = x + 4$

41. $y = -2x - 3$ **42.** $y = -4x - 1$

43. $y = -\dfrac{2}{3}x + 2$ **44.** $y = \dfrac{4}{3}x - 3$

45. $y = -\dfrac{5}{2}x - 2$ **46.** $y = -\dfrac{2}{5}x + 3$

In Problems 47–54, graph each line using the slope and y-intercept. See Objective 3.

47. $4x + y = 5$ **48.** $3x + y = 2$

49. $x + 2y = -6$ **50.** $x - 2y = -4$

51. $3x - 2y = 10$ **52.** $4x + 3y = -6$

53. $6x + 3y = -15$ **54.** $5x - 2y = 6$

In Problems 55–66, find the equation of the line with the given slope and intercept. See Objective 4.

55. slope is -1; y-intercept is 8

56. slope is 1; y-intercept is 10

57. slope is $\dfrac{6}{7}$; y-intercept is -6

58. slope is $\dfrac{4}{7}$; y-intercept is -9

59. slope is $-\dfrac{1}{3}$; y-intercept is $\dfrac{2}{3}$

60. slope is $\dfrac{1}{4}$; y-intercept is $\dfrac{3}{8}$

61. slope is undefined; x-intercept is -5

62. slope is 0; y-intercept is -2

63. slope is 0; y-intercept is 3

64. slope is undefined; x-intercept is 4

65. slope is 5; y-intercept is 0

66. slope is -3; y-intercept is 0

Mixed Practice

In Problems 67–90, graph each equation using any method you wish.

67. $y = 2x - 7$ **68.** $y = -4x + 1$

69. $3x - 2y = 24$ **70.** $2x + 5y = 30$

71. $y = -5$ **72.** $y = 4$

73. $x = -6$ **74.** $x = -3$

75. $6x - 4y = 0$ **76.** $3x + 8y = 0$

77. $y = -\dfrac{5}{3}x + 6$ **78.** $y = -\dfrac{3}{5}x + 4$

79. $2y = x + 4$ **80.** $3y = x - 9$

81. $y = \dfrac{x}{3}$ **82.** $y = -\dfrac{x}{4}$

83. $2x = -8y$ **84.** $-3x = 5y$

85. $y = -\dfrac{2x}{3} + 1$ **86.** $y = \dfrac{3x}{2} - 4$

87. $x + 2 = -7$ **88.** $y - 4 = -1$

89. $5x + y + 1 = 0$ **90.** $2x - y + 4 = 0$

Applying the Concepts

91. Weekly Salary Dien is paid a salary of $400 per week plus an 8% commission on all sales he makes during the week.

(a) Write a linear equation that calculates his weekly income, where y represents his income and x represents the amount of sales.

(b) What is Dien's weekly income if he sold $1200 worth of merchandise?

(c) Graph the equation in a rectangular coordinate system. Label the axes appropriately.

92. Car Rental To rent a car for a day, Gloria pays $75 plus $0.10 per mile.

(a) Write a linear equation that calculates the daily cost, y, to rent a car which will be driven x miles.

(b) What is the cost to drive this car for 200 miles?

(c) If Gloria paid $87.50, how many miles did she drive?

(d) Graph the equation in a rectangular coordinate system. Label the axes appropriately.

93. Cell Phone Costs The cost per minute for cell phone users has gone down over the years. In 1995, cell phone users paid, on the average, 56¢ per minute. In 2007, they paid 13¢ per minute. Assuming that the rate of decline of the cost per minute was constant, the cost per minute can be calculated by the equation $y = -3.583x + 56$, where x represents the number of years after 1995 and y represents the cost per minute of cell phone usage in cents. (SOURCE: *CTIA, The Wireless Association*)

(a) What was the cost per minute for a cell phone user in 1999?

(b) In which year did a cell phone user pay 20.17¢ per minute?

(c) Interpret the slope of $y = -3.583x + 56$.

(d) Can this trend continue indefinitely?

(e) Graph the equation in a rectangular coordinate system. Label the axes appropriately.

94. Counting Calories According to a 1989 National Academy of Sciences Report, the recommended daily intake of calories for males between the ages of 7 and 15 can be calculated by the equation $y = 125x + 1125$, where x represents the boy's age and y represents the recommended calorie intake.

(a) What is the recommended caloric intake for a 12-year-old boy?

(b) What is the age of a boy whose recommended caloric intake is 2250 calories?

(c) Interpret the slope of $y = 125x + 1125$.

(d) Why would this equation not be accurate for a 3-year-old male?

(e) Graph the equation in a rectangular coordinate system. Label the axes appropriately.

Extending the Concepts

In Problems 95–100, find the value of the missing coefficient so that the line will have the given property.

95. $2x + By = 12$; slope is $\dfrac{1}{2}$

96. $Ax + 2y = 5$; slope is $\dfrac{3}{2}$

97. $Ax - 2y = 10$; slope is -2

98. $12x + By = -1$; slope is -4

99. $x + By = \dfrac{1}{2}$; y-intercept is $-\dfrac{1}{6}$

100. $4x + By = \dfrac{4}{3}$; y-intercept is $\dfrac{2}{3}$

In Problems 101 and 102, use the following information. In business, a cost equation relates the total cost of producing a product or good such as a refrigerator, rug, or blender to the number of goods produced. The simplest cost model is the linear cost model. In the linear cost model, the slope of the linear equation represents the cost of producing one additional unit of a good. Variable cost is reported as a rate of change, such as $40 per calculator. Examples of variable costs would be labor costs and materials. The y-intercept of the linear equation represents the fixed costs of production—these are costs that exist regardless of the level of production. Fixed costs would be cost of the manufacturing facility and insurance.

101. Cost Equations Suppose the variable cost of manufacturing a graphing calculator is $40 per calculator while the daily fixed cost is $4000.

(a) Write a linear equation that relates cost y to the number of calculators manufactured x.

(b) What is the daily cost of manufacturing 500 calculators?

(c) One day, the total cost was $19,000. How many calculators were manufactured?

(d) Graph the equation relating cost and number of calculators manufactured.

102. Cost Equations Suppose the variable cost of manufacturing a cellular telephone is $35 per phone, and the daily fixed cost is $3600.

(a) Write a linear equation that relates the daily cost y to the number of cellular telephones manufactured x.

(b) What is the daily cost of manufacturing 400 cellular phones?

(c) One day, the total cost was $13,225. How many cellular phones were manufactured?

(d) Graph the equation relating cost and number of cellular telephones manufactured.

(g) $-5x + 2y = 12$ (h) $x - y = -3$

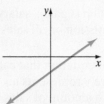

Explaining the Concepts

103. Describe the line whose graph is shown. Which of the following equations could have the graph that is shown?

(a) $y = 3x - 2$ (b) $y = -2x + 5$
(c) $y = 3$ (d) $2x + 3y = 6$
(e) $3x - 2y = 8$ (f) $4x - y = -4$

104. Without graphing, describe the orientation of each line (rises from left to right, and so on). Explain how you came to this conclusion.

(a) $y = 4x - 3$ (b) $y = -2x + 5$
(c) $y = x$ (d) $y = 4$

3.5 Point-Slope Form of a Line

OBJECTIVES

1. Find the Equation of a Line Given a Point and a Slope
2. Find the Equation of a Line Given Two Points
3. Build Linear Models Using the Point-Slope Form of a Line

Preparing for Point-Slope Form of a Line
Before getting started, take the following readiness quiz. If you get a problem wrong, go back to the section cited and review the material.

P1. Solve $y - 3 = 2(x + 1)$ for y.   [Section 2.4, pp. 116–118]

P2. Evaluate: $\dfrac{7 - 3}{4 - 2}$ [Section 1.7, p. 62]

1 Find the Equation of a Line Given a Point and a Slope

We now have two forms for the equation of a line. We have the standard equation of a line $Ax + By = C$, where A and B are not both zero, and the slope-intercept form of a line $y = mx + b$, where m is the slope and b is the y-intercept. We now introduce another form for the equation of a line.

Suppose that we have a nonvertical line with slope m containing the point (x_1, y_1). For any other point (x, y) on the line, we know from the formula for the slope of a line that

$$m = \frac{y - y_1}{x - x_1}$$

Figure 42

See Figure 42. Multiplying both sides by $x - x_1$, we can rewrite this expression as

$$m(x - x_1) = y - y_1 \quad \text{or} \quad y - y_1 = m(x - x_1)$$

POINT-SLOPE FORM OF AN EQUATION OF A LINE

An equation of a nonvertical line of slope m that contains the point (x_1, y_1) is

Slope
↓
$$y - y_1 = m(x - x_1)$$
↑ Given point ↑

The point-slope form of a line can be used to write an equation in either slope-intercept form ($y = mx + b$) or standard form ($Ax + By = C$).

EXAMPLE 1 Using the Point-Slope Form of an Equation of a Line—Positive Slope

Find the equation of a line whose slope is 3 and that contains the point $(-1, 4)$. Write the equation in slope-intercept form. Graph the line.

Solution

Because we are given the slope and a point on the line, we use the point-slope form of a line with $m = 3$ and $(x_1, y_1) = (-1, 4)$.

$$y - y_1 = m(x - x_1)$$

$m = 3, x_1 = -1, y_1 = 4:$ $\quad y - 4 = 3(x - (-1))$

$$y - 4 = 3(x + 1)$$

To put the equation in slope-intercept form, $y = mx + b$, we solve the equation for y.

Distribute: $\quad y - 4 = 3x + 3$

Add 3 to both sides: $\quad y = 3x + 7$

See Figure 43 for a graph of the line. ∎

Figure 43
$y = 3x + 7$

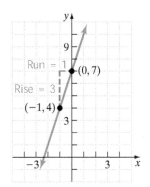

Quick ✔

1. The point-slope form of a nonvertical line whose slope is m that contains the point (x_1, y_1) is _____.
2. *True or False:* The slope of the line $y - 3 = 4(x - 1)$ is 4.

In Problems 3 and 4, find the equation of the line with the given properties. Write the equation in slope-intercept form. Graph the line.
3. $m = 3$ containing $(x_1, y_1) = (2, 1)$
4. $m = \dfrac{1}{3}$ containing $(x_1, y_1) = (3, -4)$

EXAMPLE 2 Using the Point-Slope Form of an Equation of a Line—Negative Slope

Find the equation of a line whose slope is $-\dfrac{3}{4}$ and that contains the point $(-4, 3)$. Write the equation in slope-intercept form. Graph the line.

Solution

Because we are given the slope and a point on the line, we use the point-slope form of a line with $m = -\dfrac{3}{4}$ and $(x_1, y_1) = (-4, 3)$.

Figure 44
$y = -\dfrac{3}{4}x$

$$y - y_1 = m(x - x_1)$$

$m = -\dfrac{3}{4}, x_1 = -4, y_1 = 3:$ $\quad y - 3 = -\dfrac{3}{4}(x - (-4))$

Simplify: $\quad y - 3 = -\dfrac{3}{4}(x + 4)$

Distribute: $\quad y - 3 = -\dfrac{3}{4}x - 3$

Add 3 to both sides: $\quad y = -\dfrac{3}{4}x$

See Figure 44 for a graph of the line. ∎

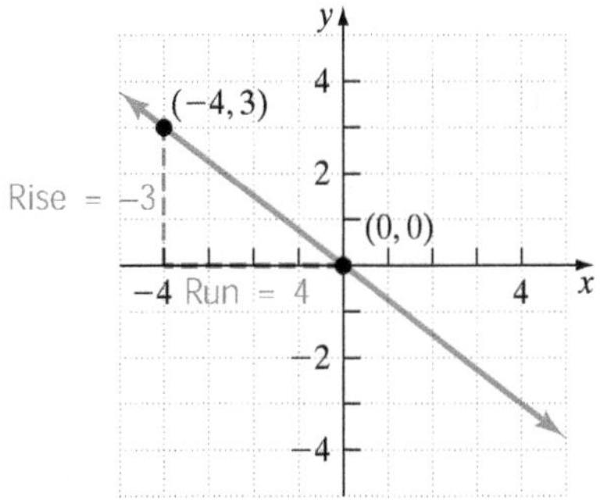

Quick ✔ *In Problems 5 and 6, find an equation of the line with the given properties. Write the equation in slope-intercept form. Graph the line.*

5. $m = -4$ containing $(x_1, y_1) = (-2, 5)$

6. $m = -\dfrac{5}{2}$ and $(x_1, y_1) = (-4, 5)$

EXAMPLE 3 Finding the Equation of a Horizontal Line

Find the equation of a horizontal line that contains the point $(-4, 2)$. Write the equation of the line in slope-intercept form. Graph the line.

Solution

The line is a horizontal line, so the slope of the line is 0. Because we know the slope and a point on the line, we use the point-slope form of a line with $m = 0$, $x_1 = -4$, and $y_1 = 2$.

$$y - y_1 = m(x - x_1)$$
$$m = 0, x_1 = -4, y_1 = 2: \quad y - 2 = 0(x - (-4))$$
$$y - 2 = 0$$
$$\text{Add 2 to both sides:} \quad y = 2 \quad \text{Slope-intercept form, } y = 0x + 2$$

See Figure 45 for a graph of the line. ■

Work Smart

When the slope of a line is 0, the equation of the line will always be in the form "y = some number."

Figure 45
$y = 2$

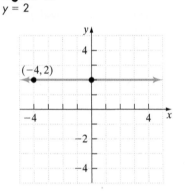

Quick ✔

7. Find the equation of a horizontal line that contains the point $(-2, 3)$. Write the equation of the line in slope-intercept form. Graph the line.

2 Find the Equation of a Line Given Two Points

From Section 3.2, we know that two points are all that is needed to graph a line. If we are given two points, we can find the equation of the line through the points by first finding the slope of the line and then using the point-slope form of a line.

EXAMPLE 4 How to Find the Equation of a Line from Two Points

Find the equation of a line through the points $(1, 3)$ and $(4, 9)$. Write the equation in slope-intercept form. Graph the line.

Step-by-Step Solution

Step 1: Find the slope of the line containing the points.

Let $(x_1, y_1) = (1, 3)$ and $(x_2, y_2) = (4, 9)$. Substitute these values into the formula for the slope of a line.

$$m = \frac{y_2 - y_1}{x_2 - x_1} = \frac{9 - 3}{4 - 1} = \frac{6}{3} = 2$$

Step 2: Substitute the slope found in Step 1 and either point into the point-slope form of a line to find the equation.

With $m = 2$, $x_1 = 1$, and $y_1 = 3$, we have

$$y - y_1 = m(x - x_1)$$
$$m = 2, x_1 = 1, y_1 = 3: \quad y - 3 = 2(x - 1)$$

Step 3: Solve the equation for y.

$$\text{Distribute the 2:} \quad y - 3 = 2x - 2$$
$$\text{Add 3 to both sides:} \quad y = 2x + 1$$

The slope-intercept form of the equation is $y = 2x + 1$. The slope of the line is 2 and the y-intercept is 1. See Figure 46 for the graph.

Figure 46
$y = 2x + 1$

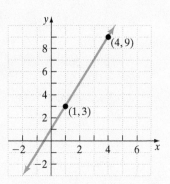

Quick ✔ *In Problems 8 and 9, find the equation of the line containing the given points. Write the equation in slope-intercept form. Graph the line.*

8. $(0, 2); (3, 5)$ **9.** $(-1, 4); (1, -2)$

Work Smart: Study Skills

To write the equation of a nonvertical line, we must know either the slope of the line and a point on the line or two points on the line.

- If the **slope** and the **y-intercept** are known, use the slope-intercept form, $y = mx + b$.
- If the **slope** and a **point** which is not the y-intercept are known, use the **point-slope** form, $y - y_1 = m(x - x_1)$.
- If **two points** are known, first find the **slope**, then use that slope and one of the **points** in the point-slope formula, $y - y_1 = m(x - x_1)$.

EXAMPLE 5 Finding the Equation of a Vertical Line from Two Points

Find the equation of a line through the points $(-3, 2)$ and $(-3, -4)$. Write the equation in slope-intercept form. Graph the line.

Solution

Figure 47
$x = -3$

Let $(x_1, y_1) = (-3, 2)$ and $(x_2, y_2) = (-3, -4)$. Substitute these values into the formula for the slope of a line.

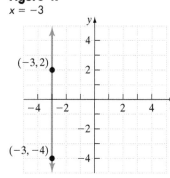

$$m = \frac{y_2 - y_1}{x_2 - x_1} = \frac{-4 - 2}{-3 - (-3)} = \frac{-6}{0}$$

Work Smart

The equation of a vertical line cannot be written in slope-intercept form.

The slope is undefined, so the line is vertical. No matter what value of y we choose, the x-coordinate of the point on the line will be -3. For this reason, the equation of the line is $x = -3$. The equation of the line cannot be written in slope-intercept form. See Figure 47 for the graph.

Quick ✔

10. Find the equation of the line containing the points $(3, 2)$ and $(3, -4)$. If possible, write the answer in slope-intercept form. Graph the line.

SUMMARY EQUATIONS OF LINES

Form of Line	Formula	Comments
Horizontal line	$y = b$	Graph is a horizontal line (slope is 0) with y-intercept b.
Vertical line	$x = a$	Graph is a vertical line (undefined slope) with x-intercept a.
Point-slope	$y - y_1 = m(x - x_1)$	Useful for finding the equation of a line, given a point and the slope, or two points.
Slope-intercept	$y = mx + b$	Useful for finding the equation of a line, given the slope and y-intercept, or for quickly determining the slope and y-intercept of the line, given the equation of the line.
Standard form	$Ax + By = C$	Straightforward to find the x- and y-intercepts.

Quick ✔

11. List the five forms of the equation of a line: _____ _____

____ _____ _____ _____

_____ .

3 Build Linear Models Using the Point-Slope Form of a Line

We can use the point-slope form of a line to build linear models from data.

EXAMPLE 6 Building a Linear Model from Data

Healthcare costs are skyrocketing. For individuals 20 years of age or older, the percentage of total income y that an individual spends on healthcare increases linearly with age x. According to data obtained from the Bureau of Labor Statistics, a 35-year-old spends about 4.0% of income on healthcare, while a 65-year-old spends about 11.2% of income on healthcare.

(a) Plot the points $(35, 4.0)$ and $(65, 11.2)$ in a rectangular coordinate system and graph the line. Find the linear equation in slope-intercept form that relates the percent of income spent on healthcare y to the age x.

(b) Use the equation found in part **(a)** to predict the percentage of income that a 50-year-old spends on healthcare.

(c) Interpret the slope.

Solution

(a) We plot the ordered pairs $(35, 4.0)$ and $(65, 11.2)$ and draw a line through the points. Be careful to start the graph at $x = 20$. Do you see why? See Figure 48.

Figure 48

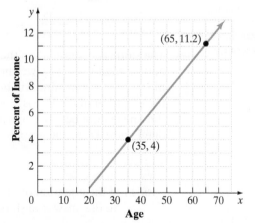

Because we know two points on the line, we will use the point-slope form of a line to find the equation of the line.

First, we must find the slope of the line:

$$m = \frac{y_2 - y_1}{x_2 - x_1} = \frac{11.2 - 4.0}{65 - 35}$$
$$= \frac{7.2}{30}$$
$$= 0.24$$

We use the point-slope form of a line with $m = 0.24$, $x_1 = 35$, and $y_1 = 4.0$:

$$y - y_1 = m(x - x_1)$$

$m = 0.24, x_1 = 35, \text{ and } y_1 = 4.0:$ $y - 4.0 = 0.24(x - 35)$

$$y - 4.0 = 0.24x - 8.4$$

Add 4.0 to both sides of the equation: $y = 0.24x - 4.4$

The equation $y = 0.24x - 4.4$ relates the percent of income spent on healthcare y to the age x.

(b) We substitute 50 for x in the equation found in part **(a),** so the predicted percentage of income spent on health care for a 50-year old is

$$y = 0.24x - 4.4$$

Let $x = 50:$ $= 0.24(50) - 4.4$

$$= 7.6$$

We predict that 7.6% of a 50-year-old's income is spent on healthcare.

(c) The slope is 0.24. The percentage of income spent on healthcare for the individual increases by 0.24% as an individual ages by one year. ∎

Quick ✔

12. Armando owns a gas station. He has found that when the price of regular unleaded gasoline is $3.90, he sells 400 gallons of gasoline between the hours of 7:00 A.M. and 8:00 A.M. When the price of regular unleaded gasoline is $4.10, he sells 380 gallons of gasoline between the hours of 7:00 A.M. and 8:00 A.M. Suppose that the relation between the quantity of gasoline sold and price is linear.

(a) Plot the points in a rectangular coordinate system and graph the line. Find the linear equation in slope-intercept form that relates quantity of gasoline sold y to the price x.

(b) Use the equation found in part **(a)** to predict the number of gallons of gasoline sold if the price is $4.00.

(c) Interpret the slope.

3.5 EXERCISES

PRACTICE   WATCH   DOWNLOAD   READ   REVIEW

1–12. *are the* Quick ✔*s that follow each* EXAMPLE

Building Skills

In Problems 13–28, find the equation of the line that contains the given point and with the given slope. Write the equation in slope-intercept form and graph the line. See Objective 1.

13. $(2, 5)$; slope $= 3$

14. $(4, 1)$; slope $= 6$

15. $(-1, 2)$; slope $= -2$

16. $(6, -3)$; slope $= -5$

17. $(8, -1)$; slope $= \dfrac{1}{4}$

18. $(-8, 2)$; slope $= -\dfrac{1}{2}$

19. $(0, 13)$; slope $= -6$

20. $(0, -4)$; slope $= 9$

21. $(5, -7)$; slope $= 0$

22. $(3, 12)$; undefined slope

23. $(-4, 5)$; undefined slope

24. $(-7, -1)$; slope $= 0$

25. $(-3, 0)$; slope $= \dfrac{2}{3}$ **26.** $(-10, 0)$; slope $= -\dfrac{4}{5}$

27. $(-8, 6)$; slope $= -\dfrac{3}{4}$ **28.** $(-4, -6)$; slope $= \dfrac{3}{2}$

In Problems 29–36, find the equation of the line that contains the given point and satisfies the given information. Write the equation in slope-intercept form, if possible. See Objectives 1 and 2.

29. Vertical line that contains $(-3, 10)$

30. Horizontal line that contains $(-6, -1)$

31. Horizontal line that contains $(-1, -5)$

32. Vertical line that contains $(4, -3)$

33. Horizontal line that contains $(0.2, -4.3)$

34. Vertical line that contains $(3.5, 2.4)$

35. Vertical line that contains $\left(\dfrac{1}{2}, \dfrac{7}{4}\right)$

36. Horizontal line that contains $\left(\dfrac{3}{2}, \dfrac{9}{4}\right)$

In Problems 37–52, find the equation of the line that contains the given points. Write the equation in slope-intercept form, if possible. See Objective 2.

37. $(0, 4)$ and $(-2, 0)$ **38.** $(0, 3)$ and $(6, 0)$

39. $(1, 2)$ and $(0, 6)$ **40.** $(2, 4)$ and $(0, 8)$

41. $(-3, 2)$ and $(1, -4)$ **42.** $(-2, 4)$ and $(2, -2)$

43. $(-3, -11)$ and $(2, -1)$ **44.** $(4, 18)$ and $(-1, 3)$

45. $(4, -3)$ and $(-3, -3)$ **46.** $(-6, 5)$ and $(7, 5)$

47. $(2, -1)$ and $(2, -9)$ **48.** $(-3, 8)$ and $(-3, 1)$

49. $(0.1, 0.6)$ and $(0.5, 0.7)$ **50.** $(0.7, 0.8)$ and $(0.2, 0.4)$

51. $\left(\dfrac{1}{2}, -\dfrac{9}{4}\right)$ and $\left(\dfrac{5}{2}, -\dfrac{1}{4}\right)$ **52.** $\left(\dfrac{1}{3}, \dfrac{12}{5}\right)$ and $\left(\dfrac{4}{3}, \dfrac{2}{5}\right)$

Mixed Practice

In Problems 53–70, find the equation of the line described. Write the equation in slope-intercept form, if possible. Graph the line.

53. Contains $(4, -2)$ with slope $= 5$

54. Contains $(3, 2)$ with slope $= 4$

55. Horizontal line that contains $(-3, 5)$

56. Vertical line that contains $(-4, 2)$

57. Contains $(1, 3)$ and $(-4, -2)$

58. Contains $(-2, -8)$ and $(2, -6)$

59. Contains $(-2, 3)$ with slope $= \dfrac{1}{2}$

60. Contains $(-8, 3)$ with slope $= \dfrac{1}{4}$

61. Vertical line that contains $(5, 2)$

62. Horizontal line that contains $(-2, -6)$

63. Contains $(3, -19)$ and $(-1, 9)$

64. Contains $(-3, 13)$ and $(4, -22)$

65. Contains $(6, 3)$ with slope $= -\dfrac{2}{3}$

66. Contains $(-6, 3)$ with slope $= -\dfrac{2}{3}$

67. Contains $(-2, 3)$ and $(4, -6)$

68. Contains $(5, -3)$ and $(-3, 3)$

69. x-intercept: 5; y-intercept: -2

70. x-intercept: -6; y-intercept: 4

Applying the Concepts

71. Shipping Packages The shipping department for a warehouse has noted that if 60 packages are shipped during a month, the total expenses for the department are \$1635. If 120 packages are shipped during a month, the total expenses for the shipping department are \$1770. Let x represent the number of packages and y represent the total expenses for the shipping department.

(a) Interpret the meaning of the point $(60, 1635)$ in the context of this problem.

(b) Plot the ordered pairs $(60, 1635)$ and $(120, 1770)$ in a rectangular coordinate system and graph the line through the points.

(c) Find the linear equation, in slope-intercept form, that relates the total expenses for the shipping department, y, to the number of packages sent, x.

(d) Use the equation found in part **(c)** to find the total expenses during a month when 200 packages were sent.

(e) Interpret the slope.

72. Retirement Plans Based on the retirement plan available by his employer, Kei knows that if he retires after 20 years, his monthly retirement income will be $3150. If he retires after 30 years, his monthly income increases to $3600. Let x represent the number of years of service and y represent the monthly retirement income.

(a) Interpret the meaning of the point $(30, 3600)$ in the context of this problem.

(b) Plot the ordered pairs $(20, 3150)$ and $(30, 3600)$ in a rectangular coordinate system and graph the line through the points.

(c) Find the linear equation, in slope-intercept form, that relates the monthly retirement income, y, to the number of years of service, x.

(d) Use the equation found in part **(c)** to find the monthly income for 15 years of service.

(e) Interpret the slope.

73. Traffic Fatalities In 1980, Kentucky had 820 traffic fatalities. In 2005, Kentucky had 985 traffic fatalities. Let x represent the number of years since 1980 and let y represent the number of traffic fatalities.

(a) Fill in the ordered pairs: (___, 820); (___, 985).

(b) Plot the ordered pairs from part **(a)** in a rectangular coordinate system and graph the line through the points.

(c) Find the linear equation, in slope-intercept form, that relates the number of traffic fatalities, y, to the number of years since 1980, x.

(d) Use the equation found in part **(c)** to predict the number of traffic fatalities in 2000.

(e) Interpret the slope.

74. U.S. Traffic Fatalities Nationwide, the statistics for traffic fatalities show a decline. In 1980, the United States had 51,091 fatal crashes while in 2005 the number dropped to 43,443. Let y represent the number of traffic fatalities, and x represent the number of years since 1980.

(a) Fill in the ordered pairs: (___, 51,091); (___, 43,443).

(b) Plot the ordered pairs from part **(a)** in a rectangular coordinate system and graph the line through the points.

(c) Find the linear equation, in slope-intercept form, that relates the number of traffic fatalities, y, to the number of years since 1980, x.

(d) Use the equation found in part **(c)** to find the number of traffic fatalities in 2000.

(e) Interpret the slope.

Extending the Concepts

Up to this point, when we knew the slope of a line and a point on the line we found the equation of the line using point-slope form. We could also use the slope-intercept form to find this equation.

For example, suppose that we were asked to find the equation of the line whose slope is 6 and that passes through the point $(2, -5)$. Let's use the slope-intercept form, $y = mx + b$, to write the equation of this line. We know $m = 6$, so we have $y = 6x + b$. We also know that $y = -5$ when $x = 2$. So we substitute 2 for x and -5 for y into the equation and solve for b.

$$y = 6x + b$$
$$\text{Let } x = 2 \text{ and } y = -5: \quad -5 = 6(2) + b$$
$$\text{Multiply:} \quad -5 = 12 + b$$
$$\text{Subtract 12 from each side:} \quad -5 - 12 = 12 - 12 + b$$
$$-17 = b$$

We now know that $b = -17$ and because we also know that $m = 6$, the equation of the line is $y = 6x - 17$. Use this technique to find the slope-intercept form of the line for Problems 75–86.

75. $(-4, 2)$; slope $= 3$ **76.** $(5, -2)$; slope $= 4$

77. $(3, -8)$; slope $= -2$ **78.** $(-1, 7)$; slope $= -5$

79. $\left(\dfrac{2}{3}, \dfrac{1}{2}\right)$; slope $= 6$ **80.** $\left(\dfrac{4}{3}, -\dfrac{3}{2}\right)$; slope $= -9$

81. $(6, -13)$ and $(-2, -5)$ **82.** $(-10, -5)$ and $(2, 7)$

83. $(5, -1)$ and $(-10, -4)$ **84.** $(-6, -3)$ and $(9, 2)$

85. $(-4, 8)$ and $(2, -1)$ **86.** $(4, -9)$ and $(8, -19)$

Explaining the Concepts

87. You are asked to write the equation of the line through the points $(3, 1)$ and $(4, 7)$ in slope-intercept form. After calculating the slope of the line, you choose the point-slope form and assign $x_1 = 3$ and $y_1 = 1$. Your friend lets $x_1 = 4$ and $y_1 = 7$. Will you and your friend obtain the same answer? Explain why or why not.

88. You are asked to write the equation of the line through $(-1, 3)$ and $(0, 4)$. Which form of a line would you choose to find the equation? Explain why you chose this form. Could you also use one of the other forms?

3.6 Parallel and Perpendicular Lines

OBJECTIVES

1. Determine Whether Two Lines Are Parallel
2. Find the Equation of a Line Parallel to a Given Line
3. Determine Whether Two Lines Are Perpendicular
4. Find the Equation of a Line Perpendicular to a Given Line

Preparing for Parallel and Perpendicular Lines

Before getting started, take the following readiness quiz. If you get a problem wrong, go back to the section cited and review the material.

P1. Determine the reciprocal of 3.   [Section 1.4, pp. 35–36]

P2. Determine the reciprocal of $-\dfrac{3}{5}$.   [Section 1.4, pp. 35–36]

1 Determine Whether Two Lines Are Parallel

When two lines in the rectangular coordinate system do not intersect (that is, they have no points in common), they are said to be *parallel*. However, rather than looking at graphs of linear equations to determine whether they are parallel or not, we can look at the equations themselves to determine whether two lines might be parallel.

> **DEFINITION**
>
> Two nonvertical lines are **parallel** if and only if their slopes are equal and they have different *y*-intercepts. Vertical lines are parallel if they have different *x*-intercepts.

Figure 49(a) shows nonvertical parallel lines. Figure 49(b) shows vertical parallel lines.

Work Smart

The use of the words "if and only if" given in the definition of parallel lines means that there are two statements being made:

If two nonvertical lines are parallel, then their slopes are equal and they have different *y*-intercepts.

If two nonvertical lines have equal slopes and different *y*-intercepts, then they are parallel.

Figure 49
Parallel lines.

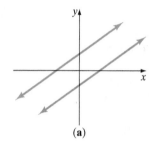

(a)   (b)

To determine whether two lines are parallel, we find the slope and *y*-intercept of each line by putting the equations of the lines in slope-intercept form. If the slopes are the same, but the *y*-intercepts are different, then the lines are parallel.

Figure 50

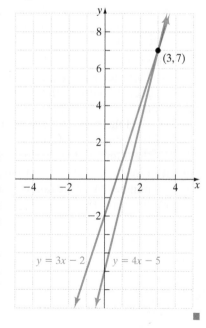

EXAMPLE 1 Determining Whether Two Lines Are Parallel

Determine whether the line $y = 4x - 5$ is parallel to $y = 3x - 2$. Graph the lines to confirm your results.

Solution

For the line $y = 4x - 5$, the slope is 4 and the *y*-intercept is -5. For the line $y = 3x - 2$, the slope is 3 and the *y*-intercept is -2. Because the lines have different slopes, they are not parallel. Figure 50 shows the graph of the two lines.

We can see from the graph in Figure 50 that the lines intersect at (3, 7). Therefore, the lines are not parallel.

EXAMPLE 2   Determining Whether Two Lines Are Parallel

Determine whether the line $-3x + y = 5$ is parallel to $6x - 2y = -2$. Graph the lines to confirm your results.

Solution

To find the slopes and y-intercepts, we solve each equation for y so that each is in slope-intercept form.

$$-3x + y = 5$$

Add $3x$ to both sides: $y = 3x + 5$

The slope of the line $-3x + y = 5$ is 3 and the y-intercept is 5.

$$6x - 2y = -2$$

Subtract $6x$ from both sides: $-2y = -6x - 2$

Divide both sides by -2: $y = \dfrac{-6x - 2}{-2}$

Divide each term in the numerator by -2: $y = 3x + 1$

The slope of $6x - 2y = -2$ is 3 and the y-intercept is 1.

Because the lines have the same slope, 3, but different y-intercepts, the lines are parallel. Figure 51 shows a graph of the two lines.   ■

Work Smart

Make sure both criteria for parallel lines are satisfied.

1. Same slope
2. Different y-intercepts

Lines with the same slope and same y-intercept are called *coincident lines*.

Figure 51

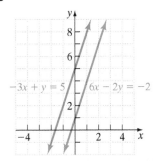

Quick ✔

1. Two nonvertical lines are parallel if and only if their _____ are equal and they have different _____. Vertical lines are parallel if they have different _____.

In Problems 2–4, determine whether the two lines are parallel. Graph the lines to confirm your results.

2. $y = 2x + 1$
$y = -2x - 3$

3. $6x + 3y = 3$
$10x + 5y = 10$

4. $4x + 5y = 10$
$8x + 10y = 20$

⌐2 Find the Equation of a Line Parallel to a Given Line

Now that we know how to identify parallel lines, we can find the equation of a line that is parallel to a given line.

EXAMPLE 3   How to Find the Equation of a Line That Is Parallel to a Given Line

Find the equation for the line that is parallel to $2x + y = 5$ and contains the point $(-1, 3)$. Write the equation of the line in slope-intercept form. Graph the lines.

Step-by-Step Solution

Step 1: Find the slope of the given line.

$$2x + y = 5$$

Subtract $2x$ from both sides: $y = -2x + 5$

The slope of the line is -2, so the slope of the parallel line is also -2.

(continued)

Step 2: Use the point-slope form of a line with the given point and the slope found in Step 1 to find the equation of the parallel line.

$$y - y_1 = m(x - x_1)$$

$m = -2, x_1 = -1, y_1 = 3:\quad y - 3 = -2(x - (-1))$

Step 3: Put the equation in slope-intercept form by solving for y.

$$y - 3 = -2(x + 1)$$

Distribute the -2: $\quad y - 3 = -2x - 2$

Add 3 to both sides: $\quad y = -2x + 1$

The equation of the line parallel to $2x + y = 5$ is $y = -2x + 1$. Figure 52 shows the graph of the parallel lines.

Figure 52

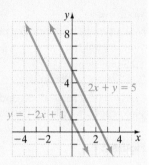

Quick ✔ *In Problems 5 and 6, find the equation of the line that contains the given point and is parallel to the given line. Write the line in slope-intercept form. Graph the lines.*

5. $y = 2x + 1$ containing $(2, 3)$

6. $3x + 2y = 4$ containing $(-2, 3)$

EXAMPLE 4 **Finding the Equation of a Line That Is Parallel to a Given Line**

Find the equation for the line that is parallel to $x = 3$ and contains the point $(1, 5)$. Graph the lines.

Solution

The equation of the given line is $x = 3$. Because this is the equation of a vertical line, the line parallel to it will also be vertical. Vertical lines have equations of the form $x = a$. The line parallel to $x = 3$ that contains the point $(1, 5)$ is $x = 1$. Figure 53 shows the graphs of the lines $x = 3$ and $x = 1$.

Figure 53

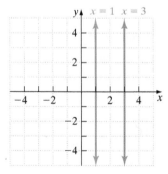

Quick ✔ *In Problems 7 and 8, find the equation of the line that contains the given point and is parallel to the given line. Write the line in slope-intercept form, if possible. Graph the lines.*

7. $x = -2$ containing $(3, 1)$

8. $y + 3 = 0$ containing $(-2, 5)$

⌐3 **Determine Whether Two Lines Are Perpendicular**

When two lines intersect at a right (90°) angle, they are said to be **perpendicular**. See Figure 54.

Just as we use the slopes of lines to determine whether two lines are parallel, we also use slopes of lines to determine whether two lines are perpendicular.

Figure 54

Perpendicular lines.

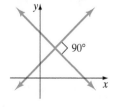

Work Smart

If m_1 and m_2 are negative reciprocals of each other, then $m_1 = \dfrac{-1}{m_2}$. For example, the numbers 4 and $-\dfrac{1}{4}$ are negative reciprocals. Watch out though, because the use of the word "*negative*" does not mean that the slope of the perpendicular line must be negative—it means that the nonvertical lines have slopes that are opposite in sign. One is positive and one is negative.

DEFINITION

Two nonvertical lines are **perpendicular** if and only if the product of their slopes is -1. Put another way, two nonvertical lines are perpendicular if their slopes are negative reciprocals of each other. Any vertical line is perpendicular to any horizontal line.

EXAMPLE 5   Finding the Slope of a Line Perpendicular to a Given Line

Find the slope of a line perpendicular to a line whose slope is (a) 5   (b) $-\dfrac{2}{3}$.

Solution

(a) To find the slope of a line perpendicular to a given line, we determine the negative reciprocal of the slope of the given line. The negative reciprocal of 5 is $\dfrac{-1}{5} = -\dfrac{1}{5}$. Any line whose slope is $-\dfrac{1}{5}$ will be perpendicular to the line whose slope is 5.

(b) The negative reciprocal of $-\dfrac{2}{3}$ is $\dfrac{-1}{-\dfrac{2}{3}} = \dfrac{3}{2}$. Any line whose slope is $\dfrac{3}{2}$ will be perpendicular to the line whose slope is $-\dfrac{2}{3}$. ∎

Quick ✔

9. Given any two nonvertical lines, if the product of their slopes is -1, then the lines are _____.

10. *True or False:* Two different lines L_1 and L_2 have slopes $m_1 = 4$ and $m_2 = -4$, so L_1 is perpendicular to L_2.

In Problems 11–13, find the slope of a line perpendicular to the line whose slope is given.

11. -4 12. $\dfrac{5}{4}$ 13. $-\dfrac{1}{5}$

EXAMPLE 6   Determining Whether Two Lines Are Perpendicular

Determine whether the line $y = 3x - 2$ is perpendicular to $y = \dfrac{1}{3}x + 1$. Graph the lines to confirm your results.

Solution

To determine whether the lines are perpendicular, we first need to find the slope of each line. If the product of the slopes is -1 (the slopes are negative reciprocals of each other), then the lines are perpendicular. The slope of $y = 3x - 2$ is $m_1 = 3$. The slope of $y = \dfrac{1}{3}x + 1$ is $m_2 = \dfrac{1}{3}$. Because the product of the slopes, $m_1 \cdot m_2 = 3 \cdot \left(\dfrac{1}{3}\right) = 1 \neq -1$, the lines are not perpendicular. Notice that the slopes are reciprocals of each other, but are not *negative* reciprocals of each other. Figure 55 shows the graph of the two lines.

Figure 55

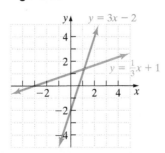

> **EXAMPLE 7** Determining Whether Two Lines Are Perpendicular

Determine whether the line $2x + 3y = -6$ is perpendicular to $3x - 2y = 2$. Graph the lines to confirm your results.

Solution

To find the slopes of the two lines, we write the equations of the lines in slope-intercept form.

$$2x + 3y = -6$$

Subtract 2x from both sides: $3y = -2x - 6$

Divide both sides by 3: $y = \dfrac{-2x - 6}{3}$

Divide 3 into each term in the numerator: $y = -\dfrac{2}{3}x - 2$

The slope of $2x + 3y = -6$ is $m_1 = -\dfrac{2}{3}$.

$$3x - 2y = 2$$

Subtract 3x from both sides: $-2y = -3x + 2$

Divide both sides by -2: $y = \dfrac{-3x + 2}{-2}$

Divide -2 into each term in the numerator: $y = \dfrac{3}{2}x - 1$

Figure 56

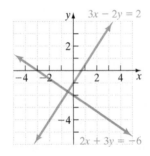

The slope of $3x - 2y = 2$ is $m_2 = \dfrac{3}{2}$.

The product of the slopes is $m_1 \cdot m_2 = -\dfrac{2}{3} \cdot \dfrac{3}{2} = -1$, so the lines are perpendicular.

Put another way, because the slopes are negative reciprocals of each other, the lines are perpendicular. See Figure 56 for the graph of the two lines. ■

Quick ✔ *In Problems 14–16, determine whether the given lines are perpendicular. Graph the lines.*

14. $y = 4x - 3$

$y = -\dfrac{1}{4}x - 4$

15. $2x - y = 3$

$x - 2y = 2$

16. $5x + 2y = 8$

$2x - 5y = 10$

⌐4 Find the Equation of a Line Perpendicular to a Given Line

Now that we know how to find the slope of a line perpendicular to a second line, we can find the equation of a line that is perpendicular to a given line.

> **EXAMPLE 8** How to Find the Equation of a Line Perpendicular to a Given Line

Find the equation of the line that is perpendicular to the line $y = 3x - 2$ and contains the point $(3, -1)$. Write the equation of the line in slope-intercept form. Graph the two lines.

Step-by-Step Solution

Step 1: Find the slope of the given line. $y = 3x - 2$

The slope of the line is 3.

Step 2: Find the slope of the perpendicular line.

The slope of the perpendicular line is the negative reciprocal of 3, which is $-\dfrac{1}{3}$.

Step 3: Use the point-slope form of a line with the given point and the slope found in Step 2 to find the equation of the perpendicular line.

$$y - y_1 = m(x - x_1)$$

$$m = -\frac{1}{3},\ x_1 = 3,\ y_1 = -1:\quad y - (-1) = -\frac{1}{3}(x - 3)$$

Step 4: Put the equation in slope-intercept form by solving for y.

$$y + 1 = -\frac{1}{3}(x - 3)$$

Distribute the $-\dfrac{1}{3}$:
$$y + 1 = -\frac{1}{3}x + 1$$

Subtract 1 from both sides:
$$y = -\frac{1}{3}x$$

The equation of the line perpendicular to $y = 3x - 2$ through $(3, -1)$ is $y = -\dfrac{1}{3}x$. Figure 57 shows the graphs of the two lines.

Figure 57

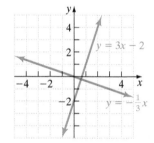

Quick ✔ *In Problems 17 and 18, find the equation of the line that contains the given point and is perpendicular to the given line. Write the line in slope-intercept form. Graph the lines.*

17. $(-4, 2);\ y = 2x + 1$

18. $(-2, -1);\ 2x + 3y = 3$

EXAMPLE 9 **Finding the Equation of a Line Perpendicular to a Given Line**

Find the equation of the line that is perpendicular to the line $x = 2$ and contains the point $(-4, 3)$. Write the equation of the line in slope-intercept form, if possible. Graph the two lines.

Solution

The line $x = 2$ is the equation of a vertical line. Therefore, the line perpendicular will be horizontal. Horizontal lines have slopes equal to 0. To find the equation of the perpendicular line we use the point-slope formula with $m = 0$, $x_1 = -4$, and $y_1 = 3$.

Work Smart

The line perpendicular to a vertical line is horizontal and vice versa.

$$y - y_1 = m(x - x_1)$$

$$m = 0,\ x_1 = -4,\ y_1 = 3:\quad y - 3 = 0(x - (-4))$$

$$y - 3 = 0$$

Add 3 to both sides:
$$y = 3$$

The equation of the line perpendicular to $x = 2$ through the point $(-4, 3)$ is $y = 3$. See Figure 58 for the graph of the two lines.

Figure 58

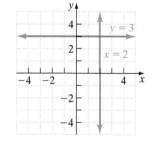

Quick ✔ *In Problems 19 and 20, find the equation of the line that contains the given point and is perpendicular to the given line. Write the line in slope-intercept form, if possible. Graph the lines.*

19. $x = -4$ containing $(-1, -5)$

20. $y + 2 = 0$ containing $(3, -2)$

3.6 EXERCISES

PRACTICE　WATCH　DOWNLOAD　READ　REVIEW

1–20. *are the* Quick ✔s *that follow each* EXAMPLE

Building Skills

In Problems 21–28, fill in the chart with the missing slopes. See Objectives 1 and 3.

	Slope of the Given Line	Slope of a Line Parallel to the Given Line	Slope of a Line Perpendicular to the Given Line
21.	$m = -3$		
22.	$m = 4$		
23.	$m = \dfrac{1}{2}$		
24.	$m = -\dfrac{1}{8}$		
25.	$m = -\dfrac{4}{9}$		
26.	$m = \dfrac{5}{2}$		
27.	$m = 0$		
28.	$m = $ undefined		

In Problems 29–42, determine if the lines are parallel, perpendicular, or neither. See Objectives 1 and 3.

29. $L_1: y = x - 3$
$L_2: y = 1 - x$

30. $L_1: y = -4x + 3$
$L_2: y = 4x - 1$

31. $L_1: y = \dfrac{3}{4}x + 2$
$L_2: y = 0.75x - 1$

32. $L_1: y = 0.8x + 6$
$L_2: y = \dfrac{4}{5}x + \dfrac{19}{3}$

33. $L_1: y = -\dfrac{5}{3}x - 6$
$L_2: y = \dfrac{3}{5}x - 1$

34. $L_1: y = 3x - 1$
$L_2: y = 6 - \dfrac{x}{3}$

35. $L_1: x + y = -3$
$L_2: y - x = 1$

36. $L_1: x - 4y = 24$
$L_2: 2x - 8y = -8$

37. $L_1: 2x - 5y = 5$
$L_2: 5x + 2y = 4$

38. $L_1: x - 2y = -8$
$L_2: x + 2y = 2$

39. $L_1: 4x - 5y - 15 = 0$
$L_2: 8x - 10y + 5 = 0$

40. $L_1: x + y = 6$
$L_2: x - y = -2$

41. $L_1: 4x = 3y + 3$
$L_2: 6y = 8x + 36$

42. $L_1: 2x - 5y - 45 = 0$
$L_2: 5x + 2y - 8 = 0$

In Problems 43–54, find the equation of the line that contains the given point and is parallel to the given line. Write the equation in slope-intercept form, if possible. See Objective 2.

43. $(4, -2); y = 3x - 1$

44. $(7, -5); y = 2x + 6$

45. $(-3, 8); y = -4x + 5$

46. $(-2, 6); y = -5x - 2$

47. $(3, -7); y = 4$

48. $(-4, 5); x = -3$

49. $(-1, 10); x = 10$

50. $(4, -8); y = -1$

51. $(10, 2); 3x - 2y = 5$

52. $(6, 7); 2x + 3y = 9$

53. $(-1, -10); x + 2y = 4$

54. $(-3, -5); 2x - 5y = 6$

In Problems 55–66, find the equation of the line that contains the given point and is perpendicular to the given line. Write the equation in slope-intercept form, if possible. See Objective 4.

55. $(3, 5); y = \dfrac{1}{2}x - 2$

56. $(4, 7); y = \dfrac{1}{3}x - 3$

57. $(-4, -1); y = -4x + 1$

58. $(-2, -5); y = -2x + 5$

59. $(-2, 1)$; x-axis

60. $(3, -6)$; y-axis

61. $(7, 5)$; y-axis

62. $(11, -6)$; x-axis

63. $(0, 0)$; $2x + 5y = 7$

64. $(0, 0)$; $6x + 4y = 3$

65. $(-10, -3)$; $5x - 3y = 4$

66. $(-6, 10)$; $3x - 5y = 2$

Mixed Practice

In Problems 67–82, find the equation of the line that has the given properties. Write the equation in slope-intercept form, if possible. Graph each line.

67. Contains $(3, -5)$; slope $= 7$

68. Contains $(-2, 10)$; slope $= 3$

69. Contains $(2, 9)$; perpendicular to the line
$y = -5x + 3$

70. Contains $(8, 3)$; parallel to the line $y = -4x + 2$

71. Contains $(6, -1)$; parallel to the line $y = -7x + 2$

72. Contains $(5, -2)$; perpendicular to the line
$y = 4x + 3$

73. Contains $(-6, 2)$ and $(-1, -8)$

74. Contains $(-4, -1)$ and $(-3, -5)$

75. Slope $= 3$, y-intercept $= -2$

76. Slope $= -2$, y-intercept $= 7$

77. Contains $(5, 1)$; parallel to the line $x = -6$

78. Contains $(2, 7)$; perpendicular to the line $x = -8$

79. Contains $(3, -2)$; parallel to the line $4x + 3y = 9$

80. Contains $(-3, -2)$; perpendicular to the line
$6x - 2y = 1$

81. Contains $(-1, -3)$; perpendicular to the line
$x - 2y = -10$

82. Contains $(-7, 2)$; parallel to the line $x + 4y = 2$

In Problems 83–90, each line contains the given points. (a) Find the slope of each line. (b) Determine if the lines are parallel, perpendicular, or neither.

83. L_1: $(0, -1)$ and $(-2, -7)$
L_2: $(-1, 5)$ and $(2, -4)$

84. L_1: $(-3, -14)$ and $(1, 2)$
L_2: $(0, 2)$ and $(-3, -10)$

85. L_1: $(2, 8)$ and $(7, 18)$
L_2: $(-2, -3)$ and $(6, 13)$

86. L_1: $(6, 0)$ and $(-2, 8)$
L_2: $(4, 1)$ and $(-6, -9)$

87. L_1: $(-2, -5)$ and $(4, -2)$
L_2: $(-8, -5)$ and $(0, -1)$

88. L_1: $(1, 6)$ and $(-1, -10)$
L_2: $(0, 1)$ and $(-2, 17)$

89. L_1: $(-6, -9)$ and $(3, 6)$
L_2: $(10, -8)$ and $(-5, 1)$

90. L_1: $(-8, -8)$ and $(4, 1)$
L_2: $(12, 8)$ and $(-4, -4)$

Applying the Concepts

A parallelogram is a quadrilateral in which both pairs of opposite sides are parallel. In Problems 91 and 92, plot the following points, draw the figure, and then use slope to determine if the figure is a parallelogram.

91. $A(-1, 1)$; $B(3, 5)$; $C(6, 4)$; $D(2, 0)$

92. $A(-1, -3)$; $B(1, -1)$; $C(5, 1)$; $D(3, -2)$

A rectangle is a parallelogram that contains one right angle. That is, one pair of sides is perpendicular. In Problems 93 and 94, plot the following points, draw the figure, and then use slope to determine if the figure is a rectangle.

93. $A(6, -1)$; $B(-3, -2)$; $C(1, -6)$; $D(2, 3)$

94. $A(1, 1)$; $B(-1, 5)$; $C(5, 8)$; $D(7, 4)$

A right triangle is a triangle that contains one right angle. In Problems 95–98, plot each point and form the triangle ABC. Verify using slope that the triangle is a right triangle.

95. $A(-2, 5)$; $B(1, 3)$; $C(3, 6)$

96. $A(-5, 3)$; $B(6, 0)$; $C(5, 5)$

97. $A(4, -3)$; $B(0, -3)$; $C(4, 2)$

98. $A(-2, 5)$; $B(12, 3)$; $C(10, -11)$

Extending the Concepts

In Problems 99 and 100, find the missing coefficient so that the lines are parallel.

99. $-3y = 6x - 12$ and $4x + By = -2$

100. $Ax + 2y = 4$ and $15x = 5y + 20$

In Problems 101 and 102, find the missing coefficient so that the lines are perpendicular.

101. $Ax + 6y = -6$ and $12 - 6y = -9x$

102. $x - By = 10$ and $3y = -6x + 9$

△**103.** The altitude of a triangle is a line segment drawn from a vertex of the triangle perpendicular to the opposite side. Plot the following points, draw triangle ABC and the segment joining points B and D, and then determine if $\overline{BD}$ is an altitude of the triangle. $A(-6, -3); B(-4, 7); C(-1, 2); D(-3, 0)$

△**104.** The coordinates of the vertices of a quadrilateral are $A(2, 1), B(4, 6), C(6, 6)$, and $D(9, 2)$. Use slopes to show that the diagonals of the quadrilateral, $\overline{AC}$ and $\overline{BD}$, are perpendicular to each other.

Explaining the Concepts

105. Describe the four possible relationships of the graphs of two lines in a rectangular coordinate system.

106. You are asked to determine if the following lines are parallel, perpendicular or neither: L_1 contains the points $(1, 1)$ and $(3, 5)$ and L_2 contains the points $(-1, -1)$ and $(4, 9)$. List the steps you would follow to make this determination and describe the criteria you would use to answer the question.

PUTTING THE CONCEPTS TOGETHER (Sections 3.1–3.6)

These problems cover important concepts from Sections 3.1 through 3.6. We designed these problems so that you can review the chapter so far and show your mastery of the concepts. Take time to work these problems before proceeding with the next section. The answers to these problems are located at the back of the text on page AN-14.

1. Given the linear equation $4x - 3y = 10$, determine whether the ordered pair $(1, -2)$ is a solution to the equation.

In Problems 2 and 3, graph each equation using the point-plotting method.

2. $y = \dfrac{2}{3}x - 1$

3. $-5x + 2y = 10$

4. Given the equation $-8x + 2y = 6$, determine

   (a) the x-intercept
   (b) the y-intercept

5. Graph the equation $4x + 3y = 6$ by finding the x-intercept and the y-intercept.

6. Given the equation $6x + 9y = -12$, determine

   (a) the slope
   (b) the y-intercept

7. Find the slope of the line that contains the points $(3, -5)$ and $(-6, -2)$.

8. Given the linear equation $2y = -5x - 4$, find

   (a) the slope of a line perpendicular to the given line
   (b) the slope of a line parallel to the given line

9. Determine whether the lines are parallel, perpendicular, or neither. Explain how you came to your conclusion.

   $L_1: 10x + 5y = 2 \qquad L_2: y = -2x + 3$

In Problems 10–16, write the equation of the line that satisfies the given conditions. Write the equation in slope-intercept form, if possible.

10. slope $= 3$ and y-intercept is 1

11. slope $= -6$ and passes through $(-1, 4)$

12. through $(4, -1)$ and $(-2, 11)$

13. through $(-8, 0)$ and perpendicular to $y = \dfrac{2}{5}x - 5$

14. through $(-8, 3)$ and parallel to $-8y + 2x = -1$

15. horizontal line through $(-6, -8)$

16. through $(2, 6)$ with undefined slope

17. Shipping Expenses The shipping department records indicate that during a week when 80 packages were shipped, the total expenses recorded for the shipping department were \$1180. During a different week 50 packages were shipped and the expenses recorded were \$850. Use the ordered pairs $(80, 1180)$ and $(50, 850)$ to determine the average rate to ship an additional package.

18. Diamonds Suppose the relation between the cost of a diamond and its weight is linear. In looking at two diamonds, we find that one of the diamonds weighs 0.7 carats and costs \$3543, while the other diamond weighs 0.8 carats and costs \$4378. (SOURCE: *diamonds.com*)

   (a) Use the ordered pairs $(0.7, 3543)$ and $(0.8, 4378)$ to find a linear equation that relates the price of a diamond to its weight.
   (b) Interpret the slope.
   (c) Predict the price of a diamond that weighs 0.76 carats.

CHAPTER 3 Activity: Graphing Practice

Focus: Graphing and identifying the graphs of linear equations and inequalities.

Time: 15–20 minutes

Group size: 3–4

Materials needed: Blank piece of paper and graph paper for each group member.

1. On each of four pieces of paper, write one of the following equations or inequalities.

   (a) $x + 3 \geq -4(y - 1)$

   (b) $4(y - 2) + 5 = 5(x + 1)$

   (c) $3(y - 7) + 4 = -2(x - 3) - 2$

   (d) $\dfrac{2}{3}(x + 2y) + \dfrac{8}{3} \geq 0$

2. Place the four papers face down on the desk and mix them up. One by one, each group member should choose a piece of paper. Do not show your choice to the other members of the group.

3. Carefully graph the chosen equation/inequality on your graph paper. Do not label your graph.

4. When finished, place the unlabeled graphs in a pile.

5. As a group, with no help from the member who drew the graph, write the equation or inequality that is drawn.

6. As a group, discuss the outcome.

CHAPTER 3 Review

Section 3.1 The Rectangular Coordinate System and Equations in Two Variables

KEY TERMS

x-axis	Ordered pair (x, y)	Quadrants
y-axis	Coordinates	Equation in two variables
Origin	x-coordinate	Sides
Rectangular or Cartesian coordinate system	y-coordinate	Satisfy
xy-plane		
Coordinate axes		

YOU SHOULD BE ABLE TO...	EXAMPLE	REVIEW EXERCISES
1 Plot points in the rectangular coordinate system (p. 175)	Examples 1 and 2	1–6
2 Determine if an ordered pair satisfies an equation (p. 179)	Example 3	7, 8
3 Create a table of values that satisfy an equation (p. 181)	Examples 4 through 7	9–16

In Problems 1–4, plot the following points in the rectangular coordinate system. Tell which quadrant each point belongs to or on which axis the point lies.

1. $A(3, -2)$

2. $B(-1, -3)$

3. $C(-4, 0)$

4. $D(0, 2)$

In Problems 5 and 6, identify the coordinates of each point labeled in the figure. Tell which quadrant each point belongs to (or on which axis the point lies).

5.

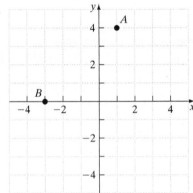

6.

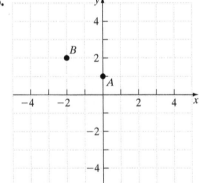

In Problems 7 and 8, determine whether the ordered pairs satisfy the given equation.

7. $y = 3x - 7$
$A(-1, -10)$
$B(-7, 0)$

8. $4x - 3y = 2$
$A(2, 2)$
$B(6, 5)$

9. Find an ordered pair that satisfies the equation $-x = 3y$ when
  (a) $x = 4$ **(b)** $y = 2$

10. Find an ordered pair that satisfies the equation $x - y = 0$ when
  (a) $x = 4$ **(b)** $y = -2$

In Problems 11–14, use the equation to complete the table. Use the table to list some of the ordered pairs that satisfy the equation.

11. $3x - 2y = 10$

x	y	(x, y)
-2		
0		
4		

12. $y = -x + 2$

x	y	(x, y)
-3		
2		
4		

13. $y = -\dfrac{1}{3}x - 4$

x	y	(x, y)
	2	
-6		
	-12	

14. $3x - 2y = 7$

x	y	(x, y)
	-8	
3		
	4	

15. Mail Order Shipping Martha purchases some clothes from a mail order catalogue. The shipping costs for her order will be $5.00 plus $2.00 per item purchased. The equation that calculates her total shipping cost, C, is given by the equation $C = 5 + 2x$, where x is the number of items purchased. Complete the table below and then graph the ordered pairs in a rectangular coordinate system.

x	C	(x, C)
1		
2		
3		

16. Department Store Wages Isabel works in a department store where her monthly earnings are $1000 plus 10% commission on her sales. Her earnings, E, are given by the equation $E = 1000 + 0.10x$, where x is Isabel's sales for the month. Complete the table below and then graph the ordered pairs in a rectangular coordinate system.

x	E	(x, E)
500		
1000		
2000		

Section 3.2 Graphing Equations in Two Variables

KEY CONCEPTS

- **Linear Equation**
  A linear equation in two variables is an equation of the form
  $Ax + By = C$, where A, B, and C are real numbers. A and B cannot
  both be zero.
- **Procedure for Finding Intercepts**
  1. To find the x-intercept(s), if any, of the graph of an equation, let $y = 0$
     in the equation and solve for x.
  2. To find the y-intercept(s), if any, of the graph of an equation, let $x = 0$
     in the equation and solve for y.
- **Vertical Line**
  A vertical line is given by the equation $x = a$, where a is the x-intercept.
- **Horizontal Line**
  A horizontal line is given by the equation $y = b$ where b is the
  y-intercept.

KEY TERMS

Graph of an equation in two variables
Point-plotting method
Complete graph
Linear equation in two variables
Standard form of an equation of a line
Line
Intercepts
x-intercept
y-intercept

YOU SHOULD BE ABLE TO...	EXAMPLE	REVIEW EXERCISES
1 Graph a line by plotting points (p. 188)	Examples 1, 3, and 4	17–22
2 Graph a line using intercepts (p. 193)	Examples 5 through 8	23–32
3 Graph vertical and horizontal lines (p. 196)	Examples 9 and 10	33–36

In Problems 17–20, graph each linear equation using the point-plotting method.

17. $y = -2x$ **18.** $y = x$

19. $4x + y = -2$ **20.** $3x - y = -1$

21. Printing Cost The cost to print pamphlets for a new healthcare clinic is a $40 set-up fee plus $2.00 per pamphlet that will be printed. The equation that calculates the total cost for printing, C, is $C = 40 + 2p$, where p is the number of pamphlets to be printed. Complete the table below and then graph the equation.

p	C	(p, C)
20		
50		
80		

22. Performance Fees The Crickets are the newest band in town and have a gig performing at a local concert. They agree that their total fee will be $500 plus an additional $3.00 per person who attends the concert. The equation that calculates the total fee for performing,

F, is $F = 500 + 3p$, where p is the number of people in attendance. Complete the table below and then graph the equation.

p	F	(p, F)
100		
200		
500		

In Problems 23 and 24, find the intercepts of each graph.

23.

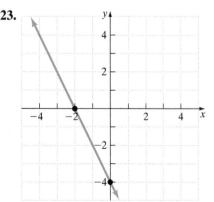

24.

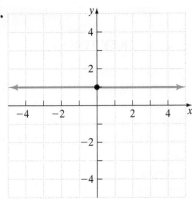

In Problems 29–32, graph each linear equation by finding its intercepts.

29. $y - 3x = 3$ **30.** $2x + 5y = 0$

31. $\dfrac{x}{3} + \dfrac{y}{2} = 1$ **32.** $y = -\dfrac{3}{4}x + 3$

In Problems 33–36, graph each vertical or horizontal line.

33. $x = -2$ **34.** $y = 3$

35. $y = -4$ **36.** $x = 1$

In Problems 25–28, find the x-intercept and y-intercept of each equation.

25. $-3x + y = 9$ **26.** $y = 2x - 6$

27. $x = 3$ **28.** $2x - 5y = 2$

Section 3.3 Slope

KEY CONCEPT	KEY TERMS
• **Slope** If $x_1 \neq x_2$, the **slope** m of the line containing (x_1, y_1) and (x_2, y_2) is defined by the formula $m = \dfrac{y_2 - y_1}{x_2 - x_1}$. The slope of a vertical line is undefined. The slope of a horizontal line is 0.	Run Rise Slope Average rate of change

YOU SHOULD BE ABLE TO...	EXAMPLE	REVIEW EXERCISES
1 Find the slope of a line given two points (p. 201)	Examples 1 and 2	37–42
2 Find the slope of vertical and horizontal lines (p. 205)	Examples 3 and 4	43–46
3 Graph a line using its slope and a point on the line (p. 206)	Examples 5 and 6	47–50
4 Work with applications of slope (p. 207)	Examples 7 and 8	51, 52

In Problems 37 and 38, find the slope of the line whose graph is shown.

37.

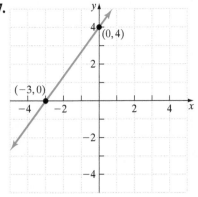

38.

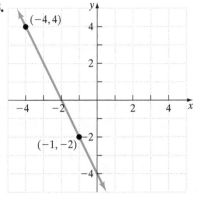

In Problems 39–46, find the slope of the line containing the given points.

39. $(-4, 6)$ and $(-3, -2)$ **40.** $(4, 1)$ and $(0, -7)$

41. $\left(\dfrac{1}{2}, -\dfrac{3}{4}\right)$ and $\left(\dfrac{5}{2}, -\dfrac{1}{4}\right)$ **42.** $\left(-\dfrac{1}{2}, \dfrac{2}{3}\right)$ and $\left(\dfrac{3}{2}, \dfrac{1}{3}\right)$

43. $(-3, -6)$ and $(-3, -10)$ **44.** $(-5, -1)$ and $(-1, -1)$

45. $\left(\dfrac{3}{4}, \dfrac{1}{2}\right)$ and $\left(-\dfrac{1}{4}, \dfrac{1}{2}\right)$ **46.** $\left(\dfrac{1}{3}, -\dfrac{3}{5}\right)$ and $\left(\dfrac{3}{9}, -\dfrac{1}{5}\right)$

In Problems 47–50, graph the line that contains the given point and has the given slope.

47. $(-2, -3); m = 4$ **48.** $(1, -3); m = -2$

49. $(0, 1); m = -\dfrac{2}{3}$ **50.** $(2, 3); m = 0$

51. Production Cost The total cost to produce 20 bicycles is \$1400 and the total cost to produce 50 bicycles is \$2750. Find and interpret the slope of the line containing the points $(20, 1400)$ and $(50, 2750)$.

52. Road Grade Scott is driving to the river on a road which falls 5 feet for every 100 feet of horizontal distance. What is the grade of this road? Express your answer as a percent.

Section 3.4   Slope-Intercept Form of a Line

KEY CONCEPT

- **Slope-intercept form of an equation of a line**
  - An equation of a line with slope m and y-intercept b is $y = mx + b$.

YOU SHOULD BE ABLE TO...	EXAMPLE	REVIEW EXERCISES
1 Use the slope-intercept form to identify the slope and y-intercept of a line (p. 211)	Examples 1 and 2	53–56
2 Graph a line whose equation is in slope-intercept form (p. 212)	Examples 3 and 4	57–62
3 Graph a line whose equation is in the form $Ax + By = C$ (p. 214)	Example 5	63, 64
4 Find the equation of a line given its slope and y-intercept (p. 214)	Example 6	65–70
5 Work with linear models in slope-intercept form. (p. 215)	Examples 7 and 8	71, 72

In Problems 53–56, find the slope and the y-intercept of the line whose equation is given.

53. $y = -x + \dfrac{1}{2}$ **54.** $y = x - \dfrac{3}{2}$

55. $3x - 4y = -4$ **56.** $2x + 5y = 8$

In Problems 57–64, use the slope and y-intercept to graph each line whose equation is given.

57. $y = \dfrac{1}{3}x + 1$ **58.** $y = -\dfrac{x}{2} - 1$

59. $y = -\dfrac{2}{3}x - 2$ **60.** $y = \dfrac{3x}{4} + 3$

61. $y = x$ **62.** $y = -2x$

63. $2x - y = -4$ **64.** $-4x + 2y = 2$

In Problems 65–70, find the equation of the line with the given slope and intercept.

65. slope is $-\dfrac{3}{4}$; y-intercept is $\dfrac{2}{3}$

66. slope is $\dfrac{1}{5}$; y-intercept is 10

67. slope is undefined; x-intercept is -12

68. slope is 0; y-intercept is -4

69. slope is 1; y-intercept is -20

70. slope is -1; y-intercept is -8

71. Car Rentals Hot Rod Car Rentals rents sports cars for \$120 plus \$80 per day. The equation that calculates the total cost C to rent a sports car is $C = 120 + 80d$, where d is the number of days that the car is used.

(a) How much will it cost to rent the car for 3 days?

(b) If the bill came to $680, how many days was the sports car rented out?

(c) Graph the equation in a rectangular coordinate system.

72. Computer Rentals Anthony plans to rent a computer to finish his master's thesis. There is no fixed fee, only a charge for each day the computer is checked out. If he keeps the computer for 22 days, he will pay $418. If his thesis advisor asks him to redo a section and he finds that he must keep the computer for 35 days, it will cost him $665.

(a) Write two ordered pairs (d, C), where d represents the number of days the computer is rented and C represents the cost. Calculate the slope of the line that contains these two points.

(b) Interpret the meaning of the slope of this line.

(c) Write an equation that represents the total cost for Anthony to rent a computer.

(d) Calculate the cost to rent a computer for 8 days.

Section 3.5 Point-Slope Form of a Line

KEY CONCEPT

- **Point-Slope Form of an Equation of a Line**
  An equation of the nonvertical line of slope m that contains the point (x_1, y_1) is $y - y_1 = m(x - x_1)$.

YOU SHOULD BE ABLE TO...	EXAMPLE	REVIEW EXERCISES
1 Find the equation of a line given a point and a slope (p. 220)	Examples 1 through 3	73–80
2 Find the equation of a line given two points (p. 222)	Examples 4 and 5	81–84
3 Build linear models using the point-slope form of a line (p. 224)	Example 6	85, 86

In Problems 73–80, find the equation of the line that contains the given point and the given slope. Write the equation in slope-intercept form, if possible.

73. $(0, -3)$; slope = 6

74. $(4, 0)$; slope = -2

75. $(3, -1)$; slope = $-\dfrac{1}{2}$

76. $(-1, -3)$; slope = $\dfrac{2}{3}$

77. $\left(-\dfrac{4}{3}, -\dfrac{1}{2}\right)$; horizontal

78. $\left(-\dfrac{4}{7}, \dfrac{8}{5}\right)$; vertical

79. $(-5, 2)$; slope is undefined

80. $(6, 0)$; slope = 0

In Problems 81–84, find the equation of the line that contains the given points. Write the equation of the line in slope-intercept form, if possible.

81. $(-7, 0)$ and $(0, 8)$

82. $(0, -6)$ and $(4, 0)$

83. $(3, 5)$ and $(-2, -10)$

84. $(-15, 1)$ and $(-5, -3)$

85. Harvesting Hay Farmer Myers noted that at the end of 3 days of harvesting, 12 acres of hay remained in his field and at the end of 5 days, 4 acres remained. Use the ordered pairs $(3, 12)$ and $(5, 4)$ to write an equation that calculates how many acres of hay, A, are left to be harvested after d days.

86. Fish Population Pat works at Scripps Institute of Oceanography and is responsible for monitoring the fish population in various waters around the world. In one bay, the sunfish population was declining at a constant rate. His initial sample netted 15 sunfish and six months later, the same location netted 13 sunfish. Use the ordered pairs $(0, 15)$ and $(6, 13)$ to write an equation that will predict how many sunfish, F, the sample will yield after m months.

Section 3.6   Parallel and Perpendicular Lines

KEY TERMS

Parallel
Perpendicular

YOU SHOULD BE ABLE TO...	EXAMPLE	REVIEW EXERCISES
1 Determine whether two lines are parallel (p. 228)	Examples 1 and 2	87, 88
2 Find the equation of a line parallel to a given line (p. 229)	Examples 3 and 4	89–94
3 Determine whether two lines are perpendicular (p. 230)	Examples 5 through 7	95–98
4 Find the equation of a line perpendicular to a given line (p. 232)	Examples 8 and 9	99–102

In Problems 87 and 88, determine if the two lines are parallel.

87. $y = -\dfrac{1}{3}x + 2$ **88.** $y = \dfrac{1}{2}x - 4$

$x - 3y = 3$ $x - 2y = 6$

In Problems 89–94, find the equation of the line that contains the given point and is parallel to the given line. Write the equation in slope-intercept form, if possible.

89. $(3, -1); y = -x + 5$

90. $(-2, 4); y = 2x - 1$

91. $(-1, 10); 3x + y = -7$

92. $(4, -5); 6x + 2y = 5$

93. $(5, 19); y\text{-axis}$

94. $(-1, -12); x\text{-axis}$

In Problems 95 and 96, determine the slope of the line perpendicular to the given line.

95. $3x - 2y = 5$ **96.** $4x - 9y = 1$

In Problems 97 and 98, determine if the two lines are perpendicular.

97. $x + 3y = 3$ **98.** $5x - 2y = 2$

$y = 3x + 1$ $y = \dfrac{2}{5}x + 12$

In Problems 99–102, write the equation of the line that contains the given point and is perpendicular to the given line. Write the equation in slope-intercept form, if possible.

99. $(-3, 4); y = -3x + 1$

100. $(4, -1); y = 2x - 1$

101. $(1, -3); 2x - 3y = 6$

102. $\left(-\dfrac{3}{5}, \dfrac{2}{5}\right); x + y = -7$

CHAPTER 3 TEST

Remember to use your Chapter Test Prep Video CD to see fully worked-out solutions to any of these problems you would like to review.

1. Determine whether the ordered pair $(-3, -2)$ is a solution to the equation $3x - 4y = -17$.

2. Given the equation $3x - 9y = 12$, determine
   (a) the x-intercept   (b) the y-intercept

3. Given the equation $4x - 3y = -24$, determine
   (a) the slope   (b) the y-intercept

In Problems 4 and 5, graph each linear equation.

4. $y = -\dfrac{3}{4}x + 2$ 5. $3x - 6y = -12$

6. Find the slope of the line that contains the points $(2, -2)$ and $(-4, -1)$.

7. Given the linear equation $3y = 2x - 1$, find
   (a) the slope of a line perpendicular to the given line.
   (b) the slope of a line parallel to the given line.

8. Determine whether the lines are parallel, perpendicular, or neither. Explain how you came to your conclusion.

$$L_1: 3x - 7y = 2$$
$$L_2: y = \frac{7}{3}x + 4$$

In Problems 9–15, write the equation of the line that satisfies the given conditions. Write the equation in slope-intercept form, if possible.

9. slope $= -4$ and y-intercept is -15

10. slope $= 2$ and contains $(-3, 8)$

11. contains $(-3, -2)$ and $(-4, 1)$

12. contains $(4, 0)$ and parallel to $y = \dfrac{1}{2}x + 2$

13. contains $(4, 2)$ and perpendicular to $4x - 6y = 5$

14. horizontal line through $(3, 5)$

15. contains $(-2, -1)$ with undefined slope

16. **Shipping Packages** The shipping department records indicate that during a week when 20 packages were shipped, the total expenses recorded for the shipping department were $560. During a different week when 30 packages were shipped, the expenses recorded were $640. Use the ordered pairs $(20, 560)$ and $(30, 640)$ to determine the average rate to ship a package.

In Problems 17–19, graph each inequality.

17. $y \geq x - 3$ 18. $-2x - 4y < 8$ 19. $x \leq -4$

CUMULATIVE REVIEW Chapters 1-3

In Problems 1–3, evaluate each expression.

1. $200 \div 25 \cdot (-2)$

2. $\dfrac{3}{4} + \dfrac{1}{6} - \dfrac{2}{3}$

3. $\dfrac{8 - 3(5 - 3^2)}{7 - 2 \cdot 6}$

4. Evaluate $x^3 + 3x^2 - 5x - 7$ for $x = -3$.

5. Simplify: $8m - 5m^2 - 3 + 9m^2 - 3m - 6$

In Problems 6 and 7, solve each equation.

6. $8(n + 2) - 7 = 6n - 5$

7. $\dfrac{2}{5}x + \dfrac{1}{6} = -\dfrac{2}{3}$

8. Solve $A = \dfrac{1}{2}h(b + B)$ for B.

In Problems 9 and 10, solve each linear inequality. Express the solution using set-builder notation and interval notation. Graph the solution set.

9. $6x - 7 > -31$

10. $5(x - 3) \geq 7(x - 4) + 3$

11. Plot the following ordered pairs in the same Cartesian plane.

$A(-3, 0) \quad B(4, -2) \quad C(1, 5)$

$D(0, 3) \quad E(-4, -5) \quad F(-5, 2)$

In Problems 12 and 13, graph the linear equation using the method you prefer.

12. $y = -\dfrac{1}{2}x + 4$

13. $4x - 5y = 15$

In Problems 14 and 15, find the equation of the line with the given properties. Express your answer in slope-intercept form.

14. Through the points $(3, -2)$ and $(-6, 10)$

15. Parallel to $y = -3x + 10$ and through the point $(-5, 7)$

16. Graph $x - 3y > 12$.

17. Computing Grades Shawn really wants an A in his geometry class. His four exam scores are 94, 95, 90, and 97. The final exam is worth two exam scores. To have an A, his average must be at least 93. What scores can Shawn score on the final exam to earn an A in the course?

18. Body Mass Index The body mass index (BMI) of a person 62 inches tall and weighing x pounds is given by $0.2x - 2$. A BMI of 30 or more is considered to be obese. For what weights would a person 62 inches tall be considered obese?

19. Supplementary Angles Two angles are supplementary. The measure of the larger angle is 15 degrees more than twice the measure of the smaller angle. Find the angle measures.

20. Cylinders Max has 100 square inches of aluminum with which to make a closed cylinder. If the radius of the cylinder must be 2 inches, how tall will the cylinder be? (Round to the nearest hundredth of an inch.)

21. Consecutive Integers Find three consecutive even integers such that the sum of the first two is 22 more than the third.

5 Exponents and Polynomials

Advertisers follow trends in consumer tastes. Did you know that the total projected worldwide spending on online social network advertising has increased in recent years? The polynomial $-32.4x^2 + 905.6x + 438$ models the projected advertising dollars to be spent on online social network advertising for the years 2006–2011, where x is the number of years after 2006. See Problem 125 in Section 5.1, page 325.

OUTLINE

The Big Picture: Putting It Together

The first two chapters of the text were devoted to reviewing and developing fundamental skills with real numbers, algebraic expressions, and equations. We will use these skills often as we proceed through the course. In particular, we will describe how new topics and skills relate to those that we already know.

This chapter introduces polynomials. Polynomial expressions, such as the one given in the chapter opener, are used to describe many situations in business, consumer affairs, the physical and biological sciences, and even the entertainment industry. In this chapter, we will learn how to add, subtract, multiply, and divide polynomial expressions. You should pay attention to the techniques for performing these operations and how they are related to the techniques for adding, subtracting, multiplying, and dividing real numbers. Why? If we think of algebra as an extension of arithmetic skills, then comprehension and understanding of the material will come more quickly and easily.

5.1 Adding and Subtracting Polynomials

Preparing for Adding and Subtracting Polynomials

Before getting started, take the following readiness quiz. If you get a problem wrong, go back to the section cited and review the material.

P1. What is the coefficient of $-4x^5$? [Section 1.8, p. 69]

P2. Combine like terms: $-3x + 2 - 2x - 6x - 7$ [Section 1.8, pp. 71–72]

P3. Use the Distributive Property to remove the parentheses: $-4(x - 3)$ [Section 1.8, p. 72]

P4. Evaluate the expression $5 - 3x$ for $x = -2$. [Section 1.8, pp. 67–68]

Recall from Section 1.8 that a term is a number or the product of a number and one or more variables raised to a power. The numerical factor of a term is the coefficient. A constant is a single number, such as 2 or $-\dfrac{3}{2}$. For example, consider Table 1, where some algebraic expressions are given along with the terms and coefficients.

Table 1		
Algebraic Expression	Terms	Coefficients
$3x + 2$	$3x, 2$	$3, 2$
$4x^2 - 7x + 5 = 4x^2 + (-7x) + 5$	$4x^2, -7x, 5$	$4, -7, 5$
$9x^2 + 7y^3$	$9x^2, 7y^3$	$9, 7$

Notice in the algebraic expression $4x^2 - 7x + 5$ given in Table 1 that we first rewrite it as a sum, $4x^2 + (-7x) + 5$, to identify the terms and coefficients.

1 Define Monomial and Determine the Degree of a Monomial

In this chapter, we study *polynomials*. Polynomials are made up of terms that are **monomials.**

Work Smart

The prefix "mono" means "one." For example, a monorail has one rail. So a monomial in one variable is either a constant or a single term with a variable in it.

In Words

The degree of a monomial can be thought of as the number of times the variable occurs as a factor. For example, because $2x^4 = 2 \cdot x \cdot x \cdot x \cdot x$, the degree of $2x^4$ is 4.

DEFINITION

A **monomial** in one variable is the product of a constant and a variable raised to a whole number $(0, 1, 2, \dots)$ power. A monomial in one variable is of the form

$$ax^k$$

where a is a constant that is any real number, x is a variable, and k is a whole number.

In a monomial of the form ax^k, where $a \neq 0$, we call k the **degree** of the monomial. The degree of a nonzero constant is zero. Because $0 = 0x = 0x^2 = 0x^3 = \dots$, we cannot assign a degree to 0. Therefore, we say 0 has no degree.

EXAMPLE 1 Monomials

MONOMIAL	COEFFICIENT	DEGREE
(a) $2x^4$	2	4
(b) $-\dfrac{7}{4}x^2$	$-\dfrac{7}{4}$	2
(c) $-x = -1 \cdot x^1$	-1	1
(d) $x^3 = 1 \cdot x^3$	1	3
(e) $8 = 8x^0$	8	0
(f) 0	0	No degree

Now let's look at some expressions that are not monomials.

EXAMPLE 2 Examples of Expressions That Are Not Monomials

(a) $5x^{\frac{1}{2}}$ is not a monomial because the exponent of the variable x is $\frac{1}{2}$ and $\frac{1}{2}$ is not a whole number.

(b) $2x^{-4}$ is not a monomial because the exponent of the variable x is -4 and -4 is not a whole number. ∎

Quick ✔

1. A _____ in one variable is the product of a number and a variable raised to a whole number power.

2. The coefficient of a monomial such as x^2 or z is ____.

In Problems 3–6, determine whether the expression is a monomial (yes or no). For those that are monomials, determine the coefficient and degree.

3. $12x^6$ 4. $3x^{-3}$

5. 10 6. $n^{\frac{1}{3}}$

So far, we have discussed only monomials in one variable. A monomial may contain more than one variable factor, such as $ax^m y^n$, where a is a constant (called the coefficient), x and y are variables, and m and n are whole numbers. An example of a monomial with more than one variable factor is $-4x^2 y^3$. The **degree of the monomial** $ax^m y^n$ is the sum of the exponents, $m + n$.

EXAMPLE 3 Monomials in More than One Variable

(a) $-4x^3 y^4$ is a monomial in x and y of degree $3 + 4 = 7$. The coefficient is -4.

(b) $10ab^5$ is a monomial in a and b of degree $1 + 5 = 6$. The coefficient is 10. ∎

Quick ✔

7. The degree of a monomial in the form $ax^m y^n$ is _____.

In Problems 8–10, determine whether the expression is a monomial (yes or no). For those that are monomials, determine the coefficient and degree.

8. $3x^5 y^2$ 9. $4ab^{\frac{1}{2}}$

10. $-x^2 y$

⌐2⌐ Define Polynomial and Determine the Degree of a Polynomial

We now turn our attention to polynomials.

> **DEFINITION**
>
> A **polynomial** is a monomial or the sum of monomials.

Work Smart

The prefix "bi" means "two" as in bicycle. The prefix "tri" means "three" as in tricycle. The prefix "poly" means "many."

We give special names to certain polynomials. For example, a polynomial with exactly one term is a monomial; a polynomial that has two different monomials is called a **binomial;** and a polynomial that contains three different monomials is called a **trinomial.** So

$-14x$ is a polynomial	but more specifically	$-14x$ is a monomial
$2x^3 - 5x$ is a polynomial	but more specifically	$2x^3 - 5x$ is a binomial
$-x^3 - 4x + 11$ is a polynomial	but more specifically	$-x^3 - 4x + 11$ is a trinomial
$3x^2 + 6xy - 2y^2$ is a polynomial	but more specifically	$3x^2 + 6xy - 2y^2$ is a trinomial

We use the term *monomial* to describe a polynomial with a *single* term, and the term *polynomial* to describe the sum of two or more monomials.

A polynomial is in **standard form** if it is written with the terms in descending order according to degree. The **degree of a polynomial** is the highest degree of all the terms of the polynomial. Remember, the degree of a nonzero constant is 0 and the number 0 has no degree.

EXAMPLE 4 **Examples of Polynomials**

POLYNOMIAL	DEGREE
(a) $7x^3 - 2x^2 + 6x + 4$	3
(b) $3 - 8x + x^2 = x^2 - 8x + 3$	2
(c) $-7x^4 + 24$	4
(d) $x^3y^4 - 3x^3y^2 + 2x^3y$	7
(e) $p^2q - 8p^3q^2 + 3 = -8p^3q^2 + p^2q + 3$	5
(f) 6	0
(g) 0	No degree

Although we have been using x to represent the variable, other letters may also be used.

$$7t^4 + 14t^2 + 8 \text{ is a polynomial (in } t) \text{ of degree 4}$$

$$-5z^2 + 3z - 6 \text{ is a polynomial (in } z) \text{ of degree 2}$$

$$8y^3 - y^2 + 2y - 12 \text{ is a polynomial (in } y) \text{ of degree 3}$$

Remember, polynomials consist of monomials. So, if any term in an algebraic expression is not a monomial, then the algebraic expression is not a polynomial.

EXAMPLE 5 **Algebraic Expressions That Are Not Polynomials**

(a) $4x^{-2} - 5x + 1$ is not a polynomial because the exponent on the first term, -2, is not a whole number.

(b) $\dfrac{4}{x^3}$ is not a polynomial because there is a variable expression in the denominator of the fraction.

(c) $4z^2 + 9z - 3z^{\frac{1}{2}}$ is not a polynomial because the exponent on the third term, $-3z^{\frac{1}{2}}$, is not a whole number.

Quick ✔

11. *True or False:* The degree of the polynomial $3ab^2 - 4a^2b^3 + \dfrac{6}{5}a^2b^2$ is 5.

12. A polynomial is said to be written in _____ if it is written with the terms in descending order according to degree.

In Problems 13–16, determine whether the algebraic expression is a polynomial (yes or no). For those that are polynomials, determine the degree.

13. $-4x^3 + 2x^2 - 5x + 3$

14. $2m^{-1} + 7$

15. $\dfrac{-1}{x^2 + 1}$

16. $5p^3q - 8pq^2 + pq$

3 Simplify Polynomials by Combining Like Terms

In Section 1.8, we learned how to combine like terms. To simplify a polynomial means to perform all indicated operations and combine like terms. One operation we perform on polynomials is addition. To add polynomials, combine the like terms of the polynomials.

EXAMPLE 6 Simplifying Polynomials: Addition

Find the sum: $(-5x^3 + 6x^2 + 2x - 7) + (3x^3 + 4x + 1)$

Solution

We can find the sum using either horizontal addition or vertical addition.

Horizontal Addition:

The idea here is to combine like terms.

$$
\begin{aligned}
(-5x^3 + 6x^2 + 2x - 7) + (3x^3 + 4x + 1) &= -5x^3 + 6x^2 + 2x - 7 + 3x^3 + 4x + 1 \\
\text{Rearrange terms:} \quad &= -5x^3 + 3x^3 + 6x^2 + 2x + 4x - 7 + 1 \\
\text{Simplify:} \quad &= -2x^3 + 6x^2 + 6x - 6
\end{aligned}
$$

Vertical Addition:

The idea here is to line up like terms in each polynomial vertically and then add the coefficients.

$$
\begin{array}{r}
-5x^3 + 6x^2 + 2x - 7 \\
3x^3 + 4x + 1 \\
\hline
-2x^3 + 6x^2 + 6x - 6
\end{array}
$$

> **Work Smart**
>
> Remember, like terms have the same variable and the same exponent on the variable.

Quick ✔

17. *True or False:* $4x^3 + 7x^3 = 11x^6$

In Problems 18 and 19, add the polynomials using either horizontal or vertical addition.

18. $(9x^2 - x + 5) + (3x^2 + 4x - 2)$

19. $(4z^4 - 2z^3 + z - 5) + (-2z^4 + 6z^3 - z^2 + 4)$

Adding polynomials in two variables is handled the same way as adding polynomials in a single variable, that is, by adding like terms.

EXAMPLE 7 Simplifying Polynomials in Two Variables: Addition

Find the sum: $(6a^2b + 11ab^2 - 4ab) + (a^2b - 3ab^2 + 9ab)$

Solution

We only present the horizontal format.

$$
\begin{aligned}
(6a^2b + 11ab^2 - 4ab) + (a^2b - 3ab^2 + 9ab) &= 6a^2b + 11ab^2 - 4ab + a^2b - 3ab^2 + 9ab \\
\text{Rearrange terms:} \quad &= 6a^2b + a^2b + 11ab^2 - 3ab^2 - 4ab + 9ab \\
\text{Simplify:} \quad &= 7a^2b + 8ab^2 + 5ab
\end{aligned}
$$

Quick ✔ *In Problem 20, simplify by adding the polynomials.*

20. $(7x^2y + x^2y^2 - 5xy^2) + (-2x^2y + 5x^2y^2 + 4xy^2)$

We can subtract polynomials using either the horizontal or vertical approach as well. However, the first step in subtracting polynomials requires that we remember the method for subtracting two real numbers. Remember,

$$
a - b = a + (-b)
$$

So, to subtract one polynomial from another, we add the opposite of each term in the polynomial following the subtraction sign and then combine like terms.

> **Work Smart**
>
> Taking the opposite of each term following the subtraction symbol is the same as multiplying each term of the polynomial by -1.

EXAMPLE 8 **Simplifying Polynomials: Subtraction**

Find the difference: $(6z^3 + 2z^2 - 5) - (-3z^3 + 9z^2 - z + 1)$

Solution

Horizontal Subtraction:

First, we write the problem as an addition problem and determine the opposite of each term following the subtraction sign.

$$(6z^3 + 2z^2 - 5) - (-3z^3 + 9z^2 - z + 1) = (6z^3 + 2z^2 - 5) + (3z^3 - 9z^2 + z - 1)$$

Remove parentheses: $= 6z^3 + 2z^2 - 5 + 3z^3 - 9z^2 + z - 1$

Rearrange terms: $= 6z^3 + 3z^3 + 2z^2 - 9z^2 + z - 5 - 1$

Simplify: $= 9z^3 - 7z^2 + z - 6$

Vertical Subtraction:

We line up like terms vertically,

$$
\begin{array}{r}
6z^3 + 2z^2 \quad\ - 5 \\
-(-3z^3 + 9z^2 - z + 1) \\
\end{array}
$$

then change the sign of each coefficient of the second polynomial, and add.

$$
\begin{array}{r}
6z^3 + 2z^2 \quad\ - 5 \\
+3z^3 - 9z^2 + z - 1 \\
\hline
9z^3 - 7z^2 + z - 6 \\
\end{array}
$$

Quick ✔ *In Problems 21 and 22, simplify by subtracting the polynomials.*

21. $(7x^3 - 3x^2 + 2x + 8) - (2x^3 + 12x^2 - x + 1)$

22. $(6y^3 - 3y^2 + 2y + 4) - (-2y^3 + 5y + 10)$

EXAMPLE 9 **Simplifying Polynomials in Two Variables: Subtraction**

Find the difference: $(2p^2q + 5pq^2 + pq) - (3p^2q + 9pq^2 - 6pq)$

Solution

$$(2p^2q + 5pq^2 + pq) - (3p^2q + 9pq^2 - 6pq) = (2p^2q + 5pq^2 + pq) + (-3p^2q - 9pq^2 + 6pq)$$

Remove parentheses: $= 2p^2q + 5pq^2 + pq - 3p^2q - 9pq^2 + 6pq$

Simplify: $= -p^2q - 4pq^2 + 7pq$

Quick ✔ *In Problems 23 and 24, subtract the polynomials.*

23. $(9x^2y + 6x^2y^2 - 3xy^2) - (-2x^2y + 4x^2y^2 + 6xy^2)$

24. $(4a^2b - 3a^2b^3 + 2ab^2) - (3a^2b - 4a^2b^3 + 5ab)$

EXAMPLE 10 **Simplifying Polynomials**

Perform the indicated operations: $(3x^2 - 2xy + y^2) - (7x^2 - y^2) + (3xy - 5y^2)$

Solution

$$(3x^2 - 2xy + y^2) - (7x^2 - y^2) + (3xy - 5y^2) = 3x^2 - 2xy + y^2 - 7x^2 + y^2 + 3xy - 5y^2$$

Rearrange terms: $= 3x^2 - 7x^2 - 2xy + 3xy + y^2 + y^2 - 5y^2$

Simplify: $= -4x^2 + xy - 3y^2$

> **Quick ✔** *In Problem 25, perform the indicated operations.*
> **25.** $(3a^2 - 5ab + 3b^2) + (4a^2 - 7b^2) - (8b^2 - ab)$

▢4 Evaluate Polynomials

To **evaluate** a polynomial, we substitute the given number for the value of the variable and simplify, just as we did in Section 1.8.

EXAMPLE 11 Evaluating a Polynomial

Evaluate the polynomial $2x^3 - 5x^2 + x - 3$ for

(a) $x = 2$ (b) $x = -3$

Solution

Work Smart

Remember the rule for order of operations: evaluate the exponent before you multiply.

(a) $2x^3 - 5x^2 + x - 3 = 2(2)^3 - 5(2)^2 + 2 - 3$
$$= 16 - 20 + 2 - 3$$
$$= -5$$

(b) $2x^3 - 5x^2 + x - 3 = 2(-3)^3 - 5(-3)^2 + (-3) - 3$
$$= -54 - 45 - 3 - 3$$
$$= -105$$

> **Quick ✔**
> **26.** Evaluate the polynomial $-2x^3 + 7x + 1$ for
> (a) $x = 0$ (b) $x = 5$ (c) $x = -4$

EXAMPLE 12 Evaluating a Polynomial in Two Variables

Evaluate the polynomial $2a^2b + 3a^2b^2 - 4ab$ for $a = -3$ and $b = -1$.

Solution

Let $a = -3$ and $b = -1$ in $2a^2b + 3a^2b^2 - 4ab$.

$$2a^2b + 3a^2b^2 - 4ab = 2(-3)^2(-1) + 3(-3)^2(-1)^2 - 4(-3)(-1)$$
$$= 2(9)(-1) + 3(9)(1) - 4(-3)(-1)$$
$$= -18 + 27 - 12$$
$$= -3$$

> **Quick ✔**
> **27.** Evaluate the polynomial $-2m^2n + 3mn - n^2$ for
> (a) $m = -2$ and $n = -4$ (b) $m = 1$ and $n = 5$

EXAMPLE 13 How Much Revenue?

The monthly revenue (in dollars) from selling x clocks is given by the polynomial $-0.3x^2 + 90x$. Evaluate the polynomial for $x = 200$ and describe the result in practical terms.

Solution

The variable x represents the number of clocks sold in a month. When we evaluate the polynomial $-0.3x^2 + 90x$ for $x = 200$, we are finding the revenue (in dollars) when 200 clocks are sold in a month. To find the revenue we replace x by 200 in the expression $-0.3x^2 + 90x$.

$$-0.3x^2 + 90x = -0.3(200)^2 + 90(200)$$
$$= -0.3(40,000) + 18,000$$
$$= -12,000 + 18,000$$
$$= 6000$$

According to the model, the revenue from selling 200 clocks in a month is $6000.   ■

Quick ✔ *Evaluate the polynomial for the given value.*

28. The polynomial $40x - 0.2x^2$ represents the monthly revenue (in dollars) realized by selling x wristwatches. Find the monthly revenue for selling 75 wristwatches by evaluating the polynomial $40x - 0.2x^2$ for $x = 75$.

5.1 EXERCISES

1–28. *are the* Quick ✔s *that follow each* EXAMPLE

Building Skills

In Problems 29–40, determine whether the given expression is a monomial (Yes or No). For those that are monomials, state the coefficient and degree. See Objective 1.

29. $\frac{1}{2}y^3$

30. $-3x^2$

31. $\frac{x^2}{7}$

32. $4m^{101}$

33. z^{-6}

34. $\frac{1}{y^7}$

35. $12mn^4$

36. $-x^6y$

37. $\frac{3}{n^2}$

38. y^{-1}

39. 4

40. $\frac{2}{3}$

In Problems 41–56, determine whether the algebraic expression is a polynomial (Yes or No). If it is a polynomial, write the polynomial in standard form, determine its degree, and state if it is a monomial, binomial, or trinomial. If it is a polynomial with more than 3 terms, identify the expression as a polynomial. See Objective 2.

41. $6x^2 - 10$

42. $4x + 1$

43. $\frac{-20}{n}$

44. $\frac{1}{x}$

45. $3y^{\frac{1}{3}} + 2$

46. $8m - 4m^{\frac{1}{2}}$

47. $\frac{1}{8}$

48. 32

49. $3t^2 - \frac{1}{2}t^4 + 6t$

50. $4x^7 - 3x^3 - 1$

51. $7x^{-1} + 4$

52. $4y^{-2} + 6y - 1$

53. $5z^3 - 10z^2 + z + 12$

54. $p^5 - 3p^4 + 7p + 8$

55. $3x^2y^2 + 2xy^4 + 4$

56. $4mn^3 - 2m^2n^3 + mn^8$

In Problems 57–70, add the polynomials. Express your answer in standard form. See Objective 3.

57. $(4x - 3) + (3x - 7)$

58. $(-13z + 4) + (9z - 10)$

59. $(-4m^2 + 2m - 1) + (2m^2 - 2m + 6)$

60. $(x^2 - 2) + (6x^2 - x - 1)$

61. $(p - p^3 + 2) + (6 - 2p^2 + p^3)$

62. $(4r^4 + 3r - 1) + (2r^4 - 7r^3 + r^2 - 10r)$

63. $(2y - 10) + (-3y^2 - 4y + 6)$

64. $(3 - 12w^2) + (2w^2 - 5 + 6w)$

65. $\left(\frac{1}{2}p^2 - \frac{2}{3}p + 2\right) + \left(\frac{3}{4}p^2 + \frac{5}{6}p - 5\right)$

66. $\left(\frac{3}{8}b^2 - \frac{3}{5}b + 1\right) + \left(\frac{5}{6}b^2 + \frac{2}{15}b - 1\right)$

67. $(5m^2 - 6mn + 2n^2) + (m^2 + 2mn - 3n^2)$

68. $(4a^2 + ab - 9b^2) + (-6a^2 - 4ab + b^2)$

69. $\quad 4n^2 \;\; - 2n + 1$
$\quad\underline{+(-6n + 4)}$

70. $\quad 8x^3 \qquad + 2x + 2$
$\quad\underline{+(-3x^2 - 4x - 2)}$

In Problems 71–84, subtract the polynomials. Express your answer in standard form. See Objective 3.

71. $(3x - 10) - (4x + 6)$

72. $(-7t + 3) - (-2t - 4)$

73. $(12x^2 - 2x - 4) - (-2x^2 + x + 1)$

74. $(3x^2 + x - 3) - (x^2 - 2x + 4)$

75. $(y^3 - 2y + 1) - (-3y^3 + y + 5)$

76. $(m^4 - 3m^2 + 5) - (3m^4 - 5m^2 - 2)$

77. $(3y^3 - 2y) - (2y + y^2 + y^3)$

78. $(2x - 4x^3) - (-3 - 2x + x^3)$

79. $\left(\dfrac{5}{3}q^2 - \dfrac{5}{2}q + 4\right) - \left(\dfrac{1}{9}q^2 + \dfrac{3}{8}q + 2\right)$

80. $\left(\dfrac{7}{4}x^2 - \dfrac{5}{8}x - 1\right) - \left(\dfrac{7}{6}x^2 + \dfrac{5}{12}x + 5\right)$

81. $(-4m^2n^2 - 2mn + 3) - (4m^2n^2 + 2mn + 10)$

82. $(4m^2n - 2mn - 4) - (10m^2n - 6mn - 3)$

83. $\quad 6x - 3$
$\quad\underline{-(10x + 2)}$

84. $\quad 6n^2 \;\; - 2n - 3$
$\quad\underline{-(4n + 7)}$

In Problems 85–90, simplify each of the following.

85. $(2x^2 - 3x + 1) + (x^2 + 9) - (4x^2 - 2x - 5)$

86. $(y^2 + 6y - 2) + (4y^2 - 9) - (2y^2 - 7y - 10)$

87. $(p^2 + 25) - (3p^2 - p + 4) - (-4p^2 - 9p + 5)$

88. $(n^2 + 4n - 5) - (2n^2 - 3n + 1) + (-n^2 - 7n + 6)$

89. $(4y - 3) + (y^3 - 8) - (2y^2 - 7y + 3)$

90. $(y^3 - 1) + (y^2 - 9) - (y^3 + 2y^2 - 7y + 3)$

In Problems 91–98, evaluate the polynomial for each of the given value(s). See Objective 4.

91. $2x^2 - x + 3$
(a) $x = 0$
(b) $x = 5$
(c) $x = -2$

92. $-x^2 + 10$
(a) $x = 0$
(b) $x = -1$
(c) $x = 1$

93. $7 - x^2$
(a) $x = 3$
(b) $x = -\dfrac{5}{2}$
(c) $x = -1.5$

94. $2 + \dfrac{1}{2}n^2$
(a) $n = 4$
(b) $n = 0.5$
(c) $n = -\dfrac{1}{4}$

95. $-x^2y + 2xy^2 - 3$
for $x = 2$ and $y = -3$

96. $-2ab^2 - 2a^2b - b^3$
for $a = 1$ and $b = -2$

97. $st + 2s^2t + 3st^2 - t^4$
for $s = -2$ and $t = 4$

98. $m^2n^2 - mn^2 + 3m^2 - 2$
for $m = \dfrac{1}{2}$ and $n = -1$

Mixed Practice

In Problems 99–114, perform the indicated operations. Express your answer in standard form.

99. $(7t - 3) - 4t$

100. $6x^2 - (18x^2 + 2)$

101. $(5x^2 + x - 4) + (-2x^2 - 4x + 1)$

102. $(4m^2 - m + 6) + (3m^2 - 4m - 10)$

103. $(2xy^2 - 3) + (7xy^2 + 4)$

104. $(-14xy + 3) - (-xy + 10)$

105. $(4 + 8y - 2y^2) - (3 - 7y - y^2)$

106. $(9 + 2z - 6z^2) - (-2 + z + 5z^2)$

107. $\left(\dfrac{5}{6}q^2 - \dfrac{1}{3}\right) + \left(\dfrac{3}{2}q^2 + 2\right)$

108. $\left(\dfrac{7}{10}t^2 - \dfrac{5}{12}t\right) + \left(\dfrac{3}{15}t^2 + \dfrac{3}{20}t - 3\right)$

109. $14d^2 - (2d - 10) - (d^2 - 3d)$

110. $3x - (5x + 1) - 4$

111. $(4a^2 - 1) + (a^2 + 5a + 2) - (-a^2 + 4)$

112. $(2b^2 + 3b - 5) - (b^2 - 4b + 1) + (b^2 + 1)$

113. $(x^2 - 2xy - y^2) - (3x^2 + xy - y^2) + (xy + y^2)$

114. $(2st^4 - 3s^2t^2 + t^4) + (7s^2t^2 - 3t^4 + 8st^4)$

115. Find the sum of $3x + 10$ and $-8x + 2$.

116. Find the sum of $4x^2 - 2x - 3$ and $-5x^2 - 2x + 7$.

117. Find the difference of $-x^2 + 2x + 3$ and $-4x^2 - 2x + 6$.

118. Find the difference of $4x - 3$ and $8x - 7$.

119. Subtract $14x^2 - 2x + 3$ from $2x - 10$.

120. Subtract $-4n - 8$ from $3n^2 + 8n - 9$.

121. What polynomial should be added to $3x - 5$ so that the sum is zero?

122. What polynomial should be added to $2a + 7b$ so that the sum is $a - b$?

Applying the Concepts

123. Height of a Ball The height above ground (in feet) of a ball dropped from the top of a 30-foot-tall building after t seconds is given by the polynomial $-16t^2 + 30$. What is the height of the ball after $\frac{1}{2}$ second?

124. Height of a Ball The height above ground (in feet) of a ball tossed upward after t seconds is given by the polynomial $-16t^2 + 32t + 100$. What is the height of the ball after 2.5 seconds?

125. Social Network Advertising Spending The projected worldwide online social network advertising spending, in millions of dollars, for the years 2006–2011 can be estimated by the polynomial $-32.4x^2 + 905.6x + 438$, where x is the number of years after 2006.

(a) Use the polynomial to estimate the projected worldwide online social network advertising spending, in millions of dollars, for the year 2006 ($x = 0$).

(b) Use the polynomial to estimate the projected worldwide online social network advertising spending, in millions of dollars, for the year 2008 ($x = 2$).

(c) Use the polynomial to estimate the projected worldwide online social network advertising spending, in millions of dollars, for the year 2011 ($x = 5$). (SOURCE: *eMarketer.com, February 2008*)

126. Stopping Distance The polynomial $1.1v + 0.06v^2$ models the number of feet it takes for a car traveling at v miles per hour to stop on dry, level concrete.

(a) How many feet will it take a car traveling 45 miles per hour to stop on dry, level concrete?

(b) How many feet will it take a car traveling 60 miles per hour to stop on dry, level concrete?

127. Manufacturing Calculators The revenue (in dollars) from manufacturing and selling x calculators in a day is given by the polynomial $-2x^2 + 120x$. The cost of manufacturing and selling x calculators in a day is given by the polynomial $0.125x^2 + 15x$.

(a) Profit is equal to revenue minus costs. Write a polynomial that represents the profit from manufacturing and selling x calculators in a day.

(b) Find the profit if 20 calculators are produced and sold each day.

128. Manufacturing DVDs Profit is equal to revenue minus cost. The revenue (in dollars) from manufacturing and selling x DVDs each day is given by the polynomial $-0.001x^2 + 6x$. The cost of manufacturing and selling x DVDs each day is given by the polynomial $0.8x + 3000$.

(a) Write a polynomial that expresses the profit from manufacturing and selling x DVDs each day.

(b) Find the profit if 1600 DVDs are produced and sold in a day.

129. Lawn Service Marissa started a lawn-care business in Tampa, Florida, in which she fertilizes lawns. Her costs are $5 per lawn for fertilizer and $10 per lawn for labor.

(a) If she charges $25 per lawn, write a polynomial that represents her weekly profit for fertilizing x lawns.

(b) If Marissa fertilizes 50 lawns in a week, what is her weekly profit?

(c) If Marissa fertilizes 50 lawns each week for 30 weeks, what is her profit?

130. Skateboard Business Kyle owns a skateboard shop. Kyle charges $40 for each skateboard he sells. The cost for manufacturing each skateboard is $12. In addition, Kyle has weekly costs of $504 regardless of how many skateboards he manufactures.

(a) If Kyle manufactures and sells x skateboards in a week, write a polynomial that represents his weekly profit.

(b) What is Kyle's weekly profit if he sells 45 skateboards per week?

(c) How many skateboards does Kyle need to sell in order to break even (profit = $0)?

△ *In Problems 131–134, write the polynomial that represents the perimeter of each figure.*

131. **132.**

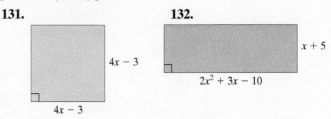

133. **134.**

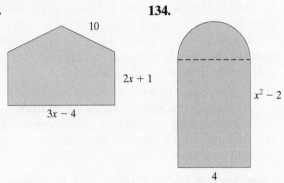

10

$2x + 1$

$3x - 4$

$x^2 - 2$

4

In Problems 135 and 136, write the polynomial that represents the unknown length.

135.

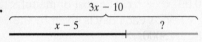

$3x - 10$

$x - 5$?

136.

?

$2x^2 + 5x$ $10x - 3$ $4x^2 - 3x + 7$

Explaining the Concepts

137. When adding polynomials you may use either a horizontal or vertical format. Explain which format you prefer and what you view as its advantages.

138. Use the two polynomials $3x - 5$ and $2x + 3$ to make up three different problems. In the directions to the first problem, use the word "evaluate"; in the second problem use the direction "solve"; and in the third use "simplify."

139. Explain how you find the degree of a polynomial in one variable. Explain how you find the degree of a polynomial in more than one variable. How do these processes differ?

5.2 Multiplying Monomials: The Product and Power Rules

OBJECTIVES

1. Simplify Exponential Expressions Using the Product Rule
2. Simplify Exponential Expressions Using the Power Rule
3. Simplify Exponential Expressions Containing Products
4. Multiply a Monomial by a Monomial

Work Smart

The natural numbers are 1, 2, 3, ….

Preparing for Multiplying Monomials: The Product and Power Rules

Before getting started, take the following readiness quiz. If you get a problem wrong, go back to the section cited and review the material.

P1. Evaluate: 4^3 [Section 1.7, pp. 59–60]

P2. Use the Distributive Property to simplify: $3(4 - 5x)$ [Section 1.8, p. 72]

In Section 1.7, we gave a definition for raising a real number to a natural number exponent. Recall that if a is a real number and n is a natural number, then the symbol a^n means that we should use a as a factor n times:

$$a^n = \underbrace{a \cdot a \cdot \ldots \cdot a}_{n \text{ factors}}$$

exponent

base

For example,

$$4^3 = \underbrace{4 \cdot 4 \cdot 4}_{3 \text{ factors}}$$

or

$$y^4 = \underbrace{y \cdot y \cdot y \cdot y}_{4 \text{ factors}}$$

In the notation a^n we call a the base and n the power or exponent. We read a^n as "a raised to the power n" or "a raised to the nth power." We usually read a^2 as "a squared" and a^3 as "a cubed." The expression 4^3 is called **exponential form** and the expression $4 \cdot 4 \cdot 4$ is called **expanded form.**

1 Simplify Exponential Expressions Using the Product Rule

We can discover several general rules for simplifying expressions with natural number exponents. The first rule that we introduce is used when multiplying two exponential expressions that have the same base. Consider the following:

In Words

When multiplying two exponential expressions with the same base, add the exponents. Then write the common base to the power of this sum.

Sum of powers 2 and 4

$$x^2 \cdot x^4 = \underbrace{(x \cdot x)}_{2 \text{ factors}}\underbrace{(x \cdot x \cdot x \cdot x)}_{4 \text{ factors}} = \underbrace{x \cdot x \cdot x \cdot x \cdot x \cdot x}_{6 \text{ factors}} = x^6$$

Same base   Same base

Preparing for…Answers   **P1.** 64
P2. $12 - 15x$

The following rule generalizes this result.

> **PRODUCT RULE FOR EXPONENTS**
>
> If a is a real number, and m and n are natural numbers, then
> $$a^m \cdot a^n = a^{m+n}$$

EXAMPLE 1 Using the Product Rule to Evaluate Numerical Expressions with Exponents

Evaluate each expression:

(a) $2^2 \cdot 2^4$ **(b)** $(-3)^2(-3)$

Solution

(a) $2^2 \cdot 2^4 = 2^{2+4}$
$= 2^6$
$= 64$

(b) $(-3)^2(-3) = (-3)^{2+1}$
$= (-3)^3$
$= -27$

EXAMPLE 2 Using the Product Rule to Simplify Algebraic Expressions with Exponents

Simplify the following expressions:

(a) $t^4 \cdot t^7$ **(b)** $a^6 \cdot a \cdot a^4$

Solution

(a) $t^4 \cdot t^7 = t^{4+7}$
$= t^{11}$

(b) $a^6 \cdot a \cdot a^4 = (a^6 \cdot a^1) \cdot a^4$
$= a^{6+1} \cdot a^4$
$= a^7 \cdot a^4$
$= a^{7+4}$
$= a^{11}$

EXAMPLE 3 Using the Product Rule to Simplify Algebraic Expressions with Exponents

Simplify the expression: $m^3 \cdot m^5 \cdot n^9$

Solution

To use the Product Rule for Exponents, the bases must be the same.
$$m^3 \cdot m^5 \cdot n^9 = m^{3+5} \cdot n^9$$
$$= m^8 n^9$$

The expression $m^8 n^9$ is in simplest form because the bases are different.

Quick ✔

1. The expression 12^3 is written in _____ form.

2. $a^m \cdot a^m = a$—.   **3.** *True or False:* $3^4 \cdot 3^2 = 9^6$

In Problems 4–8, evaluate or simplify each expression.

4. $3^2 \cdot 3$ **5.** $(-5)^2(-5)^3$ **6.** $c^6 \cdot c^2$

7. $y^3 \cdot y \cdot y^5$ **8.** $a^4 \cdot a^5 \cdot b^6$

2 Simplify Exponential Expressions Using the Power Rule

Another law of exponents applies when an exponential expression containing a power is itself raised to a power.

$$(3^2)^4 = \underbrace{3^2 \cdot 3^2 \cdot 3^2 \cdot 3^2}_{\text{4 factors}} = \underbrace{\underbrace{(3 \cdot 3)}_{\text{2 factors}} \cdot \underbrace{(3 \cdot 3)}_{\text{2 factors}} \cdot \underbrace{(3 \cdot 3)}_{\text{2 factors}} \cdot \underbrace{(3 \cdot 3)}_{\text{2 factors}}}_{2 \cdot 4 = 8 \text{ factors}} = 3^8$$

We have the following result:

In Words

If an exponential expression contains a power raised to a power, keep the base and multiply the powers.

POWER RULE FOR EXPONENTS

If a is a real number and m and n are natural numbers, then

$$(a^m)^n = a^{m \cdot n}$$

EXAMPLE 4 Using the Power Rule to Simplify Exponential Expressions

Simplify each expression. Write the answer in exponential form.

   (a) $(2^3)^2$ 　　　　　　　　　　　　　　(b) $(z^4)^2$

Solution

   (a) $(2^3)^2 = 2^{3 \cdot 2}$ 　　　　　　　(b) $(z^4)^2 = z^{4 \cdot 2}$
   $= 2^6$ 　　　　　　　　　　　　　　　$= z^8$ ■

EXAMPLE 5 Using the Power Rule to Simplify Exponential Expressions

Simplify each expression. Write the answer in exponential form.

   (a) $[(-4)^2]^3$ 　　　　　　　　　　　(b) $[(-n)^3]^5$

Solution

   (a) $[(-4)^2]^3 = (-4)^{2 \cdot 3}$
   $= (-4)^6$ 　　　　　　(b) $[(-n)^3]^5 = (-n)^{3 \cdot 5}$
   　　　　　　　　　　　　　　　　　　　$= (-n)^{15}$ ■

> Quick ✔ *In Problems 9–11, simplify each expression. Write the answer in exponential form.*
>
> **9.** $(2^2)^4$ 　　　　　　**10.** $[(-3)^3]^2$ 　　　　　　**11.** $(b^2)^5$

3 Simplify Exponential Expressions Containing Products

The next law of exponents deals with raising a product to a power. Consider the following:

$$(x \cdot y)^3 = (x \cdot y) \cdot (x \cdot y) \cdot (x \cdot y) = (x \cdot x \cdot x) \cdot (y \cdot y \cdot y) = x^3 \cdot y^3$$

The following rule generalizes this result.

In Words

When we raise a product to a power, we raise each factor to the power. (Remember, each of the numbers or variables in a multiplication problem is a factor.)

PRODUCT TO A POWER RULE FOR EXPONENTS

If a, b are real numbers and n is a natural number, then

$$(a \cdot b)^n = a^n \cdot b^n$$

EXAMPLE 6 Using the Product to a Power Rule to Simplify Exponential Expressions

Simplify each expression:

(a) $(3b^2)^4$ (b) $(-2a^2b)^3$

Solution

Each expression contains the product of factors, so we use the Product to a Power Rule, $(a \cdot b)^n = a^n \cdot b^n$.

(a)
$$(3b^2)^4 = (3)^4(b^2)^4$$
Evaluate 3^4; $(a^m)^n = a^{m \cdot n}$: $= 81b^{2 \cdot 4}$
$$= 81b^8$$

(b)
$$(-2a^2b)^3 = (-2)^3(a^2b)^3$$
$$= (-2)^3(a^2)^3(b)^3$$
Evaluate $(-2)^3$; $(a^m)^n = a^{m \cdot n}$: $= -8a^{2 \cdot 3}b^3$
$$= -8a^6b^3 \quad \blacksquare$$

Quick ✔

12. *True or False:* $(ab^3)^2 = ab^6$

In Problems 13–15, simplify each expression.

13. $(2n)^3$ **14.** $(-5x^4)^3$ **15.** $(-7a^3b)^2$

Let's summarize the three rules that we use when we find products of monomials.

RULES FOR MULTIPLYING MONOMIALS

- **Product Rule for Exponents**
  If a is a real number and m and n are natural numbers, then $a^m \cdot a^n = a^{m+n}$.
  Example: $x^4 \cdot x^3 = x^{4+3} = x^7$

- **Power Rule for Exponents**
  If a is a real number and m and n are natural numbers, then $(a^m)^n = a^{m \cdot n}$.
  Example: $(y^2)^5 = y^{10}$

- **Product to a Power Rule for Exponents**
  If a and b are real numbers and n is a natural number, then $(a \cdot b)^n = a^n \cdot b^n$.
  Example: $(2y)^3 = 2^3 \cdot y^3 = 8y^3$

Work Smart: Study Skills

Are you having trouble remembering the rules for multiplying exponents? Try making flash cards with the property on the front side, and an example or two on the back side. Also, write in words what each rule means and when it should be applied. This is a good study strategy that may apply to other topics.

---

4 Multiply a Monomial by a Monomial

To multiply two monomials with the same variable base, we multiply the coefficients of the monomials and use the Product Rule for Exponents to multiply the variable expressions.

EXAMPLE 7 Multiplying a Monomial by a Monomial: One Variable

Multiply and simplify:

(a) $(5x^2)(6x^4)$ (b) $(2p^3)(-5p^2)$

Solution

In each problem, we use the Commutative Property to rearrange factors.

(a)
$$(5x^2)(6x^4) = 5 \cdot 6 \cdot x^2 \cdot x^4$$
$a^m \cdot a^n = a^{m+n}$: $= 30x^{2+4}$
$$= 30x^6$$

(b)
$$(2p^3)(-5p^2) = 2 \cdot (-5) \cdot p^3 \cdot p^2$$
$a^m \cdot a^n = a^{m+n}$: $= -10p^{3+2}$
$$= -10p^5 \quad \blacksquare$$

| EXAMPLE 8 | Multiplying a Monomial by a Monomial: Two Variables

Multiply and simplify:

$$\textbf{(a)}\ (-3x^2y)(-7x^5y^3) \qquad\qquad \textbf{(b)}\ (2ab^3)(-a^2b)(4ab^2)$$

Solution

$$\textbf{(a)}\ (-3x^2y)(-7x^5y^3) = -3\cdot(-7)\cdot x^2\cdot x^5\cdot y\cdot y^3$$
$$a^m\cdot a^n = a^{m+n}:\qquad = 21\cdot x^{2+5}\cdot y^{1+3}$$
$$= 21x^7y^4$$

$$\textbf{(b)}\ (2ab^3)(-a^2b)(4ab^2) = 2\cdot(-1)\cdot 4\cdot a\cdot a^2\cdot a\cdot b^3\cdot b\cdot b^2$$
$$a^m\cdot a^n = a^{m+n}:\qquad = -8\cdot a^{1+2+1}\cdot b^{3+1+2}$$
$$= -8a^4b^6 \qquad\blacksquare$$

Quick ✔ *In Problems 16–18, multiply and simplify.*

16. $(2a^6)(4a^5)$ **17.** $(3m^2n^4)(-6mn^5)$

18. $\left(\dfrac{8}{3}xy^2\right)\left(\dfrac{1}{2}x^2y\right)(-12xy)$

5.2 EXERCISES

 MyMathLab

PRACTICE WATCH DOWNLOAD READ REVIEW

1–18. *are the* Quick ✔*s that follow each* EXAMPLE

Building Skills

In Problems 19–32, simplify each expression. See Objective 1.

19. $4^2\cdot 4^3$ **20.** $3\cdot 3^3$ **21.** $(-2)^3(-2)^4$

22. $(-0.3)^2(-0.3)^3$ **23.** $m^4\cdot m^5$ **24.** $a^3\cdot a^7$

25. $b^9\cdot b^{11}$ **26.** $z^8\cdot z^{23}$ ❂**27.** $x^7\cdot x$

28. $y^{13}\cdot y$ **29.** $p\cdot p^2\cdot p^6$ **30.** $b^5\cdot b\cdot b^7$

31. $(-n)^3(-n)^4$ **32.** $(-z)(-z)^5$

In Problems 33–42, simplify each expression. See Objective 2.

33. $(2^3)^2$ **34.** $(3^2)^2$ **35.** $[(-2)^2]^3$

36. $[(-2)^3]^3$ **37.** $[(-m)^9]^2$ **38.** $[(-n)^7]^3$

❂**39.** $(m^2)^7$ **40.** $(k^8)^3$ **41.** $[(-b)^4]^5$ **42.** $[(-a)^6]^3$

In Problems 43–54, simplify each expression. See Objective 3.

❂**43.** $(3x^2)^3$ **44.** $(4y^3)^2$ **45.** $(-5z^2)^2$

46. $(-6x^3)^2$ **47.** $\left(\dfrac{1}{2}a\right)^2$ **48.** $\left(\dfrac{3}{4}n^2\right)^3$

49. $(-3p^7q^2)^4$ **50.** $(-2m^2n^3)^4$ **51.** $(-2m^2n)^3$

52. $(-4ab^2)^3$ **53.** $(-5xy^2z^3)^2$ **54.** $(-3a^6bc^4)^4$

In Problems 55–68, multiply the monomials. See Objective 4.

55. $(4x^2)(3x^3)$ **56.** $(5y^6)(3y^2)$

57. $(10a^3)(-4a^7)$ **58.** $(7b^5)(-2b^4)$

❂**59.** $(-m^3)(7m)$ **60.** $(-n^6)(5n)$

61. $\left(\dfrac{4}{5}x^4\right)\left(\dfrac{15}{2}x^3\right)$ **62.** $\left(\dfrac{3}{8}y^5\right)\left(\dfrac{4}{9}y^6\right)$

63. $(2x^2y^3)(3x^4y)$ **64.** $(6a^2b^3)(2a^5b)$

65. $\left(\dfrac{1}{4}mn^3\right)(-20mn)$ **66.** $\left(\dfrac{2}{3}s^2t^3\right)(-21st)$

67. $(4x^2y)(-5xy^3)(2x^2y^2)$ **68.** $\left(\dfrac{1}{2}b\right)(-20a^2b)\left(-\dfrac{2}{3}a\right)$

Mixed Practice

In Problems 69–94, simplify each expression.

69. $x^2\cdot 4x$ **70.** $z^3\cdot 5z$ **71.** $(-x)(5x^2)$

72. $(3a^3)(-a)$ **73.** $(b^3)^2$ **74.** $(m^2)^4$

75. $(-3b)^4$ **76.** $(-4a)^2$

77. $(-6p)^2\left(\dfrac{1}{4}p^3\right)$ **78.** $(-8w)^2\left(\dfrac{3}{16}w^5\right)$

79. $(-xy)(x^2y)(-3x)^3$ **80.** $(-4a)^3(bc^2)(-b)$

81. $\left(\dfrac{3}{5}\right)(5c)(-10d^2)$ **82.** $\left(-\dfrac{7}{3}n\right)(9n^2)\left(\dfrac{5}{42}n^5\right)$

83. $(5x)^2(x^2)^3$

84. $(4y)^2(y^3)^5$

85. $(x^2y)^3(-2xy^3)$

86. $(s^2t^3)^2(3st)$

87. $(-3x)^2(2x^4)^3$

88. $(-2p^3)^2(3p)^3$

89. $\left(\frac{4}{5}q\right)^2(-5q)^2\left(\frac{1}{4}q^2\right)$

90. $\left(\frac{2}{3}m\right)^2(-3m)^3\left(\frac{3}{4}m^3\right)$

91. $(3x)^2(-2x)^4\left(\frac{1}{3}x^4\right)^2$

92. $(5y)^3(-3y)^2\left(\frac{1}{5}y^4\right)^2$

93. $-3(-5mn^3)^2\left(\frac{2}{5}m^5n\right)^3$

94. $-2(-4a^3b^2)^2\left(\frac{3}{2}ab^5\right)^3$

Applying the Concepts

△ **95. Cubes** Suppose the length of a side of a cube is x^2. Find the volume of the cube in terms of x.

△ **96. Squares** Suppose that the length of a side of a square is $3s$. Find the area of the square in terms of s.

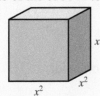

△ **97. Rectangle** Suppose that the width of a rectangle is $4x$ and its length is $12x$. Write an algebraic expression for the area of the rectangle in terms of x.

△ **98. Rectangle** Suppose that the width of a rectangle is $6a$ and its length is $8a$. Write an algebraic expression for the area of the rectangle in terms of a.

Explaining the Concepts

99. Provide a justification for the Product Rule for Exponents.

100. Provide a justification for the Power Rule for Exponents.

101. Provide a justification for the Product to a Power Rule for Exponents.

102. You simplified the expression $(-3a^2b^3)^4$ as $(-3a^2b^3)^4 = -3^4(a^2)^4(b^3)^4 = -81a^8b^{12}$. Your instructor marked your answer wrong. Find and explain the error and then rework the problem correctly.

103. Explain the difference between simplifying the expression $4x^2 + 3x^2$ and simplifying the expression $(4x^2)(3x^2)$.

104. Explain why it is incorrect to simplify the product $\left(\frac{1}{2}x^2y\right)\left(\frac{4}{3}xy^4\right)$ by multiplying by the least common denominator.

5.3 Multiplying Polynomials

OBJECTIVES
1 Multiply a Polynomial by a Monomial
2 Multiply Two Binomials Using the Distributive Property
3 Multiply Two Binomials Using the FOIL Method
4 Multiply the Sum and Difference of Two Terms
5 Square a Binomial
6 Multiply a Polynomial by a Polynomial

Preparing for Multiplying Polynomials

Before getting started, take the following readiness quiz. If you get a problem wrong, go back to the section cited and review the material.

P1. Use the Distributive Property to simplify: $2(4x - 3)$ [Section 1.8, p. 72]

P2. Find the product: $(3x^2)(-5x^3)$ [Section 5.2, pp. 329–330]

P3. Find the product: $(9a)^2$ [Section 5.2, pp. 328–329]

1 Multiply a Polynomial by a Monomial

Now that we know how to multiply two monomials, we can extend our discussion to the product of a monomial and a polynomial. If we were asked to simplify $3(2x + 1)$, we would use the Distributive Property to obtain $3(2x) + 3(1) = 6x + 3$. In general, when we multiply a polynomial by a monomial, we use the following property.

EXTENDED FORM OF THE DISTRIBUTIVE PROPERTY

$$a(b + c + \cdots + z) = a \cdot b + a \cdot c + \cdots + a \cdot z$$

where $a, b, c, \ldots, z$ are real numbers.

Preparing for...Answers   **P1.** $8x - 6$
P2. $-15x^5$ **P3.** $81a^2$

EXAMPLE 1 Multiplying a Monomial and a Trinomial Using the Extended Form of the Distributive Property

Multiply and simplify: $2x^2(x^2 + 3x + 5)$

Solution

We are multiplying a monomial by a trinomial, so we use the Extended Form of the Distributive Property and multiply each term in parentheses by $2x^2$.

$$2x^2(x^2 + 3x + 5) = 2x^2(x^2) + 2x^2(3x) + 2x^2(5)$$
$$= 2x^4 + 6x^3 + 10x^2$$ ∎

EXAMPLE 2 Multiplying a Monomial and a Trinomial

Multiply and simplify: $-2xy(3x^2 + 5xy + 2y^2)$

Solution

Use the Extended Form of the Distributive Property.

$$-2xy(3x^2 + 5xy + 2y^2) = -2xy(3x^2) + (-2xy)(5xy) + (-2xy)(2y^2)$$
$$= -6x^3y - 10x^2y^2 - 4xy^3$$ ∎

EXAMPLE 3 Multiplying a Trinomial and a Monomial

Multiply and simplify: $\left(\frac{4}{3}z^2 + 8z + \frac{1}{4}\right)\left(\frac{1}{2}z^3\right)$

Solution

$$\left(\frac{4}{3}z^2 + 8z + \frac{1}{4}\right)\left(\frac{1}{2}z^3\right) = \frac{4}{3}z^2\left(\frac{1}{2}z^3\right) + 8z\left(\frac{1}{2}z^3\right) + \frac{1}{4}\left(\frac{1}{2}z^3\right)$$
$$= \frac{2}{3}z^5 + 4z^4 + \frac{1}{8}z^3$$ ∎

Work Smart

Example 3 is an algebraic **expression** so you do not clear fractions.

Quick ✔ *In Problems 1–3, multiply and simplify.*

1. $3x(x^2 - 2x + 4)$ **2.** $-a^2b(2a^2b^2 - 4ab^2 + 3ab)$

3. $\left(5n^3 - \frac{15}{8}n^2 - \frac{10}{7}n\right)\left(\frac{3}{5}n^2\right)$

2 Multiply Two Binomials Using the Distributive Property

We now discuss how to multiply two binomials. To help understand the process, we review multiplication of two-digit numbers. Suppose we want to find $32 \cdot 14$. We proceed as follows: Multiply 2 by 4 and obtain 8, multiply 3 by 4 and obtain 12, so that $32 \cdot 4 = 128$. Now, multiply 2 by 1 and obtain 2, multiply 3 by 1 and obtain 3, so that $32 \cdot 1 = 32$. We add vertically while maintaining place value to obtain the product, 448.

$$
\begin{array}{r}
32 \\
\times 14 \\
\hline
\end{array}
$$

$$
\begin{array}{rcl}
4 \times 3 \rightarrow & 128 & \leftarrow 4 \times 2 \\
1 \times 3 \rightarrow & 32 & \leftarrow 1 \times 2 \\
\hline
& 448 &
\end{array}
$$

Now suppose we want to multiply $(3x + 2)$ and $(x + 4)$. That is, we want to find

$$
\begin{array}{r}
3x + 2 \\
\times \ x + 4 \\
\hline
\end{array}
$$

We proceed in exactly the same way as we did when multiplying two-digit numbers. Multiply 2 by 4, multiply $3x$ by 4, so that $(3x + 2) \cdot 4 = 12x + 8$. Multiply 2 by x, multiply $3x$ by x, so that $(3x + 2) \cdot x = 3x^2 + 2x$. Now add vertically and obtain the product, $3x^2 + 14x + 8$.

$$
\begin{array}{r}
3x + 2 \\
\times\ x + 4 \\
\hline
4 \cdot 3x \longrightarrow 12x + 8 \leftarrow 4 \cdot 2 \\
x \cdot 3x \rightarrow 3x^2 + \ 2x \longleftarrow x \cdot 2 \\
\hline
3x^2 + 14x + 8
\end{array}
$$

Multiplying two binomials uses exactly the same procedures that are used when multiplying two-digit numbers!

The multiplication that we just went through is known as *vertical multiplication*. We can also multiply using *horizontal multiplication*. Horizontal multiplication requires use of the Distributive Property. For example, to find $(3x + 2)(x + 4)$, we distribute $3x + 2$ to x and then distribute $3x + 2$ to 4.

$$(3x + 2)(x + 4) = (3x + 2)x + (3x + 2) \cdot 4$$

$\qquad$ Distribute x, distribute 4: $\quad = 3x \cdot x + 2 \cdot x + 3x \cdot 4 + 2 \cdot 4$

$$= 3x^2 + 2x + 12x + 8$$

$$= 3x^2 + 14x + 8$$

This is the same result that we obtained using vertical multiplication. Let's do a couple more examples using both horizontal and vertical multiplication.

EXAMPLE 4   Multiplying Two Binomials

Find the product: $(x + 3)(x - 8)$

Solution

Vertical Multiplication

$$
\begin{array}{r}
x + 3 \\
\times\ x - 8 \\
\hline
-8x - 24 \leftarrow -8(x + 3) \\
x^2 + 3x \quad\longleftarrow x(x + 3) \\
\hline
x^2 - 5x - 24
\end{array}
$$

Horizontal Multiplication

We distribute the first binomial to each term in the second binomial.

$$(x + 3)(x - 8) = (x + 3)x + (x + 3)(-8)$$
$$= x^2 + 3x - 8x - 24$$

Combine like terms: $= x^2 - 5x - 24$

In either case, $(x + 3)(x - 8) = x^2 - 5x - 24$. ■

EXAMPLE 5   Multiplying Two Binomials

Find the product: $(3x + 4)(2x - 5)$

Solution

Vertical Multiplication

$$
\begin{array}{r}
3x + 4 \\
\times\ 2x - 5 \\
\hline
-15x - 20 \leftarrow -5(3x + 4) \\
6x^2 + 8x \quad\longleftarrow 2x(3x + 4) \\
\hline
6x^2 - 7x - 20
\end{array}
$$

Horizontal Multiplication

We distribute the first binomial to each term in the second binomial.

$$(3x + 4)(2x - 5) = (3x + 4)(2x) + (3x + 4)(-5)$$
$$= 3x \cdot 2x + 4 \cdot 2x + 3x \cdot (-5) + 4 \cdot (-5)$$
$$= 6x^2 + 8x - 15x - 20$$

Combine like terms: $= 6x^2 - 7x - 20$

In either case, $(3x + 4)(2x - 5) = 6x^2 - 7x - 20$. ■

Quick ✔ *In Problems 4–6, find the product using the Distributive Property.*

4. $(x + 7)(x + 2)$ $\qquad$ **5.** $(2n + 1)(n - 3)$ $\qquad$ **6.** $(3p - 2)(2p - 1)$

3 Multiply Two Binomials Using the FOIL Method

Work Smart

The FOIL method is a form of the Distributive Property, and FOIL can be used **only** when we multiply binomials.

When multiplying two binomials, there is a second method referred to as the **FOIL method.** FOIL stands for First, Outer, Inner, Last. "First" means that we are multiplying the *first* terms in each binomial, "Outer" means we are multiplying the *outside* terms of each binomial, "Inner" means we are multiplying the *innermost* terms of each binomial, and "Last" means we are multiplying the *last* terms of each binomial. The FOIL method is illustrated below. For comparison, the horizontal method is illustrated as well.

The FOIL Method	Horizontal Multiplication Using the Distributive Property
First Last F · O · I · L $(ax + b)(cx + d) = ax \cdot cx + ax \cdot d + b \cdot cx + b \cdot d$ Inner Outer	$(ax + b)(cx + d) = (ax + b)cx + (ax + b)d$ $= ax \cdot cx + b \cdot cx + ax \cdot d + b \cdot d$ Rearrange terms: $= ax \cdot cx + ax \cdot d + b \cdot cx + b \cdot d$

The FOIL method does not give different results than the Distributive Property. Instead, it is a memory device to help when multiplying two binomials.

EXAMPLE 6 Using the FOIL Method to Multiply Two Binomials

Find the product: $(y + 3)(y + 5)$

Solution

$$(y + 3)(y + 5) = (y)(y) + (y)(5) + (3)(y) + (3)(5)$$
$$= y^2 + 5y + 3y + 15$$
$$= y^2 + 8y + 15$$

EXAMPLE 7 Using the FOIL Method to Multiply Two Binomials

Find the product: $(a + 1)(a - 3)$

Solution

$$(a + 1)(a - 3) = (a)(a) + (a)(-3) + (1)(a) + (1)(-3)$$
$$= a^2 - 3a + a - 3$$
$$= a^2 - 2a - 3$$

Quick ✔ *In Problems 7–9, find the product using the FOIL method.*

7. $(x + 3)(x + 4)$ **8.** $(y + 5)(y - 3)$ **9.** $(a - 1)(a - 5)$

EXAMPLE 8 Using the FOIL Method to Multiply Two Binomials

Find the product: $(3a + 1)(a - 4)$

Solution

$$(3a + 1)(a - 4) = (3a)(a) + (3a)(-4) + (1)(a) + (1)(-4)$$
$$= 3a^2 - 12a + a - 4$$
$$= 3a^2 - 11a - 4$$

EXAMPLE 9   Using the FOIL Method to Multiply Two Binomials

Find the product: $(3a - 4b)(5a - 2b)$

Solution

$$
\begin{aligned}
(3a - 4b)(5a - 2b) &= \overset{\text{F}}{(3a)(5a)} + \overset{\text{O}}{(3a)(-2b)} - \overset{\text{I}}{(4b)(5a)} - \overset{\text{L}}{(4b)(-2b)} \\
&= 15a^2 - 6ab - 20ab + 8b^2 \\
&= 15a^2 - 26ab + 8b^2
\end{aligned}
$$

Quick ✔ *In Problems 10–13, find the product using the FOIL method.*

10. $(2x + 3)(x + 4)$ **11.** $(3y + 5)(2y - 3)$

12. $(2a - 1)(3a - 4)$ **13.** $(5x + 2y)(3x - 4y)$

4   Multiply the Sum and Difference of Two Terms

Certain binomials have products that result in patterns. For this reason, we call these products **special products.** The first special product we discuss is a product of the form $(A - B)(A + B)$.

EXAMPLE 10   Finding a Product of the Form $(A - B)(A + B)$

Find the product: $(x - 5)(x + 5)$

Solution

$$
\begin{aligned}
(x - 5)(x + 5) &= \overset{\text{F}}{(x)(x)} + \overset{\text{O}}{(x)(5)} - \overset{\text{I}}{(5)(x)} - \overset{\text{L}}{(5)(5)} \\
&= x^2 + 5x - 5x - 25 \\
&= x^2 - 25
\end{aligned}
$$

We call products of the form $(A - B)(A + B)$ "the sum and difference of two terms." Do you see why?

In Example 10, did you notice that the outer product, $5x$, and the inner product, $-5x$, were opposites? This result is not a coincidence. The sum of the outer product and the inner product of two binomials in the form $(A - B)(A + B)$ is *always* zero, so the product $(A - B)(A + B)$ is the *difference* $A^2 - B^2$.

PRODUCT OF THE SUM AND DIFFERENCE OF TWO TERMS

$$(A - B)(A + B) = A^2 - B^2$$

EXAMPLE 11   Finding the Product of the Sum and Difference of Two Terms

Find each product:

  (a) $(2x + 5)(2x - 5)$ **(b)** $(4x - 3y)(4x + 3y)$

Solution

  (a) $(2x + 5)(2x - 5) = (2x)^2 - 5^2$
$\qquad\qquad\qquad\quad = 4x^2 - 25$

  (b) $(4x - 3y)(4x + 3y) = (4x)^2 - (3y)^2$
$\qquad\qquad\qquad\qquad\quad = 16x^2 - 9y^2$

Quick ✔

14. $(A + B)(A - B) =$ _____.

In Problems 15–17, find each product.

15. $(a - 4)(a + 4)$ **16.** $(3w + 7)(3w - 7)$ **17.** $(x - 2y^3)(x + 2y^3)$

5 Square a Binomial

Another special product involves squaring a binomial. For example, since $(x + 3)^2 = (x + 3)(x + 3)$, we use FOIL and obtain

$$(x + 3)^2 = (x + 3)(x + 3) = x^2 + 3x + 3x + 9 = x^2 + 6x + 9$$

Did you notice that the outer product and the inner product are the same, namely $3x$? Study Table 2 to discover the pattern.

Table 2				
$(n + 5)^2 =$	$(n + 5)(n + 5) =$	$n^2 + 5n + 5n + 25 =$	$n^2 + 2(5n) + 25 =$	$n^2 + 10n + 25$
$(2a - 3)^2 =$	$(2a - 3)(2a - 3) =$	$4a^2 - 6a - 6a + 9 =$	$4a^2 - 2(6a) + 9 =$	$4a^2 - 12a + 9$
$(n + 5p)^2 =$		$n^2 + 5np + 5np + 25p^2 =$	$n^2 + 2(5np) + 25p^2 =$	$n^2 + 10np + 25p^2$
$(4b - 9)^2 =$			$16b^2 - 2(4b)(9) + 81 =$	$16b^2 - 72b + 81$

The results of Table 2 lead to the following.

$$(A + B)^2 = \underbrace{A^2}_{(\text{first term})^2} + \underbrace{2AB}_{2(\text{product of terms})} + \underbrace{B^2}_{(\text{second term})^2}$$

$$(A - B)^2 = \underbrace{A^2}_{(\text{first term})^2} - \underbrace{2AB}_{2(\text{product of terms})} + \underbrace{B^2}_{(\text{second term})^2}$$

Work Smart

$(x + y)^2 \neq x^2 + y^2$

$(x - y)^2 \neq x^2 - y^2$

Whenever you feel the urge to perform an operation that you're not quite sure about, try it with actual numbers. For example, does

$(3 + 2)^2 = 3^2 + 2^2$?

NO! So

$(x + y)^2 \neq x^2 + y^2$

SQUARES OF BINOMIALS

$$(A + B)^2 = A^2 + 2AB + B^2$$
$$(A - B)^2 = A^2 - 2AB + B^2$$

The trinomials $A^2 + 2AB + B^2$ and $A^2 - 2AB + B^2$ are called **perfect square trinomials.**

EXAMPLE 12 How to Find a Product of the Form $(A + B)^2$

Find the product: $(y + 7)^2$

Step-by-Step Solution

Step 1: Because $(y + 7)^2$ is in the form $(A + B)^2$, we use $(A + B)^2 = A^2 + 2AB + B^2$ with $A = y$ and $B = 7$.

$$\underbrace{(A + B)^2} = \underbrace{A^2} + \underbrace{2AB} + \underbrace{B^2}$$
$$(y + 7)^2 = (y)^2 + 2(y)(7) + 7^2$$

Step 2: Simplify.

$$= y^2 + 14y + 49$$

EXAMPLE 13   **Finding a Product of the Form $(A - B)^2$**

Find the product: $(3 - r)^2$

Solution

$$(A - B)^2 = A^2 - 2AB + B^2$$
$$(3 - r)^2 = 3^2 - 2(3)(r) + r^2$$
$$= 9 - 6r + r^2$$

Quick ✔

18. *True or False:* $(x - y)^2 = x^2 - y^2$

19. $x^2 + 2xy + y^2$ is referred to as a _____ _____ _____.

20. *True or False:* The product of a binomial and a binomial is always a trinomial.

In Problems 21–23, find each product.

21. $(z - 9)^2$ **22.** $(p + 1)^2$ **23.** $(4 - a)^2$

EXAMPLE 14   **Finding Products of the Form $(A + B)^2$ or $(A - B)^2$**

Find each product:

   (a) $(9p - 4)^2$ **(b)** $(2x + 5y)^2$

Solution

   (a) $(9p - 4)^2 = (9p)^2 - 2(9p)4 + 4^2$
$$= 81p^2 - 72p + 16$$

   (b) $(2x + 5y)^2 = (2x)^2 + 2(2x)(5y) + (5y)^2$
$$= 4x^2 + 20xy + 25y^2$$

Work Smart

If you can't remember the formulas for a perfect square, don't panic! Simply use the fact that $(x + a)^2 = (x + a)(x + a)$ and then FOIL. The same logic applies to perfect squares of the form $(x - a)^2$.

Quick ✔   *In Problems 24–26, find each product.*

24. $(3z - 4)^2$ **25.** $(5p + 1)^2$ **26.** $(2w + 7y)^2$

For convenience, we present a summary of binomial products.

SUMMARY OF BINOMIAL PRODUCTS

- When multiplying two binomials, we can use the Distributive Property.

$$(3x + 5)(4x - 1) = (3x + 5)(4x) + (3x + 5)(-1)$$
$$= 12x^2 + 20x - 3x - 5$$
$$= 12x^2 + 17x - 5$$

- When multiplying two binomials, we can use the FOIL pattern.

$$\overset{F}{}\quad\overset{O}{}\quad\overset{I}{}\quad\overset{L}{}$$
$$(3x + 5)(4x - 1) = 3x(4x) + 3x(-1) + 5(4x) + 5(-1)$$
$$= 12x^2 - 3x + 20x - 5$$
$$= 12x^2 + 17x - 5$$

- When finding a product in the form $(A - B)(A + B)$, we use the product of the sum and difference of two terms, $A^2 - B^2$.

$$(7a + 2b)(7a - 2b) = (7a)^2 - (2b)^2$$
$$= 49a^2 - 4b^2$$

- When squaring a binomial, we use $(A + B)^2 = A^2 + 2AB + B^2$ and $(A - B)^2 = A^2 - 2AB + B^2$. The product is called a perfect square trinomial.

$$(3x + 5)^2 = (3x)^2 + 2(3x)(5) + (5)^2$$
$$= 9x^2 + 30x + 25$$
$$(4y - 3)^2 = (4y)^2 - 2(4y)(3) + (3)^2$$
$$= 16y^2 - 24y + 9$$

6 Multiply a Polynomial by a Polynomial

When we find the product of two polynomials, we make repeated use of the Extended Form of the Distributive Property. We can use either a horizontal or vertical format. In addition, it is a good idea to write each polynomial in standard form.

EXAMPLE 15 Multiplying Polynomials Using Horizontal Multiplication

Find the product: $(2x + 3)(x^2 + 5x - 1)$

Solution

We distribute $2x + 3$ to each term in the trinomial.

$$(2x + 3)(x^2 + 5x - 1) = (2x + 3)x^2 + (2x + 3) \cdot 5x + (2x + 3) \cdot (-1)$$
$$= 2x(x^2) + 3(x^2) + 2x(5x) + 3(5x) + 2x(-1) + 3(-1)$$

Simplify: $= 2x^3 + 3x^2 + 10x^2 + 15x - 2x - 3$

Combine like terms: $= 2x^3 + 13x^2 + 13x - 3$ ∎

Quick ✔

27. *True or False:* The product $(x - y)(x^2 + 2xy + y^2)$ can be found using the FOIL method.

In Problems 28 and 29, find the product using horizontal multiplication.

28. $(x - 2)(x^2 + 2x + 4)$ **29.** $(3y - 2)(y^2 + 2y + 4)$

The best way to use vertical multiplication to multiply two polynomials is to place the polynomial with more terms on top, align terms of the same degree, and then multiply. Make sure both polynomials are written in standard form.

EXAMPLE 16 Multiplying a Binomial and a Trinomial Using Vertical Multiplication

Find the product: $(2x + 3)(x^2 + 5x - 1)$

Solution

We arrange the polynomials vertically by placing the trinomial on top since it has more terms than the binomial. Now we multiply the trinomial by the 3 in the binomial and then multiply the trinomial by the $2x$ in the binomial.

$$
\begin{array}{r}
x^2 + 5x - 1 \\
\times \quad 2x + 3 \\
\hline
\end{array}
$$

$3(x^2 + 5x - 1)$: $3x^2 + 15x - 3$

$2x(x^2 + 5x - 1)$: $2x^3 + 10x^2 - 2x$

Add vertically: $2x^3 + 13x^2 + 13x - 3$ ∎

Quick ✔ *In Problems 30 and 31, find the product using vertical multiplication.*

30. $(x - 2)(x^2 + 2x + 4)$ **31.** $(3y - 1)(y^2 + 2y - 5)$

EXAMPLE 17 Multiplying Three Polynomials

Find the product: $2x(x - 4)(3x - 5)$

Solution

To find the product of three polynomials, multiply any two factors and then multiply that product by the remaining factor. We'll start by using the Distributive Property to multiply $2x$ and $(x - 4)$.

$$2x(x - 4)(3x - 5) = (2x^2 - 8x)(3x - 5)$$
$$\text{FOIL:} = 2x^2 \cdot 3x + 2x^2(-5) - 8x \cdot 3x - 8x \cdot (-5)$$
$$= 6x^3 - 10x^2 - 24x^2 + 40x$$
$$\text{Combine like terms:} = 6x^3 - 34x^2 + 40x$$

Quick ✔ *In Problems 32–34, find the product.*

32. $-2a(4a - 1)(3a + 5)$

33. $\dfrac{3}{2}(5x - 2)(2x + 8)$

34. $(x + 2)(x - 1)(x + 3)$

5.3 EXERCISES

PRACTICE   WATCH   DOWNLOAD   READ   REVIEW

1–34. *are the* Quick ✔s *that follow each* EXAMPLE

Building Skills

In Problems 35–42, use the Distributive Property to find each product. See Objective 1.

35. $2x(3x - 5)$

36. $3m(2m - 7)$

37. $\dfrac{1}{2}n(4n - 6)$

38. $\dfrac{3}{5}b(15b - 5)$

39. $3n^2(4n^2 + 2n - 5)$

40. $4w(2w^2 + 3w - 5)$

41. $(4x^2y - 3xy^2)(x^2y)$

42. $(7r + 3s^2)(2r^2s)$

In Problems 43–48, use the Distributive Property to find each product. See Objective 2.

43. $(x + 5)(x + 7)$

44. $(x + 4)(x + 10)$

45. $(y - 5)(y + 7)$

46. $(n - 7)(n + 4)$

47. $(3m - 2y)(2m + 5y)$

48. $(5n - 2y)(2n - 3y)$

In Problems 49–62, find the product using the FOIL method. See Objective 3.

49. $(x + 2)(x + 3)$

50. $(x + 3)(x + 7)$

51. $(q - 6)(q - 7)$

52. $(n - 4)(n - 5)$

53. $(2x + 3)(3x - 1)$

54. $(3z - 2)(4z + 1)$

55. $(x^2 + 3)(x^2 + 1)$

56. $(x^2 - 5)(x^2 - 2)$

57. $(7 - x)(6 - x)$

58. $(2 - y)(4 - y)$

59. $(5u + 6v)(2u + v)$

60. $(3a - 2b)(a - 3b)$

61. $(2a - b)(5a + 2b)$

62. $(3r + 5s)(6r + 7s)$

In Problems 63–72, find the product of the sum and difference of two terms. See Objective 4.

63. $(x - 3)(x + 3)$

64. $(y + 7)(y - 7)$

65. $(2z + 5)(2z - 5)$

66. $(6r - 1)(6r + 1)$

67. $(4x^2 + 1)(4x^2 - 1)$

68. $(3a^2 + 2)(3a^2 - 2)$

69. $(2x - 3y)(2x + 3y)$

70. $(8a - 5b)(8a + 5b)$

71. $\left(x - \dfrac{1}{3}\right)\left(x + \dfrac{1}{3}\right)$

72. $\left(y + \dfrac{2}{9}\right)\left(y - \dfrac{2}{9}\right)$

In Problems 73–82, find the product. See Objective 5.

73. $(x - 2)^2$

74. $(x + 4)^2$

75. $(5k - 3)^2$

76. $(6b - 5)^2$

77. $(x + 2y)^2$

78. $(3x - 2y)^2$

79. $(2a - 3b)^2$

80. $(5x + 2y)^2$

81. $\left(x + \dfrac{1}{2}\right)^2$

82. $\left(y - \dfrac{1}{3}\right)^2$

In Problems 83–96, find the product. See Objective 6.

83. $(x - 2)(x^2 + 3x + 1)$

84. $(3a - 1)(2a^2 - 5a - 3)$

85. $(2y^2 - 6y + 1)(y - 3)$

86. $(2m^2 - m + 2)(2m + 1)$

87. $(2x - 3)(x^2 - 2x - 1)$

88. $(4y + 1)(2y^2 - y - 3)$

89. $2b(b - 3)(b + 4)$

90. $5a(a + 6)(a - 1)$

91. $-\dfrac{1}{2}x(2x + 6)(x - 3)$

92. $-\dfrac{4}{3}k(k + 7)(3k - 9)$

93. $(5y^3 - y^2 + 2)(2y^2 + y + 1)$

94. $(2m^2 - m + 4)(-m^3 - 2m - 1)$

95. $(b + 1)(b - 2)(b + 3)$

96. $(2a - 1)(a + 4)(a + 1)$

Mixed Practice

In Problems 97–108, find each product.

97. $4n(3 - 2n - n^2)$

98. $2w(4 - 3w + 8w^2)$

99. $(2a - 3b)(4a + b)$

100. $(4a - 3b)(2a + b)$

101. $\left(\dfrac{1}{2}x + 3\right)\left(\dfrac{1}{2}x - 3\right)$

102. $\left(\dfrac{3}{5}n - 7\right)\left(\dfrac{3}{5}n + 7\right)$

103. $(0.5b + 3)^2$

104. $(0.2y - 5)^2$

105. $(x^2 + 1)(x^4 - 3)$

106. $(4y^2 - 5)(y^3 + 2)$

107. $(x + 2)(2x^2 - 3x - 1)$

108. $(x - 3)(3x^2 - x - 4)$

In Problems 109–122, perform the indicated operation. Express your answer as a polynomial in standard form.

109. $-\dfrac{1}{2}x^2(10x^5 - 6x^4 + 12x^3) + (x^3)^2$

110. $-\dfrac{1}{3}(27y^2 - 9y + 6) - (3y)^2$

111. $7x^2(x + 3) - 2x(x^2 - 1)$

112. $2(3a^4 + 2b^4) - 3(b^4 - 2a^4)$

113. $-3w(w - 4)(w + 3)$

114. $5y(y + 5)(y - 3)$

115. $3a(a + 4)^2$

116. $2m(m - 3)^2$

117. $(n + 3)(n - 3) + (n + 3)^2$

118. $(s + 6)(s - 6) + (s - 6)^2$

119. $(a + 6b)^2 - (a - 6b)^2$

120. $(2a + 5b)^2 - (2a - 5b)^2$

121. $(x + 1)^2 - (2x + 1)(x - 1)$

122. $(a + 3)^2 - (a + 4)(3a - 1)$

123. Square $2x + 1$.   **124.** Square $3x - 2y$.

125. Find the cube of $x - 1$.   **126.** Find the cube of $2a + b$.

127. Subtract $x - 6$ from the product of $x + 3$ and $2x - 5$.

128. Add $2x + 3$ to the product of $x + 3$ and $2x - 3$.

Applying the Concepts

In Problems 129–132, find an algebraic expression that represents the area of the shaded region.

△**129.**

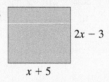

$2x - 3$

$x + 5$

△**130.**

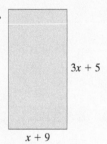

$3x + 5$

$x + 9$

△**131.**

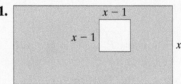

$x - 1$

$x - 1$

x

$3x - 1$

△**132.**

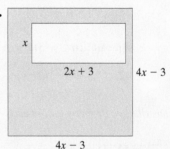

x

$2x + 3$

$4x - 3$

$4x - 3$

In Problems 133 and 134, find an algebraic expression that represents the volume of the figure.

133.

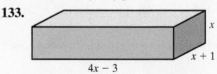

x

$x + 1$

$4x - 3$

134.

x

$x + 4$

$9 - 2x$

In Problems 135 and 136, find an algebraic expression for the area of the rectangle by finding the sum of the four interior rectangles. Then find the area of the rectangle by multiplying the width and length. Compare the two expressions. How is multiplying a binomial related to finding the area of the rectangle?

△ **135.**

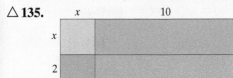

△ **136.**

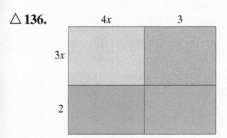

137. **Consecutive Integers** If x represents the first of three consecutive integers, write a polynomial that represents the product of the next two consecutive integers.

138. **Consecutive Integers** If x represents the first of three consecutive odd integers, write a polynomial that represents the product of the first and the third integer.

△ **139. Area of a Triangle** The base of a triangle is 2 inches shorter than twice the length of its altitude, x. Write a polynomial that represents the area of the triangle.

△ **140. Area of a Triangle** The base of a triangle is 3 feet greater in length than its altitude, x. Write a polynomial that represents the area of the triangle.

△ **141. Area of a Circle** Write a polynomial for the area of a circle with radius $(x + 2)$ feet.

△ **142. Area of a Circle** Write a polynomial for the area of a circle with radius $(2y - 3)$ meters.

△ **143. Perfect Square** Why is the expression $(a + b)^2$ called a perfect square? Consider the figure below.

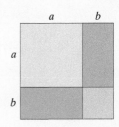

(a) Find the area of each of the four quadrilaterals.
(b) Use the result from part (a) to find the area of the entire region.
(c) Find the length and width of the entire region in terms of a and b. Use this result to find the area of the entire region. What do you notice?

△ **144. Picture Frame** A photo is 13″ by 15″ and is bordered by a matting that is x inches wide. Write the polynomial that calculates the area of the entire framed picture.

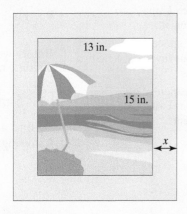

Extending the Concepts

In Problems 145–152, find the product. Write each result as a polynomial in standard form.

145. $(x - 2)(x + 2)^2$ **146.** $(x + 3)^2(x - 3)$

147. $[3 - (x + y)][3 + (x + y)]$

148. $[(x - y) + 3][(x - y) - 3]$

149. $(x + 2)^3$ **150.** $(y - 3)^3$

151. $(z + 3)^4$ **152.** $(m - 2)^4$

Explaining the Concepts

153. Explain the steps that should be followed to find the product $(3a - 5)^2$ to someone who missed the class session on squaring a binomial.

154. Explain how the product of the sum and difference of two terms can be used to calculate $19 \cdot 21$.

155. Explain when the FOIL method can be used to multiply polynomials.

156. Find and explain the error in the student's work:
$2a(a^2 + 3a) + 5a = 2a(a^2) + 2a(3a) + 2a(5a).$

5.4 Dividing Monomials: The Quotient Rule and Integer Exponents

OBJECTIVES

1. Simplify Exponential Expressions Using the Quotient Rule
2. Simplify Exponential Expressions Using the Quotient to a Power Rule
3. Simplify Exponential Expressions Using Zero as an Exponent
4. Simplify Exponential Expressions Involving Negative Exponents
5. Simplify Exponential Expressions Using the Laws of Exponents

Preparing for Dividing Monomials: The Quotient Rule and Integer Exponents

Before getting started, take the following readiness quiz. If you get a problem wrong, go back to the section cited and review the material.

P1. Find the product: $(3a^2)^3$ [Section 5.2, pp. 328–329]

P2. Evaluate: $\left(\dfrac{2}{3}\right)^2$ [Section 1.7, pp. 59–60]

P3. Find the reciprocal: **(a)** 5 **(b)** $-\dfrac{6}{7}$ [Section 1.5, p. 40]

Before we can turn our attention to dividing polynomials, we must first discuss dividing monomials.

1 Simplify Exponential Expressions Using the Quotient Rule

To find a general rule for the quotient of two exponential expressions, consider the following:

$$\frac{y^6}{y^2} = \frac{\overbrace{y \cdot y \cdot y \cdot y \cdot y \cdot y}^{6 \text{ factors}}}{\underbrace{y \cdot y}_{2 \text{ factors}}} = \underbrace{y \cdot y \cdot y \cdot y}_{4 \text{ factors}} = y^4$$

We might conclude from this result that

$$\frac{y^6}{y^2} = y^{6-2} = y^4$$

This result is true in general.

In Words

When dividing two exponential expressions with a common base, subtract the exponent in the denominator from the exponent in the numerator. Then write the base to that power.

QUOTIENT RULE FOR EXPONENTS

If a is a real number and if m and n are natural numbers, then

$$\frac{a^m}{a^n} = a^{m-n} \qquad \text{if } a \neq 0$$

EXAMPLE 1 Using the Quotient Rule to Simplify Expressions

Simplify each expression.

(a) $\dfrac{6^5}{6^3}$ **(b)** $\dfrac{n^6}{n^2}$ **(c)** $\dfrac{(-7)^8}{(-7)^6}$

Solution

(a)
$$\frac{6^5}{6^3} = 6^{5-3}$$
$$= 6^2$$
Evaluate 6^2: $= 36$

(b)
$$\frac{n^6}{n^2} = n^{6-2}$$
$$= n^4$$

(c)
$$\frac{(-7)^8}{(-7)^6} = (-7)^{8-6}$$
$$= (-7)^2$$
$$= 49 \qquad \blacksquare$$

Preparing for...Answers **P1.** $27a^6$

P2. $\dfrac{4}{9}$ **P3.** **(a)** $\dfrac{1}{5}$ **(b)** $-\dfrac{7}{6}$

EXAMPLE 2 Using the Quotient Rule to Simplify Expressions

Simplify each expression. All variables are nonzero.

(a) $\dfrac{25b^9}{15b^6}$

(b) $\dfrac{-24x^6y^4}{10x^4y}$

Solution

(a) $\dfrac{25b^9}{15b^6} = \dfrac{25}{15} \cdot \dfrac{b^9}{b^6}$

Divide out like factors;
use $\dfrac{a^m}{a^n} = a^{m-n}$: $= \dfrac{\cancel{5} \cdot 5}{\cancel{5} \cdot 3} \cdot b^{9-6}$

$= \dfrac{5}{3}b^3$

$= \dfrac{5b^3}{3}$

(b) $\dfrac{-24x^6y^4}{10x^4y} = \dfrac{-24}{10} \cdot \dfrac{x^6}{x^4} \cdot \dfrac{y^4}{y}$

Divide out like factors;
use $\dfrac{a^m}{a^n} = a^{m-n}$: $= \dfrac{-12 \cdot \cancel{2}}{5 \cdot \cancel{2}} \cdot x^{6-4} \cdot y^{4-1}$

$= -\dfrac{12}{5}x^2y^3$

$= -\dfrac{12x^2y^3}{5}$ ■

Work Smart

The expressions $\dfrac{5}{3}b^3$ and $\dfrac{5b^3}{3}$ are equivalent; the expressions $\dfrac{-12}{5}x^2y^3$ and $\dfrac{-12x^2y^3}{5}$ are also equivalent.

Quick ✔

1. $\dfrac{a^m}{a^n} =$ _____ provided that $a \neq 0$.

2. *True or False:* $\dfrac{6^{10}}{6^4} = 1^6$.

In Problems 3–5, simplify each expression. All variables are nonzero.

3. $\dfrac{3^7}{3^5}$

4. $\dfrac{14c^6}{10c^5}$

5. $\dfrac{-21w^4z^8}{14w^3z}$

☐ 2 Simplify Exponential Expressions Using the Quotient to a Power Rule

Now let's look at a quotient raised to a power:

$$\left(\dfrac{3}{2}\right)^4 = \underbrace{\left(\dfrac{3}{2}\right) \cdot \left(\dfrac{3}{2}\right) \cdot \left(\dfrac{3}{2}\right) \cdot \left(\dfrac{3}{2}\right)}_{4\ \text{factors}} = \dfrac{\overbrace{3 \cdot 3 \cdot 3 \cdot 3}^{4\ \text{factors}}}{\underbrace{2 \cdot 2 \cdot 2 \cdot 2}_{4\ \text{factors}}} = \dfrac{3^4}{2^4}$$

We are led to the following result:

QUOTIENT TO A POWER RULE FOR EXPONENTS

If a and b are real numbers and n is a natural number, then

$$\left(\dfrac{a}{b}\right)^n = \dfrac{a^n}{b^n} \qquad \text{if } b \neq 0$$

In Words

When a quotient is raised to a power, both the numerator and the denominator are raised to the indicated power.

EXAMPLE 3 Using the Quotient to a Power Rule to Simplify an Expression

Simplify the expression: $\left(\dfrac{z}{3}\right)^2$

Solution

This expression is a quotient, so we apply the Quotient to a Power Rule, raising both the numerator and the denominator to the indicated power.

$$\left(\dfrac{z}{3}\right)^2 = \dfrac{z^2}{3^2}$$

Evaluate 3^2: $= \dfrac{z^2}{9}$ ■

EXAMPLE 4 Using the Quotient to a Power Rule to Simplify Expressions

Simplify each expression. All variables are nonzero.

(a) $\left(-\dfrac{2y}{z}\right)^3$ 　　　　　　　　　　　　　　**(b)** $\left(\dfrac{3a^2}{b^3}\right)^4$

Solution

(a)

$$-\dfrac{a}{b} = \dfrac{-a}{b}\text{:} \quad \left(-\dfrac{2y}{z}\right)^3 = \left(\dfrac{-2y}{z}\right)^3$$

$$\text{Use } \left(\dfrac{a}{b}\right)^n = \dfrac{a^n}{b^n}\text{:} \quad = \dfrac{(-2y)^3}{z^3}$$

$$\text{Use } (ab)^n = a^nb^n\text{:} \quad = \dfrac{(-2)^3(y)^3}{z^3}$$

$$\text{Evaluate } (-2)^3\text{:} \quad = -\dfrac{8y^3}{z^3}$$

(b)

$$\left(\dfrac{3a^2}{b^3}\right)^4 = \dfrac{(3a^2)^4}{(b^3)^4}$$

$$\text{Use } (ab)^n = a^nb^n\text{:} \quad = \dfrac{3^4(a^2)^4}{(b^3)^4}$$

$$\begin{array}{l}\text{Evaluate } (3)^4\text{;}\\ \text{use } (a^m)^n = a^{m\cdot n}\text{:}\end{array} \quad = \dfrac{81a^{2\cdot4}}{b^{3\cdot4}}$$

$$= \dfrac{81a^8}{b^{12}} \quad\blacksquare$$

Quick ✔

6. $\left(\dfrac{a}{b}\right)^n =$ _____ provided that _____ .

In Problems 7 and 8, simplify each expression.

7. $\left(\dfrac{p}{2}\right)^4$ 　　　　　　**8.** $\left(-\dfrac{2a^2}{b^4}\right)^3$

---

❸ Simplify Exponential Expressions Using Zero as an Exponent

Now that we have fully discussed exponential expressions with natural number (or positive integer) exponents, we will extend the definition of exponential expressions to integer exponents. We begin with raising a real number to the 0 power.

> **DEFINITION OF ZERO EXPONENT**
> If a is a nonzero real number (that is, $a \neq 0$), we define
> $$a^0 = 1$$

The reason that $a^0 = 1$ is based upon the Quotient Rule for Exponents. That is,

$$\dfrac{a^n}{a^n} = a^{n-n} = a^0. \text{ In addition, } \dfrac{a^n}{a^n} = \dfrac{\overbrace{a\cdot a\cdot\ \ldots\ \cdot a}^{n\text{ factors}}}{\underbrace{a\cdot a\cdot\ \ldots\ \cdot a}_{n\text{ factors}}} = 1. \text{ Therefore, } a^0 = 1.$$

EXAMPLE 5 Using Zero as an Exponent

In the following examples, all variables are nonzero.

(a) $3^0 = 1$ 　　　　　**(b)** $x^0 = 1$ 　　　　　**(c)** $(4y)^0 = 1$

(d) $8w^0 = 8\cdot1$ 　　　**(e)** $-5^0 = -1\cdot5^0$ 　　**(f)** $(-4y)^0 = 1$

　　　 $= 8$ 　　　　　　　　 $= -1$ 　　　　　　　　　　　　　　$\blacksquare$

Work Smart

In Example 5(d), the exponent 0 applies *only* to the factor w.

Quick ✔ *In Problems 9 and 10, simplify each expression. When they occur, assume variables are nonzero.*

9. (a) $10^0 =$ _____ 　　　**(b)** $-10^0 =$ _____ 　　　**(c)** $(-10)^0 =$ _____

10. (a) $(2b)^0 =$ _____ 　　**(b)** $2b^0 =$ _____ 　　　　**(c)** $(-2b)^0 =$ _____

4   Simplify Exponential Expressions Involving Negative Exponents

Now let's look at exponents that are negative integers. Suppose that we wanted to simplify $\dfrac{z^3}{z^5}$. If we use the Quotient Rule for Exponents, we obtain

$$\frac{z^3}{z^5} = z^{3-5} = z^{-2}$$

We could also simplify this expression directly by dividing like factors:

$$\frac{z^3}{z^5} = \frac{\cancel{z} \cdot \cancel{z} \cdot \cancel{z}}{\cancel{z} \cdot \cancel{z} \cdot \cancel{z} \cdot z \cdot z} = \frac{1}{z^2}$$

This implies that $z^{-2} = \dfrac{1}{z^2}$. Considering this result, we define a raised to a negative integer power as follows:

> **DEFINITION OF NEGATIVE EXPONENT**
>
> If n is a positive integer and if a is a nonzero real number (that is, $a \neq 0$), then we define
>
> $$a^{-n} = \frac{1}{a^n}$$

Remember, the reciprocal of a nonzero number a is $\dfrac{1}{a}$. For example, the reciprocal of 7 is $\dfrac{1}{7}$ and the reciprocal of $-\dfrac{5}{8}$ is $-\dfrac{8}{5}$. Whenever we encounter a negative exponent, we should think, "take the reciprocal of the base."

EXAMPLE 6   Simplifying Exponential Expressions Containing Negative Integer Exponents

(a) $2^{-3} = \dfrac{1}{2^3}$

$= \dfrac{1}{8}$

(b) $(-5)^{-2} = \dfrac{1}{(-5)^2}$

$= \dfrac{1}{25}$

(c) $-4^{-2} = -1 \cdot 4^{-2}$

$= \dfrac{-1}{4^2}$

$= \dfrac{-1}{16}$

$= -\dfrac{1}{16}$ ∎

EXAMPLE 7   Simplifying the Sum of Exponential Expressions Containing Negative Integer Exponents

Simplify: $2^{-2} + 4^{-1}$

Solution

$$2^{-2} + 4^{-1} = \frac{1}{2^2} + \frac{1}{4^1}$$

Evaluate: $= \dfrac{1}{4} + \dfrac{1}{4}$

Find the sum: $= \dfrac{2}{4}$

Write in lowest terms: $= \dfrac{1}{2}$ ∎

Quick ✔ *In Problems 11 and 12, simplify each expression.*

11. (a) 2^{-4} **(b)** $(-2)^{-4}$ **(c)** -2^{-4} **12.** $4^{-1} - 2^{-3}$

EXAMPLE 8 Simplifying Exponential Expressions Containing a Negative Integer Exponent

Simplify each expression so that all exponents are positive. All variables are nonzero.

(a) x^{-4} (b) $(-x)^{-4}$ (c) $-x^{-4}$

Solution

(a) $x^{-4} = \dfrac{1}{x^4}$

(b) $(-x)^{-4} = \dfrac{1}{(-x)^4}$

$$= \dfrac{1}{(-1 \cdot x)^4}$$

$(ab)^n = a^n b^n: \quad = \dfrac{1}{(-1)^4 x^4}$

$(-1)^4 = 1: \quad = \dfrac{1}{x^4}$

(c) $-x^{-4} = -1 \cdot x^{-4}$

$$= -1 \cdot \dfrac{1}{x^4}$$

$$= -\dfrac{1}{x^4}$$

Quick ✔ *In Problem 13, simplify each expression so that all exponents are positive. All variables are nonzero.*

13. (a) y^{-8} (b) $(-y)^{-8}$ (c) $-y^{-8}$

EXAMPLE 9 Simplifying Expressions Containing a Negative Integer Exponent

Simplify:

(a) $2a^{-3}$ (b) $(2a)^{-3}$ (c) $(-2a)^{-3}$

In each problem, $a \neq 0$.

Solution

(a) $2a^{-3} = 2 \cdot \dfrac{1}{a^3}$

$$= \dfrac{2}{a^3}$$

(b) $(2a)^{-3} = \dfrac{1}{(2a)^3}$

$(ab)^n = a^n \cdot b^n: \quad = \dfrac{1}{2^3 \cdot a^3}$

$$= \dfrac{1}{8a^3}$$

(c) $(-2a)^{-3} = \dfrac{1}{(-2a)^3}$

$(ab)^n = a^n \cdot b^n: \quad = \dfrac{1}{(-2)^3 \cdot a^3}$

$$= \dfrac{1}{-8a^3}$$

$\dfrac{a}{-b} = -\dfrac{a}{b}: \quad = -\dfrac{1}{8a^3}$

Quick ✔ *In Problem 14, simplify each expression so that all exponents are positive. All variables are nonzero.*

14. (a) $2m^{-5}$ (b) $(2m)^{-5}$ (c) $(-2m)^{-5}$

How might we simplify $\dfrac{1}{a^{-n}}$? Because

$$\dfrac{1}{a^{-n}} = \dfrac{1}{\dfrac{1}{a^n}} = 1 \cdot \dfrac{a^n}{1} = a^n$$

we have the following result.

If a is a real number and n is an integer, then

$$\dfrac{1}{a^{-n}} = a^n \qquad \text{if } a \neq 0$$

EXAMPLE 10 Simplifying Quotients Containing Negative Integer Exponents

Simplify each expression so that all exponents are positive integers.

(a) $\dfrac{6}{2^{-3}}$ **(b)** $\dfrac{7}{n^{-2}}$ **(c)** $\dfrac{8}{3n^{-4}}$

Work Smart

$$\dfrac{6}{2^{-3}} = \dfrac{6}{\dfrac{1}{8}}$$
$$= 6 \div \dfrac{1}{8}$$
$$= 6 \cdot 8$$
$$= 48$$

Solution

(a) $\dfrac{6}{2^{-3}} = 6 \cdot 2^3 = 6 \cdot 8 = 48$ **(b)** $\dfrac{7}{n^{-2}} = 7 \cdot n^2 = 7n^2$ **(c)** $\dfrac{8}{3n^{-4}} = \dfrac{8}{3} \cdot n^4 = \dfrac{8n^4}{3}$ ■

Quick ✔ *In Problems 15–17, simplify each numerical expression. Assume all variables are nonzero.*

15. $\dfrac{1}{3^{-2}}$ **16.** $\dfrac{1}{-10^{-2}}$ **17.** $\dfrac{5}{2z^{-2}}$

EXAMPLE 11 Simplifying Quotients Containing Negative Integer Exponents

Simplify: $\left(\dfrac{3}{2}\right)^{-3}$

Solution

$$\left(\dfrac{3}{2}\right)^{-3} = \dfrac{1}{\left(\dfrac{3}{2}\right)^3}$$

Use $\left(\dfrac{a}{b}\right)^n = \dfrac{a^n}{b^n}$: $= \dfrac{1}{\dfrac{3^3}{2^3}}$

$$= \dfrac{1}{\dfrac{27}{8}}$$

$$= 1 \cdot \dfrac{8}{27}$$

$$= \dfrac{8}{27}$$ ■

Work Smart

This "shortcut" says to simplify a quotient to a negative exponent, first take the reciprocal, then raise that expression to the positive exponent power.

The following shortcut is based upon the results of Example 11:

If a and b are real numbers and n is an integer, then

$$\left(\dfrac{a}{b}\right)^{-n} = \left(\dfrac{b}{a}\right)^{n} \qquad \text{if } a \neq 0, b \neq 0$$

For example, $\left(\dfrac{3}{2}\right)^{-3} = \left(\dfrac{2}{3}\right)^{3} = \dfrac{8}{27}$.

EXAMPLE 12 Simplifying Quotients Containing Negative Exponents

Simplify $\left(-\dfrac{x^3}{4}\right)^{-2}, x \neq 0.$

Solution

$$\left(-\dfrac{x^3}{4}\right)^{-2} = \left(-\dfrac{4}{x^3}\right)^{2}$$

Use $\left(\dfrac{a}{b}\right)^n = \dfrac{a^n}{b^n}$: $= \dfrac{(-4)^2}{(x^3)^2}$

Use $(a^m)^n = a^{m \cdot n}$: $= \dfrac{16}{x^6}$ ■

Quick ✔ *In Problems 18–20, simplify each expression. All variables are nonzero.*

18. $\left(\dfrac{7}{8}\right)^{-1}$ **19.** $\left(\dfrac{3a}{5}\right)^{-2}$ **20.** $\left(-\dfrac{2}{3n^4}\right)^{-3}$

⌐5 Simplify Exponential Expressions Using the Laws of Exponents

We now summarize the Laws of Exponents where the exponents are integers.

THE LAWS OF EXPONENTS

If a and b are real numbers and if m and n are integers, then, assuming the expression is defined,

Rule		Examples
Product Rule	$a^m \cdot a^n = a^{m+n}$	$7^3 \cdot 7 = 7^4$; $x^2 \cdot x^5 = x^7$
Power Rule	$(a^m)^n = a^{m \cdot n}$	$(3^4)^2 = 3^8$; $(x^3)^2 = x^6$
Product to Power Rule	$(a \cdot b)^n = a^n \cdot b^n$	$(x^3 y)^4 = x^{12} y^4$
Quotient Rule	$\dfrac{a^m}{a^n} = a^{m-n}$, if $a \neq 0$	$\dfrac{9^5}{9^3} = 9^2$; $\dfrac{y^{11}}{y^8} = y^3$
Quotient to Power Rule	$\left(\dfrac{a}{b}\right)^n = \dfrac{a^n}{b^n}$, if $b \neq 0$	$\left(\dfrac{3}{4}\right)^2 = \dfrac{9}{16}$; $\left(\dfrac{2x}{y^2}\right)^3 = \dfrac{8x^3}{y^6}$
Zero Exponent Rule	$a^0 = 1$, if $a \neq 0$	$3^0 = 1$; $(5m)^0 = 1$ $5m^0 = 5 \cdot 1 = 5$
Negative Exponent Rules	$a^{-n} = \dfrac{1}{a^n}$, if $a \neq 0$ $\dfrac{1}{a^{-n}} = a^n$, if $a \neq 0$	$2^{-3} = \dfrac{1}{8}$; $b^{-4} = \dfrac{1}{b^4}$ $\dfrac{1}{t^{-5}} = t^5$
Quotient to a Negative Power Rule	$\left(\dfrac{a}{b}\right)^{-n} = \left(\dfrac{b}{a}\right)^n$, if $a \neq 0$, $b \neq 0$	$\left(\dfrac{5}{k}\right)^{-2} = \left(\dfrac{k}{5}\right)^2 = \dfrac{k^2}{25}$

Let's do some examples where we use one or more of the rules listed above. To evaluate or simplify these exponential expressions, ask yourself the following questions.

USING THE LAWS OF EXPONENTS

- Does the exponential expression contain numerical expressions? If so, *evaluate* them. ("Evaluate" means "find the value.")
- Is the expression a product of monomials? If so, use the Product Rule:
$$a^m \cdot a^n = a^{m+n}$$
- Is the expression a quotient (division problem)? If so, use the Quotient Rule:
$$\dfrac{a^m}{a^n} = a^{m-n}$$
- Do you see a quantity raised to a power? If so, use one of the Power Rules:
$$(a^m)^n = a^{m \cdot n}, (a \cdot b)^n = a^n \cdot b^n, \text{ or } \left(\dfrac{a}{b}\right)^n = \dfrac{a^n}{b^n}.$$
- Is there a negative exponent in the expression? Remember, a negative in an exponent means "take the reciprocal of the base." Plus, an expression is not simplified if it contains negative exponents.
- Are you required to raise a quantity to the zero power? Remember, $a^0 = 1$ for $a \neq 0$.

EXAMPLE 13 How to Simplify Exponential Expressions Using Exponent Rules

Simplify $\left(\frac{3}{2}a^3b^{-2}\right)(-12a^{-4}b^5)$. Write the answer with only positive exponents.
All variables are nonzero.

Step-by-Step Solution

Step 1: Rearrange factors.	$\left(\frac{3}{2}a^3b^{-2}\right)(-12a^{-4}b^5) = \left(\frac{3}{2}\cdot(-12)\right)(a^3\cdot a^{-4})(b^{-2}\cdot b^5)$
Step 2: Find each product.	Evaluate $\left(\frac{3}{2}\right)\cdot(-12)$; use $a^m\cdot a^n = a^{m+n}$: $= -18a^{3+(-4)}b^{-2+5}$ $= -18a^{-1}b^3$
Step 3: Simplify. Write the product so that the exponents are positive.	Use $a^{-n} = \frac{1}{a^n}$: $= -18\cdot\frac{1}{a}\cdot b^3$ $= -\frac{18b^3}{a}$

Quick ✔ *In Problems 21 and 22, simplify each expression. Write the answers with only positive exponents. All variables are nonzero.*

21. $(-4a^{-3})(5a)$ **22.** $\left(-\frac{2}{5}m^{-2}n^{-1}\right)\left(-\frac{15}{2}mn^0\right)$

EXAMPLE 14 How to Simplify Expressions Using the Quotient Rule and the Negative Exponent Rule

Simplify $-\frac{27a^7b^{-6}}{18a^{-2}b^2}$. Write the answer with only positive exponents. All variables are nonzero.

Step-by-Step Solution

Step 1: Write the quotient as the product of factors.	Use $-\frac{a}{b} = \frac{-a}{b}$: $-\frac{27a^7b^{-6}}{18a^{-2}b^2} = \frac{-27}{18}\cdot\frac{a^7}{a^{-2}}\cdot\frac{b^{-6}}{b^2}$
Step 2: Find each quotient.	Simplify $\frac{-27}{18}$; use $\frac{a^m}{a^n} = a^{m-n}$: $= \frac{-3}{2}\cdot a^{7-(-2)}\cdot b^{-6-2}$ $= -\frac{3}{2}\cdot a^9\cdot b^{-8}$
Step 3: Simplify. Write the quotient so that the exponents are positive.	Use $a^{-n} = \frac{1}{a^n}$: $= -\frac{3}{2}\cdot a^9\cdot\frac{1}{b^8}$ $= -\frac{3a^9}{2b^8}$

Quick ✔ *In Problems 23 and 24, simplify each expression. Write answers with only positive exponents. All variables are nonzero.*

23. $-\dfrac{16a^4b^{-1}}{12ab^{-4}}$ **24.** $\dfrac{45x^{-2}y^{-2}}{35x^{-4}y}$

EXAMPLE 15 Simplifying Exponential Expressions Using Exponent Rules

Simplify $\left(\dfrac{25a^{-2}b}{10ab^{-1}}\right)^{-2}$. Write the answer with only positive exponents. All variables are nonzero.

Solution

Because there are like factors inside the parentheses, we first simplify the expression within parentheses before we apply the Power Rule.

$$\left(\frac{25a^{-2}b}{10ab^{-1}}\right)^{-2} = \left(\frac{25\cdot b\cdot b}{10\cdot a^2\cdot a}\right)^{-2}$$

$\dfrac{25}{10} = \dfrac{5\cdot 5}{5\cdot 2} = \dfrac{5}{2}$; use $a^m a^n = a^{m+n}$: $= \left(\dfrac{5b^2}{2a^3}\right)^{-2}$

Use $\left(\dfrac{a}{b}\right)^{-n} = \left(\dfrac{b}{a}\right)^{n}$: $= \left(\dfrac{2a^3}{5b^2}\right)^{2}$

Use $\left(\dfrac{a}{b}\right)^{n} = \dfrac{a^n}{b^n}$: $= \dfrac{(2a^3)^2}{(5b^2)^2}$

Use $(ab)^n = a^n b^n$: $= \dfrac{2^2(a^3)^2}{5^2(b^2)^2}$

Use $(a^m)^n = a^{m\cdot n}$: $= \dfrac{4a^{3\cdot 2}}{25b^{2\cdot 2}}$

$= \dfrac{4a^6}{25b^4}$

∎

Quick ✔ *In Problems 25 and 26, simplify each expression. Write the answers with only positive exponents. All variables are nonzero.*

25. $(3y^2z^{-3})^{-2}$ **26.** $\left(\dfrac{2wz^{-3}}{7w^{-1}}\right)^{2}$

EXAMPLE 16 Simplifying Exponential Expressions Using Exponent Rules

Simplify $(6c^{-2}d)\left(\dfrac{3c^{-3}d^4}{2d}\right)^{2}$. Write the answer with only positive exponents. All variables are nonzero.

Solution

Since the quotient in the parentheses is messy, we will simplify it first.

$$(6c^{-2}d)\left(\frac{3c^{-3}d^4}{2d}\right)^{2} = \frac{6c^{-2}d}{1}\left(\frac{3c^{-3}d^{4-1}}{2}\right)^{2}$$

Use $a^{-n} = \dfrac{1}{a^n}$: $= \dfrac{6d}{c^2}\left(\dfrac{3d^3}{2c^3}\right)^{2}$

Use $\left(\dfrac{a}{b}\right)^{n} = \dfrac{a^n}{b^n}$ and $(ab)^n = a^n b^n$: $= \dfrac{6d}{c^2}\left(\dfrac{3^2(d^3)^2}{2^2(c^3)^2}\right)$

Use $(a^m)^n = a^{m\cdot n}$: $= \dfrac{6d}{c^2}\left(\dfrac{9d^6}{4c^6}\right)$

Rearrange factors: $= 6\cdot\dfrac{9}{4}\cdot\dfrac{d\cdot d^6}{c^2\cdot c^6}$

$6\cdot\dfrac{9}{4} = \cancel{6}^{3}\cdot\dfrac{9}{\cancel{4}_{2}} = \dfrac{27}{2}$; use $a^m a^n = a^{m+n}$: $= \dfrac{27}{2}\cdot\dfrac{d^{1+6}}{c^{2+6}}$

$= \dfrac{27d^7}{2c^8}$

∎

Quick ✔ *In Problems 27 and 28, simplify the expression. Write answers with only positive exponents. All variables are nonzero.*

27. $\left(\dfrac{-6p^{-2}}{p}\right)(3p^8)^{-1}$ **28.** $(-25k^5r^{-2})\left(\dfrac{2}{5}k^{-3}r\right)^{2}$

5.4 EXERCISES

PRACTICE   WATCH   DOWNLOAD   READ   REVIEW

1–28. *are the* Quick ✔s *that follow each* EXAMPLE

Building Skills

In Problems 29–38, use the Quotient Rule to simplify. All variables are nonzero. See Objective 1.

29. $\dfrac{2^{23}}{2^{19}}$

30. $\dfrac{10^5}{10^2}$

31. $\dfrac{x^{15}}{x^6}$

32. $\dfrac{x^{20}}{x^{14}}$

33. $\dfrac{16y^4}{4y}$

34. $\dfrac{9a^4}{27a}$

35. $\dfrac{-16m^{10}}{24m^3}$

36. $\dfrac{-36x^2y^5}{24xy^4}$

37. $\dfrac{-12m^9n^3}{-6mn}$

38. $\dfrac{-15r^9s^2}{-5r^8s}$

In Problems 39–46, use the Quotient to a Power Rule to simplify. All variables are nonzero. See Objective 2.

39. $\left(\dfrac{3}{2}\right)^3$

40. $\left(\dfrac{4}{9}\right)^2$

41. $\left(\dfrac{x^5}{3}\right)^3$

42. $\left(\dfrac{7}{y^2}\right)^2$

43. $\left(-\dfrac{x^5}{y^7}\right)^4$

44. $\left(-\dfrac{a^3}{b^{10}}\right)^5$

45. $\left(\dfrac{7a^2b}{c^3}\right)^2$

46. $\left(\dfrac{2mn^2}{q^3}\right)^4$

In Problems 47–58, use the Zero Exponent Rule to simplify. All variables are nonzero. See Objective 3.

47. 3^0

48. -100^0

49. $-\left(\dfrac{1}{2}\right)^0$

50. $\left(\dfrac{2}{5}\right)^0$

51. $18 \cdot 2^0$

52. $14^0 \cdot 3^0 \cdot 10$

53. $(-10)^0$

54. $(-8)^0$

55. $(24ab)^0$

56. $(-11xy)^0$

57. $24ab^0$

58. $-11xy^0$

In Problems 59–82, use the Negative Exponent Rules to simplify. Write answers with only positive exponents. All variables are nonzero. See Objective 4.

59. 10^{-3}

60. 5^{-1}

61. m^{-2}

62. k^{-2}

63. $-a^{-2}$

64. $-b^{-3}$

65. $-4y^{-3}$

66. $-7z^{-5}$

67. $2^{-1} + 3^{-2}$

68. $4^{-2} - 2^{-3}$

69. $\left(\dfrac{2}{5}\right)^{-2}$

70. $\left(\dfrac{5}{4}\right)^{-3}$

71. $\left(\dfrac{3}{z^2}\right)^{-1}$

72. $\left(\dfrac{4}{p^2}\right)^{-2}$

73. $\left(-\dfrac{2n}{m^2}\right)^{-3}$

74. $\left(-\dfrac{5}{3b^2}\right)^{-3}$

75. $\dfrac{1}{4^{-2}}$

76. $\dfrac{1}{6^{-2}}$

77. $\dfrac{6}{x^{-4}}$

78. $\dfrac{4}{b^{-3}}$

79. $\dfrac{5}{2m^{-3}}$

80. $\dfrac{9}{4t^{-1}}$

81. $\dfrac{5}{(2m)^{-3}}$

82. $\dfrac{9}{(4t)^{-1}}$

In Problems 83–92, use the Laws of Exponents to simplify. Write answers with positive exponents. All variables are nonzero. See Objective 5.

83. $\left(\dfrac{4}{3}y^{-2}z\right)\left(\dfrac{5}{8}y^{-2}z^4\right)$

84. $\left(\dfrac{3}{5}ab^{-3}\right)\left(\dfrac{5}{3}a^{-1}b^3\right)$

85. $\dfrac{-7m^7n^6}{3m^{-3}n^0}$

86. $\dfrac{13r^8t^3}{-5r^0t^{-5}}$

87. $\dfrac{21y^2z^{-3}}{3y^{-2}z^{-1}}$

88. $\dfrac{30ab^{-4}}{15a^{-1}b^{-2}}$

89. $(4x^2y^{-2})^{-2}$

90. $(5x^{-4}y^3)^{-2}$

91. $(3a^2b^{-1})\left(\dfrac{4a^{-1}b^2}{b^3}\right)^2$

92. $(5a^3b^{-4})\left(\dfrac{2ab^{-1}}{b^{-3}}\right)^2$

Mixed Practice

In Problems 93–130, simplify. Write answers with only positive exponents. All variables are nonzero.

93. $2^5 \cdot 2^{-3}$

94. $3^8 \cdot 3^{-6}$

95. $2^{-7} \cdot 2^4$

96. $10^{-4} \cdot 10^3$

97. $\dfrac{3}{3^{-3}}$

98. $\dfrac{5^4}{5^{-1}}$

99. $\dfrac{x^6}{x^{15}}$

100. $\dfrac{b^{24}}{b^{42}}$

101. $\dfrac{x^{10}}{x^{-3}}$

102. $\dfrac{a^{-4}}{a^6}$

103. $\dfrac{8x^2}{2x^5}$

104. $\dfrac{24m^4}{6m^8}$

105. $\dfrac{-27xy^3z^4}{18x^4y^3z}$

106. $\dfrac{8a^{15}b^2}{-18b^{20}}$

107. $(3x^2y^{-3})(12^{-1}x^{-5}y^{-6})$ **108.** $(-14c^2d^4)(3c^{-6}d^{-4})$

109. $(-a^4)^{-3}$ **110.** $(-x^{-2})^5$

111. $(3m^{-2})^3$ **112.** $(2z^{-1})^3$

113. $(-3x^{-2}y^{-3})^{-2}$ **114.** $(-4a^{-3}b^{-2}c^{-1})^{-1}$

115. $2p^{-4} \cdot p^{-3} \cdot p^0$ **116.** $7a^{-2} \cdot a^0 \cdot a^{-3}$

117. $(-16a^3)(-3a^4)\left(\dfrac{1}{4}a^{-7}\right)$

118. $(-3x^{-4}y)(2x^{-3}y^{-6})\left(\dfrac{1}{36}x^{10}\right)$

119. $\dfrac{8x^2 \cdot x^7}{12x^{-3} \cdot x^4}$ **120.** $\dfrac{32x^{-3} \cdot x^2}{24x^2 \cdot x^5}$

121. $(2x^{-3}y^{-2})^4(3x^2y^{-3})^{-3}$ **122.** $(4a^{-2}b)^3(2a^2b^{-4})^{-2}$

123. $\left(\dfrac{y}{2z}\right)^{-3} \cdot \left(\dfrac{3y^2}{4z^3}\right)^2$ **124.** $\left(\dfrac{s}{4t^2}\right)^3 \cdot \left(\dfrac{3s^2}{2t^4}\right)^{-4}$

125. $(4x^2y)^3 \cdot \left(\dfrac{2x}{3y}\right)^{-3}$ **126.** $(2a^5b^2)^3 \cdot \left(\dfrac{4a^{-2}b^3}{3a}\right)^{-2}$

127. $\dfrac{(5a^{-3}b^2)^2}{a^{-4}b^{-4}}(15a^{-3}b)^{-1}$ **128.** $\left(\dfrac{2x^{-4}y^{-3}}{4xy^3}\right)^{-2}(4x^2y^{-1})^{-2}$

129. $\dfrac{4x^{-3}(2x^3)}{20(x^{-3})^2}$ **130.** $\dfrac{(-2a^{-3}b^2)^{-4}}{5a^2b^2c^0}$

Applying the Concepts

△**131. Volume of a Box** The volume of a rectangular solid is given by the equation $V = l \cdot w \cdot h$. Find the volume of a shipping box whose dimensions are $l = x$ m, $w = x$ m, and $h = 3x$ m.

△**132. Volume of a Box** The volume of a rectangular solid is given by the equation $V = l \cdot w \cdot h$. Find the volume of a box whose dimensions are $l = 3n$ yards, $w = 2n$ yards, and $h = 6n$ yards.

△**133. Volume of a Cylinder** The volume of a right circular cylinder is given by the equation $V = \pi r^2 h$, where r is the radius of the circular base of the cylinder and h is its height. Rewrite this equation in terms of the diameter, d, of the base of the cylinder.

△**134. Volume of a Cylinder** The volume of a right circular cylinder is given by the equation $V = \pi r^2 h$, where r is the radius of the circular base of the cylinder and h is its height. Write an algebraic expression for the volume of a cylinder in which the radius of the circular base is equal to the height of the cylinder.

△**135. Making Buttons** How much fabric is required to cover x buttons in the shape of a circle whose radius is $3x$?

△**136. Making a Tablecloth** How much fabric is required to make a round tablecloth if the diameter of the tablecloth is $\left(\dfrac{1}{2}x\right)$ meters?

Extending the Concepts

In Problems 137–144, simplify. Write answers with only positive exponents.

137. $\dfrac{x^{2n}}{x^{3n}}$ **138.** $\dfrac{(x^{a-2})^3}{(x^{2a})^5}$

139. $\left(\dfrac{x^n y^m}{x^{4n-1}y^{m+1}}\right)^{-2}$ **140.** $\left(\dfrac{a^n b^{2m}}{ab^2}\right)^{-3}$

141. $(x^{2a}y^b z^{-c})^{3a}$ **142.** $(x^{-a}y^{-2b}z^{4c})^{2a}$

143. $\dfrac{(3a^n)^2}{(2a^{4n})^3}$ **144.** $\dfrac{y^a}{y^{4a}}$

Explaining the Concepts

145. Explain why $\dfrac{11^6}{11^4} \neq 1^2$.

146. Use the Quotient Rule and the expression $\left(\dfrac{a^n}{a^n}\right)$, $a \neq 0$, to explain why $a^0 = 1$, $a \neq 0$.

147. Explain the difference in simplifying the expressions $-12x^0$ and $(-12x)^0$.

148. Explain two different approaches to simplify $\left(\dfrac{x^8}{x^2}\right)^3$. Which do you prefer?

149. A friend of yours has a homework problem in which he must simplify $(x^3)^4$. He tells you that he thinks the answer is x^7. Is he right? If not, explain where he went wrong.

150. Explain why $-4x^{-3}$ is equal to $-\dfrac{4}{x^3}$. That is, why doesn't the factor -4 "move" to the denominator?

PUTTING THE CONCEPTS TOGETHER (Sections 5.1–5.4)

These problems cover important concepts from Sections 5.1 through 5.4. We designed these problems so that you can review the chapter so far and show your mastery of the concepts. Take time to work these problems before proceeding with the next section. The answers to these problems are located at the back of the text on page AN-22.

1. Determine whether the following algebraic expression is a polynomial (Yes or No). If it is a polynomial, state the degree and then state if it is a monomial, binomial, or trinomial: $6x^2y^4 - 8x^5 + 3$.

2. Evaluate the polynomial $-x^2 + 3x$ for the given values: **(a)** 0   **(b)** -1 **(c)** 2.

In Problems 3–11, perform the indicated operation.

3. $(6x^4 - 2x^2 + 7) - (-2x^4 - 7 + 2x^2)$

4. $(2x^2y - xy + 3y^2) + (4xy - y^2 + 3x^2y)$

5. $-2mn(3m^2n - mn^3)$ 6. $(5x + 3)(x - 4)$

7. $(2x - 3y)(4x - 7y)$ 8. $(5x + 8)(5x - 8)$

9. $(2x + 3y)^2$ 10. $2a(3a - 4)(a + 5)$

11. $(4m + 3)(4m^3 - 2m^2 + 4m - 8)$

In Problems 12–20, simplify each expression. Write answers with only positive exponents. All variables are nonzero.

12. $(-2x^7y^0z)(4xz^8)$ 13. $(5m^3n^{-2})(-3m^{-4}n)$

14. $\dfrac{-18a^8b^3}{6a^5b}$ 15. $\dfrac{16x^7y}{32x^9y^3}$

16. $\dfrac{7}{2ab^{-2}}$ 17. $\dfrac{q^{-6}rt^5}{qr^{-4}t^7}$

18. $\left(\dfrac{3}{2}r^2\right)^{-3}$ 19. $(4y^{-2}z^3)^{-2}$

20. $\left(\dfrac{3x^3y^{-3}}{2x^{-1}y^0}\right)^{-4} \cdot (2x^{-4}y^{-2})^2$

5.5   Dividing Polynomials

OBJECTIVES

☐1 Divide a Polynomial by a Monomial

☐2 Divide a Polynomial by a Binomial

Preparing for Dividing Polynomials

Before getting started, take the following readiness quiz. If you get a problem wrong, go back to the section cited and review the material.

P1. Find the quotient: $\dfrac{24a^3}{6a}$ [Section 5.4, pp. 342–343]

P2. Find the quotient: $\dfrac{-49x^3}{21x^4}$ [Section 5.4, pp. 348–349]

P3. Find the product: $3x(7x - 2)$ [Section 5.3, pp. 331–332]

P4. State the degree of $4x^2 - 2x + 1$.   [Section 5.1, pp. 318–319]

Work Smart

A polynomial is a monomial or the sum of monomials.

We have now presented a discussion of adding, subtracting, and multiplying polynomials. All that's left to discuss is polynomial division! We begin with dividing a polynomial by a monomial. Recall, when we compute a quotient using long division, such as $15\overline{)345}^{\,23}$, the number 15 is called the *divisor*, the number 345 is called the *dividend*, and the number 23 is called the *quotient*. We use the same terminology with polynomial division.

☐1   Divide a Polynomial by a Monomial

Dividing a polynomial by a monomial requires the Quotient Rule for Exponents. For convenience, we repeat the rule below.

QUOTIENT RULE FOR EXPONENTS

If a is a real number and m and n are integers, then

$$\frac{a^m}{a^n} = a^{m-n} \quad a \neq 0$$

Preparing for...Answers   **P1.** $4a^2$
P2. $-\dfrac{7}{3x}$ **P3.** $21x^2 - 6x$ **P4.** 2

In Words

To divide a polynomial by a monomial, divide each of the terms of the polynomial numerator (dividend) by the monomial denominator (divisor).

Remember, to add two rational numbers, the denominators must be the same. When we have the same denominator, we add the numerators and write the result over the common denominator. For example, $\dfrac{3}{11} + \dfrac{4}{11} = \dfrac{3+4}{11} = \dfrac{7}{11}$. When dividing a polynomial by a monomial, we reverse this process. So, if a, b, and c are monomials, we can write $\dfrac{a+b}{c}$ as $\dfrac{a}{c} + \dfrac{b}{c}$. We can extend this result to polynomials with three or more terms.

EXAMPLE 1 Dividing a Binomial by a Monomial

Divide and simplify: $\dfrac{9x^3 - 21x^2}{3x}$

Solution

We divide each term in the numerator by the denominator.

$$\frac{9x^3 - 21x^2}{3x} = \frac{9x^3}{3x} - \frac{21x^2}{3x}$$

$$\text{Use } \frac{a^m}{a^n} = a^{m-n}: \quad = \frac{9}{3}x^{3-1} - \frac{21}{3}x^{2-1}$$

$$\text{Simplify:} \quad = 3x^2 - 7x$$

EXAMPLE 2 Dividing a Trinomial by a Monomial

Divide and simplify: $\dfrac{12p^4 + 24p^3 + 4p^2}{4p^2}$

Solution

We divide each term in the numerator by the denominator.

$$\frac{12p^4 + 24p^3 + 4p^2}{4p^2} = \frac{12p^4}{4p^2} + \frac{24p^3}{4p^2} + \frac{4p^2}{4p^2}$$

$$\text{Use } \frac{a^m}{a^n} = a^{m-n}: \quad = \frac{12}{4}p^{4-2} + \frac{24}{4}p^{3-2} + \frac{4}{4}\cdot\frac{p^2}{p^2}$$

$$\text{Simplify:} \quad = 3p^2 + 6p + 1$$

Work Smart

$$\frac{12p^4 + 24p^3 + 4p^2}{4p^2}$$

$$\neq \frac{\cancel{12p^4 + 24p^3} + 4p^2}{\cancel{4p^2}}$$

$$\neq 12p^4 + 24p^3 + 1$$

You must divide *each* term in the numerator by the monomial in the denominator.

EXAMPLE 3 Dividing a Trinomial by a Monomial

Divide and simplify: $\dfrac{8a^2b^2 - 6a^2b + 5ab^2}{2a^2b^2}$

Solution

$$\frac{8a^2b^2 - 6a^2b + 5ab^2}{2a^2b^2} = \frac{8a^2b^2}{2a^2b^2} - \frac{6a^2b}{2a^2b^2} + \frac{5ab^2}{2a^2b^2}$$

$$\text{Use } \frac{a^m}{a^n} = a^{m-n}: \quad = \frac{8}{2}a^{2-2}b^{2-2} - \frac{6}{2}a^{2-2}b^{1-2} + \frac{5}{2}a^{1-2}b^{2-2}$$

$$\text{Simplify:} \quad = 4a^0b^0 - 3a^0b^{-1} + \frac{5}{2}a^{-1}b^0$$

$$\text{Use } a^0 = 1; \text{ use } a^{-n} = \frac{1}{a^n}: \quad = 4\cdot1\cdot1 - 3\cdot1\cdot\frac{1}{b} + \frac{5}{2}\cdot\frac{1}{a}\cdot1$$

$$= 4 - \frac{3}{b} + \frac{5}{2a}$$

Quick ✔

1. The first step to simplify $\dfrac{4x^4 + 8x^2}{2x}$ is to rewrite $\dfrac{4x^4 + 8x^2}{2x}$ as _____ .

In Problems 2–4, find the quotient.

2. $\dfrac{10n^4 - 20n^3 + 5n^2}{5n^2}$ **3.** $\dfrac{12k^4 - 18k^2 + 5}{2k^2}$

4. $\dfrac{x^4y^4 + 8x^2y^2 - 4xy}{4x^3y}$

2   Divide a Polynomial by a Binomial

The procedure for dividing a polynomial by a binomial is similar to the procedure for dividing two integers. Although this procedure should be familiar to you, we review it in the following example.

EXAMPLE 4   Dividing an Integer by an Integer Using Long Division

Divide 579 by 16.

Solution

$$
\begin{array}{r}
36 \quad \longleftarrow \text{ quotient} \\
\text{divisor} \longrightarrow 16\overline{)579} \quad \longleftarrow \text{ dividend} \\
\underline{48} \quad\quad \longleftarrow 3 \cdot 16 = 48 \text{ (subtract)} \\
99 \quad \longleftarrow \text{ bring down the 9} \\
\underline{96} \quad \longleftarrow 6 \cdot 16 = 96 \text{ (subtract)} \\
3 \quad \longleftarrow \text{ remainder}
\end{array}
$$

So 579 divided by 16 equals 36 with a remainder of 3. We can write this as $\dfrac{579}{16} = 36\dfrac{3}{16}$.   ∎

We can always check our work after completing a long division problem by multiplying the quotient by the divisor and adding this product to the remainder. The result should be the dividend. That is,

$$(\text{Quotient})(\text{Divisor}) + \text{Remainder} = \text{Dividend}$$

For example, we can check the results of Example 4 as follows:

$$(36)(16) + 3 = 576 + 3 = 579$$

One other comment regarding Example 4: we wrote the solution as $\dfrac{579}{16} = 36\dfrac{3}{16}$. Remember, the mixed number $36\dfrac{3}{16}$ means $36 + \dfrac{3}{16}$. So, the answer is written in the form

$$\text{Quotient} + \frac{\text{Remainder}}{\text{Divisor}}$$

Now let's go over an example that introduces "how to" divide a polynomial by a binomial using long division.

EXAMPLE 5 How to Divide a Polynomial by a Binomial Using Long Division

Find the quotient when $x^2 + 10x + 21$ is divided by $x + 7$.

Step-by-Step Solution

To divide two polynomials, we first write each polynomial in standard form (descending order of degree). The dividend is $x^2 + 10x + 21$ and the divisor is $x + 7$.

Step 1: Divide the highest degree term of the dividend, x^2, by the highest degree term of the divisor, x. Enter the result over the term x^2.	$$x \longleftarrow \frac{x^2}{x} = x$$ $$x + 7 \overline{)x^2 + 10x + 21}$$
Step 2: Multiply x by $x + 7$. Be sure to vertically align like terms.	$$\begin{array}{r} x \\ x + 7 \overline{)x^2 + 10x + 21} \\ \underline{x^2 + 7x} \longleftarrow x(x + 7) = x^2 + 7x \end{array}$$
Step 3: Subtract $x^2 + 7x$ from $x^2 + 10x + 21$.	$$\begin{array}{r} x \\ x + 7 \overline{)x^2 + 10x + 21} \\ \underline{-(x^2 + 7x)} \\ 3x + 21 \longleftarrow (x^2 + 10x + 21) - (x^2 + 7x) = 3x + 21 \end{array}$$
Step 4: Repeat Steps 1–3 treating $3x + 21$ as the dividend.	$$x + 3 \longleftarrow \frac{3x}{x} = 3$$ $$\begin{array}{r} x + 3 \\ x + 7 \overline{)x^2 + 10x + 21} \\ \underline{-(x^2 + 7x)} \\ 3x + 21 \\ \underline{-(3x + 21)} \longleftarrow 3(x + 7) = 3x + 21 \\ 0 \longleftarrow (3x + 21) - (3x + 21) = 0 \end{array}$$ The quotient is $x + 3$ and the remainder is 0.
Step 5: Check your result by showing that (Quotient)(Divisor) + Remainder = Dividend.	$$(x + 3)(x + 7) + 0 = x^2 + 10x + 21$$

The product checks, so $x^2 + 10x + 21$ divided by $x + 7$ is $x + 3$. We can express this division using fractions, as follows:

$$\frac{x^2 + 10x + 21}{x + 7} = x + 3$$

EXAMPLE 6 How to Divide a Polynomial by a Binomial Using Long Division

Find the quotient when $6x^2 + 9x - 10$ is divided by $2x - 1$.

Step-by-Step Solution

Each polynomial is in standard form. The dividend is $6x^2 + 9x - 10$ and the divisor is $2x - 1$.

Step 1: Divide the highest degree term of the dividend, $6x^2$, by the highest degree term of the divisor, $2x$. Enter the result over the term $6x^2$.	$$3x \longleftarrow \frac{6x^2}{2x} = 3x$$ $$2x - 1 \overline{)6x^2 + 9x - 10}$$

Step 2: Multiply 3x by 2x − 1. Be sure to vertically align like terms.

$$
\begin{array}{r}
3x \\
2x - 1 \overline{)6x^2 + 9x - 10} \\
\underline{6x^2 - 3x} \longleftarrow \quad 3x(2x - 1) = 6x^2 - 3x
\end{array}
$$

Step 3: Subtract $6x^2 - 3x$ from $6x^2 + 9x - 10$.

$$
\begin{array}{r}
3x \\
2x - 1 \overline{)6x^2 + 9x - 10} \\
\underline{-(6x^2 - 3x)} \\
12x - 10 \longleftarrow 6x^2 + 9x - 10 - (6x^2 - 3x) = 12x - 10
\end{array}
$$

Step 4: Repeat Steps 1–3 treating $12x - 10$ as the dividend.

$$
\begin{array}{r}
3x + 6 \longleftarrow \quad \dfrac{12x}{2x} = 6 \\
2x - 1 \overline{)6x^2 + 9x - 10} \\
\underline{-(6x^2 - 3x)} \\
12x - 10 \\
\underline{-(12x - 6)} \longleftarrow \quad 6(2x - 1) = 12x - 6 \\
-4 \longleftarrow (12x - 10) - (12x - 6) = -4
\end{array}
$$

Because the degree of -4 is less than the degree of the divisor, $2x - 1$, the process ends. The quotient is $3x + 6$ and the remainder is -4.

Step 5: Check We verify that
(Quotient)(Divisor) + Remainder = Dividend.

$$(3x + 6)(2x - 1) + (-4) = 6x^2 - 3x + 12x - 6 + (-4)$$

Combine like terms: $= 6x^2 + 9x - 10$

Work Smart

You know that you're finished dividing when the degree of the remainder is less than the degree of the divisor.

The product checks, so our answer is correct. So

$$\frac{6x^2 + 9x - 10}{2x - 1} = 3x + 6 - \frac{4}{2x - 1}.$$

Quick ✔

5. To begin a polynomial division problem, write the divisor and the dividend in _____ form.

6. To check the result of long division, multiply the _____ and the divisor and add this result to the _____. If correct, this result will be equal to the _____.

In Problems 7–9, find the quotient by performing long division.

7. $\dfrac{x^2 - 3x - 40}{x + 5}$

8. $\dfrac{2x^2 - 5x - 12}{2x + 3}$

9. $\dfrac{4x^2 + 17x + 21}{x + 3}$

[EXAMPLE 7] Dividing Two Polynomials Using Long Division

Simplify by performing long division: $\dfrac{8 - 9x + 2x^2 + 12x^3 + 5x^5}{x^2 + 3}$

Solution

Do you notice that the dividend is not written in standard form (that is, the dividend is not written in descending order of degree)? Also, when we write the dividend in standard form, do you notice that there is no x^4 term? When a term is missing, its coefficient is 0, so we rewrite the division problem as follows:

$$\frac{5x^5 + 0 \cdot x^4 + 12x^3 + 2x^2 - 9x + 8}{x^2 + 3}.$$

$$
\require{enclose}
\begin{array}{r}
5x^3 \qquad\quad -3x \;+2 \\
x^2 + 3 \enclose{longdiv}{5x^5 + 0x^4 + 12x^3 + 2x^2 - 9x + 8} \\
\end{array}
$$

$\underline{-(5x^5 \qquad\quad + 15x^3)}$ ← $5x^3(x^2 + 3)$

$-3x^3 + 2x^2 - 9x + 8$ ← $5x^5 + 12x^3 + 2x^2 - 9x + 8 - (5x^5 + 15x^3) = -3x^3 + 2x^2 - 9x + 8$

$\underline{-(-3x^3 \qquad\quad -9x)}$ ← $-3x(x^2 + 3)$

$2x^2 \qquad + 8$ ← $(-3x^3 + 2x^2 - 9x + 8) - (-3x^3 - 9x) = 2x^2 + 8$

$\underline{-(2x^2 \qquad + 6)}$ ← $2(x^2 + 3)$

2 ← Remainder

The quotient is $5x^3 - 3x + 2$ and the remainder is 2. We now check our work.

Check (Quotient)(Divisor) + Remainder = Dividend

$$(5x^3 - 3x + 2)(x^2 + 3) + 2 = 5x^5 + 15x^3 - 3x^3 - 9x + 2x^2 + 6 + 2$$
$$= 5x^5 + 12x^3 + 2x^2 - 9x + 8$$

Our answer checks, so $\dfrac{8 - 9x + 2x^2 + 12x^3 + 5x^5}{x^2 + 3} = 5x^3 - 3x + 2 + \dfrac{2}{x^2 + 3}.$ ∎

Quick ✔ *In Problems 10–12, simplify by performing long division.*

10. $\dfrac{x + 1 - 3x^2 + 4x^3}{x + 2}$ **11.** $\dfrac{2x^3 + 3x^2 + 10}{2x - 5}$ **12.** $\dfrac{4x^3 - 3x^2 + x + 1}{x^2 + 2}$

5.5 EXERCISES

PRACTICE   WATCH   DOWNLOAD   READ   REVIEW

1–12. *are the* Quick ✔s *that follow each* EXAMPLE

Building Skills

In Problems 13–30, divide and simplify. See Objective 1.

13. $\dfrac{4x^2 - 2x}{2x}$

14. $\dfrac{3x^3 - 6x^2}{3x^2}$

15. $\dfrac{9a^3 + 27a^2 - 3}{3a^2}$

16. $\dfrac{16m^3 + 8m^2 - 4}{8m^2}$

17. $\dfrac{5n^5 - 10n^3 - 25n}{25n}$

18. $\dfrac{5x^3 - 15x^2 + 10x}{5x^2}$

19. $\dfrac{15r^5 - 27r^3}{9r^3}$

20. $\dfrac{16a^5 - 12a^4 + 8a^3}{20a^4}$

21. $\dfrac{3x^7 - 9x^6 + 27x^3}{-3x^5}$

22. $\dfrac{7p^4 + 21p^3 - 3p^2}{-6p^4}$

23. $\dfrac{3z + 4z^3 - 2z^2}{8z}$

24. $\dfrac{-5y^2 + 15y^4 - 16y^5}{5y^2}$

25. $\dfrac{14x - 10y}{-2}$

26. $\dfrac{35x + 20y}{-5}$

27. $\dfrac{12y - 30x}{-2x}$

28. $\dfrac{21y^2 + 35x^2}{-7x^2}$

29. $\dfrac{25a^3b^2c + 10a^2bc^3}{-5a^4b^2c}$

30. $\dfrac{16m^2n^3 - 24m^4n^3}{-8m^3n^4}$

In Problems 31–54, find the quotient using long division. See Objective 2.

31. $\dfrac{x^2 - 4x - 21}{x + 3}$ **32.** $\dfrac{x^2 + 18x + 72}{x + 6}$

33. $\dfrac{x^2 - 9x + 20}{x - 4}$ **34.** $\dfrac{x^2 + 4x - 32}{x - 4}$

35. $\dfrac{x^3 + 4x^2 - 15x + 6}{x - 2}$ **36.** $\dfrac{x^3 - x^2 - 40x + 12}{x + 6}$

37. $\dfrac{x^4 - x^3 + 10x - 4}{x + 2}$ **38.** $\dfrac{x^4 - 2x^3 + x^2 + x - 1}{x - 1}$

39. $\dfrac{x^3 - x^2 + x + 8}{x + 1}$ **40.** $\dfrac{x^3 - 7x^2 + 15x - 11}{x - 3}$

41. $\dfrac{2x^2 - 7x - 15}{x - 5}$ **42.** $\dfrac{2x^2 + 5x - 42}{x + 6}$

43. $\dfrac{x^3 + 4x^2 - 5x + 2}{x - 2}$ **44.** $\dfrac{x^3 - 2x^2 + x + 6}{x + 1}$

45. $\dfrac{2x^4 - 3x^3 - 11x^2 - 40x - 1}{x - 4}$

46. $\dfrac{3x^4 + 7x^3 - 5x^2 + 8x + 12}{x + 3}$

47. $\dfrac{2x^3 + 7x^2 - 10x + 5}{2x - 1}$ **48.** $\dfrac{12a^3 + 11a^2 + 18a + 9}{4a + 1}$

49. $\dfrac{-24 + x^2 + x}{5 + x}$ **50.** $\dfrac{-16x + 70 + x^2}{-9 + x}$

51. $\dfrac{4x^2 + 5}{1 + 2x}$ **52.** $\dfrac{9x^2 - 14}{2 + 3x}$

53. $\dfrac{x^3 + 2x^2 - 8}{x^2 - 2}$ **54.** $\dfrac{64x^6 - 27}{4x^2 - 3}$

Mixed Practice

In Problems 55–80, perform the indicated operation.

55. $(a - 5)(a + 6)$

56. $(7n + 3m^2 + 4m) + (-6m^2 - 7n + 4m)$

57. $(2x - 8) - (3x + x^2 - 2)$

58. $3x^2(7x^2 + 2x - 3)$

59. $(2ab + b^2 - a^2) + (b^2 - 4ab + a^2)$

60. $\dfrac{3a^4b^{-2}}{6a^{-4}b^{-3}}$ **61.** $\dfrac{4 + 7x^2 - 3x^4 + 6x^3}{2x^2}$

62. $(b - 3)(b + 2)$ **63.** $\dfrac{18x^3y^{-4}z^6}{27x^{-4}y^{-12}z^{-6}}$

64. $(4ab + 6ab^2) - (12a^2b - 2ab - 3ab^2)$

65. $\dfrac{6x^2 - 28x + 30}{3x - 5}$ **66.** $\dfrac{12x^2 - 25x - 50}{3x - 10}$

67. $(n - 3)^2$ **68.** $\dfrac{-9mn^2 - 8m^2n + 12mn}{3mn}$

69. $(x^3 + x - 4x^4)(-10x^2)$

70. $(2x^3 + 6x) + (12x - x^2 - x^3)$

71. $(2pq - q^2) + (4pq - p^2 - q^2)$

72. $(4x^2 - 6x + 3) - (x - 7)$

73. $(x^2 + x - 1)(x + 5)$

74. $(x^2 - 2x + 3)(x - 4)$

75. $(7rs^2 - 2r^2s) - (2r^2s - 8rs^2)$

76. $(x + 6)^2$

77. $(x^4 - 2x^2 + x)(-3x)$

78. $2x^4(x^2 - 2x + 3)$

79. $\dfrac{3 + 6x^2 - 11x}{2x - 3} + (x + 1)$

80. $\dfrac{7x - 5 + 6x^2}{3x + 5} - (2x + 1)$

Applying the Concepts

81. Find the quotient of $(3x^4 - 6x + 12x^2)$ and $-3x^3$.

82. Divide $x - 3$ by $x + 2$.

83. Divide the sum of $x^2 + 3x - 1$ and $x - 1$ by $-2x^3$.

84. Divide the square of the difference of $x - 9$ and $x + 3$ by x^2.

△ **85. Volume of a Box** The volume of a rectangular solid is $(x^3 - 5x^2 + 6x)$ cubic feet. One side measures $(x - 2)$ feet and another measures $(x - 3)$ feet. What is the measure of the third side?

△ **86. Area of a Rectangle** A rectangle has area $(x^2 + 2x - 48)$ square inches. If one side measures $(x + 8)$ inches, what is the measurement of the other side?

△ **87. Area of a Rectangle** If the area of a rectangle is $(z^2 + 6z + 9)$ square inches and the length is $(z + 3)$ inches, what is the width?

△ **88. Area of a Triangle** If the area of a triangle is $(6a^2 - 5a - 6)$ square yards and the length of the base is $(2a - 3)$ yards, what is the height?

△ **89. Area of a Triangle** If the area of a triangle is $(6x^3 - 2x^2 - 8x)$ square feet and the height is $(3x^2 - 4x)$ feet, what is the length of the base?

△ **90. Volume of a Box** The volume of a rectangular solid is $(x^3 + 2x^2 - x - 2)$ cubic feet. One side measures $(x + 2)$ feet and another measures $(x - 1)$ feet. What is the measure of the third side?

91. Average Cost The average cost of manufacturing x computers per day is given by

$$\frac{0.004x^3 - 0.8x^2 + 180x + 5000}{x}.$$

(a) Simplify the quotient by dividing each term in the numerator by the denominator.

(b) Use this result to determine the average cost of manufacturing $x = 140$ computers in one day.

92. Average Cost The average cost of manufacturing x digital cameras per day is given by

$$\frac{0.0024x^3 - 0.4x^2 + 46x + 4000}{x}.$$

(a) Simplify the quotient by dividing each term in the numerator by the denominator.

(b) Use this result to determine the average cost of manufacturing $x = 90$ cameras in one day.

Extending the Concepts

In Problems 93 and 94, determine the value of the missing term so that the remainder is zero.

93. $\dfrac{6x^2 - 13x + ?}{2x - 3}$

94. $\dfrac{3x^2 + ? - 5}{x - 1}$

Explaining the Concepts

95. Explain how to divide polynomials when the divisor is a monomial and then when the divisor is a binomial. Which procedures are the same and which are different?

96. The first steps of a division problem are written below. Describe what has occurred. Are there any potential errors with this presentation? What would you recommend this student do to improve his or her chances of obtaining the correct answer?

$$\begin{array}{r} 2x^2 \\ x^2 - 3 \overline{)\, 2x^4 - 3x^3 + 2x + 1} \\ -(2x^4 - 6x^2) \end{array}$$

5.6 Applying Exponent Rules: Scientific Notation

OBJECTIVES

1 Convert Decimal Notation to Scientific Notation

2 Convert Scientific Notation to Decimal Notation

3 Use Scientific Notation to Multiply and Divide

Preparing for Applying Exponent Rules: Scientific Notation

Before getting started, take the following readiness quiz. If you get a problem wrong, go back to the section cited and review the material.

P1. Find the product: $(3a^6)(4.5a^4)$ [Section 5.2, pp. 326–327]

P2. Find the product: $(7n^3)(2n^{-2})$ [Section 5.4, pp. 348–350]

P3. Find the quotient: $\dfrac{3.6b^9}{0.9b^{-2}}$ [Section 5.4, pp. 348–350]

Did you know that *Spider-Man 3* had box office revenues of \$336,530,000? Did you know that the mass of a dust particle is 0.000000000753 kg? These numbers are difficult to write and difficult to read, so we use exponents to rewrite them.

1   Convert Decimal Notation to Scientific Notation

We use two types of notation to write numbers: decimal notation and scientific notation. Decimal notation is the notation we commonly see when we read the newspaper or a magazine. The numbers $336{,}530{,}000$ and 0.000000000753 kg are written in decimal notation. When we write a number in scientific notation we express that number as the product of two factors: One factor is a number between 1 and 10, including 1 but not including 10, and the other factor is an integer power of 10.

DEFINITION

When a number has been written as the product of a number x, where $1 \leq x < 10$, and a power of 10, it is said to be written in **scientific notation.** That is, a number is written in scientific notation when it is of the form

$$x \times 10^N$$

where

$$1 \leq x < 10 \text{ and } N \text{ is an integer}$$

Notice in the definition, $x < 10$. That's because when $x = 10$, we have 10^1, a power of ten. For example, in scientific notation,

$$\text{Box Office Revenue for } Spider\text{-}Man\ 3 = \$3.3653 \times 10^8 \text{ dollars}$$
$$\text{Mass of a dust particle} = 7.53 \times 10^{-10} \text{ kilograms}$$

In Words

When you have a number greater than or equal to 1, use $10^{positive\ exponent}$. When you have a number between 0 and 1, use $10^{negative\ exponent}$.

STEPS TO CONVERT FROM DECIMAL NOTATION TO SCIENTIFIC NOTATION

To change a positive number into scientific notation:

Step 1: Count the number N of decimal places that the decimal point must be moved in order to arrive at a number x, where $1 \leq x < 10$.

Step 2: If the original number is greater than or equal to 1, the scientific notation is $x \times 10^N$. If the original number is between 0 and 1, the scientific notation is $x \times 10^{-N}$.

EXAMPLE 1   How to Convert from Decimal Notation to Scientific Notation

Write 5283 in scientific notation.

Step-by-Step Solution

For a number to be in scientific notation, the decimal must be moved so that there is a single nonzero digit to the left of the decimal point. All remaining digits must appear to the right of the decimal point.

Step 1: The "understood" decimal point in 5283 follows the 3. Therefore, we will move the decimal to the left until it is between the 5 and the 2. Do you see why? This requires that we move the decimal $N = 3$ places.   5 2 8 3.

Step 2: The original number is greater than 1, so we write 5283 in scientific notation as 5.283×10^3

EXAMPLE 2 **How to Convert from Decimal Notation to Scientific Notation**

Write 0.054 in scientific notation.

Step-by-Step Solution

Step 1: Because 0.054 is less than 1, we shall move the decimal point to the right until it is between the 5 and the 4. This requires that we move the decimal $N = 2$ places.	0.054
Step 2: The original number is between 0 and 1, so we write 0.054 in scientific notation as	5.4×10^{-2}

Quick ✔

1. A number written as 3.2×10^{-6} is said to be written in _____ _____.
2. When writing 47,000,000 in scientific notation, the power of 10 will be _____ (positive or negative).
3. *True or False:* When a number is expressed in scientific notation, it is expressed as the product of a number $x, 0 \leq x < 1$, and a power of 10.

In Problems 4–9, write each number in scientific notation.

4. 432   5. 10,302   6. 5,432,000

7. 0.093   8. 0.0000459   9. 0.00000008

2 Convert Scientific Notation to Decimal Notation

Now we are going to convert a number from scientific notation to decimal notation. Study Table 3 to discover the pattern.

Table 3			
Scientific Notation	Product	Decimal Notation	Location of Decimal Point
3.69×10^{2}	3.69×100	369	moved 2 places to the right
3.69×10^{1}	3.69×10	36.9	moved 1 place to the right
3.69×10^{0}	3.69×1	3.69	didn't move
3.69×10^{-1}	3.69×0.1	0.369	moved 1 place to the left
3.69×10^{-2}	3.69×0.01	0.0369	moved 2 places to the left

The pattern in Table 3 leads to the following steps for converting a number from scientific notation to decimal notation.

STEPS TO CONVERT A NUMBER FROM SCIENTIFIC NOTATION TO DECIMAL NOTATION

Step 1: Determine the exponent, N, on the number 10.

Step 2: If the exponent is positive, then move the decimal N decimal places to the right. If the exponent is negative, then move the decimal $|N|$ decimal places to the left. Add zeros, as needed.

EXAMPLE 3   How to Convert from Scientific Notation to Decimal Notation

Write 2.3×10^3 in decimal notation.

Step-by-Step Solution

Step 1: Determine the exponent on the number 10.	The exponent on the 10 is 3.
Step 2: Since the exponent is positive, we move the decimal point 3 places to the right. Notice we add zeros to the right of 3, as needed.	2,300

So, $2.3 \times 10^3 = 2300$.   ∎

EXAMPLE 4   How to Convert from Scientific Notation to Decimal Notation

Write 4.57×10^{-5} in decimal notation.

Step-by-Step Solution

Step 1: Determine the exponent on the number 10.		The exponent on the 10 is -5.
Step 2: Since the exponent is negative, we move the decimal point 5 places to the left.	Add zeros to the left of the original decimal point.	0.00004.57

So, $4.57 \times 10^{-5} = 0.0000457$.   ∎

Quick ✔

10. To write 3.2×10^{-6} in decimal notation, move the decimal point in 3.2 six places to the ___.

11. *True or False:* To convert 2.4×10^3 to decimal notation, move the decimal three places to the right.

In Problems 12–16, write each number in decimal notation.

12. 3.1×10^2 **13.** 9.01×10^{-1} **14.** 1.7×10^5

15. 7×10^0 **16.** 8.9×10^{-4}

3   Use Scientific Notation to Multiply and Divide

The Laws of Exponents make it relatively straightforward to multiply and divide numbers that are written in scientific notation. The two Laws of Exponents that we make use of are the Product Rule, $a^m \cdot a^n = a^{m+n}$, and the Quotient Rule, $\dfrac{a^m}{a^n} = a^{m-n}$. We will use these laws where the base is 10 as follows:

$$10^m \cdot 10^n = 10^{m+n} \quad \text{and} \quad \frac{10^m}{10^n} = 10^{m-n}$$

EXAMPLE 5   Multiplying Using Scientific Notation

Perform the indicated operation. Express the answer in scientific notation.

$$(3 \times 10^2) \cdot (2.5 \times 10^5)$$

Solution

$$(3 \times 10^2) \cdot (2.5 \times 10^5) = (3 \cdot 2.5) \times (10^2 \cdot 10^5)$$

Multiply $3 \cdot 2.5$; use $a^m \cdot a^n = a^{m+n}$: $= 7.5 \times 10^7$ ∎

EXAMPLE 6 Multiplying Using Scientific Notation

Perform the indicated operation. Express the answer in scientific notation.

(a) $(4 \times 10^{-2}) \cdot (6 \times 10^8)$ **(b)** $(3.2 \times 10^{-3}) \cdot (4.8 \times 10^{-4})$

Solution

(a)
$$(4 \times 10^{-2}) \cdot (6 \times 10^8) = (4 \cdot 6) \times (10^{-2} \cdot 10^8)$$

Multiply $4 \cdot 6$; use $a^m \cdot a^n = a^{m+n}$: $= 24 \times 10^6$

Convert 24 to scientific notation: $= (2.4 \times 10^1) \times 10^6$

Use $a^m \cdot a^n = a^{m+n}$: $= 2.4 \times 10^7$

(b)
$$(3.2 \times 10^{-3}) \cdot (4.8 \times 10^{-4}) = (3.2 \cdot 4.8) \times (10^{-3} \cdot 10^{-4})$$

Multiply $3.2 \cdot 4.8$; use $a^m \cdot a^n = a^{m+n}$: $= 15.36 \times 10^{-7}$

Convert 15.36 to scientific notation: $= (1.536 \times 10^1) \times 10^{-7}$

Use $a^m \cdot a^n = a^{m+n}$: $= 1.536 \times 10^{-6}$

Quick ✔ *In Problems 17–20, perform the indicated operation. Express the answer in scientific notation.*

17. $(3 \times 10^4) \cdot (2 \times 10^3)$ **18.** $(2 \times 10^{-2}) \cdot (4 \times 10^{-1})$

19. $(5 \times 10^{-4}) \cdot (3 \times 10^7)$ **20.** $(8 \times 10^{-4}) \cdot (3.5 \times 10^{-2})$

EXAMPLE 7 Dividing Using Scientific Notation

Perform the indicated operation. Express the answer in scientific notation.

(a) $\dfrac{6 \times 10^6}{2 \times 10^2}$ **(b)** $\dfrac{2.4 \times 10^4}{3 \times 10^{-2}}$

Solution

(a)
$$\frac{6 \times 10^6}{2 \times 10^2} = \frac{6}{2} \times \frac{10^6}{10^2}$$

Divide $\dfrac{6}{2}$; use $\dfrac{a^m}{a^n} = a^{m-n}$: $= 3 \times 10^4$

(b)
$$\frac{2.4 \times 10^4}{3 \times 10^{-2}} = \frac{2.4}{3} \times \frac{10^4}{10^{-2}}$$

Divide $\dfrac{2.4}{3}$; use $\dfrac{a^m}{a^n} = a^{m-n}$: $= 0.8 \times 10^{4-(-2)}$

Convert 0.8 to scientific notation: $= (8 \times 10^{-1}) \times 10^6$

Use $a^m \cdot a^n = a^{m+n}$: $= 8 \times 10^5$

Quick ✔ *In Problems 21–24, perform the indicated operation. Express the answer in scientific notation.*

21. $\dfrac{8 \times 10^6}{2 \times 10^1}$ **22.** $\dfrac{2.8 \times 10^{-7}}{1.4 \times 10^{-3}}$

23. $\dfrac{3.6 \times 10^3}{7.2 \times 10^{-1}}$ **24.** $\dfrac{5 \times 10^{-2}}{8 \times 10^2}$

EXAMPLE 8 Finding Newspaper Circulation

In 2006, *USA Today* had a daily circulation of 2.5×10^6 newspapers. What was the circulation of *USA Today* in the month of April when *USA Today* was published 21 times? (*Note: USA Today* does not publish on weekends.) Express the answer in scientific notation and in decimal notation. (SOURCE: *Information Please Almanac*)

Solution

To find the total monthly circulation for the newspaper in April, we multiply the number of daily copies by the number of publication days. There are 21 publication days in April.

Let's first change 21 to scientific notation: $21 = 2.1 \times 10^1$. So we have

$$(2.5 \times 10^6) \cdot (2.1 \times 10^1) = (2.5 \cdot 2.1) \times (10^6 \cdot 10^1)$$
$$= 5.25 \times 10^7$$
$$= 52,500,000 \text{ newspapers.}$$

A total of 52,500,000 copies of *USA Today* were circulated in April 2006.

Quick ✔

25. Saudi Arabia produced nearly 8.72×10^6 barrels of crude oil per day in August 2007. How many barrels of oil did Saudi Arabia produce in August 2007? Express the solution in scientific notation and decimal notation. (SOURCE: *U.S. Department of Energy*)

26. By 2009, Saudi Arabia is expected to increase its crude oil production to 12 million barrels per day. How many barrels of oil will Saudi Arabia produce in August 2009? Express the solution in scientific notation and decimal notation. (SOURCE: *U.S. Department of Energy*)

5.6 EXERCISES

PRACTICE   WATCH   DOWNLOAD   READ   REVIEW

1–26. *are the* Quick ✔*s that follow each* EXAMPLE

Building Skills

In Problems 27–42, write each number in scientific notation. See Objective 1.

27. 300,000

28. 421,000,000

29. 64,000,000

30. 8,000,000,000

31. 0.00051

32. 0.0000001

33. 0.000000001

34. 0.0000283

35. 8,007,000,000

36. 401,000,000

37. 0.0000309

38. 0.000201

39. 620

40. 8

41. 4

42. 120

In Problems 43–54, a number is given in decimal notation. Write the number in scientific notation. See Objective 1.

43. World Population At the beginning of 2008, the population of the world was approximately 6,656,000,000 persons.

44. United States Population At the beginning of 2008, the population of the United States was approximately 303,609,000 persons.

45. Stock Exchange Monthly Total Volume The total reported volume of the NASDAQ Exchange in February 2008 was 70,510,000,000 shares. (SOURCE: *NASDAQ*)

46. Pets There were approximately 13,400,000 pet reptiles in the United States in 2007.

47. NASA Rover In 2003, NASA launched *Spirit,* an unmanned rover designed to land on the planet Mars and explore its surface. On the day *Spirit* landed on Mars, the distance from Earth to Mars was 170,200,000 kilometers.

48. NASA Rover A second unmanned rover, *Opportunity*, landed on Mars in January 2004. On the day *Opportunity* landed on Mars, the distance from Earth to Mars was 198,700,000 miles.

49. Smallpox Virus The diameter of a smallpox virus is 0.00003 mm.

50. Human Blood Cell The diameter of a human blood cell is 0.0075 mm.

51. Dust Mites Dust mites are microscopic bugs that are a major cause of allergies and asthma. They are approximately 0.00000025 m in length.

52. DNA The length of a DNA molecule can exceed 0.025 inches in some organisms.

53. Mass of a Penny The mass of the United States' Lincoln penny is approximately 0.00311 kg.

54. Physics The radius of a typical atom is approximately 0.00000000010 m.

In Problems 55–70, write each number in decimal notation. See Objective 2.

55. 4.2×10^5 **56.** 3.75×10^2

57. 1×10^8 **58.** 6×10^6

59. 3.9×10^{-3} **60.** 6.1×10^{-6}

61. 4×10^{-1} **62.** 5×10^{-4}

63. 3.76×10^3 **64.** 4.9×10^{-1}

65. 8.2×10^{-3} **66.** 5.4×10^5

67. 6×10^{-5} **68.** 5.123×10^{-3}

69. 7.05×10^6 **70.** 7×10^8

In Problems 71–76, a number is given in scientific notation. Write the number in decimal notation. See Objective 2.

71. Time A femtosecond is equal to 1×10^{-15} second.

72. Dust Particle The mass of a dust particle is 7.53×10^{-10} kg.

73. Vitamin A One-A-Day vitamin pill contains 2.25×10^{-3} grams of zinc.

74. Water Molecule The diameter of a water molecule is 3.85×10^{-7} m.

75. Coffee Shops It is predicted that by the year 2010, there will be more than 5×10^5 coffee shops in the United States.

76. Motor Vehicles In 2007, there were approximately 9.4×10^4 registered drivers aged 85 and over in New York State. (SOURCE: *U.S. Department of Transportation*)

In Problems 77–88, perform the indicated operations. Express your answer in scientific notation. See Objective 3.

77. $(2 \times 10^6)(1.5 \times 10^3)$

78. $(3 \times 10^{-4})(8 \times 10^{-5})$

79. $(1.2 \times 10^0)(7 \times 10^{-3})$

80. $(4 \times 10^7)(2.5 \times 10^{-4})$

81. $\dfrac{9 \times 10^4}{3 \times 10^{-4}}$ **82.** $\dfrac{6 \times 10^3}{1.2 \times 10^5}$

83. $\dfrac{2 \times 10^{-3}}{8 \times 10^{-5}}$ **84.** $\dfrac{4.8 \times 10^7}{1.2 \times 10^2}$

85. $\dfrac{56,000}{0.00007}$ **86.** $\dfrac{0.000275}{2500}$

87. $\dfrac{300,000 \times 15,000,000}{0.0005}$ **88.** $\dfrac{24,000,000,000}{0.00006 \times 2000}$

Applying the Concepts

89. Speed of Light Light travels at the rate of 1.86×10^5 miles per second. How far does light travel in one minute (6.0×10^1 seconds)?

90. Speed of Sound Sound travels at the rate of 1.127×10^3 feet per second. How far does sound travel in one minute (6.0×10^1 seconds)?

91. Garbage In 2006, the total waste generated in the United States was 5.026×10^{11} pounds. Also in 2006, the United States population was 3.0×10^8 people. Determine the garbage per capita (per person) in the United States in the year 2006.

92. Fossil Fuels In 2006, the United States imported 5.124×10^8 gallons of oil per day. The United States population in 2006 was approximately 3.0×10^8 people. Determine the per capita number of gallons of oil imported into the United States daily in 2006.

93. Ice Cream Consumption Total U.S. consumption of ice cream and related frozen desserts in 2006 amounted to about 1.55 billion gallons. (SOURCE: *U.S. Department of Agriculture*)

(a) Write 1.55 billion gallons in scientific notation.
(b) The population of the United States in 2006 was approximately 300,000,000 persons. Express this number in scientific notation.
(c) Use your answers to parts **(a)** and **(b)** to find, to the nearest tenth of a gallon, the average number of gallons of ice cream and frozen desserts that were consumed per person in the United States in 2006.

94. M&M'S® Candy Over 400 million M&M'S® candies are produced in the United States every day. (SOURCE: *Mars.com*)

(a) Write 400 million in scientific notation.

(b) Assuming a 30-day month, how many M&M'S® candies are produced in a month in the United States? Write this answer in scientific notation.

(c) The population of the United States is approximately 303,000,000 persons. Express this number in scientific notation.

(d) Use your answers to parts **(b)** and **(c)** to find, to the nearest whole, the average number of M&M'S candies eaten per person per month in the United States.

95. U.S. Pet Ownership According to the 2007–2008 National Pet Owners Survey, there are approximately 179.1 million pet birds, dogs, and cats in the United States. (SOURCE: *American Pet Products Manufacturers Association*)

(a) Write 179.1 million in scientific notation

(b) There are about 44.8 million pet dogs in the United States. Write 44.8 million in scientific notation.

(c) Use the answers to parts **(a)** and **(b)** to determine what percentage, to the nearest percent, of the number of pet birds, dogs, and cats owned in the United States were dogs, according to the survey.

96. Pet Reptiles According to the 2007–2008 National Pet Owners Survey, there are approximately 230.6 million pets in the United States, excluding fish.

(SOURCE: *American Pet Products Manufacturers Association*)

(a) Write 230.6 million in scientific notation.

(b) There are about 13.4 million pet reptiles in the United States. Write 13.4 million in scientific notation.

(c) Use the answers to parts **(a)** and **(b)** to determine what percentage, to the nearest whole percent, of the number of pets in the United States are reptiles, according to the survey.

Extending the Concepts

Scientists often need to measure very small things, such as cells. They use the following units of measure:

millimeter (mm) = 1×10^{-3} *meter*   *micron (μm)* = 1×10^{-6} *meter*

nanometer (nm) = 1×10^{-9} *meter*   *picometer (pm)* = 1×10^{-12} *meter*

Write the following measurements in meters using scientific notation:

97. 250 μm   **98.** 60.4 nm

99. 800 pm   **100.** 40 mm

101. 71.5 nm   **102.** 200 μm

Assume a cell is in the shape of a sphere. Given that the volume of a sphere is $V = \frac{4}{3}\pi r^3$, *find the volume of a cell whose radius is given. Express the answer as a multiple of* π *in cubic meters.*

103. 21 μm   **104.** 0.75 nm

105. 6 nm   **106.** 108 μm

Explaining the Concepts

107. Explain how to convert a number written in decimal notation to scientific notation.

108. Explain how to convert a number written in scientific notation to decimal notation.

109. Dana thinks that the number 34.5×10^4 is correctly written in scientific notation. Is Dana correct? If so, explain why. If not, explain why the answer is wrong and write the correct answer.

110. Explain why scientific notation is used to perform calculations that involve multiplying and dividing but not adding and subtracting.

CHAPTER 5 Activity: What Is the Question?

Focus: Using exponent rules, using scientific notation, and performing operations with polynomials

Time: 15–20 minutes

Group size: 2 or 4

In this activity you will work as a team to solve eight multiple-choice questions. However, these questions are different from most multiple-choice questions. You are given the answer to a problem and must determine which of the multiple-choice options has the correct question for the given answer.

Before beginning the activity, decide how you will approach this task as a team. For example:

- If there are 2 members on your team, one member will always examine choices (a) and (b) and the other will always examine choices (c) and (d).

- If there are 4 members on your team, one member will always examine choice (a), another member will always examine choice (b), and so on.

1. The answer is $-3x^2 - 10x$. What is the question?

(a) Simplify: $2x - 3x(x^2 + 4)$

(b) Find the quotient: $\dfrac{6x^3 - 20x^2}{-2x}$

(c) Simplify: $-3x(x^2 + 3) + 1$

(d) Find the quotient: $\dfrac{-6x^4 - 20x^3}{2x^2}$

2. The answer is $-10x^4y^8$. What is the question?

(a) Simplify: $(-5x^2y^4)^2$

(b) Simplify: $(5x^3y^3)(-2xy^5)$

(c) Simplify: $\dfrac{-30x^{-2}y^6}{3x^2y^{-2}}$

(d) Simplify: $(5x^2y^4)(-2x^2y^2)$

3. The answer is $12x^2 - 16x - 3$. What is the question?

(a) Multiply: $(6x - 1)(2x + 3)$

(b) Divide: $\dfrac{24x^3 - 32x^2 + 6x}{2x}$

(c) Multiply: $(6x + 1)(2x - 3)$

(d) Simplify: $(14x^2 - x + 2) - (2x^2 + 16x + 5)$

4. The answer is $x^2 + 5x + 6$. What is the question?

(a) Find the product: $(x + 6)(x - 1)$

(b) Simplify: $2x^2 + 7x + 9 - (x^2 - 2x - 3)$

(c) Find the product: $(x + 2)(x + 3)$

(d) Simplify: $(x + 6)^2$

5. The answer is 3. What is the question?

(a) What is the name of the variable in $16z^2 + 3z - 5$?

(b) What is the degree of the polynomial $2mn + 6m - 3$?

(c) How many terms are in the polynomial $2mn + 6m - 3$?

(d) What is the coefficient of b in the polynomial $3a^2b - 9a + 5b$?

6. The answer is 43. What is the question?

(a) Evaluate: $4x^2 - 2x + 1$ for $x = -3$

(b) Evaluate: $2x^2 + 3x - 4$ for $x = -2$

(c) Evaluate: $-x^2 - 5x + 1$ for $x = -1$

(d) Evaluate: $x^2 + 4x - 8$ for $x = -5$

7. The answer is $\dfrac{2x^5}{y^5}$. What is the question?

(a) Simplify: $(6x^{-4}y)^0\left(\dfrac{12x^{-1}y^{-2}}{x^{-4}y^3}\right)$

(b) Simplify: $(6x^{-3}y^0)^{-1}\left(\dfrac{12xy^{-3}}{x^{-2}y^2}\right)$

(c) Simplify: $(6x^2y^0)^{-1}\left(\dfrac{12x^{-2}y^3}{xy^{-4}}\right)$

(d) Simplify: $(6x^{-2}y^0)^{-1}\left(\dfrac{12x^0y^{-2}}{x^{-3}y^3}\right)$

8. The answer is 2.5×10^{-8}. What is the question?

(a) Find the quotient: $\dfrac{2 \times 10^3}{8 \times 10^{-4}}$

(b) Find the product: $(5 \times 10^{-4}) \cdot (5 \times 10^{-4})$

(c) Find the quotient: $\dfrac{2 \times 10^{-3}}{8 \times 10^4}$

(d) Find the product: $(5 \times 10^{12}) \cdot (5 \times 10^{-4})$

CHAPTER 5 Review

Section 5.1   Adding and Subtracting Polynomials

KEY CONCEPTS	KEY TERMS
• In a monomial in the form ax^k, k is the degree of the monomial and k is a whole number. • The degree of a polynomial is the highest degree of all the terms of the polynomial.	Monomial Degree of a monomial Polynomial Binomial Trinomial Standard form Degree of a polynomial

YOU SHOULD BE ABLE TO...	EXAMPLE	REVIEW EXERCISES
1 Define monomial and determine the degree of a monomial (p. 317)	Examples 1 through 3	1–4
2 Define polynomial and determine the degree of a polynomial (p. 318)	Examples 4 and 5	5–10
3 Simplify polynomials by combining like terms (p. 319)	Examples 6 through 10	11–16
4 Evaluate polynomials (p. 322)	Examples 11 through 13	17–20

In Problems 1–4, determine whether the given expression is a monomial (Yes or No). For those that are monomials, state the coefficient and the degree.

1. $4x^3$

2. $6x^{-3}$

3. $m^{\frac{1}{2}}$

4. mn^2

In Problems 5–10, determine whether the algebraic expression is a polynomial (Yes or No). If it is a polynomial, state the degree and then state if it is a monomial, binomial, or trinomial.

5. $4x^6 - 4x^{\frac{1}{2}}$

6. $\dfrac{3}{x} - \dfrac{1}{x^2}$

7. 6

8. $3x^3 - 4xy^4$

9. $-2x^5y - 7x^4y + 7$

10. $\dfrac{1}{2}x^3 + 2x^{10} - 5$

In Problems 11–14, perform the indicated operation.

11. $(6x^2 - 2x + 1) + (3x^2 + 10x - 3)$

12. $(-7m^3 - 2mn) + (8m^3 - 5m + 3mn)$

13. $(4x^2y + 10x) - (5x^2y - 2x)$

14. $(3y^2 - yz + 3z^2) - (10y^2 + 5yz - 6z^2)$

15. Find the sum of $-6x^2 + 5$ and $4x^2 - 7$.

16. Subtract $20y^2 - 10y + 5$ from $-18y + 10$.

In Problems 17–20, evaluate the polynomial for the given value(s).

17. $3x^2 - 5x$
  (a) $x = 0$
  (b) $x = -1$
  (c) $x = 2$

18. $-x^2 + 3$
  (a) $x = 0$
  (b) $x = -1$
  (c) $x = \dfrac{1}{2}$

19. $x^2y + 2xy^2$ for $x = -2$ and $y = 1$

20. $4a^2b^2 - 3ab + 2$ for $a = -1$ and $b = -3$

Section 5.2 Multiplying Monomials: The Product and Power Rules

KEY CONCEPTS	KEY TERMS
• **Product Rule for Exponents** If a is a real number and m and n are natural numbers, then $a^m \cdot a^n = a^{m+n}$ • **Power Rule for Exponents** If a is a real number and m and n are natural numbers, then $(a^m)^n = a^{m \cdot n}$ • **Product to a Power Rule for Exponents** If a and b are real numbers and n is a natural number, then $(a \cdot b)^n = a^n \cdot b^n$	Base Power Exponent

YOU SHOULD BE ABLE TO...	EXAMPLE	REVIEW EXERCISES
1 Simplify exponential expressions using the Product Rule (p. 326)	Examples 1 through 3	21, 22, 25, 26
2 Simplify exponential expressions using the Power Rule (p. 328)	Examples 4 and 5	23, 24, 27, 28
3 Simplify exponential expressions containing products (p. 328)	Example 6	29–32
4 Multiply a monomial by a monomial (p. 329)	Examples 7 and 8	33–40

In Problems 21–32, simplify each expression.

21. $6^2 \cdot 6^5$

22. $\left(-\dfrac{1}{3}\right)^2\left(-\dfrac{1}{3}\right)^3$

23. $(4^2)^6$

24. $[(-1)^4]^3$

25. $x^4 \cdot x^8 \cdot x$

26. $m^4 \cdot m^2$

27. $(r^3)^4$

28. $(m^8)^3$

29. $(4x)^3(4x)^2$

30. $(-2n)^3(-2n)^3$

31. $(-3x^2y)^4$

32. $(2x^3y^4)^2$

In Problems 33–40, multiply.

33. $3x^2 \cdot 5x^4$

34. $-4a \cdot 9a^3$

35. $-8y^4 \cdot (-2y)$

36. $12p \cdot (-p^5)$

37. $\dfrac{8}{3}w^3 \cdot \dfrac{9}{2}w$

38. $\dfrac{1}{3}z^2 \cdot \left(-\dfrac{9}{4}z\right)$

39. $(3x^2)^3 \cdot (2x)^2$

40. $(-4a)^2 \cdot (5a^4)$

Section 5.3 Multiplying Polynomials

KEY CONCEPTS

- **Extended form of the Distributive Property**
  $a(b + c + \cdots + z) = a \cdot b + a \cdot c + \cdots + a \cdot z$ where $a, b, c, \ldots, z$ are real numbers.

- **FOIL Method for multiplying two binomials**
  $$\overset{\text{F}\quad\text{O}\quad\text{I}\quad\text{L}}{(ax + b)(cx + d) = ax \cdot cx + ax \cdot d + b \cdot cx + b \cdot d}$$

- **Product of the Sum and Difference of Two Terms**
  $(A - B)(A + B) = A^2 - B^2$

- **Squares of Binomials**
  $(A + B)^2 = A^2 + 2AB + B^2$
  $(A - B)^2 = A^2 - 2AB + B^2$

KEY TERMS

FOIL method
Special products
Sum and difference of two terms
Squares of binomials
Perfect square trinomial

YOU SHOULD BE ABLE TO...	EXAMPLE	REVIEW EXERCISES
1 Multiply a polynomial by a monomial (p. 331)	Examples 1 through 3	41, 42
2 Multiply two binomials using the Distributive Property (p. 332)	Examples 4 and 5	43–46
3 Multiply two binomials using the FOIL method (p. 334)	Examples 6 through 9	49–54
4 Multiply the sum and difference of two terms (p. 335)	Examples 10 and 11	55, 56, 59, 60, 63, 64
5 Square a binomial (p. 336)	Examples 12 through 14	57, 58, 61, 62, 65, 66
6 Multiply a polynomial by a polynomial (p. 338)	Examples 15 through 17	47, 48

In Problems 41–48, multiply using the Distributive Property.

41. $-2x^3(4x^2 - 3x + 1)$ **42.** $\frac{1}{2}x^4(4x^3 + 8x^2 - 2)$

43. $(3x - 5)(2x + 1)$ **44.** $(4x + 3)(x - 2)$

45. $(x + 5)(x - 8)$ **46.** $(w - 1)(w + 10)$

47. $(4m - 3)(6m^2 - m + 1)$

48. $(2y + 3)(4y^4 + 2y^2 - 3)$

In Problems 49–54, use the FOIL method to find each product.

49. $(x + 5)(x + 3)$ **50.** $(2x - 1)(x - 8)$

51. $(2m + 7)(3m - 2)$ **52.** $(6m - 4)(8m + 1)$

53. $(3x + 2y)(7x - 3y)$ **54.** $(4x - y)(5x + 3y)$

In Problems 55–66, find the special products.

55. $(x - 4)(x + 4)$ **56.** $(2x + 5)(2x - 5)$

57. $(2x + 3)^2$ **58.** $(7x - 2)^2$

59. $(3x + 4y)(3x - 4y)$ **60.** $(8m - 6n)(8m + 6n)$

61. $(5x - 2y)^2$ **62.** $(2a + 3b)^2$

63. $(x - 0.5)(x + 0.5)$ **64.** $(r + 0.25)(r - 0.25)$

65. $\left(y + \dfrac{2}{3}\right)^2$ **66.** $\left(y - \dfrac{1}{2}\right)^2$

Section 5.4   Dividing Monomials: The Quotient Rule and Integer Exponents

KEY CONCEPTS

- **Quotient Rule for Exponents**
  If a is a nonzero real number and if m and n are integers, then $\dfrac{a^m}{a^n} = a^{m-n}$.

- **Definition of Zero as an Exponent**
  If a is a nonzero real number, we define $a^0 = 1$.

- **Quotient to a Power Rule for Exponents**
  If a and b are real numbers and n is an integer, then $\left(\dfrac{a}{b}\right)^n = \dfrac{a^n}{b^n}$ if $b \neq 0$.
  If n is negative or 0, then a cannot be 0.

- **Definition of a Negative Exponent**
  If n is a positive integer and if a is a nonzero real number, then we define
  $a^{-n} = \dfrac{1}{a^n}$ and $\dfrac{1}{a^{-n}} = a^n$.

- **Quotient to a Negative Power**
  If a and b are real numbers and n is an integer, then $\left(\dfrac{a}{b}\right)^{-n} = \left(\dfrac{b}{a}\right)^n$ if $a \neq 0, b \neq 0$.

YOU SHOULD BE ABLE TO...	EXAMPLE	REVIEW EXERCISES
1 Simplify exponential expressions using the Quotient Rule (p. 342)	Examples 1 and 2	67–70, 75, 76
2 Simplify exponential expressions using the Quotient to a Power Rule (p. 343)	Examples 3 and 4	77–80
3 Simplify exponential expressions using zero as an exponent (p. 344)	Example 5	71–74
4 Simplify exponential expressions involving negative exponents (p. 345)	Examples 6 through 12	81–86
5 Simplify exponential expressions using the Laws of Exponents (p. 348)	Examples 13 through 16	87–92

In Problems 67–92, simplify. Write answers with only positive exponents. All variables are nonzero.

67. $\dfrac{6^5}{6^3}$

68. $\dfrac{7}{7^4}$

69. $\dfrac{x^{16}}{x^{12}}$

70. $\dfrac{x^3}{x^{11}}$

71. 5^0

72. -5^0

73. $m^0, \, m \neq 0$

74. $-m^0, \, m \neq 0$

75. $\dfrac{25x^3y^7}{10xy^{10}}$

76. $\dfrac{3x^4y^2}{9x^2y^{10}}$

77. $\left(\dfrac{x^3}{y^2}\right)^5$

78. $\left(\dfrac{7}{x^2}\right)^3$

79. $\left(\dfrac{2m^2n}{p^4}\right)^3$

80. $\left(\dfrac{3mn^2}{p^5}\right)^4$

81. -5^{-2}

82. $\dfrac{1}{4^{-3}}$

83. $\left(\dfrac{2}{3}\right)^{-4}$

84. $\left(\dfrac{1}{3}\right)^{-3}$

85. $2^{-2} + 3^{-1}$

86. $4^{-1} - 2^{-3}$

87. $\dfrac{16x^{-3}y^4}{24x^{-6}y^{-1}}$

88. $\dfrac{15x^0y^{-6}}{35xy^4}$

89. $(2m^{-3}n)^{-4}(3m^{-4}n^2)^2$

90. $(4m^{-6}n^0)^3(3m^{-6}n^3)^{-2}$

91. $\left(\dfrac{3rs^{-1}}{4s^2}\right)^{-2} \cdot (2r^{-6}t^0)^{-1}$

92. $(6r^4s^{-3})^2 \cdot \left(\dfrac{3r^4s}{2r^{-2}s^{-2}}\right)^{-3}$

Section 5.5 Dividing Polynomials

KEY CONCEPTS	KEY TERMS
• If a, b, and c are monomials, $\dfrac{a+b}{c} = \dfrac{a}{c} + \dfrac{b}{c}$. • (Quotient)(Divisor) + Remainder = Dividend	Divisor Dividend Quotient Remainder

YOU SHOULD BE ABLE TO...	EXAMPLE	REVIEW EXERCISES
⊓ Divide a polynomial by a monomial (p. 353)	Examples 1 through 3	93–98
⊠ Divide a polynomial by a binomial (p. 355)	Examples 4 through 7	99–104

In Problems 93–104, divide each of the following.

93. $\dfrac{36x^7 - 24x^6 + 30x^2}{6x^2}$

94. $\dfrac{15x^5 + 25x^3 - 30x^2}{5x}$

95. $\dfrac{16n^8 + 4n^5 - 10n}{4n^5}$

96. $\dfrac{30n^6 - 20n^5 - 16n^3}{5n^5}$

97. $\dfrac{2p^8 + 4p^5 - 8p^3}{-16p^5}$

98. $\dfrac{3p^4 - 6p^2 + 9}{-6p^2}$

99. $\dfrac{8x^2 - 2x - 21}{2x + 3}$

100. $\dfrac{3x^2 + 17x - 6}{3x - 1}$

101. $\dfrac{6x^2 + x^3 - 2x + 1}{x - 1}$

102. $\dfrac{-6x + 2x^3 - 7x^2 + 8}{x - 2}$

103. $\dfrac{x^3 + 8}{x + 2}$

104. $\dfrac{3x^3 + 2x - 7}{x - 5}$

Section 5.6 Applying Exponent Rules: Scientific Notation

KEY CONCEPTS	KEY TERMS
• **Definition of Scientific Notation** A number is written in scientific notation when it is of the form $x \times 10^N$, where $1 \le x < 10$ and N is an integer. • **Convert from Decimal Notation to Scientific Notation** To change a positive number into scientific notation: **Step 1:** Count the number N of decimal places that the decimal point must be moved to arrive at a number x, where $1 \le x < 10$. **Step 2:** If the original number is greater than or equal to 1, the scientific notation is $x \times 10^N$. If the original number is between 0 and 1, the scientific notation is $x \times 10^{-N}$. • **Convert from Scientific Notation to Decimal Notation** **Step 1:** Determine the exponent, N, on the number 10. **Step 2:** If the exponent is positive, then move the decimal point N decimal places to the right. If the exponent is negative, then move the decimal point $|N|$ decimal places to the left.	Decimal notation Scientific notation

YOU SHOULD BE ABLE TO...	EXAMPLE	REVIEW EXERCISES
⊓ Convert decimal notation to scientific notation (p. 361)	Examples 1 and 2	105–110
⊠ Convert scientific notation to decimal notation (p. 362)	Examples 3 and 4	111–116
③ Use scientific notation to multiply and divide (p. 363)	Examples 5 through 8	117–122

In Problems 105–110, write in scientific notation.

105. 27,000,000

106. 1,230,000,000

107. 0.00006

108. 0.00000305

109. 3

110. 8

In Problems 111–116, write in decimal notation.

111. 6×10^{-4}

112. 1.25×10^{-3}

113. 6.13×10^5

114. 8×10^4

115. 3.7×10^{-1}

116. 5.4×10^7

In Problems 117–122, perform the indicated operations. Express your answer in scientific notation.

117. $(1.2 \times 10^{-5})(5 \times 10^8)$

118. $(1.4 \times 10^{-10})(3 \times 10^2)$

119. $\dfrac{2.4 \times 10^{-6}}{1.2 \times 10^{-8}}$

120. $\dfrac{5 \times 10^6}{25 \times 10^{-3}}$

121. $\dfrac{200,000 \times 4,000,000}{0.0002}$

122. $\dfrac{1,200,000}{0.003 \times 2,000,000}$

CHAPTER 5 TEST

Remember to use your Chapter Test Prep Video CD to see fully worked-out solutions to any of these problems you would like to review.

 CHAPTER Test Prep VIDEOS

1. Determine whether the algebraic expression $6x^5 - 2x^4$ is a polynomial (Yes or No). If it is a polynomial, state the degree and then state if it is a monomial, binomial, or trinomial.

2. Evaluate the polynomial $3x^2 - 2x + 5$ for the given values:

   (a) $x = 0$ **(b)** $x = -2$ **(c)** $x = 3$

In Problems 3–11, perform the indicated operation.

3. $(3x^2y^2 - 2x + 3y) + (-4x - 6y + 4x^2y^2)$

4. $(8m^3 + 6m^2 - 4) - (5m^2 - 2m^3 + 2)$

5. $-3x^3(2x^2 - 6x + 5)$

6. $(x - 5)(2x + 7)$

7. $(2x - 7)^2$

8. $(4x - 3y)(4x + 3y)$

9. $(3x - 1)(2x^2 + x - 8)$

10. $\dfrac{6x^4 - 8x^3 + 9}{3x^3}$

11. $\dfrac{3x^3 - 2x^2 + 5}{x + 3}$

In Problems 12–16, simplify each expression. Write answers with only positive exponents. All variables are nonzero.

12. $(4x^3y^2)(-3xy^4)$

13. $\dfrac{18m^5n}{27m^2n^6}$

14. $\left(\dfrac{m^{-2}n^0}{m^{-7}n^4}\right)^{-6}$

15. $(4x^{-3}y)^{-2}(2x^4y^{-3})^4$

16. $(2m^{-4}n^2)^{-1} \cdot \left(\dfrac{16m^0n^{-3}}{m^{-3}n^2}\right)$

17. Write 0.000012 in scientific notation.

18. Write 2.101×10^5 in decimal notation.

In Problems 19 and 20, perform the indicated operation. Express your answer in scientific notation.

19. $(2.1 \times 10^{-6}) \cdot (1.7 \times 10^{10})$

20. $\dfrac{3 \times 10^{-4}}{15 \times 10^2}$

CUMULATIVE REVIEW CHAPTERS 1–5

1. Use the set $\left\{-6, -\dfrac{4}{2}, 0, 1.4, \sqrt{7}, \sqrt{25}\right\}$. List all of the elements that are

   (a) natural   **(b)** whole   **(c)** integers

   (d) rational   **(e)** irrational   **(f)** real

In Problems 2 and 3, evaluate each expression.

2. $-\dfrac{1}{2} + \dfrac{2}{3} \div 4 \cdot \dfrac{1}{3}$

3. $2 + 3[3 + 10(-1)]$

In Problems 4 and 5, simplify each algebraic expression.

4. $6x^3 - (-2x^2 + 3x) + 3x^2$

5. $-4(6x - 1) + 2(3x + 2)$

6. Solve: $-2(3x - 4) + 6 = 4x - 6x + 10$

7. Translate the following statement into an equation. DO NOT SOLVE. Four times the difference of a number and 5 is equal to 10 more than twice the number.

8. Paycheck Kathy's monthly paycheck from her part-time job working at an electronics store totaled $659.20. This amount included a 3% raise over her previous month's earnings. What were Kathy's monthly earnings before the 3% raise?

9. Driving Cheyenne and Amber live 306 miles apart. They start driving toward each other and meet in three hours. If Cheyenne drives 12 miles per hour faster than Amber, find Amber's driving speed.

10. Solve and graph the following inequality: $-5x + 2 > 17$

11. Evaluate $\dfrac{x^2 - y^2}{z}$ when $x = 3$, $y = -2$, and $z = -10$.

12. Find the slope of the line through $(-3, 8)$ and $(1, 2)$.

13. Graph the line $2x + 3y = 24$ by finding the intercepts.

14. Graph the line $y = -3x + 8$.

15. Solve the system of linear equations:
$$\begin{cases} 2x - 3y = 27 \\ -4x + 2y = -27 \end{cases}$$

16. Solve the system of linear equations:
$$\begin{cases} 3x - 2y = 8 \\ -6x + 4y = 8 \end{cases}$$

In Problems 17–23, perform the indicated operation.

17. $(4x^2 + 6x) - (-x + 5x^2) + (6x^3 - 2x^2)$

18. $(4m - 3)(7m + 2)$

19. $(3m - 2n)(3m + 2n)$

20. $(7x + y)^2$

21. $(2m + 5)(2m^2 - 5m + 3)$

22. $\dfrac{14xy^2 + 7x^2y}{7x^2y^2}$

23. $\dfrac{x^3 + 27}{x + 3}$

In Problems 24–27, simplify the expression. Write your answers with only positive exponents. All variables are nonzero.

24. $(4m^0n^3)(-6n)$

25. $\dfrac{25m^{-6}n^{-2}}{-10m^{-4}n^{-10}}$

26. $\left(\dfrac{2xy^4}{z^{-2}}\right)^{-6}$

27. $(x^4y^{-2})^{-4} \cdot \left(\dfrac{6x^{-4}y^3}{3y^{-8}}\right)^{-1}$

28. Write 0.0000605 in scientific notation.

29. Write 2.175×10^6 in decimal notation.

30. Perform the indicated operation. Write your answer in scientific notation.
$$(3.4 \times 10^8)(2.1 \times 10^{-3})$$

6 Factoring Polynomials

The owners of A & L Auto Sales want to hang decorative banners to draw potential customers' attention to their extensive used car offerings. They have 10 feet of wire to attach banners and know that, according to zoning regulations, the distance from the pole to the point where the wire attaches to the ground must be 2 feet greater than the height of the pole. How tall can the pole be? To find the height of the pole, we use the Pythagorean Theorem. See Problem 39 in Section 6.7 on page 431.

OUTLINE

The Big Picture: Putting It Together

In Chapter 5, we learned how to multiply polynomials. We began by multiplying a monomial and a polynomial using the Distributive Property. We then learned how to multiply two binomials, and, in general, how to multiply two polynomials. In this chapter, we reverse the process. That is, we want to write a polynomial as a product of two or more polynomials. This process is called *factoring*, which leads to a "big picture" idea of mathematics. Whenever we perform an operation, we want a technique to "undo" the operation. Here, factoring "undoes" multiplication.

In Chapter 2, we solved linear (first-degree) equations such as $2x + 5 = 8$. In this chapter, we discuss how factoring can be used to solve equations such as $2x^2 + 7x + 3 = 0$. The approach requires that we rewrite $2x^2 + 7x + 3$ as the product of two polynomials of degree 1. This ultimately leads us to solving two linear equations—something we already know how to do! This is one of the goals of algebra: Simplify a problem until it becomes a problem you already know how to solve!

Factoring is important for solving equations, but also will play a major role in Chapters 7, 8, and 9, so be sure to work hard to learn the factoring techniques presented in this chapter.

6.1 Greatest Common Factor and Factoring by Grouping

OBJECTIVES

1. Find the Greatest Common Factor of Two or More Expressions
2. Factor Out the Greatest Common Factor in Polynomials
3. Factor Polynomials by Grouping

Preparing for Greatest Common Factor and Factoring by Grouping

Before getting started, take the following readiness quiz. If you get a problem wrong, go back to the section cited and review the material.

P1. Write 48 as the product of prime numbers. [Section 1.2, p. 9]

P2. Distribute: $2(5x - 3)$ [Section 1.8, pp. 70–71]

P3. Find the product: $(2x + 5)(x - 3)$ [Section 5.3, pp. 330–335]

Consider the following products:

$$5 \cdot 3 = 15$$
$$5(y + 5) = 5y + 25$$
$$(3x - 1)(x + 5) = 3x^2 + 14x - 5$$

The expressions on the left side are called **factors** of the expression on the right side. For example, $3x - 1$ and $x + 5$ are factors of $3x^2 + 14x - 5$. In the last chapter, we learned how to multiply factors to obtain a product. For example, we learned how to multiply expressions such as $3x - 1$ and $x + 5$ to obtain the polynomial $3x^2 + 14x - 5$.

In this chapter, we learn how to obtain the factors of a polynomial such as $3x^2 + 14x - 5$. That is, we learn how to write $3x^2 + 14x - 5$ as $(3x - 1)(x + 5)$.

In Words

Factoring is "undoing" multiplication.

DEFINITION

To **factor** a polynomial means to write the polynomial as a product of two or more polynomials.

The process of factoring reverses the process of multiplying, as shown below.

$$\text{Factored form} \quad \longrightarrow \quad \overset{\text{Multiplication}}{\underset{\text{Factoring}}{3(x - 7) = 3x - 21}} \quad \longleftarrow \quad \text{Product}$$

1 Find the Greatest Common Factor of Two or More Expressions

If you look carefully at the illustration above, you will notice that 3 is the largest number that divides evenly into both $3x$ and 21 in the expression $3x - 21$. For this reason, 3 is the greatest common factor of $3x - 21$.

DEFINITION

The **greatest common factor (GCF)** of a list of polynomials is the largest expression that divides evenly into all the polynomials.

Preparing for...Answers **P1.** $3 \cdot 2^4$
P2. $10x - 6$ **P3.** $2x^2 - x - 15$

Writing $3x - 21$ as $3(x - 7)$ is referred to as factoring out the greatest common factor. But how can we find the GCF? The following example shows us how.

EXAMPLE 1 How to Find the GCF of a List of Numbers

Find the GCF of 12 and 18.

Step-by-Step Solution

Step 1: Write each number as the product of prime factors.	$12 = 2 \cdot 2 \cdot 3$ $18 = 2 \quad \cdot 3 \cdot 3$
Step 2: Determine the common prime factors.	The common factors are 2 and 3.
Step 3: Find the product of the common factors found in Step 2. This number is the GCF.	The GCF is $2 \cdot 3 = 6$.

EXAMPLE 2 Finding the GCF of a List of Numbers

Find the GCF of 24, 40, and 72.

Solution

We write each number as the product of prime factors.

$$24 = 4 \cdot 6 = 2 \cdot 2 \cdot 2 \cdot 3$$
$$40 = 4 \cdot 10 = 2 \cdot 2 \cdot 2 \cdot \quad 5$$
$$72 = 8 \cdot 9 = 2 \cdot 2 \cdot 2 \cdot 3 \cdot 3$$

Because all three numbers contain three factors of 2, the GCF is $2 \cdot 2 \cdot 2 = 8$. ■

Notice the greatest common factor in Example 2 could be written as 2^3. The exponent 3 represents the number of times the factor 2 appears in the factorization of each number.

> **Work Smart**
>
> Remember, a prime number is a number greater than 1 that has no factors other than itself and 1. For example, 3, 7, and 13 are prime numbers while 4 ($= 2 \cdot 2$), 12 ($= 2 \cdot 2 \cdot 3$), and 35 ($= 5 \cdot 7$) are not prime.
>
> Also, it is helpful to align the common factors vertically.

Quick ✔

1. The largest expression that divides evenly into a set of numbers is called the _____ _____ _____.

2. In the product $(3x - 2)(x + 4) = 3x^2 + 10x - 8$, the polynomials $(3x - 2)$ and $(x + 4)$ are called _____ of the polynomial $3x^2 + 10x - 8$.

In Problems 3–5, find the greatest common factor of each list of numbers.

3. 32, 40   4. 12, 45   5. 21, 35, 84

What if we want to find the greatest common factor among two or more expressions that contain variables? The approach to finding the GCF is the same as it is for numbers. Consider x^3, x^5, and x^6, which can be written as the product of factors of x as follows:

$$x^3 = x \cdot x \cdot x$$
$$x^5 = x \cdot x \cdot x \cdot x \cdot x$$
$$x^6 = x \cdot x \cdot x \cdot x \cdot x \cdot x$$

> **Work Smart**
>
> The GCF of a variable factor is the lowest power of that variable.

Each of the terms contains three factors of x, so the greatest common factor is x^3. It is no coincidence that the exponent of the GCF is 3, the smallest exponent of x^3, x^5, and x^6. This approach to finding the GCF for variable expressions will work in general. We illustrate how to find the GCF of two expressions in the next example.

EXAMPLE 3 Finding the Greatest Common Factor

Find the greatest common factor (GCF) of $8y^4$ and $12y^2$.

Solution

Step 1: We determine the GCF of the coefficients, 8 and 12.

$$8 = 2 \cdot 2 \cdot 2$$
$$12 = 2 \cdot 2 \quad \cdot 3$$

The GCF of the coefficients is $2 \cdot 2 = 4$.

Step 2: The variable factors are y^4 and y^2. For each variable, determine the smallest exponent that each variable is raised to. The GCF of y^4 and y^2 is y^2.

Step 3: The product of the common factors found in Steps 1 and 2 is the GCF. The GCF is $4y^2$. ■

> **SUMMARY** STEPS TO FIND THE GREATEST COMMON FACTOR
>
> **Step 1:** Find the GCF of the coefficients of each variable factor.
>
> **Step 2:** For each variable factor common to all the terms, determine the smallest exponent that the variable factor is raised to.
>
> **Step 3:** Find the product of the common factors found in Steps 1 and 2. This expression is the GCF.

EXAMPLE 4 Finding the Greatest Common Factor

Find the GCF:

    (a) $3x^3, 9x^2, 21x$ **(b)** $10x^5y^4, 15x^2y^3, 25x^3y^5$

Solution

We determine the GCF of the coefficients and then determine the variable factor with the smallest exponent. The product of these two factors is the GCF.

    (a) The coefficients, 3, 9, and 21, written as products of prime numbers, are

$$\text{Factor the coefficients as products of primes:} \quad \begin{aligned} 3 &= 3 \\ 9 &= 3 \cdot 3 \\ 21 &= 3 \cdot \quad 7 \end{aligned}$$

The GCF of the coefficients is 3.
    The variable factors are x^3, x^2, and x. The smallest exponent is 1, so the GCF of the variable factors is x. Therefore, the GCF of $3x^3$, $9x^2$, and $21x$ is $3x$.

    (b) The coefficients are 10, 15, and 25. We write these coefficients as products of prime numbers.

$$\text{Factor the coefficients as products of primes:} \quad \begin{aligned} 10 &= 5 \cdot 2 \\ 15 &= 5 \cdot \quad 3 \\ 25 &= 5 \cdot \qquad 5 \end{aligned}$$

The GCF of the coefficients is 5.
    The GCF of x^5, x^2, and x^3 is x^2. The GCF of y^4, y^3, and y^5 is y^3. Therefore, the GCF of $10x^5y^4$, $15x^2y^3$, and $25x^3y^5$ is $5x^2y^3$.   ■

Quick ✔ *In Problems 6–8, find the greatest common factor (GCF).*
6. $14y^3, 35y^2$ **7.** $6z^3, 8z^2, 12z$ **8.** $4x^3y^5, 8x^2y^3, 24xy^4$

The greatest common factor can be a binomial, as illustrated in the following example.

EXAMPLE 5 The GCF as a Binomial

Find the greatest common factor of each pair of expressions.

    (a) $3(x - 1)$ and $8(x - 1)$ **(b)** $2(z + 3)(z + 5)$ and $4(z + 5)^2$

Solution

    (a) There is no common factor between the coefficients, 3 and 8. However, each expression has $x - 1$ as a factor, so the GCF of $3(x - 1)$ and $8(x - 1)$ is $x - 1$.
    (b) The GCF between 2 and 4 is 2. The GCF between $(z + 3)(z + 5)$ and $(z + 5)^2$ is $z + 5$. The GCF of the expressions $2(z + 3)(z + 5)$ and $4(z + 5)^2$ is $2(z + 5)$.   ■

Quick ✔ *In Problems 9 and 10, find the greatest common factor (GCF).*
9. $7(2x + 3)$ and $-4(2x + 3)$ **10.** $9(k + 8)(3k - 2)$ and $12(k - 1)(k + 8)^2$

$\boxed{2}$ Factor Out the Greatest Common Factor in Polynomials

The first step in factoring any polynomial is to look for the greatest common factor of the terms of the polynomial. Once the GCF is identified, we use the Distributive Property "in reverse" to factor the polynomial as shown below.

$$ab + ac = a(b + c) \quad \text{or} \quad ab - ac = a(b - c)$$

When we use this method, we say that we "factor out" the greatest common factor. Example 6 illustrates the method.

$\boxed{\text{EXAMPLE 6}}$ How to Factor Out the Greatest Common Factor in a Polynomial

Factor $2x - 10$ by factoring out the greatest common factor.

Step-by-Step Solution

Step 1: Find the GCF of the terms of the polynomial.	The terms of $2x - 10$ are $2x$ and -10. The GCF of $2x$ and -10 is 2.
Step 2: Rewrite each term as the product of the GCF and the remaining factor.	$2x - 10 = 2(x) - 2(5)$
Step 3: Factor out the GCF.	$= 2(x - 5)$
Step 4: Check	$2(x - 5) = 2(x) - 2(5)$ $= 2x - 10$

Work Smart

The Distributive Property comes in handy again for factoring out the GCF. Note how it is used in the check step, too.

So $2x - 10 = 2(x - 5)$.

Below we summarize the steps to follow when factoring out the greatest common factor.

> **STEPS TO FACTOR A POLYNOMIAL USING THE GREATEST COMMON FACTOR**
>
> **Step 1:** Identify the greatest common factor (GCF) of the terms that make up the polynomial.
> **Step 2:** Rewrite each term as the product of the GCF and the remaining factor.
> **Step 3:** Use the Distributive Property "in reverse" to factor out the GCF.
> **Step 4:** Check using the Distributive Property.

$\boxed{\text{EXAMPLE 7}}$ Factoring Out the Greatest Common Factor in a Binomial

Factor the binomial $9z^3 + 36z^2$ by factoring out the greatest common factor.

Solution

The greatest common factor between 9 and 36 is 9. The greatest common factor between z^3 and z^2 is z^2. Therefore, the GCF is $9z^2$.

Rewrite each term as the product
of the GCF and the remaining factor: $\quad 9z^3 + 36z^2 = 9z^2(z) + 9z^2(4)$

Factor out the GCF: $\quad = 9z^2(z + 4)$

Check $\quad 9z^2(z + 4) = 9z^2(z) + 9z^2(4)$

$= 9z^3 + 36z^2$

So $9z^3 + 36z^2 = 9z^2(z + 4)$.

EXAMPLE 8 Factoring Out the Greatest Common Factor in a Trinomial

Factor the trinomial $6a^2b^2 - 8ab^3 + 18a^3b^4$ by factoring out the greatest common factor.

Solution

The GCF of $6a^2b^2 - 8ab^3 + 18a^3b^4$ is $2ab^2$. We now rewrite each term as the product of the GCF and the remaining factor.

$$6a^2b^2 - 8ab^3 + 18a^3b^4 = 2ab^2(3a) - 2ab^2(4b) + 2ab^2(9a^2b^2)$$

Factor out the GCF: $= 2ab^2(3a - 4b + 9a^2b^2)$

Check $2ab^2(3a - 4b + 9a^2b^2) = 2ab^2(3a) - 2ab^2(4b) + 2ab^2(9a^2b^2)$
$$= 6a^2b^2 - 8ab^3 + 18a^3b^4$$

So $6a^2b^2 - 8ab^3 + 18a^3b^4 = 2ab^2(3a - 4b + 9a^2b^2)$. ■

> Quick ✔
>
> **11.** To ____ a polynomial means to write the polynomial as a product of two or more polynomials.
>
> **12.** When we factor a polynomial using the GCF, we use the _____ Property in reverse.
>
> *In Problems 13–16, factor each polynomial by factoring out the greatest common factor.*
>
> **13.** $5z^2 + 30z$ **14.** $12p^2 - 12p$
>
> **15.** $16y^3 - 12y^2 + 4y$ **16.** $6m^4n^2 + 18m^3n^4 - 22m^2n^5$

When the coefficient of the term of highest degree is negative, we factor the negative out of the polynomial as part of the GCF.

EXAMPLE 9 Factoring Out a Negative as Part of the GCF

Factor $-7a^3 + 14a$ by factoring out the greatest common factor.

Solution

This binomial is written in standard form. Since the coefficient on the highest-degree term, $-7a^3$, is negative, we factor the negative out as part of the GCF. So we use $-7a$ as the greatest common factor.

$$-7a^3 + 14a = -7a(a^2) + (-7a)(-2)$$

Factor out the GCF: $= -7a(a^2 - 2)$

Check $-7a(a^2 - 2) = -7a(a^2) + (-7a)(-2)$
$$= -7a^3 + 14a$$

So $-7a^3 + 14a = -7a(a^2 - 2)$. ■

> Quick ✔ *In Problems 17 and 18, factor out the greatest common factor.*
>
> **17.** $-4y^2 + 8y$ **18.** $-6a^3 + 12a^2 - 3a$

As we have discovered, the greatest common factor may be a binomial.

EXAMPLE 10 Factoring Out a Binomial as the Greatest Common Factor

Factor out the greatest common binomial factor: $5x(x - 2) + 3(x - 2)$

Solution

Do you see that $x - 2$ is common to both terms? The GCF is the binomial $x - 2$.

$$5x(x - 2) + 3(x - 2) = 5x(x - 2) + 3(x - 2)$$

Factor out $x - 2$: $= (x - 2)(5x + 3)$

Check $(x - 2)(5x + 3) = (x - 2)5x + (x - 2)3$
$$= 5x(x - 2) + 3(x - 2)$$

So $5x(x - 2) + 3(x - 2) = (x - 2)(5x + 3)$. ■

Quick ✔

19. *True or False:* We factor $(2x + 1)(x - 3) + (2x + 1)(2x + 7)$ as $(2x + 1)^2(3x + 4)$.

In Problems 20 and 21, factor out the greatest common factor.

20. $2a(a - 5) + 3(a - 5)$ **21.** $7z(z + 5) - 4(z + 5)$

③ Factor Polynomials by Grouping

Work Smart

Try factoring by grouping when a polynomial contains four terms.

Sometimes a common factor does not occur in every term of the polynomial. If a polynomial contains four terms, it may be possible to find a GCF of the first two terms and a different GCF of the second two terms and have the same remaining factor from each pair. When this happens, the common factor can be factored out of each group of terms. This technique is called **factoring by grouping,** as is illustrated in the next example.

EXAMPLE 11   How to Factor by Grouping

Factor by grouping: $3x - 3y + ax - ay$

Step-by-Step Solution

Step 1: Group terms with common factors.	$3x - 3y + ax - ay = (3x - 3y) + (ax - ay)$
Step 2: In each grouping, factor out the GCF.	$= 3(x - y) + a(x - y)$
Step 3: Factor out the common factor, $x - y$, that remains.	$= (x - y)(3 + a)$
Step 4: Check	Multiply: $(x - y)(3 + a) = 3x + ax - 3y - ay$ Rearrange terms: $= 3x - 3y + ax - ay$

So $3x - 3y + ax - ay = (x - y)(3 + a)$.

Based upon Example 11, we have the following steps for factoring by grouping.

Work Smart

We could have written the answer to Example 11 as $(3 + a)(x - y)$. Do you know why?

STEPS TO FACTOR A POLYNOMIAL BY GROUPING

Step 1: Group the terms with common factors.
Step 2: In each grouping, factor out the greatest common factor (GCF).
Step 3: If the remaining factor in each grouping is the same, factor it out.
Step 4: Check your work by finding the product of the factors.

Quick ✔ *In Problem 22, factor by grouping.*

22. $4x + 4y + bx + by$

EXAMPLE 12   Factoring by Grouping

Factor by grouping: $5x - 5y - 4bx + 4by$

Solution

First, we group terms with common factors. Be careful when grouping the third and fourth terms because of the minus sign with $-4bx$.

Work Smart

Notice we factor out $-4b$ in the second grouping. If we factor out $4b$ instead, we do not end up with the common factor, $x - y$.

$$5x - 5y - 4bx + 4by = (5x - 5y) + (-4bx + 4by)$$

Factor out the common factor in each group: $= 5(x - y) + (-4b)(x - y)$
Factor out the common factor that remains: $= (x - y)(5 - 4b)$

Check   Multiply: $(x - y)(5 - 4b) = 5x - 4bx - 5y + 4by$
Rearrange terms: $= 5x - 5y - 4bx + 4by$

So $5x - 5y - 4bx + 4by = (x - y)(5 - 4b)$.

In Example 12, we could have rearranged terms using the Commutative Property of Addition to write the problem $5x - 5y - 4bx + 4by$ as $5x - 4bx - 5y + 4by$ and factored as follows.

$$5x - 4bx - 5y + 4by = x(5 - 4b) - y(5 - 4b)$$
$$= (5 - 4b)(x - y)$$

Because $(5 - 4b)(x - y) = (x - y)(5 - 4b)$ by the Commutative Property of Multiplication, the answer is equivalent to the result of Example 12.

Work Smart

Sometimes it will be necessary to rearrange terms before factoring by grouping.

> **Quick** ✔ *In Problems 23 and 24, factor by grouping.*
> **23.** $6az - 2a - 9bz + 3b$ **24.** $8b + 4 - 10ab - 5a$

Whenever we encounter a factoring problem, the first thing we should always do is look for a common factor. The next example illustrates this idea.

EXAMPLE 13 Factoring by Grouping

Factor: $3x^3 + 12x^2 - 6x - 24$

Solution

Work Smart

Whenever factoring, always look for a GCF first.

Do all four terms contain a common factor? Yes!! There is a GCF of 3, so we factor it out.

$$3x^3 + 12x^2 - 6x - 24 = 3(x^3 + 4x^2 - 2x - 8)$$

Now we group terms with common factors.

$$3(x^3 + 4x^2 - 2x - 8) = 3[(x^3 + 4x^2) + (-2x - 8)]$$

Factor out the common factor in each group: $= 3[(x^2(x + 4) + (-2)(x + 4)]$

Factor out the common factor that remains: $= 3(x + 4)(x^2 - 2)$

Check   Multiply: $3(x + 4)(x^2 - 2) = 3(x^3 - 2x + 4x^2 - 8)$

Distribute the 3: $= 3x^3 - 6x + 12x^2 - 24$

Rearrange terms: $= 3x^3 + 12x^2 - 6x - 24$

So $3x^3 + 12x^2 - 6x - 24 = 3(x + 4)(x^2 - 2)$.   ■

> **Quick** ✔ *In Problems 25 and 26, factor by grouping.*
> **25.** $3z^3 + 12z^2 + 6z + 24$ **26.** $2n^4 + 2n^3 - 4n^2 - 4n$

6.1 EXERCISES

PRACTICE   WATCH   DOWNLOAD   READ   REVIEW

1–26. *are the* Quick ✔s *that follow each* EXAMPLE

Building Skills

In Problems 27–46, find the greatest common factor, GCF, of each group of expressions. See Objective 1.

27. $8, 6$ **28.** $49, 35$

29. $15, 14$ **30.** $6, 55$

31. $12, 28, 48$ **32.** $35, 42, 63$

33. x^{10}, x^2, x^8 **34.** y^3, y^5, y

35. $7x, 14x^3$ **36.** $8a^4, 20a^2$

37. $45a^2b^3, 75ab^2c$ **38.** $26xy^2, 39x^2y$

39. $4a^2bc^3, 6ab^2c^2, 8a^2b^2c^4$ **40.** $2x^2yz, xyz^2, 5x^3yz^2$

41. $3(x - 1)$ and $6(x + 1)$ **42.** $8(x + y)$ and $9(x + y)$

43. $2(x - 4)^2$ and $4(x - 4)^3$ **44.** $6(a - b)$ and $15(a - b)^3$

45. $12(x + 2)(x - 3)^2$ and $18(x - 3)^2(x - 2)$

46. $15(2a - 1)^2(2a + 1)$ and $18(2a - 1)^3(2a + 3)^2$

In Problems 47–70, factor the GCF from the polynomial. See Objective 2.

47. $12x - 18$

48. $3a + 6$

49. $-3x^2 + 12x$

50. $-9b^2 - 6ab$

51. $5x^2y - 15x^3y^2$

52. $8a^3b^2 + 12a^5b^2$

53. $3x^3 + 6x^2 - 3x$

54. $5x^4 + 10x^3 - 25x^2$

55. $-5x^3 + 10x^2 - 15x$

56. $-2y^2 + 10y - 14$

57. $9m^5 - 18m^3 - 12m^2 + 81$

58. $5z^2 + 10z^4 - 15z^3 - 45z^5$

59. $-12z^3 + 16z^2 - 8z$

60. $-22n^4 + 18n^2 + 14n$

61. $10 - 5b - 15b^3$

62. $14m^2 - 16m^3 - 24m^4$

63. $15a^2b^4 - 60ab^3 + 45a^3b^2$

64. $12r^3s^2 + 3rs - 6rs^4$

65. $(x - 3)x - (x - 3)5$

66. $a(a - 5) + 6(a - 5)$

67. $x^2(x - 1) + y^2(x - 1)$

68. $(b + 2)a^2 - (b + 2)b$

69. $x^2(4x + 1) + 2x(4x + 1) + 5(4x + 1)$

70. $s^2(s^2 + 1) + 4s(s^2 + 1) + 7(s^2 + 1)$

In Problems 71–80, factor by grouping. See Objective 3.

71. $xy + 3y + 4x + 12$

72. $x^2 + ax + 2a + 2x$

73. $yz + z - y - 1$

74. $mn - 3n + 2m - 6$

75. $x^3 - x^2 + 2x - 2$

76. $z^3 + 4z^2 + 3z + 12$

77. $2t^3 - t^2 - 4t + 2$

78. $x^3 - x^2 - 5x + 5$

79. $2t^4 - t^3 - 6t + 3$

80. $6yz - 8y - 9z + 12$

Mixed Practice

In Problems 81–102, factor each polynomial.

81. $4y - 20$

82. $3z - 21$

83. $28m^3 + 7m^2 + 63m$

84. $10x^3 - 15x^2 - 5x$

85. $12m^3n^2p - 18m^2n$

86. $4s^2t^3 - 24st$

87. $(2p - 1)(p + 3) + (7p + 4)(p + 3)$

88. $(3x - 2)(4x + 1) + (3x - 2)(x - 10)$

89. $18ax - 9ay - 12bx + 6by$

90. $6xm + 3xn - 4ym - 2yn$

91. $(x - 2)(x - 3) + (x - 2)$

92. $(a + 2)(2b - 1) - (2b - 1)$

93. $15x^4 - 6x^3 + 30x^2 - 12x$

94. $2a^3 - 4a^2 + 8a - 16$

95. $-3x^3 + 6x^2 - 9x$

96. $-8z^4 - 12z^3 + 28z^2$

97. $-12b + 16b^2$

98. $-8a + 20a^2$

99. $12xy + 9x - 8y - 6$

100. $-12mxz - 3xz + 24mx + 6x$

101. $\dfrac{1}{3}x^3 - \dfrac{2}{9}x^2$

102. $\dfrac{3}{4}p^4 - \dfrac{1}{4}p^3$

Applying the Concepts

103. Height of a Toy Rocket The height of a toy rocket after t seconds when fired straight up from the ground with an initial speed of 150 feet per second is given by the polynomial $-16t^2 + 150t$. Write the polynomial $-16t^2 + 150t$ in factored form.

104. Height of a Ball The height of a ball after t seconds when thrown straight up from a height of 48 feet with an initial speed of 80 feet per second is given by the polynomial $-16t^2 + 80t + 48$. Write the polynomial $-16t^2 + 80t + 48$ in factored form.

105. Selling Calculators A manufacturer of calculators found that the number of calculators sold at a price of p dollars is given by the polynomial $21,000 - 150p$. Write $21,000 - 150p$ in factored form.

106. Revenue A manufacturer of a gas clothes dryer has found that the revenue (in dollars) from selling clothes dryers at a price of p dollars is given by the expression $-4p^2 + 4000p$. Write $-4p^2 + 4000p$ in factored form.

△**107. Area of a Rectangle** A rectangle has an area of $(8x^5 - 28x^3)$ square feet. Write $8x^5 - 28x^3$ in factored form.

△**108. Area of a Parallelogram** A parallelogram has an area of $(18n^4 - 15n^3 + 6n)$ square cm. Write $18n^4 - 15n^3 + 6n$ in factored form.

△**109. Surface Area** The surface area of a cylindrical can whose radius is r inches and height is 4 inches is given by $S = (2\pi r^2 + 8\pi r)$ square inches. Express the surface area in factored form.

△**110. Surface Area** The surface area of a cylindrical can whose radius is r inches and height is 8 inches is given by $S = (2\pi r^2 + 16\pi r)$ square inches. Express the surface area in factored form.

In Problems 111 and 112, the area of the polygon is given. Write a polynomial that represents the missing length.

△**111.**

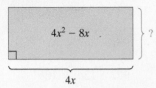

△**112.**

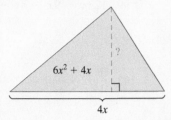

Extending the Concepts

In Problems 113–120, find the missing factor.

113. $8x^{3n} + 10x^n = 2x^n \cdot ?$

114. $3x^{2n+2} + 6x^{6n} = 3x^{2n} \cdot ?$

115. $3 - 4x^{-1} + 2x^{-3} = x^{-3} \cdot ?$

116. $1 - 3x^{-1} + 2x^{-2} = x^{-2} \cdot ?$

117. $x^2 - 3x^{-1} + 2x^{-2} = x^{-2} \cdot ?$

118. $2x^2 + x^{-3} - x^{-4} = x^{-4} \cdot ?$

119. $\dfrac{6}{35}x^4 - \dfrac{1}{7}x^2 + \dfrac{2}{7}x = \dfrac{2}{7}x \cdot ?$

120. $\dfrac{2}{15}x^3 - \dfrac{1}{9}x^2 + \dfrac{1}{3}x = \dfrac{1}{3}x \cdot ?$

Explaining the Concepts

121. Write a list of steps for finding the greatest common factor and then write a second list of steps for factoring the GCF from a polynomial.

122. Describe how to factor a negative from a polynomial. What types of errors might happen during this process?

123. Explain the error in the following student's work:
$$3a(x + y) - 4b(x + y) = (3a - 4b)(x + y)^2.$$

124. On a test, your answer for factoring $5z(x - 4) - 6(x - 4)$ was $(x - 4)(5z - 6)$. Your friend Jack's answer was $(5z - 6)(x - 4)$. Explain why both answers are correct.

6.2 Factoring Trinomials of the Form $x^2 + bx + c$

OBJECTIVES

1. Factor Trinomials of the Form $x^2 + bx + c$
2. Factor Out the GCF, Then Factor $x^2 + bx + c$

Preparing for Factoring Trinomials of the Form $x^2 + bx + c$

Before getting started, take the following readiness quiz. If you get a problem wrong, go back to the section cited and review the material.

P1. Find two factors of 18 whose sum is 11. [Section 1.2, p. 9]

P2. Find two factors of -24 whose sum is -2. [Section 1.4, pp. 30–34]

P3. Find two factors of -12 whose sum is 1. [Section 1.4, pp. 30–34]

P4. Find two factors of 35 whose sum is -12. [Section 1.4, pp. 30–34]

P5. Determine the coefficients of $3x^2 - x - 4$. [Section 1.8, p. 69]

P6. Find the product: $-5p(p + 4)$ [Section 5.3, pp. 331–332]

P7. Find the product: $(z - 1)(z + 4)$ [Section 5.3, pp. 332–335]

In this section, we factor trinomials of degree 2. Because the word **quadratic** means "relating to a square," these trinomials are called *quadratic trinomials.*

DEFINITION

A **quadratic trinomial** is a polynomial of the form $ax^2 + bx + c, a \neq 0$ where a represents the coefficient of the squared (second-degree) term, b represents the coefficient of the linear (first-degree) term, and c represents the constant.

Preparing for...Answers **P1.** 9 and 2
P2. -6 and 4 **P3.** 4 and -3
P4. -7 and -5 **P5.** 3, -1, -4
P6. $-5p^2 - 20p$ **P7.** $z^2 + 3z - 4$

When the trinomial is written in standard form (descending order of degree) the coefficient of the squared term is also called the **leading coefficient.** We begin by looking at quadratic trinomials where the leading coefficient, a, is 1. Examples of quadratic trinomials whose leading coefficient is 1 are

$$x^2 + 4x + 3 \qquad a^2 + 4a - 21 \qquad p^2 - 11p + 18$$

⌐1 Factor Trinomials of the Form $x^2 + bx + c$

The idea behind factoring a second-degree trinomial of the form $x^2 + bx + c$ is to see whether it can be written as the product of two first-degree polynomials.

For example,

$$\text{Factored form} \rightarrow (x + 3)(x - 7) = x^2 - 4x - 21 \leftarrow \text{Product}$$

Multiplication $\rightarrow$

$\leftarrow$ Factoring

The factors of $x^2 - 4x - 21$ are $x + 3$ and $x - 7$. Notice the following:

$$x^2 - 4x - 21 = (x + 3)(x - 7)$$

The sum of -7 and 3 is -4.

The product of -7 and 3 is -21.

In general, if $x^2 + bx + c = (x + m)(x + n)$, then $mn = c$ and $m + n = b$. We illustrate how to factor a trinomial of the form $x^2 + bx + c$ in the following example.

⌐EXAMPLE 1 How to Factor a Trinomial of the Form $x^2 + bx + c$, where c Is Positive

Factor: $x^2 + 7x + 12$

Step-by-Step Solution

Step 1: When we compare $x^2 + 7x + 12$ with $x^2 + bx + c$, we see that $b = 7$ and $c = 12$. We are looking for factors of $c = 12$ whose sum is $b = 7$. We begin by listing all factors of 12 and computing the sum of these factors.

Integers Whose Product Is 12	1, 12	2, 6	3, 4	−1, −12	−2,−6	−3,−4
Sum	13	8	7	−13	−8	−7

We can see that $3 \cdot 4 = 12$ and $3 + 4 = 7$, so $m = 3$ and $n = 4$.

Step 2: We write the trinomial in the form $(x + m)(x + n)$.

$$x^2 + 7x + 12 = (x + 3)(x + 4)$$

Step 3: Check

Multiply: $(x + 3)(x + 4) = x^2 + 4x + 3x + 3(4) = x^2 + 7x + 12$

So $x^2 + 7x + 12 = (x + 3)(x + 4)$.   ∎

We summarize the steps for factoring a trinomial of the form $x^2 + bx + c$ below.

STEPS TO FACTOR A TRINOMIAL OF THE FORM $x^2 + bx + c$

Step 1: Find the pair of integers whose product is c and whose sum is b. That is, determine m and n such that $mn = c$ and $m + n = b$.

Step 2: Write $x^2 + bx + c = (x + m)(x + n)$.

Step 3: Check your work by multiplying the binomials.

In Example 1, notice that the coefficient of the middle term is positive and the constant is positive. **If the coefficient of the middle term and the constant are both positive, then m and n must both be positive.**

EXAMPLE 2 Factoring a Trinomial of the Form $x^2 + bx + c$, where c Is Positive

Factor: $p^2 - 11p + 24$

Solution

We first identify $b = -11$ and $c = 24$. We are looking for factors of $c = 24$ whose sum is $b = -11$. We begin by listing all factors of 24 and computing the sum of these factors.

Integers Whose Product Is 24	1,24	2,12	3, 8	4, 6	−1, −24	−2, −12	−3, −8	−4, −6
Sum	25	14	11	10	−25	−14	−11	−10

We can see that $-3 \cdot (-8) = 24$ and $-3 + (-8) = -11$, so $m = -3$ and $n = -8$. Now we write the trinomial in the form $(p + m)(p + n)$.

$$p^2 - 11p + 24 = (p + (-3))(p + (-8))$$
$$= (p - 3)(p - 8)$$

Check

Multiply: $(p - 3)(p - 8) = p^2 - 8p - 3p + (-3)(-8)$
$$= p^2 - 11p + 24$$

So $p^2 - 11p + 24 = (p - 3)(p - 8)$. ∎

In Example 2, notice that the coefficient of the middle term is negative and the constant is positive. **If the coefficient of the middle term is negative and the constant is positive, then m and n must both be negative.**

Quick ✔

1. A _____ _____ is a polynomial of the form $ax^2 + bx + c, a \neq 0$.

2. When factoring $x^2 - 10x + 24$, the signs of the factors of 24 must both be _____.

3. *True or False:* $4 + 4x + x^2$ has a leading coefficient of 4.

In Problems 4 and 5, factor each trinomial.

4. $y^2 + 9y + 20$

5. $z^2 - 9z + 14$

EXAMPLE 3 **Factoring a Trinomial of the Form $x^2 + bx + c$, where c Is Negative**

Factor: $z^2 + 3z - 28$

Solution

We see that $b = 3$ and $c = -28$. We are looking for factors of $c = -28$ whose sum is $b = 3$. We begin by listing all factors of -28 and computing the sum of these factors. Because c is negative, we know that one of the factors must be positive and the other negative. And because the coefficient of the middle term is odd, one of the factors of 28 is odd and the other is even. We list only the integers whose product is -28.

Integers Whose Product Is -28	$-1, 28$	$-4, 7$	$1, -28$	$4, -7$
Sum	27	3	-27	-3

We can see that $-4 \cdot 7 = -28$ and $-4 + 7 = 3$, so $m = -4$ and $n = 7$. We write the trinomial in the form $(z + m)(z + n)$.

$$\begin{aligned} z^2 + 3z - 28 &= (z + (-4))(z + 7) \\ &= (z - 4)(z + 7) \end{aligned}$$

Check

$$\begin{aligned} \text{Multiply:}\quad (z - 4)(z + 7) &= z^2 + 7z - 4z + (-4)(7) \\ &= z^2 + 3z - 28 \end{aligned}$$

Thus, $z^2 + 3z - 28 = (z - 4)(z + 7)$. ∎

In Example 3, notice that the coefficient of the middle term is positive and the constant is negative. **If the constant is negative, then m and n must have opposite signs.** In addition, **if the coefficient of the middle term is positive, then the factor with the larger absolute value must be positive.**

EXAMPLE 4 **Factoring a Trinomial of the Form $x^2 + bx + c$, where c Is Negative**

Factor: $z^2 - 7z - 18$

Solution

To factor the expression, what do we want to find? We need factors of $c = -18$ whose sum is $b = -7$. We begin by listing all factors of -18 and computing the sum of these factors.

Integers Whose Product Is -18	$-1, 18$	$-2, 9$	$-3, 6$	$1, -18$	$2, -9$	$3, -6$
Sum	17	7	3	-17	-7	-3

We can see that $2 \cdot (-9) = -18$ and $2 + (-9) = -7$, so $m = 2$ and $n = -9$. We write the trinomial in the form $(z + m)(z + n)$.

$$\begin{aligned} z^2 - 7z - 18 &= (z + 2)(z + (-9)) \\ &= (z + 2)(z - 9) \end{aligned}$$

Check

$$\begin{aligned} \text{Multiply:}\quad (z + 2)(z - 9) &= z^2 - 9z + 2z + 2(-9) \\ &= z^2 - 7z - 18 \end{aligned}$$

So $z^2 - 7z - 18 = (z + 2)(z - 9)$. ∎

In Example 4, notice that the coefficient of the middle term is negative and the constant is also negative. **If the coefficient of the middle term is negative and the constant is negative, then m and n must have opposite signs and the factor with the larger absolute value must be negative.**

Quick ✔

6. *True or False:* When factoring $x^2 - 10x - 24$, the factors of 24 must have opposite signs.

In Problems 7 and 8, factor each trinomial.

7. $y^2 - 2y - 15$ **8.** $w^2 + w - 12$

Table 1 summarizes the four possibilities for factoring a quadratic trinomial in the form $x^2 + bx + c = (x + m)(x + n)$.

Table 1		
Form	Signs of m and n	Example
$x^2 + bx + c$, where b and c are both positive	Both factors are positive.	$x^2 + 3x + 2 = (x + 2)(x + 1)$
$x^2 + bx + c$, where b is negative and c is positive	Both factors are negative.	$a^2 - 7a + 12 = (a - 4)(a - 3)$
$x^2 + bx + c$, where b is positive and c is negative	Factors are opposite in sign and the factor with the larger absolute value is positive.	$y^2 + 2y - 24 = (y + 6)(y - 4)$
$x^2 + bx + c$, where b is negative and c is negative	Factors are opposite in sign and the factor with the larger absolute value is negative.	$b^2 - 4b - 21 = (b - 7)(b + 3)$

DEFINITION

A polynomial that cannot be written as the product of two other polynomials (other than 1 or -1) is said to be a **prime polynomial.**

EXAMPLE 5 Identifying a Prime Trinomial

Show that $y^2 + 10y + 12$ is prime.

Solution

We are looking for factors of $c = 12$ whose sum is $b = 10$. Because both b and c are positive, we know that the factors of 12 must both be positive, so we only list positive factors of 12 and the sum of these factors.

Integers Whose Product Is 12	1, 12	2, 6	3, 4
Sum	13	8	7

There are no factors of 12 whose sum is 10. Therefore, $y^2 + 10y + 12$ is prime. ∎

Quick ✔ *In Problems 9 and 10, factor the trinomial. If the trinomial cannot be factored, state that it is prime.*

9. $z^2 - 5z + 8$ **10.** $q^2 + 4q - 45$

If a trinomial has more than one variable, we take the same approach that we used for trinomials in one variable. So trinomials of the form

$$x^2 + bxy + cy^2$$

will factor as

$$(x + my)(x + ny)$$

where

$$mn = c \quad \text{and} \quad m + n = b$$

EXAMPLE 6 Factoring Trinomials in Two Variables

Factor: $p^2 + 4pq - 21q^2$

Solution

The trinomial $p^2 + 4pq - 21q^2$ will factor as $(p + mq)(p + nq)$, where $mn = -21$ and $m + n = 4$. We are looking for factors of $c = -21$ whose sum is $b = 4$. We list factors of -21, but because c is negative and b is positive, we know that the factors of -21 will have opposite signs, and the factor of -21 with the larger absolute value will be positive.

Integers Whose Product Is −21	−1, 21	−3, 7
Sum	20	4

We can see that $-3 \cdot 7 = -21$ and $-3 + 7 = 4$, so $m = -3$ and $n = 7$. We write the trinomial in the form $(p + mq)(p + nq)$.

$$\begin{aligned} p^2 + 4pq - 21q^2 &= (p + (-3)q)(p + 7q) \\ &= (p - 3q)(p + 7q) \end{aligned}$$

Check

$$\begin{aligned} \text{Multiply:} \quad (p - 3q)(p + 7q) &= p^2 + 7pq - 3pq - 21q^2 \\ &= p^2 + 4pq - 21q^2 \end{aligned}$$

We conclude that $p^2 + 4pq - 21q^2 = (p - 3q)(p + 7q)$.   ■

Quick ✔ *In Problems 11 and 12, factor each trinomial.*

11. $x^2 + 9xy + 20y^2$ **12.** $m^2 + mn - 42n^2$

EXAMPLE 7 Factoring a Trinomial Not Written in Standard Form

Factor: $2w + w^2 - 8$

Solution

Do you notice that the trinomial is not in standard form, $ax^2 + bx + c$? We will first write it in standard form (descending order of degree) and then factor.

$$2w + w^2 - 8 = w^2 + 2w - 8$$

We now look for factors of $c = -8$ whose sum is $b = 2$. Since the coefficient of w is positive and the constant term is negative, we know that the factor with the larger absolute value will be positive.

Integers Whose Product Is −8	−1, 8	−2, 4
Sum	7	2

We see that $-2 \cdot 4 = -8$ and $-2 + 4 = 2$, so $m = -2$ and $n = 4$. The factors are $(w - 2)(w + 4)$.

Check

Multiply: $(w - 2)(w + 4) = w^2 + 4w - 2w + (-2)(4)$
$= w^2 + 2w - 8$

So $w^2 + 2w - 8 = (w - 2)(w + 4)$. ∎

Quick ✔

13. Write each trinomial in standard form.

(a) $-12 - x + x^2$ (b) $9n + n^2 - 10$

In Problems 14 and 15, factor each polynomial.

14. $-56 + n^2 + n$ **15.** $y^2 + 35 - 12y$

2 Factor Out the GCF, Then Factor $x^2 + bx + c$

Some algebraic expressions can be factored as trinomials in the form $x^2 + bx + c$ after we factor out a greatest common factor.

EXAMPLE 8 Factoring Trinomials with a Common Factor

Factor: $3u^3 - 21u^2 - 90u$

Solution

Did you notice that there is a GCF of $3u$ in the trinomial? We factor the $3u$ out:
$$3u^3 - 21u^2 - 90u = 3u(u^2 - 7u - 30)$$

We now concentrate on factoring the trinomial in parentheses, $u^2 - 7u - 30$. We are looking for factors of $c = -30$ whose sum is $b = -7$. Because c is negative and b is negative, the factor of -30 with the larger absolute value will be negative.

Integers Whose Product Is −30	1, −30	2, −15	3, −10	5, −6
Sum	−29	−13	−7	−1

We can see that $3(-10) = -30$ and $3 + (-10) = -7$, so $m = 3$ and $n = -10$. We write the trinomial in the form $(u + m)(u + n)$.
$$u^2 - 7u - 30 = (u + 3)(u - 10)$$

So we have
$$3u^3 - 21u^2 - 90u = 3u(u^2 - 7u - 30)$$
$$= 3u(u + 3)(u - 10)$$

Work Smart

We could have checked the result of Example 8 as follows:
$3u(u + 3)(u - 10)$
$= (3u^2 + 9u)(u - 10)$
$= 3u^3 - 30u^2 + 9u^2 - 90u$
$= 3u^3 - 21u^2 - 90u$

Check

Multiply: $3u(u + 3)(u - 10) = 3u(u^2 - 10u + 3u - 30)$
Combine like terms: $= 3u(u^2 - 7u - 30)$
Distribute: $= 3u^3 - 21u^2 - 90u$

So $3u^3 - 21u^2 - 90u = 3u(u + 3)(u - 10)$. ∎

We say that a polynomial is **factored completely** if each factor in the final factorization is prime. For example, $3x^2 - 6x - 45 = (x - 5)(3x + 9)$ is not factored completely because the binomial $3x + 9$ has a common factor of 3. However, $3x^2 - 6x - 45 = 3(x - 5)(x + 3)$ is factored completely.

Quick ✔

16. *True or False:* The polynomial $(x - 3)(3x + 6)$ is factored completely.

In Problems 17 and 18, completely factor each trinomial.

17. $4m^2 - 16m - 84$ **18.** $3z^3 + 12z^2 - 15z$

As we stated in the last section, sometimes the leading coefficient may be negative. If this is the case, we factor out the negative to make our factoring lives easier.

EXAMPLE 9 Factoring Trinomials with a Negative Leading Coefficient

Factor completely: $-w^2 - 5w + 24$

Solution

Work Smart

It's easier to factor a trinomial in standard form when the leading coefficient is positive.

We notice that the leading coefficient is -1. It is easier to factor a trinomial when the leading coefficient is positive, so we will use -1 as the GCF and rewrite $-w^2 - 5w + 24$ as

$$-w^2 - 5w + 24 = -1(w^2 + 5w - 24)$$

To factor $w^2 + 5w - 24$, we look for two integers whose product is -24 and whose sum is 5. Since we have a negative product, but a positive sum, we know that one factor will be positive, and the other negative. Because the coefficient of the middle term is odd, one of the factors of -24 is odd and the other is even. Further, we know that the factor of -24 with the larger absolute value will be positive.

Integers Whose Product Is -24	$-1, 24$	$-3, 8$
Sum	23	5

We factor $w^2 + 5w - 24$ as $(w - 3)(w + 8)$. But remember that we already factored out the greatest common factor, -1, so

$$-w^2 - 5w + 24 = -1(w^2 + 5w - 24)$$
$$= -1(w - 3)(w + 8)$$
$$= -(w - 3)(w + 8)$$

Quick ✔ *In Problems 19 and 20, factor each trinomial completely.*

19. $-w^2 - 3w + 10$ **20.** $-2a^2 - 8a + 24$

6.2 EXERCISES

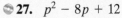

| PRACTICE | WATCH | DOWNLOAD | READ | REVIEW |

1–20. *are the* Quick ✔s *that follow each* EXAMPLE

Building Skills

In Problems 21–42, factor each trinomial completely. If the trinomial cannot be factored, say it is prime. See Objective 1.

21. $x^2 + 5x + 6$ **22.** $p^2 + 7p + 6$

23. $m^2 + 9m + 18$ **24.** $n^2 + 12n + 20$

25. $x^2 - 15x + 36$ **26.** $z^2 - 13z + 36$

☉ **27.** $p^2 - 8p + 12$ **28.** $z^2 - 7z + 12$

29. $x^2 - x - 12$ **30.** $y^2 - 8y - 9$

31. $x^2 + x - 20$ **32.** $y^2 + 6y - 40$

☉ **33.** $z^2 + 12z - 45$ **34.** $t^2 + 2t - 38$

35. $x^2 - 5xy + 6y^2$ **36.** $x^2 - 14xy + 24y^2$

37. $r^2 + rs - 6s^2$

38. $p^2 + 5pq - 14q^2$

39. $x^2 - 3xy - 4y^2$

40. $x^2 + 9xy - 36y^2$

41. $z^2 + 7zy + y^2$

42. $m^2 + 16mn + 48n^2$

In Problems 43–56, factor each trinomial completely by factoring out the GCF first and then factoring the resulting trinomial. See Objective 2.

43. $3x^2 + 3x - 6$

44. $5x^2 + 30x + 40$

45. $3n^3 - 24n^2 + 45n$

46. $4p^4 - 4p^3 - 8p^2$

47. $5x^2z - 20xz - 160z$

48. $8x^2z^2 - 56xz^2 + 80z^2$

49. $-3x^2 + x^3 - 18x$

50. $30x - 2x^2 - 100$

51. $-2y^2 + 8y - 8$

52. $-3x^2 - 18x - 15$

53. $4x^3 - 32x^2 + x^4$

54. $-75x + x^3 + 10x^2$

55. $2x^2 + x^3 - 15x$

56. $x^3 - 20x - 8x^2$

Mixed Practice

In Problems 57–90, factor each polynomial completely. If the polynomial cannot be factored, say that it is prime.

57. $x^2 - 3xy - 28y^2$

58. $x^2 - 9xy - 36y^2$

59. $x^2 + x + 6$

60. $t^2 - 8t - 7$

61. $k^2 - k - 20$

62. $x^2 - 2x - 35$

63. $x^2 + xy - 30y^2$

64. $p^2 - 6pq + 5q^2$

65. $s^2t^2 - 8st + 15$

66. $x^2y^2 + 3xy + 2$

67. $-3p^3 + 3p^2 + 6p$

68. $-2z^3 - 2z^2 + 24z$

69. $-x^2 - x + 6$

70. $-r^2 - 12r - 36$

71. $g^2 - 4g + 21$

72. $x^2 - x + 6$

73. $n^4 - 30n^2 - n^3$

74. $-16x + x^3 - 6x^2$

75. $m^2 + 2mn - 15n^2$

76. $x^2 + 7xy + 12y^2$

77. $35 + 12s + s^2$

78. $25 + 10x + x^2$

79. $n^2 - 9n - 45$

80. $x^2 - 6x - 42$

81. $m^2n^2 - 8mn + 12$

82. $x^2y^2 - 3xy - 18$

83. $-x^3 + 12x^2 + 28x$

84. $-3r^3 + 6r^2 - 3r$

85. $y^2 - 12y + 36$

86. $x^2 - 15x + 54$

87. $-36x + 20x^2 - 2x^3$

88. $-20mn^2 + 30m^2n - 5m^3$

89. $-21x^3y - 14xy^2$

90. $-12x^2y + 8xy^3$

Applying the Concepts

91. Punkin Chunkin In a recent Punkin Chunkin contest, in which a pumpkin is shot in the air with a homemade cannon, the height of a pumpkin after t seconds was given by the trinomial $(-16t^2 + 64t + 80)$ feet. Write this polynomial in factored form.

92. Punkin Chunkin In a recent Punkin Chunkin contest, in which a pumpkin is shot into the air with a catapult, the height of a pumpkin after t seconds was given by the trinomial $(-16t^2 + 16t + 32)$ feet. Write this polynomial in factored form.

△**93. A Rectangular Field** The trinomial $(x^2 + 9x + 18)$ square meters represents the area of a rectangular field. Find two binomials that might represent the length and width of the field.

△**94. Another Rectangular Field** The trinomial $(x^2 + 6x + 8)$ square yards represents the area of a rectangular field. Find two binomials that might represent the length and width of the field.

△**95. Area as a Polynomial** The area of a triangle is given by the trinomial $\left(\dfrac{1}{2}x^2 + x - \dfrac{15}{2}\right)$ square inches. Find algebraic expressions for the base and height of the triangle. (*Hint:* Factor out $\dfrac{1}{2}$ as a common factor.)

△**96. Triangle Trinomial** The area of a triangle is given by the trinomial $\left(\dfrac{1}{2}x^2 + 5x + 12\right)$ square kilometers. Find algebraic expressions for the base and height of the triangle. (*Hint:* Factor out $\dfrac{1}{2}$ as a common factor.)

Extending the Concepts

In Problems 97–100, find all possible values of b so that the trinomial is factorable.

97. $x^2 + bx + 6$

98. $x^2 + bx - 10$

99. $x^2 + bx - 21$

100. $x^2 + bx + 12$

In Problems 101–104, find all possible positive values of c so that the trinomial is factorable.

101. $x^2 - 2x + c$

102. $x^2 - 3x + c$

103. $x^2 - 7x + c$

104. $x^2 + 6x + c$

Explaining the Concepts

105. The answer key to your algebra exam said the factored form of a trinomial is $(x - 1)(x - 2)$. You have $(1 - x)(2 - x)$ on your paper. Is your answer marked correct or incorrect? Explain your reasoning.

106. In the trinomial $x^2 + bx + c$, both b and c are negative. Explain how to factor the trinomial. Make up a trinomial and then use your rules to factor it.

6.3 Factoring Trinomials of the Form $ax^2 + bx + c$, $a \neq 1$

OBJECTIVES

⌐1⌐ Factor $ax^2 + bx + c$, $a \neq 1$, Using Trial and Error

⌐2⌐ Factor $ax^2 + bx + c$, $a \neq 1$, Using Grouping

Preparing for Factoring Trinomials of the Form $ax^2 + bx + c$, $a \neq 1$

Before getting started, take the following readiness quiz. If you get a problem wrong, go back to the section cited and review the material.

P1. List the prime factorization of 24.   [Section 1.2, p. 9]

P2. Determine the coefficients of $5x^2 - 3x + 7$.   [Section 1.8, p. 69]

P3. Find the product: $(2x + 7)(3x - 1)$ [Section 5.3, pp. 332–335]

In this section, we factor quadratic trinomials of the form $ax^2 + bx + c$ in which the leading coefficient, a, is not 1. Examples of quadratic trinomials of the form $ax^2 + bx + c$, $a \neq 1$, are

$$2x^2 + 3x + 1 \qquad 5y^2 - y - 4 \qquad 10z^2 - 7z + 6$$

Before we begin to factor these quadratic trinomials, let's review multiplication of binomials using FOIL.

Factored Form	F	O	I	L	Polynomial
$(2x + 3)(x + 4) =$	$2x^2 +$	$8x +$	$3x +$	$12 =$	$2x^2 + 11x + 12$
$(3x - 4)(x + 7) =$	$3x^2 +$	$21x -$	$4x -$	$28 =$	$3x^2 + 17x - 28$
$(5m - 2n)(3m - n) =$	$15m^2 -$	$5mn -$	$6mn +$	$2n^2 =$	$15m^2 - 11mn + 2n^2$

To factor a trinomial in the form $ax^2 + bx + c$, $a \neq 1$, we reverse the FOIL multiplication process. That is, we will be given a trinomial such as $2x^2 + 11x + 12$, and we will write it as the product $(2x + 3)(x + 4)$. To factor trinomials in this form, we have two methods that can be used.

1. Trial and error

2. Factoring by grouping

There are pros and cons to both methods. We will point out these pros and cons as we proceed. We start with factoring by trial and error.

⌐1⌐ Factor $ax^2 + bx + c$, $a \neq 1$, Using Trial and Error

The idea behind using trial and error is to list various binomials and multiply to find their product until the combination of binomials that results in the original trinomial is found. While this method may sound haphazard, experience and logic will play a role in minimizing the number of possibilities that you must try before a factored form is found. The following example illustrates the method.

Preparing for...Answers **P1.** $2^3 \cdot 3$
P2. $5, -3, 7$ **P3.** $6x^2 + 19x - 7$

⌐**EXAMPLE 1**⌐ **How to Factor $ax^2 + bx + c$, $a \neq 1$, Using Trial and Error**

Factor: $2x^2 + 7x + 5$

Step-by-Step Solution

Step 1: List the possibilities for the first terms of each binomial whose product is ax^2.	We list possible ways of representing the first term, $2x^2$. Since 2 is a prime number, we have one possibility: $$(2x + \underline{})(x + \underline{})$$

(continued)

Step 2: List the possibilities for the last terms of each binomial whose product is c.

The last term, 5, is also prime. It has the factors $(1)(5)$ and $(-1)(-5)$. However, did you notice that the coefficient of x, 7, is positive? To produce a positive sum, $7x$, we must have two positive factors. So we do not include the factors $(-1)(-5)$ in our trials.

Step 3: Write out all the combinations of factors found in Steps 1 and 2. Multiply the binomials until a product is found that equals the trinomial.

Possible Factorization of $2x^2 + 7x + 5$	Product
$(2x + 1)(x + 5)$	$2x^2 + 11x + 5$
$(2x + 5)(x + 1)$	$2x^2 + 7x + 5$

The second row is the factorization that works, so $2x^2 + 7x + 5 = (2x + 5)(x + 1)$.

We summarize the steps used in Example 1 below.

STEPS TO FACTOR $ax^2 + bx + c$, $a \neq 1$, USING TRIAL AND ERROR: a, b, AND c HAVE NO COMMON FACTORS

Step 1: List the possibilities for the first terms of each binomial whose product is ax^2.
$$(\_x + \quad)(\_x + \quad) = ax^2 + bx + c$$

Step 2: List the possibilities for the last terms of each binomial whose product is c.
$$(\_x + \square)(\_x + \square) = ax^2 + bx + c$$

Step 3: Write out all the combinations of factors found in Steps 1 and 2. Multiply the binomials until a product is found that equals the trinomial.

Quick ✔

1. *True or False:* To check if a trinomial has been factored correctly, multiply the binomials and verify that the product is the original trinomial.

In Problems 2 and 3, factor each trinomial.

2. $3x^2 + 5x + 2$ 3. $7y^2 + 22y + 3$

EXAMPLE 2 Factoring $ax^2 + bx + c$, $a \neq 1$, Using Trial and Error

Factor completely: $7x^2 - 18x + 8$

Solution

We list possible ways of representing the first term, $7x^2$. Since 7 is a prime number, we have
$$(7x + \_\_)(x + \_\_)$$
Let's look at the last term, 8, and list its factors:

Factors of 8	
$1 \cdot 8$	$-1 \cdot -8$
$2 \cdot 4$	$-2 \cdot -4$

Now let's concentrate on the middle term, $-18x$. To produce a negative sum, $-18x$, from a positive product, 8, we must have two *negative* factors. So we do not include the factors $1 \cdot 8$ or $2 \cdot 4$ in our trials. Now we list the possible combinations of factors. We also highlight the sum of the "outer" and "inner" products.

Possible Factorization	Product
$(7x - 1)(x - 8)$	$7x^2 - 57x + 8$
$(7x - 8)(x - 1)$	$7x^2 - 15x + 8$
$(7x - 2)(x - 4)$	$7x^2 - 30x + 8$
$(7x - 4)(x - 2)$	$7x^2 - 18x + 8$

We see that $7x^2 - 18x + 8 = (7x - 4)(x - 2)$. ∎

Quick ✔ *In Problems 4 and 5, factor each trinomial completely.*

4. $3x^2 - 13x + 12$ **5.** $5p^2 - 21p + 4$

EXAMPLE 3 Factoring $ax^2 + bx + c$, $a \neq 1$, Using Trial and Error

Factor completely: $10x^2 - 13x - 3$

Solution

We list possible ways of representing the first term, $10x^2$.

$$(10x + \_\_)(x + \_\_)$$
$$(5x + \_\_)(2x + \_\_)$$

The last term, -3, has factors $-1 \cdot 3$ or $1 \cdot -3$.
  We list the possible combinations of factors. We also write the sum of the "outer" and "inner" products in blue ink.

Possible Factorization	Product
$(10x - 1)(x + 3)$	$10x^2 + 29x - 3$
$(10x + 3)(x - 1)$	$10x^2 - 7x - 3$
$(10x - 3)(x + 1)$	$10x^2 + 7x - 3$
$(10x + 1)(x - 3)$	$10x^2 - 29x - 3$
$(5x - 1)(2x + 3)$	$10x^2 + 13x - 3$
$(5x + 3)(2x - 1)$	$10x^2 + x - 3$
$(5x - 3)(2x + 1)$	$10x^2 - x - 3$
$(5x + 1)(2x - 3)$	$10x^2 - 13x - 3$

The row with the correct factorization is highlighted. So
$10x^2 - 13x - 3 = (5x + 1)(2x - 3)$. ∎

Quick ✔ *In Problems 6 and 7, factor each trinomial completely.*

6. $2n^2 - 17n - 9$ **7.** $4w^2 - 5w - 6$

Factoring trinomials of the form $ax^2 + bx + c$, $a \neq 1$ can at first seem overwhelming. There are so many possibilities! Plus, the technique may at first seem haphazard. In fact, however, calling the technique "trial and error" is not quite truth in advertising because some thought is necessary to reduce the list of possible factors. To keep the list of possibilities small, here are some questions you should ask yourself before you begin to factor.

HINTS FOR USING TRIAL AND ERROR TO FACTOR $ax^2 + bx + c$, $a \neq 1$

- Is the constant c positive? If so, then the factors of the constant, c, must be the same sign as the coefficient of the middle term, b. For example,

$$2a^2 + 11a + 5 = (2a + 1)(a + 5)$$
$$2a^2 - 11a + 5 = (2a - 1)(a - 5)$$

- Is the constant c negative? If so, then the factors of c must have opposite signs. For example,

$$10b^2 + 19b - 15 = (5b - 3)(2b + 5)$$
$$10b^2 - 19b - 15 = (5b + 3)(2b - 5)$$

- If $ax^2 + bx + c$ has no common factor, then the binomials in the factored form cannot have common factors either.

- Is the value of b small? If so, then choose factors of a and factors of c that are close to each other. If the value of b is large, then choose factors of a and factors of c that are far from each other.

- Is the value of b correct, but has the wrong sign? Then interchange the signs in the binomial factors.

EXAMPLE 4 Factoring $ax^2 + bx + c$, $a \neq 1$, Using Trial and Error

Factor completely: $18x^2 + 3x - 10$

Solution

Remember, the first step in any factoring problem is to look for common factors. There are no common factors in $18x^2 + 3x - 10$. We list all possible ways of representing $18x^2$.

$$(18x + \underline{\ \ })(x + \underline{\ \ })$$
$$(9x + \underline{\ \ })(2x + \underline{\ \ })$$
$$(6x + \underline{\ \ })(3x + \underline{\ \ })$$

Let's look at the last term, -10, and list its factors:

Factors of -10	
$-10 \cdot 1$	$10 \cdot -1$
$-5 \cdot 2$	$5 \cdot -2$

Before we list the possible combinations of factors, we ask some questions. Is the coefficient of the middle term of the polynomial $18x^2 + 3x - 10$ small? Yes, it is $+3$. Because this middle term is positive and small, the binomial factors we list should have outer and inner products that sum to a positive, small number. Therefore, we will start with $(6x + \underline{\ \ })(3x + \underline{\ \ })$ and the factors $(2)(-5)$ and $(-2)(5)$. We do not use $6x + 2$ or $6x - 2$ as possible factors because there is a common factor of 2 in these binomials and the trinomial to be factored has no common factors.

Let's try $(6x - 5)(3x + 2)$.

$$(6x - 5)(3x + 2) = 18x^2 + 12x - 15x - 10$$
$$= 18x^2 - 3x - 10$$

Close! The only problem is that the middle term has the opposite sign of the one that we want. Therefore, let's flip-flop the signs of -5 and 2 in the binomials and try $(6x + 5)(3x - 2)$.

$$(6x + 5)(3x - 2) = 18x^2 - 12x + 15x - 10$$
$$= 18x^2 + 3x - 10$$

It works! So, $18x^2 + 3x - 10 = (6x + 5)(3x - 2)$.

The moral of the story in Example 4 is that the name *trial and error* is a bit misleading. With some thought, you won't have to choose binomial factors haphazardly "until the cows come home" provided you use the helpful hints given and some care.

Quick ✔

8. When factoring $ax^2 + bx + c$ and b is a small number, choose factors of a and factors of c that are ____ to each other.

In Problems 9 and 10, factor each trinomial completely.

9. $12x^2 + 17x + 6$ **10.** $12y^2 + 32y - 35$

EXAMPLE 5 Factoring Trinomials with Two Variables Using Trial and Error

Factor completely: $48x^2 + 4xy - 30y^2$

Solution

Did you notice that there is a greatest common factor of 2? We first factor out this GCF and obtain the polynomial $2(24x^2 + 2xy - 15y^2)$. The trinomial in parentheses will factor in the form $24x^2 + 2xy - 15y^2 = (\_x + \_y)(\_x + \_y)$.

List all possible ways of representing $24x^2$: $(24x + \_y)(x + \_y)$
$(12x + \_y)(2x + \_y)$
$(8x + \_y)(3x + \_y)$
$(6x + \_y)(4x + \_y)$

We list the factors of the coefficient of the last term, -15:

Factors of -15	
$-15 \cdot 1$	$15 \cdot -1$
$-5 \cdot 3$	$5 \cdot -3$

We do not use $24x + 3y$, $12x + 3y$, $3x + 3y$, or $6x + 3y$ as possible factors because there is a common factor in these binomials, and a common factor does not exist in the trinomial $24x^2 + 2xy - 15y^2$. Also, since the middle term has a small coefficient, we will start with $(6x + \_y)(4x + \_y)$ and the factors $(3)(-5)$ and $(-3)(5)$.
   Let's try $(6x - 5y)(4x + 3y)$.

$$(6x - 5y)(4x + 3y) = 24x^2 - 2xy - 15y^2$$

Close! The only problem is that the middle term has the opposite sign of the one that we want. Therefore, let's flip-flop the signs of -5 and 3 in the binomials and try $(6x + 5y)(4x - 3y)$.

$$(6x + 5y)(4x - 3y) = 24x^2 - 18xy + 20xy - 15y^2$$
$$= 24x^2 + 2xy - 15y^2$$

So, $48x^2 + 4xy - 30y^2 = 2(6x + 5y)(4x - 3y)$.   ■

Quick ✔

11. What is the first step in factoring any polynomial?

In Problems 12 and 13, factor each trinomial completely.

12. $8x^2 - 28x - 60$ **13.** $90x^2 + 21xy - 6y^2$

EXAMPLE 6 Factoring a Trinomial with a Negative Leading Coefficient

Factor: $-14x^2 + 29x + 15$

Solution

While there are no common factors in $-14x^2 + 29x + 15$, notice that the coefficient of the squared term is negative. Factor -1 out of the trinomial to obtain

$$-14x^2 + 29x + 15 = -1(14x^2 - 29x - 15)$$

Now factor the expression in parentheses and obtain

$$\begin{aligned} -14x^2 + 29x + 15 &= -1(14x^2 - 29x - 15) \\ &= -1(7x + 3)(2x - 5) \\ &= -(7x + 3)(2x - 5) \end{aligned}$$

So $-14x^2 + 29x + 15 = -(7x + 3)(2x - 5)$. ∎

Quick ✔

14. *True or False:* The trinomial $12x^2 + 22x + 6$ is completely factored as $(4x + 6)(3x + 1)$.

In Problems 15 and 16, factor each trinomial completely.

15. $-6y^2 + 23y + 4$ **16.** $-6x^2 - 3x + 45$

2 Factor $ax^2 + bx + c$, $a \neq 1$, Using Grouping

We now introduce a second method for factoring trinomials of the form $ax^2 + bx + c$, $a \neq 1$, which uses factoring by grouping, introduced in Section 6.1. The next example illustrates the procedure.

EXAMPLE 7 How to Factor $ax^2 + bx + c$, $a \neq 1$, by Grouping

Factor: $3x^2 + 14x + 15$

Step-by-Step Solution

First, we notice that $3x^2 + 14x + 15$ has no common factors. Comparing $3x^2 + 14x + 15$ to $ax^2 + bx + c$, we find that $a = 3$, $b = 14$, and $c = 15$.

Step 1: Find the value of ac.	The value of $a \cdot c = 3 \cdot 15 = 45$.
Step 2: Find the pair of integers, m and n, whose product is ac and whose sum is b.	We want to determine the integers whose product is 45 and whose sum is 14. Because both 14 and 45 are positive, we only list the positive factors of 45.

Integers Whose Product Is 45	1, 45	3, 15	5, 9
Sum	46	18	14

Step 3: Write $ax^2 + bx + c$ as $ax^2 + mx + nx + c$.	Write $3x^2 + 14x + 15$ as $3x^2 + 9x + 5x + 15$

$$14x = 9x + 5x$$

Step 4: Factor the expression in Step 3 by grouping.	$3x^2 + 9x + 5x + 15 = (3x^2 + 9x) + (5x + 15)$

Common factor in 1st group: $3x$;
common factor in 2nd group: 5: $= 3x(x + 3) + 5(x + 3)$

Factor out $x + 3$: $= (x + 3)(3x + 5)$

Step 5: **Check** Multiply out the factored form.	$\begin{aligned}(x + 3)(3x + 5) &= 3x^2 + 5x + 9x + 15 \\ &= 3x^2 + 14x + 15\end{aligned}$

So $3x^2 + 14x + 15 = (x + 3)(3x + 5)$. ∎

We summarize below the steps used in Example 7.

STEPS TO FACTOR $ax^2 + bx + c$, $a \neq 1$, BY GROUPING: a, b, AND c HAVE NO COMMON FACTORS

Step 1: Find the value of ac.

Step 2: Find the pair of integers, m and n, whose product is ac and whose sum is b.

Step 3: Write $ax^2 + bx + c = ax^2 + mx + nx + c$.

Step 4: Factor the expression in Step 3 by grouping.

Step 5: Check by multiplying the factors.

EXAMPLE 8   Factoring $ax^2 + bx + c$, $a \neq 1$, by Grouping

Factor: $12x^2 - x - 1$

Solution

First, we see that there is no common factor in the expression $12x^2 - x - 1$. Comparing $12x^2 - x - 1$ to $ax^2 + bx + c$, we see that $a = 12$, $b = -1$, and $c = -1$.

The value of $a \cdot c$ is $12(-1) = -12$. We want to determine the integers whose product is -12 and whose sum is -1. Because the product $a \cdot c$ is negative, -12, we know that one integer will be positive and the other negative. Since the value of b is negative ($b = -1$), we know the factor of -12 with the larger absolute value will be negative.

Integers Whose Product Is -12	1, -12	2, -6	3, -4
Sum	-11	-4	-1

The integers whose product is -12 and whose sum is -1 are 3 and -4.

Write $12x^2 - x - 1$ as $12x^2 + 3x - 4x - 1$, and factor by grouping.

$$-x = 3x - 4x$$

$$12x^2 + 3x - 4x - 1 = (12x^2 + 3x) + (-4x - 1)$$

Common factor in 1st group: $3x$;
common factor in 2nd group: -1: $= 3x(4x + 1) - 1(4x + 1)$

Factor out $4x + 1$: $= (4x + 1)(3x - 1)$

Check

$$(4x + 1)(3x - 1) = 12x^2 - 4x + 3x - 1$$
$$= 12x^2 - x - 1$$

So $12x^2 - x - 1 = (4x + 1)(3x - 1)$.   ∎

Work Smart

In Example 8, we could have written $12x^2 - x - 1$ as $12x^2 - 4x + 3x - 1$ and obtained the same result.

Quick ✔

17. When factoring $6x^2 + x - 1$ using grouping, $ac =$ ___ and $b =$ ___ .

18. *True or False:* To factor $2x^2 - 13x + 6$ using grouping, find factors whose product is 6 and sum is -13.

In Problems 19 and 20, factor each trinomial completely.

19. $3x^2 - 2x - 8$ **20.** $10z^2 + 21z + 9$

The advantage of factoring quadratic trinomials of the form $ax^2 + bx + c$, $a \neq 1$, by grouping is that it is algorithmic (that is, step by step). However, if the product $a \cdot c$ gets large, then there are a lot of factors of ac whose sum must be determined. This can get overwhelming. Under these circumstances, it may be better to try trial and error.

EXAMPLE 9 Factoring $ax^2 + bx + c$, $a \neq 1$, by Grouping

Factor: $18x^2 - 33x - 30$

Solution

The first question we ask is, "Is there a greatest common factor in the expression $18x^2 - 33x - 30$?" Yes, there is a GCF of 3, so we first factor out the 3.

$$18x^2 - 33x - 30 = 3(6x^2 - 11x - 10)$$

Now we factor the remaining trinomial, $6x^2 - 11x - 10$, by grouping. We see that $a = 6, b = -11$, and $c = -10$. The value of $a \cdot c = 6(-10) = -60$.

Now, we want to determine the integers whose product is -60 and whose sum is -11.

Integers Whose Product Is −60	1, −60	2, −30	3, −20	4, −15	5, −12	6, −10
Sum	−59	−28	−17	−11	−7	−4

The integers whose product is -60 and whose sum is -11 are 4 and -15.
Write $6x^2 - 11x - 10$ as $6x^2 + 4x - 15x - 10$.

$$-11x = 4x - 15x$$

Now, factor by grouping.

$$6x^2 + 4x - 15x - 10 = (6x^2 + 4x) + (-15x - 10)$$

Common factor in 1st group: $2x$;
common factor in 2nd group: -5: $= 2x(3x + 2) - 5(3x + 2)$
Factor out $3x + 2$: $= (3x + 2)(2x - 5)$

Check

$$3(3x + 2)(2x - 5) = 3(6x^2 - 15x + 4x - 10)$$
$$= 3(6x^2 - 11x - 10)$$
$$= 18x^2 - 33x - 30$$

So, $18x^2 - 33x - 30 = 3(3x + 2)(2x - 5)$.

Quick ✔ *In Problems 21 and 22, factor the trinomial completely.*
21. $24x^2 + 6x - 9$ **22.** $-10n^2 + 17n - 3$

Work Smart

Let's compare the two methods presented in this section, trial and error and factoring by grouping, by factoring $3x^2 + 10x + 8$. The first question to ask is: Is there a GCF? No, there's not, so let's continue.

Trial and Error

Step 1: The coefficient of x^2, 3, is prime, so we list the possibilities for the binomial factors: $(3x + \_)(x + \_)$.

Step 2: The last term, 8, is not prime. Its factors are $(1)(8)$ or $(2)(4)$ or $(-1)(-8)$ or $(-2)(-4)$. Since $c = 8$ is positive and the coefficient of the middle term is also positive, we'll consider only $(1)(8)$ and $(2)(4)$.

Grouping

Step 1: For the polynomial $3x^2 + 10x + 8$, $a = 3$ and $c = 8$; the value of ac is $3 \cdot 8 = 24$.

Step 2: The two integers whose product is $ac = 24$ and whose sum is $b = 10$ are 6 and 4.

Step 3: Rewrite $3x^2 + 10x + 8$ as $3x^2 + 10x + 8 = 3x^2 + 6x + 4x + 8$.

	Trial and Error		**Grouping**

Step 3: The coefficient of the middle term is not large, so let's start by trying $(3x + 4)(x + 2)$.

$(3x + 4)(x + 2) = 3x^2 + 10x + 8$

It works! Therefore,
$3x^2 + 10x + 8 = (3x + 4)(x + 2)$.

Step 4: Factor the expression
$3x^2 + 6x + 4x + 8$ by grouping.
$3x^2 + 6x + 4x + 8$
$= 3x(x + 2) + 4(x + 2)$
$= (x + 2)(3x + 4)$
So $3x^2 + 10x + 8 = (x + 2)(3x + 4)$.

Because $(3x + 4)(x + 2) = (x + 2)(3x + 4)$, we see that both methods give the same result. Which method do you prefer?

6.3 EXERCISES

PRACTICE   WATCH   DOWNLOAD   READ   REVIEW

1–22. are the Quick ✓s that follow each EXAMPLE

Building Skills

In Problems 23–46, factor each polynomial completely using the trial and error method. Hint: None of the polynomials is prime. See Objective 1.

23. $2x^2 + 5x + 3$

24. $3x^2 + 16x + 5$

25. $5n^2 + 7n + 2$

26. $7z^2 + 22z + 3$

27. $5y^2 + 2y - 3$

28. $11z^2 + 32z - 3$

29. $-4p^2 + 11p + 3$

30. $-6w^2 + 11w + 2$

31. $5w^2 + 13w - 6$

32. $3x^2 + 16x - 12$

33. $7t^2 + 37t + 10$

34. $5x^2 + 16x + 3$

35. $6n^2 - 17n + 10$

36. $11p^2 - 46p + 8$

37. $2 - 11x + 5x^2$

38. $4 - 17x + 4x^2$

39. $2x^2 + 3xy + y^2$

40. $3x^2 + 7xy + 2y^2$

41. $2m^2 - 3mn - 2n^2$

42. $3y^2 + 7yz - 6z^2$

43. $6x^2 + 2xy - 4y^2$

44. $6x^2 - 14xy - 12y^2$

45. $-2x^2 - 7x + 15$

46. $-6x^2 - 3x + 45$

In Problems 47–70, factor each polynomial completely using the grouping method. Hint: None of the polynomials is prime. See Objective 2.

47. $2x^2 + 13x + 15$

48. $3x^2 + 22x + 7$

49. $5w^2 + 13w - 6$

50. $7n^2 - 27n - 4$

51. $4w^2 - 8w - 5$

52. $4x^2 + 4x - 3$

53. $27z^2 + 3z - 2$

54. $25t^2 + 5t - 2$

55. $6y^2 - 5y - 6$

56. $20t^2 + 21t + 4$

57. $4m^2 + 8m - 5$

58. $6m^2 - 5m - 4$

59. $12n^2 + 19n + 5$

60. $12p^2 - 23p + 5$

61. $-5 - 9x + 18x^2$

62. $-4 - 3x + 10x^2$

63. $12x^2 + 2xy - 4y^2$

64. $18x^2 + 6xy - 4y^2$

65. $8x^2 + 28x + 12$

66. $30m^2 - 85m + 60$

67. $7x - 5 + 6x^2$

68. $15 + 8x - 12x^2$

69. $-8p^2 + 6p + 9$

70. $-10y^2 + 47y + 15$

Mixed Practice

In Problems 71–96, factor completely. If a polynomial cannot be factored, say it is prime.

71. $15x^2 - 23x + 4$ **72.** $12x^3 - 11x^2 - 15x$

73. $-13y + 12 - 4y^2$ **74.** $2x + 12x^2 - 24$

75. $10x^2 - 8xy - 24y^2$ **76.** $12n^2 + 7n - 10$

77. $8 - 18x + 9x^2$ **78.** $18x^2 + 88x - 10$

79. $-12x + 9 - 24x^2$ **80.** $-24z^2 + 18z + 2$

81. $4x^3y^2 - 8x^2y^3 - 4x^2y^2$ **82.** $9x^3y + 6x^2y + 3xy$

83. $4m^2 + 13mn + 3n^2$ **84.** $4m^2 - 19mn + 12n^2$

85. $6x^2 - 17x - 12$ **86.** $8x^2 + 14x - 7$

87. $48xy + 24x^2 - 30y^2$ **88.** $-20y^2 + 6x^2 + 7xy$

89. $18m^2 + 39mn - 24n^2$ **90.** $63y^3 + 60xy^3 + 12x^2y^3$

91. $-6x^3 + 10x^2 - 4x^4$ **92.** $21n^2 - 18n^3 + 9n$

93. $30x + 22x^2 - 24x^3$ **94.** $48x - 74x^2 + 28x^3$

95. $6x^2(x^2 + 1) - 25x(x^2 + 1) + 14(x^2 + 1)$

96. $10x^2(x - 1) - x(x - 1) - 2(x - 1)$

Applying the Concepts

△ **97. Area of a Triangle** A triangle has area described by the polynomial $\left(3x^2 + \dfrac{13}{2}x - 14\right)$ square meters. Find the base and height of the triangle. *Hint:* Factor out $\dfrac{1}{2}$ as a common factor.

△ **98. Area of a Rectangle** A rectangle has area described by the polynomial $6x^2 + x - 1$ square centimeters. Find the length and width of the rectangle.

99. Suppose that we know one factor of $6x^2 - 11x - 10$ is $3x + 2$. What is the other factor?

100. Suppose that we know one factor of $8x^2 + 22x - 21$ is $2x + 7$. What is the other factor?

Extending the Concepts

In Problems 101–104, factor completely.

101. $27z^4 + 42z^2 + 16$ **102.** $15n^6 + 7n^3 - 2$

103. $3x^{2n} + 19x^n + 6$ **104.** $2x^{2n} - 3x^n - 5$

In Problems 105 and 106, find all possible integer values of b so that the polynomial is factorable.

105. $3x^2 + bx - 5$ **106.** $6x^2 + bx + 7$

Explaining the Concepts

107. Describe when you would use trial and error and when you would use grouping to factor a trinomial. Make up two examples that demonstrate your reasoning.

108. How can you tell if a trinomial is not factorable? Make up an example to demonstrate your reasoning.

6.4 Factoring Special Products

OBJECTIVES

1. Factor Perfect Square Trinomials
2. Factor the Difference of Two Squares
3. Factor the Sum or Difference of Two Cubes

Preparing for Factoring Special Products

Before getting started, take the following readiness quiz. If you get a problem wrong, go back to the section cited and review the material.

P1. Evaluate: 5^2 [Section 1.7, pp. 59–60]

P2. Evaluate: $(-2)^3$ [Section 1.7, pp. 59–60]

P3. Find the product: $(5p^2)^3$ [Section 5.2, pp. 328–329]

P4. Find the product: $(3z + 2)^2$ [Section 5.3, pp. 336–337]

P5. Find the product: $(4m + 5)(4m - 5)$ [Section 5.3, pp. 335–336]

Preparing for...Answers **P1.** 25
P2. -8 **P3.** $125p^6$ **P4.** $9z^2 + 12z + 4$
P5. $16m^2 - 25$

In Section 5.3, we presented three binomial products that were "special products" that occur when we multiply two binomials. We briefly review two of them here.

Pattern	Product	Example
Squaring a binomial	$(A + B)^2 = A^2 + 2AB + B^2$	$(3a + 5)^2 = (3a)^2 + 2(3a)(5) + 5^2$
		$= 9a^2 + 30a + 25$
	$(A - B)^2 = A^2 - 2AB + B^2$	$(2p - 3)^2 = (2p)^2 - 2(2p)(3) + 3^2$
		$= 4p^2 - 12p + 9$
Product of the sum and difference of two terms	$(A + B)(A - B) = A^2 - B^2$	$(4z + 7)(4z - 7) = (4z)^2 - 7^2$
		$= 16z^2 - 49$

Recall that $A^2 + 2AB + B^2$ and $A^2 - 2AB + B^2$ are called perfect square trinomials. We call $A^2 - B^2$ the difference of two squares.

In this section, we look at polynomials that can be categorized as having "special formulas" for factoring. Why would we want to learn a method for factoring using "special formulas"? If you recognize a polynomial as a perfect square trinomial or the difference of two squares, you'll be able to factor it quickly without using trial and error or the grouping method.

We begin with factoring perfect square trinomials.

1   Factor Perfect Square Trinomials

When we use the formulas $(A + B)^2 = A^2 + 2AB + B^2$ and $(A - B)^2 = A^2 - 2AB + B^2$ in reverse, we obtain a method for factoring perfect square trinomials.

In Words

A perfect square trinomial is a trinomial in which the first term and the third term are perfect squares and the second term is either 2 times or −2 times the product of the expressions being squared in the first and third terms.

Work Smart

The first five perfect squares are 1, 4, 9, 16, and 25.

PERFECT SQUARE TRINOMIALS

$$A^2 + 2AB + B^2 = (A + B)^2$$
$$A^2 - 2AB + B^2 = (A - B)^2$$

Perfect square trinomials can be factored quickly when they are recognized. For a polynomial to be a perfect square trinomial, two conditions must be satisfied.

1. The first and last terms must be perfect squares. Any variable raised to an even exponent is a perfect square. So, x^2, $x^4 = (x^2)^2$, $x^6 = (x^3)^2$ are all perfect squares. Examples of perfect squares are

49	because	$7^2 = 49$
121	because	$11^2 = 121$
$9x^2$	because	$(3x)^2 = 9x^2$
$25a^4$	because	$(5a^2)^2 = 25a^4$

2. The "middle term" must equal 2 times or −2 times the product of the expressions being squared in the first and last term.

Let's look at an example.

EXAMPLE 1   How to Factor Perfect Square Trinomials

Factor completely: $z^2 + 6z + 9$

Step-by-Step Solution

Step 1: Determine whether the first term and the third term are perfect squares.	The first term, z^2, is the square of z and the third term, 9, is the square of 3.
Step 2: Determine whether the middle term is 2 times or −2 times the product of the expressions being squared in the first and last term.	The middle term, $6z$, is 2 times the product of z and 3.

(continued)

Step 3: Use $A^2 + 2AB + B^2 = (A + B)^2$ to factor the expression.

$$A^2 + 2 \cdot A \cdot B + B^2$$
$$\downarrow \quad \downarrow \downarrow \quad \downarrow$$
$$z^2 + 6z + 9 = z^2 + 2 \cdot z \cdot 3 + 3^2$$
Factor as $(A + B)^2$ with $A = z$ and $B = 3$: $= (z + 3)^2$

Step 4: Check

$$(z + 3)^2 = (z + 3)(z + 3)$$
$$= z^2 + 3z + 3z + 9$$
$$= z^2 + 6z + 9$$

So $z^2 + 6z + 9 = (z + 3)^2$. ∎

EXAMPLE 2 Factoring Perfect Square Trinomials

Factor completely:

(a) $4x^2 - 20x + 25$ **(b)** $9x^2 + 42xy + 49y^2$

Solution

(a) The first term, $4x^2$, is the square of $2x$, and the third term, 25, is the square of 5. The middle term, $-20x$, is -2 times the product of $2x$ and 5. We use $A^2 - 2AB + B^2 = (A - B)^2$ to factor the expression.

$$A^2 \quad -2 \cdot A \cdot B \ + B^2$$
$$\downarrow \qquad \downarrow \ \downarrow \ \downarrow$$
$$4x^2 - 20x + 25 = (2x)^2 - 2 \cdot 2x \cdot 5 + (5)^2$$
$$= (2x - 5)^2$$

Therefore, $4x^2 - 20x + 25 = (2x - 5)^2$. We leave the check to you.

(b) The first term, $9x^2$, is the square of $3x$, and the third term, $49y^2$, is the square of $7y$. The middle term, $42xy$, is 2 times the product of $3x$ and $7y$. We factor as $A^2 + 2AB + B^2 = (A + B)^2$.

$$A^2 \ + 2 \cdot A \ \cdot B \ + \ B^2$$
$$\downarrow \qquad \downarrow \ \downarrow \qquad \downarrow$$
$$9x^2 + 42xy + 49y^2 = (3x)^2 + 2 \cdot 3x \cdot 7y + (7y)^2$$
$$= (3x + 7y)^2$$

So, $9x^2 + 42xy + 49y^2 = (3x + 7y)^2$. We leave the check to you. ∎

Quick ✔

1. The expression $A^2 + 2AB + B^2$ is called a _____ _____ _____.

2. $A^2 - 2AB + B^2 =$ _____.

In Problems 3–5, factor each trinomial completely.

3. $x^2 - 12x + 36$ **4.** $16x^2 + 40x + 25$ **5.** $9a^2 - 60ab + 100b^2$

EXAMPLE 3 Factoring a Trinomial

Factor completely, if possible: $b^2 - 10b + 36$

Solution

The first term, b^2, is the square of b. The third term, 36, is the square of 6. Is the middle term, $-10b$, -2 times the product of the expressions being squared in the first and last term?

$$-2(b)(6) = -12b \neq -10b.$$

So $b^2 - 10b + 36$ is not a perfect square trinomial. Can we factor $b^2 - 10b + 36$ using another strategy? The trinomial $b^2 - 10b + 36$ is in the form $x^2 + bx + c$, so we need two integers whose product is 36 and whose sum is -10. We choose negative factors of 36, since the coefficient of the middle term is negative. The possibilities are $(-1)(-36), (-2)(-18), (-3)(-12),$ or $(-9)(-4)$. None of these factors sum to -10. We conclude that $b^2 - 10b + 36$ is prime. ∎

Quick ✔ *In Problems 6–8, factor each trinomial completely, if possible.*

6. $z^2 - 8z + 16$ **7.** $4n^2 + 12n + 9$ **8.** $y^2 + 13y + 35$

EXAMPLE 4 Factoring a Perfect Square Trinomial Having a GCF

Factor completely: $32m^4 - 48m^2 + 18$

Solution

Do you remember the first step in any factoring problem? It is to look for the GCF. Notice there is a common factor of 2 in the trinomial, so we factor it out.

$$32m^4 - 48m^2 + 18 = 2(16m^4 - 24m^2 + 9)$$

Work Smart

m^4 is a square because $m^4 = (m^2)^2$.

We now examine the trinomial $16m^4 - 24m^2 + 9$. The first term, $16m^4$, is the square of $4m^2$. The third term, 9, is the square of 3. The middle term, $-24m^2$, is -2 times the product of $4m^2$ and 3.

$$
\begin{array}{ccccc}
 & A^2 & -2 \cdot A \cdot B & + B^2 & \\
 & \downarrow & \downarrow\ \downarrow\ \downarrow & & \\
16m^4 - 24m^2 + 9 = & (4m^2)^2 & -2 \cdot 4m^2 \cdot 3 & + 3^2 & \\
\text{Factor as } (A-B)^2: & = & (4m^2 - 3)^2 &
\end{array}
$$

Work Smart

Don't forget the GCF that was factored out in the first step.

Therefore,

$$
\begin{aligned}
32m^4 - 48m^2 + 18 &= 2(16m^4 - 24m^2 + 9) \\
&= 2(4m^2 - 3)^2
\end{aligned}
$$
∎

We leave the check to you.

Quick ✔

9. The first thing we look for when factoring a trinomial is the ____ ____ ____.

In Problems 10 and 11, factor each trinomial completely.

10. $4z^2 + 24z + 36$ **11.** $50a^3 + 80a^2 + 32a$

Perfect square trinomials can also be factored using trial and error or grouping, but if you recognize the perfect square pattern, you won't have to use either of these approaches.

In Words

The difference of two squares is just that! A perfect square minus a perfect square. This pattern is easy to recognize: Just look for two squares that have been subtracted.

2 Factor the Difference of Two Squares

Do you recall finding products such as $(x + 2y)(x - 2y)$ in Chapter 5? We found that $(x + 2y)(x - 2y) = x^2 - (2y)^2 = x^2 - 4y^2$. In general,

$$(A - B)(A + B) = A^2 - B^2$$

We will now reverse the multiplication process and find the factors of the difference of two squares.

DIFFERENCE OF TWO SQUARES

$$A^2 - B^2 = (A - B)(A + B)$$

EXAMPLE 5 Factoring the Difference of Two Squares

Factor completely:

(a) $n^2 - 81$ (b) $16x^2 - 9y^2$

Solution

(a) We notice that $n^2 - 81$ is the difference of two squares, n^2 and $81 = 9^2$. So

$$\overset{\overset{\textstyle A^2 \quad - \quad B^2}{\downarrow \qquad \downarrow}}{n^2 - 81 = (n)^2 - (9)^2}$$
$$A^2 - B^2 = (A - B)(A + B): \quad = (n - 9)(n + 9)$$

> **Work Smart**
>
> Remember that the Commutative Property of Multiplication tells us that the order of the factors in the answer doesn't matter:
>
> $(a - b)(a + b) = (a + b)(a - b)$

You can check the answer to any of these differences of two squares by using FOIL. To check Example 5(a),

Check $(n - 9)(n + 9) = n^2 + 9n - 9n - 81$
$$= n^2 - 81$$

Our answer checks, so $n^2 - 81 = (n - 9)(n + 9)$.

(b) We notice that $16x^2 - 9y^2$ is the difference of two squares, $16x^2 = (4x)^2$ and $9y^2 = (3y)^2$. So

$$\overset{\overset{\textstyle A^2 \quad - \quad B^2}{\downarrow \qquad \downarrow}}{16x^2 - 9y^2 = (4x)^2 - (3y)^2}$$
$$A^2 - B^2 = (A - B)(A + B): \quad = (4x - 3y)(4x + 3y)$$

Check $(4x - 3y)(4x + 3y) = 16x^2 + 12xy - 12xy - 9y^2$
$$= 16x^2 - 9y^2$$

Our answer checks, so $16x^2 - 9y^2 = (4x - 3y)(4x + 3y)$.   ■

Quick ✔

12. $4m^2 - 81n^2$ is called the _____ of _____ and factors into two binomials.

13. $P^2 - Q^2 = ($ _____ $)($ _____ $)$

In Problems 14–16, factor completely.

14. $z^2 - 25$ **15.** $81m^2 - 16n^2$ **16.** $16a^2 - \dfrac{4}{9}b^2$

For the remainder of the examples in the section, we will leave the check of the factorization to you.

EXAMPLE 6 Factoring the Difference of Two Squares

Factor completely:

(a) $49k^4 - 100$ (b) $p^4 - 1$

Solution

(a) Because $49k^4 = (7k^2)^2$ and $100 = 10^2$, we have the difference of two squares. So

$$\overset{\overset{\textstyle A^2 \quad - \quad B^2}{\downarrow \qquad \downarrow}}{49k^4 - 100 = (7k^2)^2 - 10^2}$$
$$A^2 - B^2 = (A - B)(A + B): \quad = (7k^2 - 10)(7k^2 + 10)$$

So, $49k^4 - 100 = (7k^2 - 10)(7k^2 + 10)$.

(b) The expressions p^4 and 1 are both perfect squares. $p^4 = (p^2)^2$ and $1 = 1^2$. So

$$\overset{\overset{\textstyle A^2 \quad - \quad B^2}{\downarrow \qquad \downarrow}}{p^4 - 1 = (p^2)^2 - 1^2}$$
$$A^2 - B^2 = (A - B)(A + B): \quad = (p^2 - 1)(p^2 + 1)$$

But $p^2 - 1$ is a difference of two squares! So we factor again:

$$= (p - 1)(p + 1)(p^2 + 1)$$

So $p^4 - 1 = (p - 1)(p + 1)(p^2 + 1)$.   ∎

You may be asking yourself, "What about the sum of two squares—how does it factor?" The answer is that if a and b are real numbers, **the sum of two squares, $a^2 + b^2$, is prime and does not factor.** So, if a variable represents a real number, binomials such as $a^2 + 1$ or $4y^2 + 81$ are prime.

Quick ✔

17. *True or False:* $x^2 + 9$ is prime.

In Problems 18 and 19, factor each polynomial completely.

18. $100k^4 - 81w^2$ **19.** $x^4 - 16$

EXAMPLE 7   Factoring the Difference of Two Squares Containing a GCF

Factor completely: $50x^2 - 72y^2$

Solution

What's the first thing we look for when we factor? A greatest common factor! The GCF of 50 and 72 is 2, so we first factor out the GCF:

$$50x^2 - 72y^2 = 2(25x^2 - 36y^2)$$

Difference of two squares with $A = 5x$ and $B = 6y$: $= 2[(5x)^2 - (6y)^2]$

Factor as $(A - B)(A + B)$: $= 2(5x - 6y)(5x + 6y)$

So, $50x^2 - 72y^2 = 2(5x - 6y)(5x + 6y)$.   ∎

Quick ✔

20. *True or False:* $4x^2 - 16y^2$ factors completely as $(2x - 4y)(2x + 4y)$.

In Problems 21 and 22, factor each polynomial completely.

21. $147x^2 - 48$ **22.** $-27a^3b + 75ab^3$

3   Factor the Sum or Difference of Two Cubes

Consider the following products:

$$(A + B)(A^2 - AB + B^2) = A^3 - A^2B + AB^2 + A^2B - AB^2 + B^3$$
$$= A^3 + B^3$$
$$(A - B)(A^2 + AB + B^2) = A^3 + A^2B + AB^2 - A^2B - AB^2 - B^3$$
$$= A^3 - B^3$$

These products show us that we can factor the sum or difference of two cubes as follows:

THE SUM OF TWO CUBES

$$A^3 + B^3 = (A + B)(A^2 - AB + B^2)$$

THE DIFFERENCE OF TWO CUBES

$$A^3 - B^3 = (A - B)(A^2 + AB + B^2)$$

Notice in the formulas that the sign between the cubes matches the sign in the first set of parentheses and that the sign in the middle of the trinomial factor must be opposite the sign between the cubes. Also remember that the perfect cubes are $1^3 = 1, 2^3 = 8, 3^3 = 27$, and so on. Any variable raised to a multiple of 3 is a perfect cube. So $x^3, x^6 = (x^2)^3, x^9 = (x^3)^3$, and so on, are all perfect cubes.

EXAMPLE 8 **Factoring the Sum or Difference of Two Cubes**

Factor completely: $x^3 - 8$

Solution

We notice that we have the difference of two cubes, x^3 and $8 = 2^3$. We let $A = x$ and $B = 2$ in the factoring formula for the difference of two cubes.

$$A^3 - B^3 = (A - B)(A^2 + AB + B^2)$$

$$x^3 - 8 = x^3 - 2^3 = (x - 2)(x^2 + x(2) + 2^2)$$
$$= (x - 2)(x^2 + 2x + 4)$$

So $x^3 - 8 = (x - 2)(x^2 + 2x + 4)$. ∎

EXAMPLE 9 **Factoring the Sum or Difference of Two Cubes**

Factor completely: $8m^3 + 125n^6$

Solution

Because $8m^3 = (2m)^3$ and $125n^6 = (5n^2)^3$, the expression $8m^3 + 125n^6$ is the sum of two cubes. We let $A = 2m$ and $B = 5n^2$ in the factoring formula for the sum of two cubes.

$$8m^3 + 125n^6 = (2m)^3 + (5n^2)^3$$
$$= (2m + 5n^2)[(2m)^2 - (2m)(5n^2) + (5n^2)^2]$$
$$= (2m + 5n^2)(4m^2 - 10mn^2 + 25n^4)$$

So $8m^3 + 125n^6 = (2m + 5n^2)(4m^2 - 10mn^2 + 25n^4)$. ∎

Quick ✔

23. The binomial $27x^3 + 64y^3$ is called the ___ of ___ ___.
24. *True or False:* $(x - 1)(x^2 - x + 1)$ can be factored further.

In Problems 25 and 26, factor each polynomial completely.
25. $z^3 + 125$ **26.** $8p^3 - 27q^6$

EXAMPLE 10 **Factoring the Sum or Difference of Two Cubes Having a GCF**

Factor completely: $250x^4 + 54x$

Solution

Remember, the first step in any factoring problem is to look for a common factor. Here, we have a common factor of $2x$.

$$250x^4 + 54x = 2x(125x^3 + 27)$$
$$(5x)^3 = 125x^3 \text{ and } 3^3 = 27: \quad = 2x[(5x)^3 + 3^3]$$
$$= 2x(5x + 3)(25x^2 - 15x + 9)$$

So $250x^4 + 54x = 2x(5x + 3)(25x^2 - 15x + 9)$. ∎

Quick ✔ *In Problems 27 and 28, factor each polynomial completely.*
27. $54a - 16a^4$ **28.** $-375b^3 + 3$

6.4 EXERCISES

PRACTICE   WATCH   DOWNLOAD   READ   REVIEW

1–28. *are the* Quick ✔s *that follow each* EXAMPLE

Building Skills

In Problems 29–38, factor each perfect square trinomial completely. See Objective 1.

29. $x^2 + 10x + 25$

30. $m^2 + 12m + 36$

31. $4p^2 - 4p + 1$

32. $9a^2 - 12a + 4$

● 33. $16x^2 + 24x + 9$

34. $16y^2 - 72y + 81$

35. $x^2 - 4xy + 4y^2$

36. $4a^2 + 20ab + 25b^2$

37. $4z^2 - 12z + 9$

38. $25k^2 - 70k + 49$

In Problems 39–48, factor each difference of two squares completely. See Objective 2.

39. $16x^2 - 49y^2$

40. $36m^2 - 25n^2$

● 41. $4x^2 - 25$

42. $25m^2 - 9$

43. $100n^8 - 81p^4$

44. $36s^6 - 49t^4$

45. $k^8 - 256$

46. $a^4 - 16$

47. $25p^4 - 49q^2$

48. $36b^4 - 121a^2$

In Problems 49–58, factor each sum or difference of two cubes completely. See Objective 3.

● 49. $27 + x^3$

50. $8v^3 + 1$

51. $8x^3 - 27y^3$

52. $64r^3 - 125s^3$

● 53. $x^6 - 8y^3$

54. $m^9 - 27n^6$

55. $27c^3 + 64d^9$

56. $125y^3 + 27z^6$

57. $16x^3 + 250y^3$

58. $40x^3 + 135y^6$

Mixed Practice

In Problems 59–94, factor completely. If the polynomial is prime, state so.

59. $16m^2 + 40mn + 25n^2$

60. $25p^2q^2 - 80pq + 64$

61. $18 - 12x + 2x^2$

62. $50 + 20x + 2x^2$

63. $48a^3 + 72a^2 + 27a$

64. $12n^3 - 36n^2 + 27n$

65. $2x^3 + 10x^2 + 16x$

66. $-5y^3 + 20y^2 - 80y$

67. $x^4y^2 - x^2y^4$

68. $16a^2b^2 - 25a^4b^2$

69. $x^8 - 25y^{10}$

70. $32a^3 + 4b^6$

71. $2t^4 - 54t$

72. $16x^5 - 54x^2$

73. $3s^7 + 24s$

74. $4x - 4x^3$

75. $2x^5 - 162x$

76. $48z^4 - 3$

77. $x^3y - xy^3$

78. $x^4 - 225x^2$

79. $x^3y^3 + 1$

80. $8r^3s^3 + t^3$

81. $3n^2 + 14n + 36$

82. $12m^2 - 14m + 21$

83. $2x^2 - 8x + 8$

84. $3x^2 + 18x + 27$

85. $9x^2 + y^2$

86. $16a^2 + 49b^2$

87. $x^4y^3 + 216xy^3$

88. $54b^5 - 16b^2$

89. $48n^4 - 24n^3 + 3n^2$

90. $18x^2 - 24x^3 + 8x^4$

91. $2x(x^2 - 4) + 5(x^2 - 4)$

92. $4z(z^2 - 9) + 3(z^2 - 9)$

93. $2y^3 + 5y^2 - 32y - 80$

94. $m^3 + 2m^2 - 25m - 50$

Applying the Concepts

△**95.** **Area of a Square** The area of a square is given by the polynomial $(4x^2 + 20x + 25)$ square meters. What is an algebraic expression for the length of one side of the square?

△**96.** **Area of a Square** The area of a square is given by the polynomial $(9x^2 - 6x + 1)$ square feet. What is an algebraic expression for the length of one side of the square?

Extending the Concepts

In Problems 97–106, factor completely and then simplify, if possible.

97. $(x - 2)^2 - (x + 1)^2$

98. $(m - p)^2 - (m + p)^2$

99. $(x - y)^3 + y^3$

100. $(z + 1)^3 - z^6$

101. $(x + 1)^2 - 9$

102. $(x + 3)^2 - 25$

103. $2a^2(x + 1) - 17a(x + 1) + 30(x + 1)$

104. $25a^2(x - 1)^2 - 5a(x - 1)^2 - 2(x - 1)^2$

105. $5(x + 2)^2 - 7(x + 2) - 6$

106. $9(2a + b)^2 + 6(2a + b) - 8$

Explaining the Concepts

107. Create a list of steps for factoring the sum or difference of two cubes.

108. Explain why the polynomial $4x^2 - 9$ is factorable, but the polynomial $4x^2 + 9$ is prime.

109. Explain the error in factoring the polynomial $x^3 + y^3$ as the product $(x + y)(x^2 - xy + y^2) = (x + y)(x - y)^2$.

110. Factor $x^6 - 1$ first as a difference of two squares and then as a difference of two cubes. Are the factors the same? Explain your results.

6.5 Summary of Factoring Techniques

OBJECTIVE

1 Factor Polynomials Completely

1 Factor Polynomials Completely

We have one objective in this section—to put together all the various factoring techniques we have discussed in Sections 6.1–6.4. Recall that we say that a polynomial is factored completely if each factor in the final factorization is prime. Here we present guidelines for factoring any polynomial.

STEPS FOR FACTORING

Step 1: Is there a greatest common factor? If so, factor out the greatest common factor (GCF).

Step 2: Count the number of terms.

Step 3: (a) 2 terms (Binomials)

- Is it the difference of two squares? If so,

$$A^2 - B^2 = (A - B)(A + B)$$

- Is it the sum of two squares? If so, stop! The expression is prime.
- Is it the difference of two cubes? If so,

$$A^3 - B^3 = (A - B)(A^2 + AB + B^2)$$

- Is it the sum of two cubes? If so,

$$A^3 + B^3 = (A + B)(A^2 - AB + B^2)$$

(b) 3 terms (Trinomials)

- Is it a perfect square trinomial? If so,

$$A^2 + 2AB + B^2 = (A + B)^2 \quad \text{or} \quad A^2 - 2AB + B^2 = (A - B)^2$$

- Is the coefficient of the squared term 1? If so,

$$x^2 + bx + c = (x + m)(x + n) \text{ where } mn = c \text{ and } m + n = b$$

- Is the coefficient of the squared term different from 1? If so, factor using trial and error or grouping.

(c) 4 terms

- Use factoring by grouping.

Step 4: Check your work by multiplying out the factors.

EXAMPLE 1   How to Factor Completely

Factor completely: $2x^2 - 4x - 48$

Step-by-Step Solution

Step 1: Is there a GCF?	Yes. We factor out the GCF, 2. $$2x^2 - 4x - 48 = 2(x^2 - 2x - 24)$$
Step 2: Identify the number of terms in the polynomial in parentheses.	This polynomial has three terms in parentheses.
Step 3: We concentrate on the trinomial in parentheses, $x^2 - 2x - 24$. It is not a perfect square trinomial. The leading coefficient is 1, so we try $(x + m)(x + n)$, where $mn = c$ and $m + n = b$.	We need to find two factors of -24 whose sum is -2. Since $-6(4) = -24$ and $-6 + 4 = -2$, we have that $m = -6$ and $n = 4$. $$2(x^2 - 2x - 24) = 2(x - 6)(x + 4)$$
Step 4: Check	Multiply: $2(x - 6)(x + 4) = 2(x^2 + 4x - 6x - 24)$ $= 2(x^2 - 2x - 24)$ Distribute: $= 2x^2 - 4x - 48$

So, $2x^2 - 4x - 48 = 2(x - 6)(x + 4)$.   ∎

Quick ✔

1. The first step in any factoring problem is to look for the _____ _____.

In Problems 2 and 3, factor each polynomial completely.

2. $2p^2 + 8p - 90$ **3.** $-45x^2 + 3xy + 6y^2$

EXAMPLE 2   How to Factor Completely

Factor completely: $25p^2 - 9q^2$

Step-by-Step Solution

Step 1: Is there a GCF?	There is no GCF.
Step 2: Identify the number of terms in the polynomial.	There are two terms.
Step 3: Because the first term, $25p^2 = (5p)^2$, and the second term, $9q^2 = (3q)^2$, are both perfect squares, we have the difference of two squares.	$25p^2 - 9q^2 = ((5p)^2 - (3q)^2)$ $A^2 - B^2 = (A - B)(A + B):\ = (5p - 3q)(5p + 3q)$
Step 4: Check	Multiply: $(5p - 3q)(5p + 3q) = 25p^2 + 15pq - 15pq - 9q^2$ Combine like terms: $= 25p^2 - 9q^2$

So, $25p^2 - 9q^2 = (5p - 3q)(5p + 3q)$.   ∎

Quick ✔ *In Problems 4 and 5, factor each polynomial completely.*

4. $100x^2 - 81y^2$ **5.** $2ab^2 - 242a$

EXAMPLE 3 How to Factor Completely

Factor completely: $12x^2 + 36xy + 27y^2$

Step-by-Step Solution

Step 1: We notice that the coefficients 12, 36, and 27 are all multiples of 3, so we factor out the GCF of 3.	$12x^2 + 36xy + 27y^2 = 3(4x^2 + 12xy + 9y^2)$
Step 2: Identify the number of terms in the polynomial in parentheses.	There are three terms in the polynomial in parentheses.
Step 3: We concentrate on the polynomial in parentheses. Is it a perfect square trinomial? The first term is a perfect square, $4x^2 = (2x)^2$. The third term is also a perfect square, $9y^2 = (3y)^2$. The middle term is 2 times the product of $2x$ and $3y$. The polynomial in parentheses is a perfect square trinomial.	$3(4x^2 + 12xy + 9y^2) = 3[(2x)^2 + 2(2x)(3y) + (3y)^2]$ $A^2 + 2AB + B^2 = (A + B)^2: \; = 3(2x + 3y)^2$
Step 4: Check	Multiply: $\begin{aligned} 3(2x + 3y)^2 &= 3(2x + 3y)(2x + 3y) \\ &= 3(4x^2 + 6xy + 6xy + 9y^2) \\ &= 3(4x^2 + 12xy + 9y^2) \\ &= 12x^2 + 36xy + 27y^2 \end{aligned}$

So, $12x^2 + 36xy + 27y^2 = 3(2x + 3y)^2$. ■

Quick ✔ *In Problems 6 and 7, factor each polynomial completely.*
6. $p^2 - 12pq + 36q^2$ **7.** $75x^2 + 90x + 27$

EXAMPLE 4 Factoring Completely

Factor completely: $16m^3 + 54$

Solution

Notice that there is a greatest common factor of 2. Let's factor it out. The polynomial in the parentheses has two terms.

$$16m^3 + 54 = 2(8m^3 + 27)$$

Sum of two cubes with $A = 2m$ and $B = 3$: $= 2[(2m)^3 + 3^3]$

$A^3 + B^3 = (A + B)(A^2 - AB + B^2)$: $= 2[(2m + 3)((2m)^2 - (2m)(3) + (3)^2)]$

$$= 2(2m + 3)(4m^2 - 6m + 9)$$

Check $\begin{aligned} 2(2m + 3)(4m^2 - 6m + 9) &= 2[8m^3 - 12m^2 + 18m + 12m^2 - 18m + 27] \\ &= 2[8m^3 + 27] \\ &= 16m^3 + 54 \end{aligned}$

So, $16m^3 + 54 = 2(2m + 3)(4m^2 - 6m + 9)$. ■

Quick ✔ *In Problems 8 and 9, factor each polynomial completely.*
8. $125y^3 - 64$ **9.** $-24a^3 + 3b^3$

EXAMPLE 5 Factoring Completely

Factor completely: $-5x^5 + 80x$

Solution

We know that the first thing to look for is a greatest common factor. Because the leading coefficient is negative we factor out a negative as part of the GCF. The GCF is $-5x$.

$$-5x^5 + 80x = -5x(x^4 - 16)$$

Work Smart

Check each factor to determine if any factor can be factored again.

There are two terms in the factor in parentheses. The terms x^4 and 16 are perfect squares since $x^4 = (x^2)^2$ and $16 = 4^2$. So $x^4 - 16$ is a difference of two squares with $A = x^2$ and $B = 4$.

$$-5x(x^4 - 16) = -5x(x^2 - 4)(x^2 + 4).$$

Difference of two squares with $A = x$ and $B = 2$: $= -5x(x - 2)(x + 2)(x^2 + 4)$

Check $\quad -5x(x - 2)(x + 2)(x^2 + 4) = -5x(x^2 - 4)(x^2 + 4)$
$$= -5x(x^4 - 16)$$
$$= -5x^5 + 80x$$

So, $-5x^5 + 80x = -5x(x - 2)(x + 2)(x^2 + 4)$. ∎

Quick ✔

10. *True or False:* The polynomial $x^4 - 81 = (x^2 - 9)(x^2 + 9)$ is factored completely.

In Problems 11 and 12, factor each polynomial completely.

11. $x^4 - 1$ **12.** $-36x^2y + 16y$

EXAMPLE 6 Factoring Completely

Factor completely: $4x^3 - 6x^2 - 36x + 54$

Solution

Is there a greatest common factor among these four terms? Yes! The GCF is 2. Also notice that there are four terms, so we attempt to factor by grouping.

Factor out the GCF of 2: $4x^3 - 6x^2 - 36x + 54 = 2(2x^3 - 3x^2 - 18x + 27)$
Factor by grouping: $= 2[(2x^3 - 3x^2) + (-18x + 27)]$
Factor out common factor in each group: $= 2[x^2(2x - 3) - 9(2x - 3)]$
Factor out $2x - 3$: $= 2(2x - 3)(x^2 - 9)$
$x^2 - 9$ is the difference of two squares: $= 2(2x - 3)(x - 3)(x + 3)$

Work Smart: Study Skills

You know how to begin factoring a polynomial—look for the GCF. But do you know when a polynomial is factored completely? That is, do you know when to stop? Which of the following is not completely factored?

(a) $(x + 5)(2x + 6)$
(b) $(z - 3)(z + 3)(z^2 + 9)$
(c) $(2n - 5)(5n + 7)$
(d) $(4y - 3yz)(2 + 7z)$

Did you recognize that (a) and (d) are not completely factored because each has a common factor in one of the binomials?

Check $\quad 2(2x - 3)(x - 3)(x + 3) = 2(2x - 3)(x^2 - 9)$
$$= 2(2x^3 - 18x - 3x^2 + 27)$$
$$= 4x^3 - 6x^2 - 36x + 54$$

So, $4x^3 - 6x^2 - 36x + 54 = 2(2x - 3)(x - 3)(x + 3)$. ∎

Quick ✔

13. When factoring a polynomial with four terms, try factoring by _____.

14. *True or False:* $ax - ay + 4x - 4y$ can be factored by grouping.

In Problems 15 and 16, factor each polynomial completely.

15. $2x^3 + 3x^2 + 4x + 6$ **16.** $6x^3 + 9x^2 - 6x - 9$

EXAMPLE 7 **Factoring Completely**

Factor completely: $-4xy^2 + 4xy + 12x$

Solution

Notice that each term has a common factor of $-4x$, so we factor out $-4x$ as the GCF.

$$-4xy^2 + 4xy + 12x = -4x(y^2 - y - 3)$$

We now concentrate on the polynomial in parentheses, which has three terms, $y^2 - y - 3$. It is not a perfect square trinomial (because 3 is not a perfect square). We look for two factors of -3 whose sum is -1. There are no such factors, so $y^2 - y - 3$ is prime.

Check $-4x(y^2 - y - 3) = -4xy^2 + 4xy + 12x$

So, $-4xy^2 + 4xy + 12x = -4x(y^2 - y - 3)$.

Quick ✔ *In Problems 17 and 18, factor each polynomial completely.*

17. $-3z^2 + 9z - 21$ **18.** $6xy^2 + 15x^3$

6.5 EXERCISES

PRACTICE   WATCH   DOWNLOAD   READ   REVIEW

1–18. *are the* Quick ✔*s that follow each* EXAMPLE

Mixed Practice

In Problems 19–90, factor completely. If a polynomial cannot be factored, say it is prime.

19. $x^2 - 100$ **20.** $x^2 - 256$

21. $t^2 + t - 6$ **22.** $n^2 + 5n + 6$

23. $x + y + 2ax + 2ay$ **24.** $xy - 2ay + 3bx - 6ab$

25. $a^3 - 8$ **26.** $1 - y^9$

27. $a^2 - ab - 6b^2$ **28.** $x^2 - xy - 30y^2$

29. $2x^2 - 5x - 7$ **30.** $12n^2 - 23n + 5$

31. $2x^2 - 6xy - 20y^2$ **32.** $2x^2 + 4xy - 6y^2$

33. $9 - a^2$ **34.** $25 - m^2$

35. $u^2 - 14u + 33$ **36.** $x^2 + 5x - 6$

37. $xy - ay - bx + ab$ **38.** $2x^3 - x^2 - 18x + 9$

39. $w^2 + 6w + 8$ **40.** $x^2 - 8x + 15$

41. $36a^2 - 49b^4$ **42.** $100x^2 - 25y^2$

43. $x^2 + 2xm - 8m^2$ **44.** $s^2 - 11st + 24t^2$

45. $6x^2y^2 - 13xy + 6$ **46.** $6s^2t^2 + st - 1$

47. $x^3 + x^2 + x + 1$ **48.** $x^3 - 3x^2 + 2x - 6$

49. $12z^2 + 12z + 18$ **50.** $3y^2 + 6y + 3$

51. $14c^2 + 19c - 3$ **52.** $24x^2 + 66x + 45$

53. $27m^3 + 64n^6$ **54.** $8x^6 + 125y^3$

55. $2j^6 - 2j^2$ **56.** $48m - 3m^9$

57. $8a^2 + 18ab - 5b^2$ **58.** $10p^2 - 15q^2 + 19pq$

59. $2a^3 + 6a$ **60.** $4t^4 + 16t^2$

61. $12z^2 - 3$ **62.** $8n^3 - 18n$

63. $x^2 - x + 6$ **64.** $n^2 + 2n + 8$

65. $16a^4 + 2ab^3$ **66.** $24p^3q + 81q^4$

67. $p^2q^2 + 6pq - 7$ **68.** $x^2y^2 + 20xy + 96$

69. $s^2(s + 2) - 4(s + 2)$ **70.** $x^2(x + y) - 16(x + y)$

71. $-12x^3 + 2x^2 + 2x$ **72.** $-3x^3 - 13x^2 + 10x$

73. $10v^2 - 2 - v$ **74.** $27h - 5 + 18h^2$

75. $4n^2 - n^4 + 3n^3$ **76.** $4x - 2x^2 - 2x^3$

77. $-4a^3b + 2a^2b - 2ab$ **78.** $-4x^3y + 4x^2y - 4xy$

79. $12p - p^3 + p^2$ **80.** $-9x - 3x^3 - 12x^2$

81. $-32x^3 + 72xy^2$ **82.** $-48p^4 + 75p^2$

83. $2n^3 - 10n^2 - 6n + 30$ **84.** $6x^4 + 3x^3 - 24x^2 - 12x$

85. $16x^2 + 4x - 12$

86. $36x^2 + 30x - 24$

87. $14x^2 + 3x^4 + 8$

88. $14 + 53r^3 + 14r^6$

89. $-2x^3y + x^2y^2 + 3xy^3$

90. $6a^3 - 5a^2b + ab^2$

Applying the Concepts

91. Profit on Newspapers The revenue for selling x newspapers is given by the expression $x^3 + 8x$. The cost to produce x newspapers is $8x^2 - 7x$. If profit is calculated as revenue minus costs, write an expression, in factored form, that calculates the profit from selling x newspapers.

92. Profit on T-shirts Candy and her boyfriend produce silk-screened T-shirts. The cost to produce n T-shirts is given by the expression $12n - 2n^2$ and the revenue for selling the same number of T-shirts is $n^3 + 2n^2$. Write an expression, in factored form, that calculates the profit from selling n T-shirts.

△**93. Volume of a Box** The volume of a box is given by the formula $V = lwh$. The volume of the box is represented by the expression $(4x^3 - 10x^2 - 6x)$ cubic feet. Factor this expression to determine algebraic expressions for the dimensions of the box.

△**94. Volume of a Box** The volume of a box is given by the formula $V = lwh$. The volume of the box is represented by the expression $(18x^3 + 3x^2 - 6x)$ cubic centimeters. Factor this expression to determine algebraic expressions for the dimensions of the box.

Extending the Concepts

Although the most common pattern for factoring a polynomial with four terms is to group the first two terms and group the second two terms, it is not the only possibility. In the following examples, the polynomial has been written as three terms in the first group

and a single term in the second group. Study the example and then try to find a grouping that will factor each polynomial.

$$x^2 + 2xy + y^2 - z^2 = (x^2 + 2xy + y^2) - z^2$$
$$= (x + y)^2 - z^2$$
$$= (x + y + z)(x + y - z)$$

In Problems 95–98, factor completely.

95. $4m^2 - 4mn + n^2 - p^2$ **96.** $b^2 + 2bc + c^2 - a^2$

97. $x^2 - y^2 + 2yz - z^2$ **98.** $16x^2 - y^2 - 8y - 16$

In Problems 99–102, see if you can extend the concept presented in Problems 95–98 to find a creative way to group and then factor each of the following. You may need to rearrange the terms.

99. $x^2 - 2xy + y^2 - 6x + 6y + 8$

100. $a^2 + 2ab + b^2 - a - b - 6$

101. $x^2 + 2xy + y^2 - a^2 + 2ab - b^2$

102. $x^2 - 4mx + 4m^2 - y^2 + 4ny - 4n^2$

Explaining the Concepts

103. You are grading the paper of a student who factors the polynomial $x^2 + 4x - 3x - 12$ by grouping as follows:

$$(x^2 + 4x)(-3x - 12) = x(x + 4) - 3(x - 4)$$
$$= (x - 3)(x + 4)$$

Did the student correctly factor the polynomial? What comments would you write on the student's paper?

104. Describe the method of factoring you find most difficult. Write a polynomial and factor it using this method.

PUTTING THE CONCEPTS TOGETHER (Sections 6.1–6.5)

These problems cover important concepts from Sections 6.1 through 6.5. We designed these problems so that you can review the chapter so far and show your mastery of the concepts. Take time to work these problems before proceeding with the next section. The answers to these problems are located at the back of the text on page AN-25.

1. Find the GCF of $10x^3y^4z$, $15x^5y$, and $25x^2y^7z^3$.

In Problems 2–16, factor each polynomial completely. If the polynomial cannot be factored, say it is prime.

2. $x^2 - 3x - 4$ **3.** $x^6 - 27$

4. $6x(2x + 1) + 5z(2x + 1)$

5. $x^2 + 5xy - 6y^2$ **6.** $x^3 + 64$

7. $4x^2 + 49y^2$ **8.** $3x^2 + 12xy - 36y^2$

9. $12z^5 - 44z^3 - 24z^2$ **10.** $x^2 + 6x - 5$

11. $4m^4 + 5m^3 - 6m^2$ **12.** $5p^2 - 17p + 6$

13. $10m^2 + 25m - 6m - 15$ **14.** $36m^2 + 6m - 6$

15. $4m^2 - 20m + 25$ **16.** $5x^2 - xy - 4y^2$

17. Surface Area The surface area of a right circular cylinder is given by the formula $S = 2\pi rh + 2\pi r^2$. Write the right side of this formula in factored form.

18. Rocket Height A toy rocket is launched upward from the ground with an initial velocity of 48 feet per second. Its height, h, in feet, after t seconds, is given by the equation $h = 48t - 16t^2$. Write the right side of this equation in factored form.

6.6 Solving Polynomial Equations by Factoring

OBJECTIVES

1 Solve Quadratic Equations Using the Zero-Product Property

2 Solve Polynomial Equations of Degree Three or Higher Using the Zero-Product Property

Preparing for Solving Polynomial Equations by Factoring

Before getting started, take the following readiness quiz. If you get a problem wrong, go back to the section cited and review the material.

P1. Solve: $x + 5 = 0$ [Section 2.1, pp. 86–87]

P2. Solve: $2(x - 4) - 10 = 0$ [Section 2.2, pp. 94–97]

P3. Evaluate $2x^2 + 3x - 4$ when **(a)** $x = 2$ **(b)** $x = -1$.   [Section 1.8, pp. 67–68]

In Sections 6.1–6.5, we learned how to factor polynomial expressions. A question that you may have been asking yourself is, "Why do I care about factoring? What good is it?" It turns out that there are many uses of factoring, but one use that we can present now is that factoring is essential for solving *polynomial equations*.

Work Smart

Remember, the degree of a polynomial in one variable is the value of the **largest exponent** on the variable. For example, the degree of $4x^3 - 9x^2 + 1$ is 3.

DEFINITIONS

A **polynomial equation** is any equation that contains only polynomial expressions. The **degree of a polynomial equation** is the degree of the polynomial expression in the equation.

Some examples of polynomial equations are

$$4x + 5 = 17 \qquad\qquad 2x^2 - 5x - 3 = 0 \qquad\qquad y^3 + 4y^2 = 3y + 18$$

Polynomial equation   Polynomial equation   Polynomial equation
of degree 1   of degree 2   of degree 3

We learned how to solve polynomial equations of degree 1 back in Chapter 2. We now learn how to solve polynomial equations of degree 2.

1 Solve Quadratic Equations Using the Zero-Product Property

If a polynomial equation can be solved using factoring, we make use of the following property.

THE ZERO-PRODUCT PROPERTY

If the product of two factors is zero, then at least one of the factors is 0. That is,

if $ab = 0$, then $a = 0$ or $b = 0$ or both a and b are 0.

For example, if $2x = 0$, then either $2 = 0$ or $x = 0$. Since $2 \neq 0$, it must be that $x = 0$.

EXAMPLE 1 Using the Zero-Product Property

Solve: $(x + 4)(2x - 5) = 0$

Solution

We have the product of two factors, $x + 4$ and $2x - 5$, set equal to 0. According to the Zero-Product Property, the value of at least one of the factors must equal 0. Therefore, we set each of the factors equal to 0 and solve each equation separately.

$$x + 4 = 0 \qquad\text{or}\qquad 2x - 5 = 0$$

Subtract 4 from both sides: $x = -4$ Add 5 to both sides: $2x = 5$

Divide both sides by 2: $\dfrac{2x}{2} = \dfrac{5}{2}$

$$x = \dfrac{5}{2}$$

Check

$$x = -4$$

$$(x + 4)(2x - 5) = 0$$

$$(-4 + 4)(2(-4) - 5) \stackrel{?}{=} 0$$

$$0(-13) \stackrel{?}{=} 0$$

$$0 = 0 \quad \text{True}$$

$$x = \frac{5}{2}$$

$$(x + 4)(2x - 5) = 0$$

$$\left(\frac{5}{2} + 4\right)\left(2 \cdot \left(\frac{5}{2}\right) - 5\right) \stackrel{?}{=} 0$$

$$\left(\frac{13}{2}\right)(5 - 5) \stackrel{?}{=} 0$$

$$\frac{13}{2} \cdot 0 \stackrel{?}{=} 0$$

$$0 = 0 \quad \text{True}$$

The solution set is $\left\{-4, \frac{5}{2}\right\}$.   ■

Quick ✔

1. The Zero-Product Property states that if $ab = 0$, then either _____ or _____.

In Problems 2 and 3, use the Zero-Product Property to solve the equation.

2. $x(x + 3) = 0$ **3.** $(x - 2)(4x + 5) = 0$

The Zero-Product Property comes in handy when we need to solve quadratic equations.

DEFINITION

A **quadratic equation** is an equation that can be written in the form

$$ax^2 + bx + c = 0$$

where $a, b,$ and c are real numbers and $a \neq 0$.

The following are examples of quadratic equations.

$$2x^2 + 5x - 3 = 0 \qquad -6z^2 + 12z = 0 \qquad y^2 - 25 = 0 \qquad p^2 + 12p = -36$$

Notice that the equation $y^2 - 25 = 0$ is a quadratic equation even though it is missing the "y" term. The equation $-6z^2 + 12z = 0$ is a quadratic equation even though it is missing a constant term.

A quadratic equation is a specific type of a polynomial equation. The term "quadratic" means "of, or relating to, a square." There are many real-world situations that are modeled by these second-degree equations, such as problems involving revenue for selling x units of a good. Additionally, quadratic equations can be used to describe the height of a projectile over time.

Sometimes a quadratic equation is called a **second-degree equation** because the highest power of the variable in a quadratic equation is two.

DEFINITION

A quadratic equation is said to be in **standard form** if it is written in the form $ax^2 + bx + c = 0$.

For example, the equation $2x^2 + x - 5 = 0$ is in standard form, while the equation $p^2 + 12p = -36$ is not in standard form. To write $p^2 + 12p = -36$ in standard form, we add 36 to both sides of the equation to obtain $p^2 + 12p + 36 = 0$.

When a quadratic equation is written in standard form, $ax^2 + bx + c = 0$, it may be possible to factor the expression $ax^2 + bx + c$ as the product of two first-degree polynomials. If it is possible to factor the trinomial, we can then use the Zero-Product Property to solve the quadratic equation.

EXAMPLE 2 How to Solve a Quadratic Equation by Factoring

Solve: $x^2 - 4x - 21 = 0$

Step-by-Step Solution

Step 1: Is the equation in standard form? Yes, it is written in the form $ax^2 + bx + c = 0$.	$x^2 - 4x - 21 = 0$
Step 2: Factor the expression on the left side of the equation.	Two integers whose product is -21 and whose sum is -4 are -7 and 3. $(x + 3)(x - 7) = 0$
Step 3: Set each factor equal to 0.	$x + 3 = 0$ or $x - 7 = 0$
Step 4: Solve each first-degree equation.	$x = -3$ or $x = 7$
Step 5: Check	$x^2 - 4x - 21 = 0$ $x^2 - 4x - 21 = 0$ $x = -3$: $(-3)^2 - 4(-3) - 21 \stackrel{?}{=} 0$ $x = 7$: $7^2 - 4(7) - 21 \stackrel{?}{=} 0$ $9 + 12 - 21 \stackrel{?}{=} 0$ $49 - 28 - 21 \stackrel{?}{=} 0$ $0 = 0$ True $0 = 0$ True

The solution set is $\{-3, 7\}$.

Look at Step 3 in the solution to Example 2. To solve a quadratic equation, we wish to put the equation into a form that we already know how to solve. That is, we "transform" the quadratic equation $x^2 - 4x - 21 = 0$ into two linear equations, $x + 3 = 0$ or $x - 7 = 0$. We will present methods for solving $ax^2 + bx + c = 0$ when we cannot factor the expression $ax^2 + bx + c$ later in the text.

STEPS TO SOLVE A QUADRATIC EQUATION BY FACTORING

Step 1: Write the quadratic equation in standard form, $ax^2 + bx + c = 0$.

Step 2: Factor the polynomial on the left side of the equation.

Step 3: Set each factor found in Step 2 equal to zero using the Zero-Product Property.

Step 4: Solve each first-degree equation for the variable.

Step 5: Check your answers by substituting the values of the variable into the *original* equation.

EXAMPLE 3 Solving a Quadratic Equation Not in Standard Form

Solve: $3x^2 + 5x = 14x$

Solution

We first write the equation in standard form, $ax^2 + bx + c = 0$.

$$3x^2 + 5x = 14x$$

Subtract $14x$ from both sides of the equation: $3x^2 - 9x = 0$

Factor: $3x(x - 3) = 0$

Set each factor equal to 0: $3x = 0$ or $x - 3 = 0$

Solve each first-degree equation: $x = 0$ or $x = 3$

Check Substitute $x = 0$ and $x = 3$ into the original equation.

$$3x^2 + 5x = 14x \qquad\qquad 3x^2 + 5x = 14x$$

$$x = 0: \quad 3(0)^2 + 5(0) \stackrel{?}{=} 14(0) \qquad\qquad x = 3: \quad 3(3)^2 + 5(3) \stackrel{?}{=} 14(3)$$

$$0 = 0 \quad \text{True} \qquad\qquad\qquad 27 + 15 \stackrel{?}{=} 42$$

$$42 = 42 \quad \text{True}$$

The solution set is $\{0, 3\}$. ∎

Quick ✔

4. A _____ equation is an equation that can be written in the form $ax^2 + bx + c = 0$, where $a, b,$ and c are real numbers and $a \neq 0$.

5. Quadratic equations are also known as _____ -degree equations.

6. *True or False:* $3x + x^2 = 6$ is written in standard form.

In Problems 7–10, use the Zero-Product Property to solve the equation.

7. $p^2 - 6p + 8 = 0$ **8.** $2t^2 - 5t = 3$

9. $2x^2 + 3x = 5$ **10.** $z^2 + 20 = -9z$

EXAMPLE 4 Solving a Quadratic Equation Not in Standard Form

Solve: $3m^2 - 3m = 2 - 2m$

Solution

Once again, we first write the quadratic equation in standard form, $ax^2 + bx + c = 0$.

$$3m^2 - 3m = 2 - 2m$$

Add $2m$ to both sides and
subtract 2 from both sides: $3m^2 - 3m + 2m - 2 = 2 - 2 - 2m + 2m$

$$3m^2 - m - 2 = 0$$

Factor $3m^2 - m - 2$: $(3m + 2)(m - 1) = 0$

Set each factor equal to 0: $3m + 2 = 0 \quad \text{or} \quad m - 1 = 0$

Solve each first-degree equation: $3m = -2 \quad \text{or} \quad m = 1$

$$m = -\frac{2}{3}$$

Check Check the two solutions by substituting $m = -\dfrac{2}{3}$ and $m = 1$ in the original equation. We leave this to you.

The solution set is $\left\{ -\dfrac{2}{3}, 1 \right\}$. ∎

Quick ✔ *In Problems 11 and 12, solve each quadratic equation by factoring.*

11. $5k^2 + 3k - 1 = 3 - 5k$ **12.** $3x^2 + 9x = 4 - 2x$

EXAMPLE 5 Solving a Quadratic Equation Not in Standard Form

Solve: $(2x + 5)(x - 3) = 6x$

Solution

$$(2x + 5)(x - 3) = 6x$$

Multiply using FOIL: $\quad 2x^2 - x - 15 = 6x$

Write in standard form: $\quad 2x^2 - 7x - 15 = 0$

Factor the polynomial: $\quad (2x + 3)(x - 5) = 0$

Set each factor equal to 0: $\quad 2x + 3 = 0 \quad$ or $\quad x - 5 = 0$

Solve each first-degree equation: $\quad 2x = -3 \quad$ or $\quad x = 5$

$$x = -\frac{3}{2}$$

Check We leave it to you to substitute $x = -\dfrac{3}{2}$ and $x = 5$ into the original equation to verify the answer.

The solution set is $\left\{-\dfrac{3}{2}, 5\right\}$.

Quick ✔

13. *True or False:* $x(x - 3) = 4$ means that $x = 4$ or $x - 3 = 4$.

In Problems 14 and 15, solve each quadratic equation by factoring.

14. $(x - 3)(x + 5) = 9$ **15.** $(x + 3)(2x - 1) = 7x - 3x^2$

EXAMPLE 6 Solving a Quadratic Equation Not in Standard Form

Solve: $4k^2 + 9 = -12k$

Solution

$$4k^2 + 9 = -12k$$

Write in standard form: $\quad 4k^2 + 12k + 9 = 0$

Factor the trinomial using
$A^2 + 2AB + B^2 = (A + B)^2$: $\quad (2k + 3)^2 = 0$

Set each factor equal to 0: $\quad 2k + 3 = 0 \quad$ or $\quad 2k + 3 = 0$

Solve each first-degree equation: $\quad 2k = -3 \qquad\qquad 2k = -3$

$$k = -\frac{3}{2} \qquad\qquad k = -\frac{3}{2}$$

Check Substitute $k = -\dfrac{3}{2}$ into the original equation to verify that the solution is correct.

The solution set is $\left\{-\dfrac{3}{2}\right\}$.

Notice in Example 6 that the solution $k = -\dfrac{3}{2}$ occurred twice. When this occurs, the solution is called a **double root.**

Quick ✔ *In Problem 16, solve the quadratic equation by factoring.*

16. $9p^2 + 16 = 24p$

EXAMPLE 7 Solving a Quadratic Equation Containing a GCF

Solve: $-3x^2 + 6x + 72 = 0$

Solution

$$-3x^2 + 6x + 72 = 0$$

Factor out the GCF, -3: $\quad -3(x^2 - 2x - 24) = 0$

Factor the trinomial: $\quad -3(x - 6)(x + 4) = 0$

Set each factor equal to 0: $\quad -3 = 0 \quad$ or $\quad x - 6 = 0 \quad$ or $\quad x + 4 = 0$

Solve each first-degree equation: $\qquad\qquad\qquad\qquad x = 6 \qquad\qquad x = -4$

The statement $-3 = 0$ is false. So the solutions are 6 and -4.

Check Substitute $x = 6$ and $x = -4$ into the original equation to check.

The solution set is $\{-4, 6\}$. ∎

Another technique that we could have used in Example 7 is to use the Multiplication Property of Equality and divide both sides of the equation by -3. Then we would solve the quadratic equation $x^2 - 2x - 24 = 0$ and also obtain the solutions $x = -4$ or $x = 6$.

Quick ✔ *In Problems 17 and 18, solve the quadratic equation by factoring.*

17. $4x^2 + 12x - 72 = 0$ **18.** $-2x^2 + 2x = -12$

EXAMPLE 8 Throwing a Ball from the Top of a Building

A ball is thrown vertically upward from the top of a building 96 feet tall with an initial velocity of 80 feet per second. Solve the equation $-16t^2 + 80t + 96 = 192$ to find the time t (in seconds) at which the ball is 192 feet from the ground. See Figure 1.

Solution

Figure 1

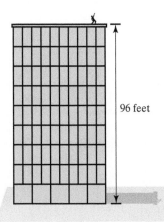

96 feet

$$-16t^2 + 80t + 96 = 192$$

Write the quadratic equation in standard form: $\quad -16t^2 + 80t + 96 - 192 = 192 - 192$

$$-16t^2 + 80t - 96 = 0$$

Factor out the GCF, -16: $\quad -16(t^2 - 5t + 6) = 0$

Factor the trinomial: $\quad -16(t - 3)(t - 2) = 0$

Set each factor equal to 0: $\quad -16 = 0 \quad$ or $\quad t - 3 = 0 \quad$ or $\quad t - 2 = 0$

Solve each first-degree equation: $\qquad\qquad\qquad\qquad t = 3 \quad$ or $\qquad t = 2$

The statement $-16 = 0$ is false. The solutions are $t = 3$ or $t = 2$. After 2 seconds and 3 seconds the ball will be 192 feet from the ground. Do you see why? ∎

19. A toy rocket is shot directly up from the ground with an initial velocity of 80 feet per second. Solve the equation $-16t^2 + 80t = 64$ to find the time (in seconds) at which the toy rocket is 64 feet from the ground.

$\boxed{2}$ Solve Polynomial Equations of Degree Three or Higher Using the Zero-Product Property

The Zero-Product Property is also used to solve higher-degree polynomial equations.

$\boxed{\text{EXAMPLE 9}}$ How to Solve a Polynomial Equation of Degree Three or Higher

Solve: $18x^3 + 3x^2 - 6x = 0$

Step-by-Step Solution

Step 1: Write the equation in standard form.	$18x^3 + 3x^2 - 6x = 0$
Step 2: Factor the polynomial on the left side of the equation.	$3x(6x^2 + x - 2) = 0$ $3x(3x + 2)(2x - 1) = 0$
Step 3: Set each factor equal to 0.	$3x = 0$ or $3x + 2 = 0$ or $2x - 1 = 0$
Step 4: Solve each first-degree equation.	$x = 0$ $3x = -2$ $2x = 1$ $x = -\dfrac{2}{3}$ $x = \dfrac{1}{2}$
Step 5: Check each solution by substituting $x = 0$, $x = -\dfrac{2}{3}$, and $x = \dfrac{1}{2}$ into the original equation.	We leave the check to you.

Work Smart

Do not divide both sides of the equation by the factor $3x$. We can divide both sides by a constant, but not by a variable because the variable may have a value of zero.

The solution set is $\left\{ 0, -\dfrac{2}{3}, \dfrac{1}{2} \right\}$.

20. *True or False:* $x^3 - 4x^2 - 12x = 0$ can be solved using the Zero-Product Property.

In Problems 21 and 22, solve each polynomial equation.

21. $(4x - 5)(x^2 - 9) = 0$ **22.** $3x^3 + 9x^2 + 6x = 0$

6.6 EXERCISES

PRACTICE   WATCH   DOWNLOAD   READ   REVIEW

1–22. *are the* Quick ✔s *that follow each* EXAMPLE

Building Skills

In Problems 23–30, solve each equation using the Zero-Product Property. See Objective 1.

23. $2x(x + 4) = 0$

24. $3x(x + 9) = 0$

25. $(n + 3)(n - 9) = 0$

26. $(a + 8)(a - 4) = 0$

27. $(3p + 1)(p - 5) = 0$

28. $(4z - 3)(z + 4) = 0$

29. $(5y + 3)(2 - 7y) = 0$

30. $(6m - 5)(3 - 8m) = 0$

In Problems 31–34, identify each equation as a linear equation or a quadratic equation. See Objective 1.

31. $3(x + 4) - 1 = 5x + 2$

32. $2x + 1 - (x + 7) = 3x + 1$

33. $x^2 - 2x = 8$

34. $(x + 2)(x - 2) = 14$

In Problems 35–58, solve each quadratic equation by factoring. See Objective 1.

35. $x^2 - 3x - 4 = 0$

36. $x^2 + 2x - 63 = 0$

37. $n^2 + 9n + 14 = 0$

38. $p^2 - 5p - 24 = 0$

39. $4x^2 + 2x = 0$

40. $14x - 49x^2 = 0$

41. $2x^2 - 3x - 2 = 0$

42. $3x^2 + x - 14 = 0$

43. $a^2 - 6a + 9 = 0$

44. $k^2 + 12k + 36 = 0$

45. $6x^2 = 36x$

46. $2x^2 = 5x$

47. $n^2 - n = 6$

48. $a^2 - 6a = 16$

49. $b^2 + 18 = 11b$

50. $m^2 - 30 = 7m$

51. $1 - 5m = -4m^2$

52. $4p - 3 = -4p^2$

53. $n(n - 2) = 24$

54. $p(p + 1) = 2$

55. $(x - 2)(x - 3) = 56$

56. $(x + 5)(x - 3) = 9$

57. $(c + 2)^2 = 9$

58. $(2a - 1)^2 = 16$

In Problems 59–64, solve each polynomial equation by factoring. See Objective 2.

59. $2x^3 + 2x^2 - 12x = 0$

60. $3x^3 + x^2 - 14x = 0$

61. $y^3 + 3y^2 - 4y - 12 = 0$

62. $m^3 + 2m^2 - 9m - 18 = 0$

63. $2x^3 + 3x^2 = 8x + 12$

64. $-2x + 3 = 3x^2 - 2x^3$

Mixed Practice

In Problems 65–90, solve each equation. Be careful; the problems represent a mix of linear, quadratic, and third-degree polynomial equations.

65. $(5x + 3)(x - 4) = 0$

66. $(3x - 2)(x + 5) = 0$

67. $p^2 - p - 20 = 0$

68. $z^2 - 13z + 40 = 0$

69. $4w + 3 = 2w - 7$

70. $7y + 3 = 2y - 12$

71. $4a^2 - 25a = 21$

72. $5m^2 = 18m + 8$

73. $2a(a + 1) = a^2 + 8$

74. $2y(y + 5) = y^2 + 11$

75. $2x^3 + x^2 = 32x + 16$

76. $2n^3 + 4 = n^2 + 8n$

77. $4(b - 3) - 3b = 8$

78. $2(p - 3) = p + 1$

79. $y^2 + 5y = 5(y + 20)$

80. $3z^2 + 7z = 7(z + 21)$

81. $(a + 3)(a - 5)(3a + 2) = 0$

82. $(w - 6)(w + 5)(2w - 3) = 0$

83. $(2k - 3)(2k^2 - 9k - 5) = 0$

84. $(7m - 11)(3m^2 - m - 2) = 0$

85. $(w - 3)^2 = 9 + 2w$

86. $3(k + 2)^2 = 5k + 8$

87. $\frac{1}{2}x^2 + \frac{5}{4}x = 3$

88. $z^2 + \frac{29}{4}z = 6$

89. $8x^2 + 44x = 24$

90. $9q^2 = 3q + 6$

Applying the Concepts

91. Tossing a Ball A ball is thrown vertically upward from the top of a building 80 feet tall with an initial velocity of 64 feet per second. Solve the equation $-16t^2 + 64t + 80 = 128$ to find the time t (in seconds) at which the ball is 128 feet from the ground.

92. Tossing a Ball A ball is thrown vertically upward from the ground with an initial velocity of 64 feet per second. Solve the equation $-16t^2 + 64t = 48$ to find the time t (in seconds) at which the ball is 48 feet from the ground.

93. Water Balloon A water balloon is dropped from a height of 40 feet. Solve the equation $-16t^2 + 40 = 24$ to find the time t (in seconds) at which the water balloon is 24 feet from the ground.

94. Flying Money A stunt-man dropped a bag containing fake money from a hot-air balloon at a height of 240 feet. Solve the equation $-16t^2 + 240 = 96$ to find the time t (in seconds) at which the bag was 96 feet from the ground.

95. Consecutive Integers The product of two consecutive integers is 12. Find the integers.

96. Consecutive Odd Integers The product of two consecutive odd integers is 143. Find the integers.

97. Consecutive Even Integers Find three consecutive even integers such that the product of the first and the third is 96.

98. Consecutive Odd Integers Find three consecutive odd integers such that the product of the second and the third is 99.

△**99. Rectangle** The length and width of two sides of a rectangle are consecutive odd integers. The area of the rectangle is 255 square units. Find the dimensions of the rectangle.

△**100. Garden Area** The State University Landscape Club wants to establish a horticultural garden near the administration building. The length and width of the space that is available are consecutive even integers, and the area of the garden is 440 square feet. Find the dimensions of the garden.

The equation $N = \dfrac{t^2 - t}{2}$ models the number of soccer games that must be scheduled in a league with t teams, when each team plays every other team exactly once. Use this equation to solve Problems 101 and 102.

101. If a league has 28 games scheduled, how many teams are in the league?

102. If a league has 36 games scheduled, how many teams are in the league?

Extending the Concepts

103. Write a polynomial equation in factored form with integer coefficients that has $x = 3$ and $x = -5$ as solutions. What is the degree of this polynomial equation?

104. Write a polynomial equation in factored form with integer coefficients that has $x = 0$ and $x = -8$ as solutions. What is the degree of this polynomial equation?

105. Write a polynomial equation in factored form with integer coefficients that has $z = 6$ as a double root. What is the degree of this polynomial equation?

106. Write a polynomial equation in factored form with integer coefficients that has $x = -2$ as a double root. What is the degree of this polynomial equation?

107. Write a polynomial equation in factored form with integer coefficients that has $x = -3$, $x = 1$ and $x = 5$ as solutions. What is the degree of this polynomial equation?

108. Write a polynomial equation in factored form with integer coefficients that has $a = \dfrac{1}{2}$, $a = \dfrac{2}{3}$, and $a = 1$ as solutions. What is the degree of this polynomial equation?

In Problems 109–112, solve for x in each equation.

109. $x^2 - ax + bx - ab = 0$

110. $x^2 + ax - 6a^2 = 0$

111. $2x^3 - 4ax^2 = 0$

112. $4x^2 - 6ax + 10bx - 15ab = 0$

Explaining the Concepts

113. A student solved a quadratic equation using the following procedure. Explain the student's error and then work the problem correctly.

$$15x^2 = 5x$$
$$\frac{15x^2}{x} = \frac{5x}{x}$$
$$15x = 5$$
$$x = \frac{5}{15} = \frac{1}{3}$$

114. A student solved a quadratic equation using the following procedure. Explain the student's error and then work the problem correctly.

$$(x - 4)(x + 3) = -6$$
$$x - 4 = -6 \quad \text{or} \quad x + 3 = -6$$
$$x = -2 \qquad\qquad x = -9$$

115. When solving polynomial equations, we always begin by writing the equation in standard form. Explain why this is important.

116. Explain the difference between a quadratic polynomial and a quadratic equation.

6.7 Modeling and Solving Problems with Quadratic Equations

OBJECTIVES

 1 Model and Solve Problems Involving Quadratic Equations

2 Model and Solve Problems Using the Pythagorean Theorem

Preparing for Modeling and Solving Problems with Quadratic Equations
Before getting started, take the following readiness quiz. If you get a problem wrong, go back to the section cited and review the material.

P1. Evaluate: 15^2 [Section 1.7, pp. 59–60]

P2. Solve: $x^2 - 5x - 14 = 0$ [Section 6.6, pp. 416–422]

The solutions to many applied problems require solving polynomial equations by factoring. For example, the height of a projectile over time, the area of a triangular sail, and the dimensions of a big-screen TV may be found by solving a polynomial equation.

1 Model and Solve Problems Involving Quadratic Equations

Let's begin by solving a quadratic equation to determine the time at which a projectile is at a certain height.

EXAMPLE 1 Projectile Motion

A child throws a ball upward off a cliff from a height of 240 feet above sea level. The height h of the ball above the water (in feet) at any time t (in seconds) can be modeled by the equation

$$h = -16t^2 + 32t + 240$$

See Figure 2.

(a) When will the height of the ball be 240 feet above sea level?

(b) When will the ball strike the water?

Figure 2

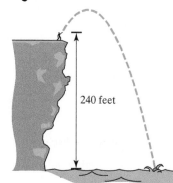

240 feet

Solution

(a) To determine when the height of the ball will be 240 feet above sea level, we let $h = 240$ and solve the resulting equation.

$$-16t^2 + 32t + 240 = 240$$

Write the equation in standard form: $-16t^2 + 32t = 0$

Factor out $-16t$: $-16t(t - 2) = 0$

Set each factor equal to 0: $-16t = 0$ or $t - 2 = 0$

Solve each first degree equation: $t = 0$ or $t = 2$

The ball will be at a height of 240 feet the instant the ball leaves the child's hand and after 2 seconds of flight.

(b) The ball will strike the water at the instant its height is 0. So we let $h = 0$ and solve the resulting equation.

$$-16t^2 + 32t + 240 = 0$$

Factor out -16: $-16(t^2 - 2t - 15) = 0$

Factor the trinomial: $-16(t - 5)(t + 3) = 0$

Set each factor equal to 0: $-16 = 0$ or $t - 5 = 0$ or $t + 3 = 0$

Solve each first degree equation: $t = 5$ or $t = -3$

The equation $-16 = 0$ is false, and since t represents time, we discard the solution $t = -3$. Therefore, the ball will strike the water after 5 seconds. ∎

Quick ✔

1. A model rocket is fired straight up from the ground. The height h of the rocket (in feet) at any time t (in seconds) can be modeled by the equation $h = -16t^2 + 160t$.

(a) When will the height of the rocket be 384 feet from the ground?

(b) When will the rocket strike the ground?

In the next two examples, we will employ the problem-solving strategy first presented in Section 2.5.

EXAMPLE 2 Geometry: Area of a Rectangle

A carpet installer finds that the length of a rectangular hallway is 3 feet more than twice the width. If the area of the hallway is 44 square feet, what are the dimensions of the hallway? See Figure 3.

Solution

Figure 3

Step 1: Identify This is a geometry problem involving the area of a rectangle.

Step 2: Name Because we know less about the width of the hallway, we let w represent the width. The length of the hallway is 3 feet more than twice the width, so we let $2w + 3$ represent the length.

Step 3: Translate We are given that the area of the hallway is 44 square feet. We know that the area of a rectangle = (length)(width), so we have

$$\text{area} = (\text{length})(\text{width})$$
$$44 = (2w + 3)(w) \qquad \text{The Model}$$

Step 4: Solve We now proceed to solve the equation. Do you recognize this equation as being a quadratic equation? The first step is to put the equation in standard form, $ax^2 + bx + c = 0$.

$$w(2w + 3) = 44$$

Distribute: $\qquad 2w^2 + 3w = 44$

Subtract 44 from both sides: $\qquad 2w^2 + 3w - 44 = 0$

Factor: $\qquad (2w + 11)(w - 4) = 0$

Set each factor equal to 0: $\qquad 2w + 11 = 0 \quad \text{or} \quad w - 4 = 0$

Solve each first degree equation: $\qquad 2w = -11 \quad \text{or} \qquad w = 4$

$$\frac{2w}{2} = -\frac{11}{2}$$

$$w = -\frac{11}{2}$$

Step 5: Check Since w represents the width of the rectangular hallway, we discard the solution $w = -\dfrac{11}{2}$. If the width of the hallway is 4 feet, then the length would be $2w + 3 = 2(4) + 3 = 11$ feet. The area of a hallway that is 4 feet by 11 feet is $4(11) = 44$ square feet. We have the right answer!

Step 6: Answer The dimensions of the hallway are 4 feet by 11 feet. ■

> **Quick ✔**
>
> **2.** A rectangular plot of land has length that is 3 kilometers less than twice its width. If the area of the land is 104 square kilometers, what are the dimensions of the land?

EXAMPLE 3 Geometry: Area of a Triangle

The height of a triangle is 5 inches less than the length of the base, and the area of the triangle is 42 square inches. Find the height of the triangle.

Solution

Step 1: Identify This is a geometry problem involving the area of a triangle.

Step 2: Name The height of the triangle is 5 inches less than the length of the base. We will let b represent the length of the base and $b - 5$ represent the height of the triangle. See Figure 4.

Figure 4

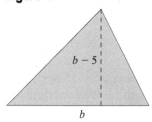

Step 3: Translate We know that the area of a triangle is given by the formula
Area $= \frac{1}{2}$(base)(height). Further, we are given the area of the triangle to be
42 square feet, so

$$\text{Area} = \frac{1}{2}(\text{base})(\text{height})$$

$$42 = \frac{1}{2}(b)(b-5) \qquad \text{The Model}$$

Step 4: Solve Our model is a quadratic equation, so we first put the equation in standard form, $ax^2 + bx + c = 0$.

Work Smart

Multiply only the $\frac{1}{2}$ by 2—don't multiply the factors b and $(b-5)$ by 2 also.

$$42 = \frac{1}{2}(b)(b-5)$$

Multiply by 2 to clear fractions: $2(42) = 2\left[\frac{1}{2}(b)(b-5)\right]$

$$84 = b(b-5)$$

Distribute: $84 = b^2 - 5b$

Subtract 84 from both sides: $0 = b^2 - 5b - 84$

Factor: $0 = (b-12)(b+7)$

Set each factor equal to 0: $b - 12 = 0 \quad \text{or} \quad b + 7 = 0$

Solve each first degree equation: $b = 12 \quad \text{or} \quad b = -7$

Step 5: Check Since b represents the base of the triangle, we discard the solution $b = -7$. Do you see why? The base of the triangle is 12 inches, so the height is $b - 5 = 12 - 5 = 7$ inches. The area of a triangle that has a base of 12 inches and a height of 7 inches is $\frac{1}{2} \cdot 12 \cdot 7 = 42$ square inches. We have the right answer!

Step 6: Answer The height of the triangle is 7 inches.   ■

Quick ✔

3. The base of a triangular garden is 4 yards longer than the height, and the area of the garden is 48 square yards. Find the dimensions of the triangle.

⌐2 Model and Solve Problems Using the Pythagorean Theorem

The Pythagorean Theorem is a statement about right triangles.

DEFINITIONS

A **right triangle** is one that contains a **right angle,** that is, an angle of 90°. The side of the triangle opposite the 90° angle is called the **hypotenuse;** the remaining two sides are called **legs.**

Figure 5

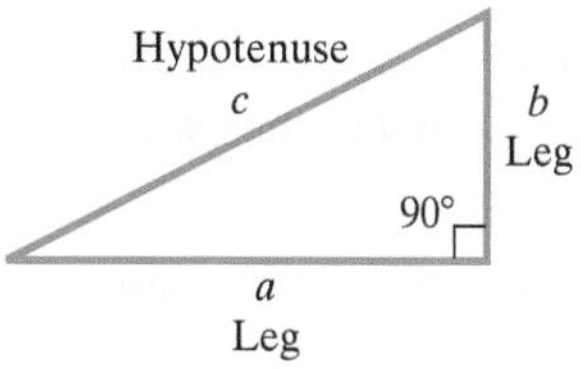

Hypotenuse
c

b
Leg

90°

a
Leg

In Figure 5 we use c to represent the length of the hypotenuse and a and b to represent the lengths of the legs. Notice the use of the symbol ⌐ to show the 90° angle.
      We now state the Pythagorean Theorem.

THE PYTHAGOREAN THEOREM

In a right triangle, the square of the length of the hypotenuse is equal to the sum of the squares of the lengths of the legs. That is, in the right triangle shown in Figure 5,

$$a^2 + b^2 = c^2 \quad \text{or} \quad \text{leg}^2 + \text{leg}^2 = \text{hypotenuse}^2$$

EXAMPLE 4 Using the Pythagorean Theorem

Find the lengths of the sides of the right triangle in Figure 6.

Solution

Figure 6 shows a right triangle, so we use the Pythagorean Theorem, $a^2 + b^2 = c^2$. The legs have lengths x and $x + 7$, and the hypotenuse has length 13. We substitute into the equation $a^2 + b^2 = c^2$.

Figure 6

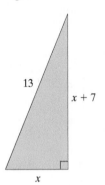

$$a^2 + b^2 = c^2$$

Substitute $a = x$, $b = x + 7$, $c = 13$: $\quad x^2 + (x + 7)^2 = 13^2$

$(A + B)^2 = A^2 + 2AB + B^2$: $\quad x^2 + x^2 + 14x + 49 = 169$

Combine like terms: $\quad 2x^2 + 14x + 49 = 169$

Write the equation in standard form: $\quad 2x^2 + 14x - 120 = 0$

Factor out GCF 2: $\quad 2(x^2 + 7x - 60) = 0$

$$2(x + 12)(x - 5) = 0$$

Set each factor equal to 0: $\quad 2 = 0 \quad$ or $\quad x + 12 = 0 \quad$ or $\quad x - 5 = 0$

Solve each first degree equation: $\quad\quad\quad\quad\quad\quad x = -12 \quad$ or $\quad x = 5$

The equation $2 = 0$ is false, and the solution $x = -12$ makes no sense because x represents the length of a leg of a right triangle. So $x = 5$ is the length of one leg of the triangle. The other leg is $x + 7 = 5 + 7 = 12$.

To check our solutions, let's replace a by 5 and b by 12 and see if our solutions satisfy the Pythagorean Theorem. Does $5^2 + 12^2 = 13^2$? Is $25 + 144 = 169$? Yes! Our answers are correct. ∎

Quick ✔

4. Find the length of each leg of the right triangle pictured below.

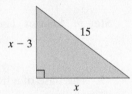

5. One leg of a right triangle is 17 inches longer than the other leg. The hypotenuse has a length of 25 inches. Find the lengths of the two legs of the triangle.

EXAMPLE 5 Will the Television Fit in the Media Cabinet?

A rectangular 20-inch television screen (measured diagonally) is 4 inches wider than it is tall. Will this TV fit in your new media cabinet that is 20 inches wide?

Solution

Step 1: Identify This is a geometry problem involving the lengths of the sides of a right triangle.

Step 2: Name We know that the diagonal of the television screen (hypotenuse) is 20 inches long. Let x represent the height of the screen. The screen is 4 inches wider than it is tall, so $x + 4$ represents the width.

Step 3: Translate We know that the Pythagorean Theorem tells us the relationship between the lengths of the sides of a right triangle, so we use $a^2 + b^2 = c^2$.

$$a^2 + b^2 = c^2$$

Substitute $a = x$, $b = x + 4$, $c = 20$: $\quad x^2 + (x + 4)^2 = 20^2$

Work Smart

Remember

$(x + 4)^2 \neq x^2 + 16$

$(x + 4)^2 = x^2 + 8x + 16$

Step 4: Solve We now proceed to solve the equation. The first step is to put the quadratic equation in standard form, $ax^2 + bx + c = 0$.

$$x^2 + (x + 4)^2 = 20^2$$

$(A + B)^2 = A^2 + 2AB + B^2$: $x^2 + x^2 + 8x + 16 = 400$

Combine like terms: $2x^2 + 8x + 16 = 400$

Subtract 400 from both sides: $2x^2 + 8x - 384 = 0$

Factor: $2(x^2 + 4x - 192) = 0$

Factor: $2(x + 16)(x - 12) = 0$

Set each factor equal to 0: $2 = 0$ or $x + 16 = 0$ or $x - 12 = 0$

Solve: $x = -16$ or $x = 12$

Step 5: Check The statement $2 = 0$ is false. Since x represents the length of the shorter leg of the triangle, we discard the solution $x = -16$. If the shorter leg of the triangle (height of the TV) is 12 inches, then the longer leg (width of the television) would be $x + 4 = 12 + 4 = 16$ inches. Does $12^2 + 16^2 = 20^2$? Since $144 + 256 = 400$, our answer is correct!

Step 6: Answer The television screen is 16 inches wide, so it will fit in the new cabinet.

Quick ✔

6. A rectangular 10-inch television screen (measured diagonally) is 2 inches wider than it is tall. What are the dimensions of the TV screen?

6.7 EXERCISES

PRACTICE   WATCH   DOWNLOAD   READ   REVIEW

1–6. are the Quick ✔*s that follow each* EXAMPLE

Building Skills

In Problems 7–10, use the given area to find the missing sides of the rectangle. See Objective 1.

△ **7.** $A = 56$

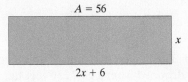

x

$2x + 6$

△ **8.** $A = 250$ △ **9.** $A = 18$

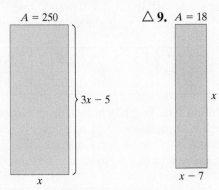

$3x - 5$ x

x $x - 7$

△ **10.** $A = 364$

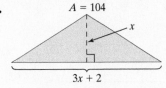

x

$x + 12$

In Problems 11–14, use the given area to find the height and base of the triangle. See Objective 1.

△ **11.** $A = 104$

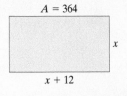

x

$3x + 2$

△ **12.** $A = 42$

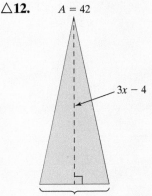

$3x - 4$

x

△ **13.**

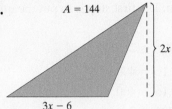

$A = 144$
$2x$
$3x - 6$

△ **14.**

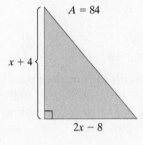

$A = 84$
$x + 4$
$2x - 8$

In Problems 15–18, use the given area to find the dimensions of the quadrilateral. See Objective 1.

△ **15.**

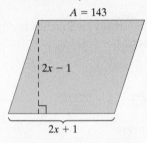

$A = 143$
$2x - 1$
$2x + 1$

△ **16.**

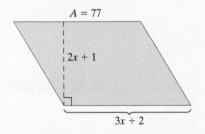

$A = 77$
$2x + 1$
$3x + 2$

△ **17.**

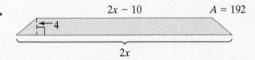

$2x - 10$ $A = 192$
4
$2x$

△ **18.**

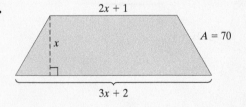

$2x + 1$
x
$A = 70$
$3x + 2$

In Problems 19–22, use the Pythagorean Theorem to find the lengths of the sides of the triangle. See Objective 2.

△ **19.**

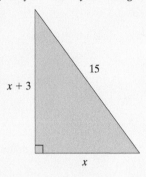

15
$x + 3$
x

△ **20.**

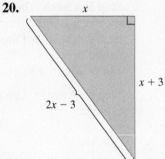

x
$x + 3$
$2x - 3$

△ **21.**

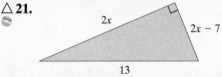

$2x$
$2x - 7$
13

△ **22.**

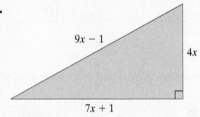

$9x - 1$
$4x$
$7x + 1$

Applying the Concepts

23. Projectile Motion The height, h in feet, of an object t seconds after it is dropped from a cliff 256 feet tall is given by the equation $h = -16t^2 + 256$. Suppose you dropped your glasses off the cliff. Fill in the table below to find the height of your glasses at each time, t.

Time, in Seconds	0	0.5	1	1.5	2	2.5	3	3.5	4
Height, in Feet									

24. Projectile Motion The height, h in feet, of an object t seconds after it is propelled from ground level is given by the equation $h = -16t^2 + 64t$. Fill in the table below to find the height of the object at each time, t.

Time, in Seconds	0	0.5	1	1.5	2	2.5	3	3.5	4
Height, in Feet									

25. Projectile Motion If $h = -16t^2 + 96t$ represents the height of a rocket, in feet, t seconds after it was fired, when will the rocket hit the ground? (*Hint:* The rocket is on the ground when $h = 0$.)

26. Projectile Motion If $h = -16t^2 + 96t$ represents the height of a rocket, in feet, t seconds after it was fired, when will the rocket be 144 feet high?

△**27. Rectangular Room** The length of a rectangular room is 8 meters more than the width. If the area of the room is 48 square meters, find the dimensions of the room.

△**28. Rectangular Room** The width of a rectangular room is 4 feet less than the length. If the area of the room is 21 square feet, find the dimensions of the room.

△**29. Sailboat** The sail on a sailboat is in the shape of a triangle. If the height of the sail is 3 times the length of the base and the area is 54 square feet, find the dimensions of the sail.

△**30. Triangle** The base of a triangle is 2 meters more than the height. If the area of the triangle is 24 square meters, find the base and height of the triangle.

31. Big-Screen TV Your big-screen TV measures 50 inches on the diagonal. If the front of the TV measures 40 inches across the bottom, find the height of the TV.

32. Big-Screen TV Hannah owns a 29-inch TV (that is, it measures 29 inches on the diagonal). If the television is 20 inches tall, find the distance across the bottom.

△**33. Dimensions of a Rectangle** The length of a rectangle is 1 mm more than twice the width. If the area is 300 square mm, find the dimensions of the rectangle.

△**34. Playing Field Dimensions** The length of a rectangular playing field is 3 yards less than twice the width. If the area of the field is 104 square yards, what are its dimensions?

△**35. Rectangle and Square** A rectangle and a square have the same area. The width of the rectangle is 6 cm less than the side of the square and the length of the rectangle is 5 cm more than twice the side of the square. What are the dimensions of the rectangle?

△**36. Square and Rectangle** A rectangle and a square have the same area. The width of the rectangle is 2 in. less than the side of the square and the length of the rectangle is 3 in. less than twice the side of the square. What are the dimensions of the rectangle?

△**37. Watching the World Series** David is an avid baseball fan and has purchased a plasma TV just in time to watch the World Series. The TV screen is 17 inches taller than it is wide and there is a $1\frac{1}{2}$-inch-wide casing that surrounds the TV screen.

(a) David begins to install the TV and remembers that he was told that it measures 53 inches on the diagonal, including the casing. What are the dimensions of the TV screen?

(b) What size opening is required to fit the TV into David's entertainment center?

△**38. Jasper's Big-Screen TV** Jasper purchased a new big-screen TV. The TV screen is 10 inches taller than it is wide and is surrounded by a casing that is 2 inches wide.

(a) Jasper lost his tape measure but sees on the box that the TV measures 50 inches on the diagonal, including the casing. What are the dimensions of the TV screen?

(b) Jasper knows that the size of the opening where he wants the TV installed is 29 by 42 inches. Will this TV fit into his space?

△**39. How Tall Is the Pole?** The owners of A & L Auto Sales want to hang decorative banners to draw potential customers' attention to their extensive used car offerings. They have 10 feet of wire to attach banners and know that, according to zoning regulations, the  distance from the pole to the point that the wire attaches to the ground must be 2 feet greater than the height of the pole. How tall can the pole be?

△**40. Sailing on Lake Erie** A sail on a sailboat is in the shape of a right triangle. The longest side of the sail is 13 feet long and one side of the sail is 7 feet longer than the other. Find the dimensions of the sail.

Extending the Concepts

△**41. Gardening** Beth has 28 feet of fence to enclose a small garden. The length of the garden lies along her house, so only three sides require fencing. Find the dimensions of the garden if she encloses 98 square feet of the garden with the fence.

△**42. Volume of a Box** A rectangular solid has a square base and is 8 meters high. What are the dimensions of the base if the volume of the solid is 128 cubic meters?

Explaining the Concepts

43. In a projectile motion problem, you have two positive numbers that satisfy the word problem. Explain the meaning of each of these numbers and then give a case where you would have only one positive solution.

44. Can the Pythagorean Theorem be used to find the length of a side of any triangle? Explain your answer.

CHAPTER 6 Activity: Which One Does Not Belong?

Focus: Factoring polynomials.
Time: 20–30 minutes
Group size: 3–4

Each group member should decide which polynomial from each row does not belong. Answers will vary. As a group, discuss each

member's results. Each group member should be prepared to explain WHY that particular polynomial does not belong with the other three. Be creative!

	A	B	C	D
1.	$15x^2 - 10ax - 15xy + 10ay$	$xr - 3xs - ry + 3sy$	$2ax - 14bx - 2ay + 14by$	$3ab - 3ay - 3bx + 3xy$
2.	$-x^2 - x + 6$	$3x^2 + 39x + 120$	$2x^2 - 12xy - 54y^2$	$7x^2 + 7x - 140$
3.	$3x^2 - 16x + 21$	$6x^2 - 3x + 15$	$3x^2 - 13x - 56$	$3x^2 + x + 1$
4.	$9a^2 + 30a + 25$	$16x^2 - 24x + 9$	$4x^2 - 12xy + 9y^2$	$18s^2 - 60s + 9$
5.	$4x^2 + 13x + 10$	$16x^2 + 40xy + 25y^2$	$16x^2 - 25y^2$	$8x^2 - 2xy - 15y^2$

CHAPTER 6 Review

Section 6.1   Greatest Common Factor and Factoring by Grouping

KEY CONCEPTS	KEY TERMS
• **To find the greatest common factor of two or more expressions,** **Step 1:** Find the GCF of the coefficients of each variable expression. **Step 2:** For each variable, determine the smallest exponent that the variable is raised to. **Step 3:** Find the product of the common factors found in Steps 1 and 2. This expression is the GCF. • **To factor a polynomial using the greatest common factor,** **Step 1:** Identify the greatest common factor (GCF) of the terms that make up the polynomial. **Step 2:** Rewrite each term as the product of the GCF and the remaining factor. **Step 3:** Use the Distributive Property "in reverse" to factor out the GCF. **Step 4:** Check using the Distributive Property.	Factors Greatest common factor Factoring by grouping

YOU SHOULD BE ABLE TO...	EXAMPLE	REVIEW EXERCISES
1̄ Find the greatest common factor (GCF) of two or more expressions (p. 376)	Examples 1 through 5	1–10
2̄ Factor out the greatest common factor in polynomials (p. 379)	Examples 6 through 10	11–16
3̄ Factor polynomials by grouping (p. 381)	Examples 11 through 13	17–20

In Problems 1–10, find the greatest common factor, GCF, of each group of expressions.

1. 24, 36

2. 27, 54

3. 10, 20, 30

4. 8, 16, 28

5. x^4, x^2, x^8

6. m^3, m, m^5

7. $30a^2b^4, 45ab^2$

8. $18x^4y^2z^3, 24x^3y^5z$

9. $4(2a + 1)^2$ and $6(2a + 1)^3$

10. $9(x - y)$ and $18(x - y)$

In Problems 11–16, factor the GCF from the polynomial.

11. $-18a^3 - 24a^2$

12. $-9x^2 + 12x$

13. $15y^2z + 5y^7z + 20y^3z$

14. $7x^3y - 21x^2y^2 + 14xy^3$

15. $x(5 - y) + 2(5 - y)$

16. $z(a + b) + y(a + b)$

In Problems 17–20, factor by grouping.

17. $5m^2 + 2mn + 15mn + 6n^2$

18. $2xy + y^2 + 2x^2 + xy$

19. $8x + 16 - xy - 2y$

20. $xy^2 + x - 3y^2 - 3$

Section 6.2   Factoring Trinomials of the Form $x^2 + bx + c$

KEY CONCEPT	KEY TERMS
• **To factor a trinomial of the form $x^2 + bx + c$, we use the following steps.** **Step 1:** Find the pair of integers whose product is c and whose sum is b. That is, determine m and n such that $mn = c$ and $m + n = b$. **Step 2:** Write $x^2 + bx + c = (x + m)(x + n)$. **Step 3:** Check your work by multiplying the binomials.	Quadratic trinomial Leading coefficient Prime polynomial

YOU SHOULD BE ABLE TO...	EXAMPLE	REVIEW EXERCISES
1 Factor trinomials of the form $x^2 + bx + c$ (p. 385)	Examples 1 through 7	21–28
2 Factor out the GCF, then factor $x^2 + bx + c$ (p. 390)	Examples 8 and 9	29–34

In Problems 21–34, factor completely. If the polynomial cannot be factored, say it is prime.

21. $x^2 + 5x + 6$

22. $x^2 + 6x + 8$

23. $x^2 - 21 - 4x$

24. $3x + x^2 - 10$

25. $m^2 + m + 20$

26. $m^2 - 6m - 5$

27. $x^2 - 8xy + 15y^2$

28. $m^2 + 4mn - 5n^2$

29. $-p^2 - 11p - 30$

30. $-y^2 + 2y + 15$

31. $3x^3 + 33x^2 + 36x$

32. $4x^2 + 36x + 32$

33. $2x^2 - 2xy - 84y^2$

34. $4y^3 + 12y^2 - 40y$

Section 6.3   Factoring Trinomials of the Form $ax^2 + bx + c$, $a \neq 0$

KEY CONCEPTS

• **Factoring $ax^2 + bx + c$, $a \neq 1$, using trial and error: a, b, and c have no common factors**

Step 1: List the possibilities for the first terms of each binomial whose product is ax^2.

$$(\_\,x + \_)(\_\,x + \_) = ax^2 + bx + c$$

Step 2: List the possibilities for the last terms of each binomial whose product is c.

$$(\_\,x + \square)(\_\,x + \square) = ax^2 + bx + c$$

Step 3: Write out all the combinations of factors found in Steps 1 and 2. Multiply the binomials out until a product is found that equals the trinomial.

• **Factoring $ax^2 + bx + c$, $a \neq 1$, by grouping: a, b, and c have no common factors**

Step 1: Find the value of ac.

Step 2: Find the pair of integers, m and n, whose product is ac and whose sum is b.

Step 3: Write $ax^2 + bx + c = ax^2 + mx + nx + c$.

Step 4: Factor the expression in Step 3 by grouping.

Step 5: Check by multiplying the factors.

YOU SHOULD BE ABLE TO...	EXAMPLE	REVIEW EXERCISES
1 Factor $ax^2 + bx + c$, $a \neq 1$, using trial and error (p. 393)	Examples 1 through 6	35–44
2 Factor $ax^2 + bx + c$, $a \neq 1$, using grouping (p. 398)	Examples 7 through 9	35–44

In Problems 35–44, factor completely using any method you wish. If a polynomial cannot be factored, say it is prime.

35. $5y^2 + 14y - 24$

36. $6y^2 - 41y - 7$

37. $-5x + 2x^2 + 3$

38. $23x + 6x^2 + 7$

39. $2x^2 - 7x - 6$

40. $8m^2 + 18m + 9$

41. $9m^3 + 30m^2n + 21mn^2$

42. $14m^2 + 16mn + 2n^2$

43. $15x^3 + x^2 - 2x$

44. $6p^4 + p^3 - p^2$

Section 6.4   Factoring Special Products

KEY CONCEPTS	KEY TERMS
• **Perfect Square Trinomials** $A^2 + 2AB + B^2 = (A + B)^2$ $A^2 - 2AB + B^2 = (A - B)^2$ • **Difference of Two Squares** $A^2 - B^2 = (A - B)(A + B)$ • **Sum or Difference of Two Cubes** $A^3 + B^3 = (A + B)(A^2 - AB + B^2)$ $A^3 - B^3 = (A - B)(A^2 + AB + B^2)$	Perfect square trinomial Difference of two squares Sum of two cubes Difference of two cubes

YOU SHOULD BE ABLE TO...	EXAMPLE	REVIEW EXERCISES
1 Factor perfect square trinomials (p. 403)	Examples 1 through 4	45–50
2 Factor the difference of two squares (p. 405)	Examples 5 through 7	51–56
3 Factor the sum or difference of two cubes (p. 407)	Examples 8 through 10	57–62

In Problems 45–62, factor completely. If a polynomial cannot be factored, say it is prime.

45. $4x^2 - 12x + 9$

46. $x^2 - 10x + 25$

47. $x^2 + 6xy + 9y^2$

48. $9x^2 + 24xy + 4y^2$

49. $8m^2 + 8m + 2$

50. $2m^2 - 24m + 72$

51. $4x^2 - 25y^2$

52. $49x^2 - 36y^2$

53. $x^2 + 25$

54. $x^2 + 100$

55. $x^4 - 81$

56. $x^4 - 625$

57. $m^3 + 27$

58. $m^3 + 125$

59. $27p^3 - 8$

60. $64p^3 - 1$

61. $y^9 + 64z^6$

62. $8y^3 + 27z^6$

Section 6.5   Summary of Factoring Techniques

KEY CONCEPT

Steps for Factoring

Step 1: Is there a greatest common factor? If so, factor out the greatest common factor (GCF).

Step 2: Count the number of terms.

Step 3: (a) 2 terms (Binomials)

- Is it the difference of two squares? If so,
$$A^2 - B^2 = (A - B)(A + B)$$
- Is it the sum of two squares? If so, Stop! The expression is prime.
- Is it the difference of two cubes? If so,
$$A^3 - B^3 = (A - B)(A^2 + AB + B^2)$$
- Is it the sum of two cubes? If so,
$$A^3 + B^3 = (A + B)(A^2 - AB + B^2)$$

(b) 3 terms (Trinomials)

- Is it a perfect square trinomial? If so,
$$A^2 + 2AB + B^2 = (A + B)^2 \quad \text{or} \quad A^2 - 2AB + B^2 = (A - B)^2$$
- Is the leading coefficient 1? If so,
$$x^2 + bx + c = (x + m)(x + n) \text{ where } mn = c \text{ and } m + n = b$$
- Is the coefficient of the squared term different from 1? If so, factor using trial and error or grouping.

(c) 4 terms

- Use factoring by grouping

Step 4: Check your work by multiplying out the factors.

YOU SHOULD BE ABLE TO...	EXAMPLE	REVIEW EXERCISES
⏰ Factor polynomials completely (p. 410)	Examples 1 through 7	63–78

In Problems 63–78, factor completely. If a polynomial cannot be factored, say it is prime.

63. $15a^3 - 6a^2b - 25ab^2 + 10b^3$

64. $12a^2 - 9ab + 4ab - 3b^2$

65. $x^2 - xy - 48y^2$

66. $x^2 - 10xy - 24y^2$

67. $x^3 - x^2 - 42x$

68. $3x^6 - 30x^5 + 63x^4$

69. $6x^2 + 11x + 3$

70. $10z^2 + 9z - 9$

71. $27x^3 + 8$

72. $8z^3 - 1$

73. $4y^2 + 18y - 10$

74. $5x^3y^2 - 8x^2y^2 + 3xy^2$

75. $25k^2 - 81m^2$

76. $x^4 - 9$

77. $16m^2 + 1$

78. $m^4 + 25$

Section 6.6   Solving Polynomial Equations by Factoring

KEY CONCEPT	KEY TERMS
• **The Zero-Product Property** If the product of two factors is zero, then at least one of the factors is 0. That is, if $ab = 0$, then $a = 0$ or $b = 0$ or both a and b are 0.	Polynomial equation Degree of a polynomial equation Quadratic equation Second-degree equation Standard form

YOU SHOULD BE ABLE TO...	EXAMPLE	REVIEW EXERCISES
1 Solve quadratic equations using the Zero-Product Property (p. 416)	Examples 1 through 8	79–88
2 Solve polynomial equations of degree three or higher using the Zero-Product Property (p. 422)	Example 9	89–92

In Problems 79–92, solve each equation by factoring.

79. $(x - 4)(2x - 3) = 0$ **80.** $(2x + 1)(x + 7) = 0$

81. $x^2 - 12x - 45 = 0$ **82.** $x^2 - 7x + 10 = 0$

83. $3x^2 + 6x = 0$ **84.** $4x^2 + 18x = 0$

85. $3x(x + 1) = 2x^2 + 5x + 3$

86. $2x^2 + 6x = (3x + 1)(x + 3)$

87. $5x^2 + 7x + 16 = 3x^2 - 5x$

88. $8x^2 - 10x = -2x + 6$

89. $x^3 = -11x^2 + 42x$

90. $-3x^2 = -x^3 + 18x$

91. $(3x - 4)(x^2 - 9) = 0$

92. $(2x + 5)(x^2 + 4x + 4) = 0$

Section 6.7 Modeling and Solving Problems with Quadratic Equations

KEY CONCEPT	KEY TERMS
• **The Pythagorean Theorem** In a right triangle, the square of the length of the hypotenuse is equal to the sum of the squares of the lengths of the legs. That is, if a and b are the lengths of the legs and c is the length of the hypotenuse, then $a^2 + b^2 = c^2$ or $\text{leg}^2 + \text{leg}^2 = \text{hypotenuse}^2$.	Right triangle Right angle Hypotenuse Legs

YOU SHOULD BE ABLE TO...	EXAMPLE	REVIEW EXERCISES
1 Model and solve problems involving quadratic equations (p. 425)	Examples 1 through 3	93–96
2 Model and solve problems using the Pythagorean Theorem (p. 427)	Examples 4 and 5	97, 98

93. Geysers If $h = -16t^2 + 80t$ represents the height of a jet of water from a geyser t seconds after the geyser erupts, when will the water hit the ground?

94. More Geysers If $h = -16t^2 + 80t$ represents the height of the jet of water from a geyser at time t, when will the jet of water be 96 feet high?

△ **95. Tabletop** The length of a rectangular tabletop is 3 feet shorter than twice its width. If the area of the tabletop is 54 square feet, what are the dimensions of the tabletop?

△ **96. Tarp** The length of a rectangular tarp is 1 yard shorter than twice its width. If the area of the tarp is 15 square yards, what are the dimensions of the tarp?

△ **97. Right Triangle** The shorter leg of a right triangle is 2 feet shorter than the longer leg. The hypotenuse is 10 feet. How long is each leg?

△ **98. Right Triangle** The shorter leg of a right triangle is 14 feet shorter than the longer leg. The hypotenuse is 26 feet. How long is each leg?

CHAPTER 6 TEST

Remember to use your Chapter Test Prep Video CD to see fully worked-out solutions to any of these problems you would like to review.

1. Find the GCF of $16x^5y^2$, $20x^4y^6$, and $24x^6y^8$.

In Problems 2–16, factor each polynomial completely. If the polynomial cannot be factored, say it is prime.

2. $x^4 - 256$

3. $18x^3 - 9x^2 - 27x$

4. $xy - 7y - 4x + 28$

5. $27x^3 + 125$

6. $y^2 - 8y - 48$

7. $6m^2 - m - 5$

8. $4x^2 + 25$

9. $4(x - 5) + y(x - 5)$

10. $3x^2y - 15xy - 42y$

11. $x^2 + 4x + 12$

12. $2x^6 - 54y^3$

13. $9x^3 + 39x^2 + 12x$

14. $6m^2 + 7m + 2$

15. $4m^2 - 6mn + 4$

16. $25x^2 + 70xy + 49y^2$

In Problems 17 and 18, solve the equation by factoring.

17. $5x^2 = -16x - 3$

18. $5x^3 - 20x^2 + 20x = 0$

19. The length of a rectangle is 8 inches shorter than three times its width. If the area of the rectangle is 35 square inches, find the dimensions of the rectangle.

20. The hypotenuse of a right triangle is one inch longer than the longer leg. The shorter leg is 7 inches shorter than the longer leg. Find the length of all three sides of the triangle.

8 Roots and Radicals

Did you ever think that dropping a water balloon from the top of a building could have a mathematical context? The time t that it takes for an object to fall h feet is modeled by the formula $t = \sqrt{\dfrac{h}{16}}$. See Problems 99 and 100 on page 573.

The Big Picture: Putting It Together

Multiplication of polynomial expressions was presented in Chapter 5. Chapter 6 presented the idea that polynomial multiplication can be "undone" by factoring. Throughout your mathematics career, you will learn a process and a method for "undoing" the process.

This chapter discusses the process of "undoing" integer exponents. The focus of Sections 8.1–8.2 is on "undoing" the squaring operation (raising real numbers to the second power). This technique involves a symbol called a radical. Once the idea of how radicals "undo" exponents is understood, the presentation shifts to addition, subtraction, multiplication, and division of radical expressions. After we have a complete understanding of simplifying radical expressions, we turn our attention to solving equations involving these radical expressions in Section 8.6. Finally, Section 8.7 deals with "undoing" positive integer exponents that are 3 or greater. In Section 8.7, we also extend the idea of raising a real number to an integer exponent (Chapter 5) by discussing how to raise a real number to a rational exponent.

8.1 Introduction to Square Roots

Preparing for Introduction to Square Roots

Before getting started, take the following readiness quiz. If you get a problem wrong, go to the section cited and review the material.

In Problems 1–3, use the set $\left\{ -4, \dfrac{5}{3}, 0, \sqrt{2}, 6.95, 13, \pi \right\}$.

P1. Which of the numbers are integers? [Section 1.3, pp. 20–24]

P2. Which of the numbers are rational numbers? [Section 1.3, pp. 20–24]

P3. Which of the numbers are irrational numbers? [Section 1.3, pp. 20–24]

P4. Evaluate: **(a)** $\left(\dfrac{3}{2}\right)^2$ **(b)** $(0.4)^2$ [Section 1.7, pp. 59–60]

In Section 1.7, we introduced the concept of exponents. Exponents are used to indicate repeated multiplication. For example, 4^2 means $4 \cdot 4$, so $4^2 = 16$; $(-6)^2$ means $(-6) \cdot (-6)$, so $(-6)^2 = 36$. In this section, we will reverse the process of raising a number to the second power and ask questions such as, "What number, or numbers, when squared, give me 16?"

1 Evaluate Square Roots

If asked, "What is 5^2?", you would respond "25." If asked, "What is $(-5)^2$?", you would also respond "25." If instead you were asked, "What number, when squared, results in 25?", you may have to think for a while, but eventually you would respond, "Either −5 or 5."

In Words

Taking the square root of a number "undoes" raising a number to the second power.

DEFINITION

For any real numbers a and b, b is a **square root** of a if $b^2 = a$.

Put another way, the square roots of a are the numbers whose square give a.

For example, the square roots of 25 are −5 and 5 because $(-5)^2 = 25$ and $5^2 = 25$. The square roots of 144 are −12 and 12 because $(-12)^2 = 144$ and $12^2 = 144$.

EXAMPLE 1 Finding the Square Roots of Numbers

Find the square roots: **(a)** 36 **(b)** 0

Solution

(a) 6 is a square root of 36 because $6^2 = 36$.

−6 is also a square root of 36 because $(-6)^2 = 36$.

(b) 0 is the only square root of 0 because only $0^2 = 0$. ∎

EXAMPLE 2 Finding the Square Roots of Numbers

Work Smart

When finding square roots of fractions, look at the numerator and denominator separately.

Find the square roots: **(a)** $\dfrac{16}{49}$ **(b)** 0.09

Solution

(a) $-\dfrac{4}{7}$ is a square root of $\dfrac{16}{49}$ because $\left(-\dfrac{4}{7}\right)^2 = \dfrac{16}{49}$ and $\dfrac{4}{7}$ is also a square root of $\dfrac{16}{49}$ because $\left(\dfrac{4}{7}\right)^2 = \dfrac{16}{49}$.

(b) −0.3 is a square root of 0.09 because $(-0.3)^2 = 0.09$ and 0.3 is a square root of 0.09 because $(0.3)^2 = 0.09$. ∎

Preparing for...Answers **P1.** −4, 0, 13

P2. $-4, \dfrac{5}{3}, 0, 6.95, 13$ **P3.** $\sqrt{2}, \pi$

P4. (a) $\dfrac{9}{4}$ **(b)** 0.16

Quick ✔

1. For any real numbers a and b, b is a square root of a if __ = __.

In Problems 2–4, find the square roots of each real number.

2. 64   **3.** $\dfrac{25}{49}$ **4.** 0.36

Notice in Examples 1 and 2 that every positive number has a positive square root and a negative square root. When we want only the positive square root of a number, we use the symbol $\sqrt{}$, called a **radical,** to denote the **principal square root,** or nonnegative (zero or positive) square root. For example, if we want the positive square root of 25, we would write $\sqrt{25} = 5$. We read $\sqrt{25} = 5$ as "the positive square root of 25 is 5." But what if we want the negative square root of a real number? In that case, we use the expression $-\sqrt{25} = -5$ to obtain the negative square root of 25.

PROPERTIES OF SQUARE ROOTS

- Every positive real number has two square roots, one positive and one negative.
- The square root of 0 is 0. In symbols, $\sqrt{0} = 0$.
- We use the symbol $\sqrt{}$, called a radical, to denote the nonnegative square root of a real number. The nonnegative square root is called the principal square root.
- The number under the radical is called the **radicand.** For example, the radicand in $\sqrt{25}$ is 25.

EXAMPLE 3 Evaluating Square Roots

Evaluate: **(a)** $\sqrt{64}$ **(b)** $-\sqrt{81}$

Solution

   (a) The notation $\sqrt{64}$ means that we want the positive number whose square is 64. Because $8^2 = 64$, we have that
$$\sqrt{64} = 8$$

   (b) The notation $-\sqrt{81}$ means that we want the negative number whose square is 81. So
$$-\sqrt{81} = -1 \cdot \sqrt{81} = -1 \cdot 9 = -9$$

EXAMPLE 4 Evaluating Square Roots

Evaluate: **(a)** $\sqrt{\dfrac{1}{4}}$ **(b)** $-\sqrt{0.01}$

Solution

   (a) $\sqrt{\dfrac{1}{4}} = \dfrac{1}{2}$ because $\left(\dfrac{1}{2}\right)^2 = \dfrac{1}{4}$.

   (b) $-\sqrt{0.01} = -0.1$ because $0.1^2 = 0.01$.

Quick ✔

5. The number represented by $\sqrt{a}$ is called the _____ _____ ___ of a.

6. In the expression $\sqrt{4x}$, the $4x$ is called the _____.

In Problems 7–10, evaluate each square root.

7. $\sqrt{100}$ **8.** $-\sqrt{9}$ **9.** $\sqrt{\dfrac{25}{49}}$ **10.** $\sqrt{0.36}$

$$1^2 = 1 \qquad 5^2 = 25$$
$$2^2 = 4 \qquad 6^2 = 36$$
$$3^2 = 9 \qquad 7^2 = 49$$
$$4^2 = 16 \qquad 8^2 = 64$$

and so on.

Figure 1

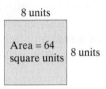

A rational number is a **perfect square** if it is the square of a rational number. For example, 64, 81, $\frac{1}{4}$, and 0.01 are all perfect squares because their square roots are rational numbers. (Refer back to Examples 3 and 4.) We can think of perfect squares geometrically as in Figure 1, where we have a square whose area is 64 square units. The square root of the area, $\sqrt{64}$, gives us the length of each side of the square, 8 units.

EXAMPLE 5 Evaluating an Expression Containing Square Roots

Evaluate: $-4\sqrt{25}$

Solution

The expression $-4\sqrt{25}$ is asking us to find -4 times the positive square root of 25. So we first find the positive square root of 25 and then multiply this result by -4.

$$-4\sqrt{25} = -4 \cdot 5$$
$$= -20$$

EXAMPLE 6 Evaluating an Expression Containing Square Roots

Evaluate:

(a) $\sqrt{9} + \sqrt{16}$ **(b)** $\sqrt{9 + 16}$ **(c)** $\sqrt{64 - 4 \cdot 7 \cdot 1}$

Solution

(a) $\sqrt{9} + \sqrt{16} = 3 + 4$ **(b)** $\sqrt{9 + 16} = \sqrt{25}$
$$= 7 \qquad\qquad\qquad\qquad\qquad\qquad = 5$$

(c) $\sqrt{64 - 4 \cdot 7 \cdot 1} = \sqrt{64 - 28}$
$$= \sqrt{36}$$
$$= 6$$

Quick ✔ *In Problems 11–14, evaluate each expression.*

11. $2\sqrt{36}$ **12.** $\sqrt{25 + 144}$ **13.** $\sqrt{25} + \sqrt{144}$ **14.** $\sqrt{25 - 4 \cdot 3 \cdot (-2)}$

2 Determine Whether a Square Root Is Rational, Irrational, or Not a Real Number

Because there is no rational number whose square is 5, $\sqrt{5}$ is not a rational number. In fact, $\sqrt{5}$ is an *irrational* number. Remember, an irrational number is a number that cannot be written as the quotient of two integers.

What if we wanted to evaluate $\sqrt{-16}$? Because any positive real number squared is positive, any negative real number squared is also positive, and 0 squared is 0, there is no real number whose square is -16. We conclude: **Negative real numbers do not have square roots that are real numbers!**

The following comments regarding square roots are important.

MORE PROPERTIES OF SQUARE ROOTS

- The square root of a perfect square number is a rational number.
- The square root of a positive rational number that is not a perfect square is an irrational number. For example, $\sqrt{20}$ is an irrational number because 20 is not a perfect square.
- The square root of a negative real number is not a real number. For example, $\sqrt{-2}$ is not a real number.

If needed, find decimal approximations for irrational square roots using a calculator.

EXAMPLE 7 Approximating Square Roots

Approximate $\sqrt{5}$ by writing it rounded to two decimal places.

Solution

We know that $\sqrt{4} = 2$ and $\sqrt{9} = 3$, so it seems reasonable to expect $\sqrt{5}$ to be between 2 and 3 since 5 is between 4 and 9. We use a calculator or Appendix A and find $\sqrt{5} \approx 2.23607$. Rounded to two decimal places, we have $\sqrt{5} \approx 2.24$. ∎

> Quick ✔ *In Problems 15 and 16, express each square root as a decimal rounded to two decimal places.*
>
> **15.** $\sqrt{35}$ **16.** $-\sqrt{6}$

Work Smart

The notation $\approx$ means "is approximately equal to."

EXAMPLE 8 Determining Whether a Square Root of an Integer Is Rational, Irrational, or Not a Real Number

Determine if each square root is rational, irrational, or not a real number. Then evaluate each real square root, if possible. For each square root that is irrational, express the square root as a decimal rounded to two decimal places.

  (a) $\sqrt{51}$ **(b)** $\sqrt{169}$ **(c)** $\sqrt{-81}$

Solution

  (a) $\sqrt{51}$ is irrational because 51 is not a perfect square. There is no rational number whose square is 51. Using a calculator or Appendix A, we find $\sqrt{51} \approx 7.14$.
  (b) $\sqrt{169}$ is a rational number because $13^2 = 169$, so $\sqrt{169} = 13$.
  (c) $\sqrt{-81}$ is not a real number. There is no real number whose square is -81. ∎

Work Smart

$\sqrt{-81}$ is not a real number, but $-\sqrt{81}$ is because $-\sqrt{81} = -9$. Note the placement of the negative sign!

> Quick ✔
>
> **17.** *True or False:* If a positive number is not a perfect square, then its square root is an irrational number.
>
> *In Problems 18–21, determine whether each square root is rational, irrational, or not a real number. Evaluate each square root, if possible. For each square root that is irrational, round your answer to two decimal places.*
>
> **18.** $\sqrt{49}$ **19.** $\sqrt{71}$ **20.** $\sqrt{-25}$ **21.** $-\sqrt{16}$

⌐3 Find Square Roots of Variable Expressions

What is $\sqrt{4^2}$? Because $4^2 = 16$, we have that $\sqrt{4^2} = \sqrt{16} = 4$. Based on this result, we might conclude that $\sqrt{a^2} = a$ for any real number a. Before we jump to this conclusion, let's consider $\sqrt{(-4)^2}$. Our "formula" says that $\sqrt{a^2} = a$, so we would think that $\sqrt{(-4)^2} = -4$, right? Wrong! $\sqrt{(-4)^2} = \sqrt{16} = 4$. So $\sqrt{4^2} = 4$ and $\sqrt{(-4)^2} = 4$. Regardless of whether the "a" in $\sqrt{a^2}$ is positive or negative, the result ends up being positive. So to say that $\sqrt{a^2} = a$ would not be correct. How can we fix our "formula"? In Section 1.3, we learned that $|a|$ will be a positive number if a is nonzero. From this, we have the following result:

For any **real number** a,

$$\sqrt{a^2} = |a|$$

In Words

The square root of a nonzero number squared will always be positive. The absolute value ensures this.

For example, $\sqrt{(-4)^2} = |-4| = 4$. We use this result when evaluating square roots that have variable expressions because it guarantees the result will be nonnegative regardless of whether the variable is negative, positive, or zero.

EXAMPLE 9 **Finding Square Roots of Variable Expressions**

(a) $\sqrt{(2x)^2} = |2x| = 2|x|$ for any real number x.

(b) $\sqrt{(a-4)^2} = |a-4|$ for any real number a. ∎

Quick ✔

22. For any real number a, $\sqrt{a^2} = \underline{\quad}$.

In Problems 23–25, simplify each square root. The variable represents any real number.

23. $\sqrt{b^2}$ **24.** $\sqrt{(4p)^2}$ **25.** $\sqrt{(w+3)^2}$

If it is stated that $a \geq 0$, then the absolute value bars are not needed because $|a| = a$ when $a \geq 0$. So $\sqrt{a^2} = a$ when $a \geq 0$.

EXAMPLE 10 **Finding Square Roots of Variable Expressions**

Simplify each square root.

(a) $\sqrt{(3y)^2}, y \geq 0$ **(b)** $\sqrt{(b+3)^2}, b+3 \geq 0$

Solution

(a) $\sqrt{(3y)^2} = 3y$ because $y \geq 0$.

(b) $\sqrt{(b+3)^2} = b+3$ because $b+3 \geq 0$. ∎

Quick ✔ *In Problems 26–28, simplify each square root.*

26. $\sqrt{(5b)^2}, b \geq 0$ **27.** $\sqrt{(z-6)^2}, z-6 \geq 0$

28. $\sqrt{(2h-5)^2}, 2h-5 \geq 0$

8.1 EXERCISES

MyMathLab

 PRACTICE   WATCH   DOWNLOAD   READ   REVIEW

1–28. *are the* Quick ✔*s that follow each* **EXAMPLE**

Building Skills

In Problems 29–36, find the value(s) of each expression. See Objective 1.

29. the square roots of 1   **30.** the square roots of 4

31. the square roots of $\frac{1}{9}$ **32.** the square roots of $\frac{9}{4}$

33. the square roots of 36   **34.** the square roots of 49

35. the square roots of 0.25   **36.** the square roots of 0.16

In Problems 37–60, find the exact value of each square root without a calculator. See Objective 1.

37. $\sqrt{144}$ **38.** $\sqrt{4}$

39. $-\sqrt{9}$ **40.** $-\sqrt{1}$

41. $\sqrt{225}$ **42.** $\sqrt{169}$

43. $\sqrt{\dfrac{1}{121}}$ **44.** $\sqrt{\dfrac{1}{49}}$

45. $\sqrt{0.04}$ **46.** $\sqrt{0.09}$

47. $-6\sqrt{9}$ **48.** $-4\sqrt{4}$

49. $\sqrt{\dfrac{16}{81}}$ **50.** $\sqrt{\dfrac{25}{9}}$

51. $5\sqrt{49}$ **52.** $4\sqrt{16}$

53. $\sqrt{36+64}$ **54.** $\sqrt{81+144}$

55. $\sqrt{36}+\sqrt{64}$ **56.** $\sqrt{81}+\sqrt{144}$

57. $\sqrt{4-(4)(1)(-15)}$ **58.** $\sqrt{9-(4)(1)(-10)}$

59. $\sqrt{49-(4)(15)(-2)}$ **60.** $\sqrt{100-(4)(8)(3)}$

In Problems 61–66, use a calculator or Appendix A to find the approximate value of the square root, rounded to the indicated place. See Objective 2.

61. $\sqrt{8}$ to 3 decimal places

62. $\sqrt{12}$ to 3 decimal places

63. $\sqrt{30}$ to the nearest hundredth

64. $\sqrt{18}$ to the nearest hundredth

65. $\sqrt{57}$ to the nearest tenth

66. $\sqrt{42}$ to the nearest tenth

In Problems 67–76, tell if the square root is rational, irrational, or not a real number. If the square root is rational, find the exact value; if the square root is irrational, write the approximate value rounded to two decimal places. See Objective 2.

67. $\sqrt{-4}$

68. $\sqrt{-100}$

69. $\sqrt{400}$

70. $\sqrt{900}$

71. $\sqrt{\dfrac{1}{4}}$

72. $\sqrt{\dfrac{49}{64}}$

73. $\sqrt{54}$

74. $\sqrt{24}$

75. $\sqrt{50}$

76. $\sqrt{12}$

In Problems 77–82, simplify each square root. See Objective 3.

77. $\sqrt{d^2}, d \geq 0$

78. $\sqrt{k^2}, k \geq 0$

79. $\sqrt{(x-9)^2}$

80. $\sqrt{(y-16)^2}, y-16 \geq 0$

81. $\sqrt{(2m-n)^2}, 2m-n \geq 0$ **82.** $\sqrt{(p+q)^2}$

Mixed Practice

In Problems 83–98, evaluate each square root if possible. If the square root is irrational, write the approximate value rounded to two decimal places. If the square root is not a real number, so state.

83. $\sqrt{3}$

84. $\sqrt{2}$

85. $\sqrt{0.4}$

86. $\sqrt{\dfrac{4}{81}}$

87. $\sqrt{-2}$

88. $\sqrt{-10}$

89. $3\sqrt{4}$

90. $-10\sqrt{9}$

91. $3\sqrt{\dfrac{25}{9}} - \sqrt{169}$

92. $2\sqrt{\dfrac{9}{4}} - \sqrt{4}$

93. $\sqrt{3-19}$

94. $\sqrt{5-9}$

95. $\sqrt{7^2 - (4)(-2)(-3)}$

96. $\sqrt{13^2 - (4)(-6)(-6)}$

97. $\sqrt{(11-8)^2 + (11-5)^2}$ **98.** $\sqrt{(-3-5)^2 + (-5-(-1))^2}$

Applying the Concepts

The area, A, of a square whose side has length s is given by $A = s^2$. We can calculate the length, s, of the side of a square as the positive square root of the area, A, using $s = \sqrt{A}$. In Problems 99–102, find the length of the side of the square whose area is given.

△ **99.** 625 square feet   △ **100.** 256 square meters

△ **101.** 256 square kilometers   △ **102.** 400 square inches

The area, A, of a circle whose radius is r is given by the formula $A = \pi r^2$. We can calculate the radius when the area is given using $r = \sqrt{\dfrac{A}{\pi}}$. In Problems 103–106, find the radius of the circle with the following areas.

△ **103.** 49π square meters   △ **104.** 25π square feet

△ **105.** 196π square inches   △ **106.** 289π square centimeters

△ **107. Great Pyramid at Giza** The volume V of a pyramid with a square base s and height h is $V = \dfrac{1}{3}s^2 h$. If we solve this formula for s, we obtain $s = \sqrt{\dfrac{3V}{h}}$. The Great Pyramid at Giza, built around 2500 B.C., has a volume of approximately 7,700,000 cubic meters. Find the length, to the nearest meter, of the side of the Great Pyramid if you know that the height is approximately 146 meters.

△ **108. Sun Pyramid** Use the formula given in Problem 107 to the find the length, to the nearest foot, of the side of the Sun Pyramid if the volume of the pyramid is approximately 114,000,000 cubic feet and the height is 210 feet. The Sun Pyramid was built in the ancient city of Teotihuacán, around 200 A.D.

Extending the Concepts

In Problems 109–112, simplify each expression.

109. $\sqrt{\sqrt{16}}$

110. $\sqrt{\sqrt{81}}$

111. $\sqrt{5 \cdot \sqrt{25}}$

112. $\sqrt{2 \cdot \sqrt{4}}$

Explaining the Concepts

113. Explain why $-\sqrt{9}$ is a real number but $\sqrt{-9}$ is not a real number.

114. You don't have a calculator handy but need an estimate for $\sqrt{20}$. Explain how you might find an approximate value for this number without a calculator.

CHAPTER 8 Review

Section 8.1 Introduction to Square Roots

KEY CONCEPTS	KEY TERMS
• The principal square root of any positive number is positive. • The principal square root of 0 is 0 because $0^2 = 0$. That is, $\sqrt{0} = 0$. • The square root of a perfect square is a rational number. • The square root of a positive rational number that is not a perfect square is an irrational number. • The square root of a negative real number is not a real number. • For any real number a, $\sqrt{a^2} = |a|$. If $a \geq 0$, $\sqrt{a^2} = a$.	Square root Radical Principal square root Radicand Perfect square

YOU SHOULD BE ABLE TO...	EXAMPLE	REVIEW EXERCISES
1 Evaluate square roots (p. 530)	Examples 1 through 6	1–12
2 Determine whether a square root is rational, irrational, or not a real number (p. 532)	Examples 7 and 8	13–16
3 Find square roots of variable expressions (p. 533)	Examples 9 and 10	17, 18

In Problems 1 and 2, find the value of each expression.

1. the square roots of 4   **2.** the square roots of 81

In Problems 3–12, find the exact value of each expression.

3. $-\sqrt{1}$

4. $-\sqrt{25}$

5. $\sqrt{0.16}$

6. $\sqrt{0.04}$

7. $\dfrac{3}{2}\sqrt{\dfrac{25}{36}}$

8. $\dfrac{4}{3}\sqrt{\dfrac{81}{4}}$

9. $\sqrt{25 - 9}$

10. $\sqrt{169 - 25}$

11. $\sqrt{9^2 - (4)(5)(-18)}$

12. $\sqrt{13^2 - (4)(-3)(-4)}$

In Problems 13–16, determine whether each square root rational, irrational, or not a real number. Then evaluate t square root. For each square root that is irrational, use a calculator or Appendix A to round your answer to two decimal places.

13. $-\sqrt{9}$

14. $-\dfrac{1}{2}\sqrt{48}$

15. $\sqrt{14}$

16. $\sqrt{-2}$

In Problems 17 and 18, simplify each square root. Assum that the variable can be any real number.

17. $\sqrt{(4x - 9)^2}$

18. $\sqrt{(16m - 25)^2}$

Appendix A
Table of Square Roots

n	$\sqrt{n}$	n	$\sqrt{n}$	n	$\sqrt{n}$	n	$\sqrt{n}$
1	1	26	5.09902	51	7.14143	76	8.71780
2	1.41421	27	5.19615	52	7.21110	77	8.77496
3	1.73205	28	5.29150	53	7.28011	78	8.83176
4	2	29	5.38516	54	7.34847	79	8.88819
5	2.23607	30	5.47723	55	7.41620	80	8.94427
6	2.44949	31	5.56776	56	7.48331	81	9
7	2.64575	32	5.65685	57	7.54983	82	9.05539
8	2.82843	33	5.74456	58	7.61577	83	9.11043
9	3	34	5.83095	59	7.68115	84	9.16515
10	3.16228	35	5.91608	60	7.74597	85	9.21954
11	3.31662	36	6	61	7.81025	86	9.27362
12	3.46410	37	6.08276	62	7.87401	87	9.32738
13	3.60555	38	6.16441	63	7.93725	88	9.38083
14	3.74166	39	6.24500	64	8	89	9.43398
15	3.87298	40	6.32456	65	8.06226	90	9.48683
16	4	41	6.40312	66	8.12404	91	9.53939
17	4.12311	42	6.48074	67	8.18535	92	9.59166
18	4.24264	43	6.55744	68	8.24621	93	9.64365
19	4.35890	44	6.63325	69	8.30662	94	9.69536
20	4.47214	45	6.70820	70	8.36660	95	9.74679
21	4.58258	46	6.78233	71	8.42615	96	9.79796
22	4.69042	47	6.85565	72	8.48528	97	9.84886
23	4.79583	48	6.92820	73	8.54400	98	9.89949
24	4.89898	49	7	74	8.60233	99	9.94987
25	5	50	7.07107	75	8.66025	100	10

Appendix B
Geometry Review

B.1 Lines and Angles

OBJECTIVES

1. Understand the Terms *Point*, *Line*, and *Plane*
2. Work with Angles
3. Find the Measures of Angles Formed by Parallel Lines

The word *geometry* comes from the Greek words "geo," meaning "earth" and "metra," meaning "measure." The Greek scholar Euclid collected and organized the geometry known in his day into a logical system more than two thousand years ago. Euclid's system forms the basis of the geometry we still study today.

1 Understand the Terms *Point*, *Line*, and *Plane*

A **point** has no size, only position, and is usually designated by a capital letter as shown below.

$$\bullet$$
$$P$$

Figure 1

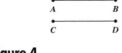

A **line** is a set of points extending infinitely far in opposite directions. A line has no width or height, just length and is uniquely determined by two points. For example, the line in Figure 1 is passing through the points A and B. The notation for the line shown is $\overleftrightarrow{AB}$.

Figure 2

A **ray** is a half-line with one **endpoint,** which extends infinitely far in one direction. See Figure 2. The notation for the ray shown is $\overrightarrow{AB}$.

Figure 3

A **line segment** is a portion of a line that has a beginning and an end. See Figure 3. If two line segments have the same length, they are said to be **congruent.** Notations for the congruent line segments shown are $\overline{AB}$ and $\overline{CD}$.

Figure 4

A **plane** is the set of points that forms a flat surface that extends indefinitely. A plane has no thickness. See Figure 4. The arrows indicate that the plane extends indefinitely in each direction.

2 Work with Angles

Figure 5

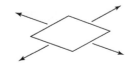

Suppose we draw two rays with a common endpoint as shown in Figure 5. The amount of rotation from one ray to the second ray is called the **angle** between the rays. The common endpoint is called the **vertex.** In Figure 5, the name of the angle is $\angle ABC$, $\angle CBA$, or $\angle B$. Angles are measured in **degrees,** which is symbolized °. One full rotation represents 360°. The notation $m\angle A = 60°$ means "the measure of angle A is 60 degrees." Because 60° is $\frac{1}{6}$ of 360°, an angle whose measure is 60° is $\frac{1}{6}$ of a full rotation. If two angles have the same measure, they are called **congruent.**

Some angles are classified by their measure.

Work Smart

One full rotation is represented below.

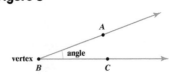

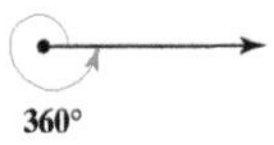

DEFINITION

An angle that measures 90° is called a **right angle.** The symbol ⌐ is used to denote a right angle. A right angle has $\frac{1}{4}$ of a full rotation. See Figure 6(a).

An angle whose measure is between 0° and 90° is called an **acute angle.** See Figure 6(b).

An angle whose measure is between 90° and 180° is called an **obtuse angle.** See Figure 6(c).

An angle whose measure is 180° is called a **straight angle.** A straight angle is $\frac{1}{2}$ of a full rotation. See Figure 6(d).

Figure 6

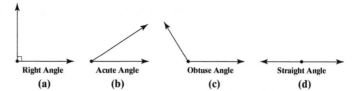

Right Angle (a)   Acute Angle (b)   Obtuse Angle (c)   Straight Angle (d)

Quick ✔

1. If two line segments have the same length, they are said to be _____.
2. The amount of rotation from one ray to a second ray is called the ____ between the rays.
3. An angle that measures 90° is called a ____ angle.

In Problems 4–7, classify each angle as right, acute, obtuse, or straight.

4.   5.   6.   7.

DEFINITION

Two angles whose measures sum to 90° are called **complementary** angles. Each angle is the **complement** of the other. Two angles whose measures sum to 180° are called **supplementary** angles. Each angle is the **supplement** of the other. See Figure 7.

Figure 7

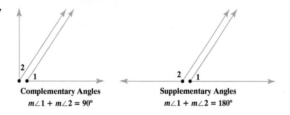

Complementary Angles
$m\angle 1 + m\angle 2 = 90°$

Supplementary Angles
$m\angle 1 + m\angle 2 = 180°$

EXAMPLE 1 Finding the Complement of an Angle

Find the complement of an angle whose measure is 18°.

Solution

Two angles are complementary if their sum is 90°. The measure of an angle that is complementary to an angle whose measure is 18° is $90° - 18° = 72°$. ∎

EXAMPLE 2 Finding the Supplement of an Angle

Find the supplement of an angle whose measure is 97°.

Solution

Two angles are supplementary if their sum is 180°. The measure of an angle that is supplementary to an angle whose measure is 97° is $180° - 97° = 83°$. ∎

Quick ✔

8. *True or False:* Two angles whose measures sum to 180° are called complementary.

In Problems 9 and 10, find the complement and supplement of each angle.

9. 15°   10. 60°

3 Find the Measures of Angles Formed by Parallel Lines

Lines that lie in the same plane are called **coplanar.**

DEFINITION

Parallel lines are lines in the same plane that never meet as shown in Figure 8(a). **Intersecting lines** meet or cross in one point. See Figure 8(b). Two lines that intersect to form right (90°) angles are called **perpendicular lines.** Figure 8(c) shows perpendicular lines.

Figure 8

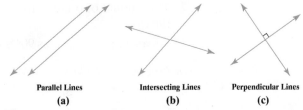

| Parallel Lines | Intersecting Lines | Perpendicular Lines |
| (a) | (b) | (c) |

When two lines intersect they form four angles. Two angles that are opposite each other are called **vertical angles.** Vertical angles have equal measures. **Adjacent angles** have the same vertex and share a side. In Figure 9, angles 1 and 3 are vertical angles and angles 1 and 2 are adjacent angles. Angles 1 and 2 are also supplementary angles. Other pairs of adjacent angles are angles 2 and 3, angles 3 and 4, and angles 1 and 4.

A line that cuts two parallel lines is called a **transversal.** In Figure 10, lines m and n are parallel and the transversal is labeled t. In this figure, there are certain angles with special names.

- There are 4 pairs of **corresponding angles:**

$$\angle 1 \text{ and } \angle 5, \quad \angle 2 \text{ and } \angle 6, \quad \angle 3 \text{ and } \angle 7, \quad \angle 4 \text{ and } \angle 8$$

- There are 2 pairs of **alternate interior angles:**

$$\angle 3 \text{ and } \angle 5, \quad \angle 4 \text{ and } \angle 6$$

Parallel lines and these angles are related in the following way.

PARALLEL LINES CUT BY A TRANSVERSAL

If two parallel lines are cut by a transversal, then
- Corresponding angles are equal in measure.
- Alternate interior angles are equal in measure.

EXAMPLE 3 Finding the Measure of Corresponding and Alternate Interior Angles

Given that lines m and n are parallel, t is a transversal, and the measure of angle 1 is 85°, find the measures of angles 2, 3, 4, 5 and 6.

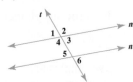

Solution

$m\angle 2 = 180° - 85° = 95°$ because $\angle 1$ and $\angle 2$ are supplementary angles.

$m\angle 3 = 85°$ because $\angle 1$ and $\angle 3$ are vertical angles.

$m\angle 4 = 180° - 85° = 95°$ because $\angle 3$ and $\angle 4$ are supplementary angles. $\angle 1$ and $\angle 4$ are also supplementary angles.

$m\angle 5 = 85°$ because $\angle 1$ and $\angle 5$ are corresponding angles.

$m\angle 6 = 85°$ because $\angle 1$ and $\angle 6$ are alternate interior angles. ∎

Figure 9

$m\angle 1 = m\angle 3$
$m\angle 2 = m\angle 4$

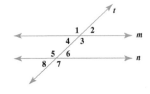

Figure 10

Quick ✔

11. _____ lines are lines in the same plane that never meet.

12. *True or False:* Two intersecting lines form four angles. The two vertical angles are supplementary.

13. *True or False:* If two parallel lines are cut by a transversal, the corresponding angles are equal in measure.

14. Find the measure of angles 1–7 given that lines m and n are parallel and t is a transversal.

B.1 EXERCISES

MyMathLab *Powered by CourseCompass™ and MathXL®*

PRACTICE   WATCH   DOWNLOAD   READ   REVIEW

1–14. *are the* Quick ✔*s that follow each* EXAMPLE

Building Skills

In Problems 15–22, classify each angle as right, acute, obtuse, or straight. See Objective 2.

15.

16.

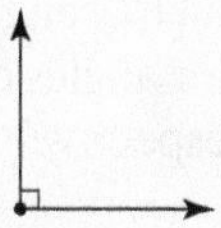

17.

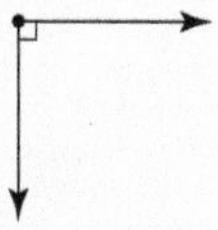

18.

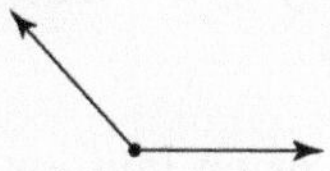

19.

20.

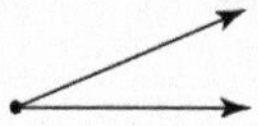

21.

22.

In Problems 23–26, find the complement of each angle. See Objective 2.

23. 32°   **24.** 19°

25. 73°   **26.** 51°

In Problems 27–30, find the supplement of each angle. See Objective 2.

27. 67°   **28.** 145°

29. 8°   **30.** 106°

In Problems 31 and 32, find the measure of angles 1–7 given that lines m and n are parallel and t is a transversal. See Objective 3.

31.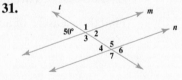

32.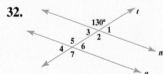

B.2 Polygons

OBJECTIVES

1. Define *Polygon*
2. Work with Triangles
3. Identify Quadrilaterals
4. Work with Circles

In Words

Vertices is the plural form of the word "vertex." The word *polygon* comes from the Greek words "poly," which means "many," and "gon," which means "angle."

1   Define *Polygon*

A **polygon** is a closed figure in a plane consisting of line segments that meet at the **vertices.** A **regular polygon** is a polygon in which the sides are congruent and the angles are congruent. Figure 11 shows four regular polygons.

Figure 11

Regular polygons: All the sides are the same length; all the angles have the same measure.

(a)

(b)

(c)

(d)

A polygon is named according to the number of sides. Table 1 summarizes the names of the polygons with 3 to 10 sides. A **triangle** is a polygon with three sides. Figure 11(a) is a regular triangle. A **quadrilateral** is a polygon with four sides. Figure 11(b) is a regular quadrilateral (also known as a *square*). A **pentagon** is a polygon with five sides. Figure 5(c) is a regular pentagon. An **octagon** is a polygon with eight sides. Figure 5(d) shows a regular octagon.

Table 1	
Polygons	
Number of Sides	Name of Polygon
3	Triangle
4	Quadrilateral
5	Pentagon
6	Hexagon
7	Heptagon
8	Octagon
9	Nonagon
10	Decagon

Figure 12

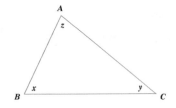

2 Work with Triangles

Figure 12 shows triangle ABC. In triangle ABC angles A, B and C are called **interior angles.** The sum of the measures of the interior angles of a triangle is $180°$. If x, y, and z represent the measures of angles A, B, and C, respectively, then

$$x + y + z = 180°$$

EXAMPLE 1   Finding the Measure of an Interior Angle of a Triangle

Find the measure of angle C in the triangle.

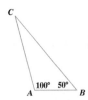

Solution

The measure of angle A is $100°$ and the measure of angle B is $50°$. We compute the measure of angle C as

$$m\angle C = 180° - 50° - 100° = 30°$$

We classify triangles by the lengths of their sides. A triangle in which all three sides are congruent is called an **equilateral** triangle. A triangle in which exactly two sides are congruent is called an **isosceles** triangle, and a triangle in which none of the sides are congruent is called a **scalene** triangle. See Figure 13.

Figure 13

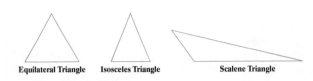

Equilateral Triangle   Isosceles Triangle   Scalene Triangle

Figure 14

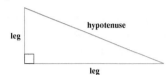

A **right triangle** is a triangle that contains a right (90°) angle. In a right triangle, the longest side is called the **hypotenuse,** and the remaining two sides are called **legs.** See Figure 14.

EXAMPLE 2 Finding the Measure of an Angle of a Right Triangle

Find the measure of angle B in the right triangle.

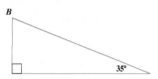

Solution

There are 180° degrees in a triangle and the right angle measures 90° so

$$m\angle B = 180° - 90° - 35° = 55°$$

Quick ✔

1. A triangle in which two sides are congruent is called a(n) _____ triangle.
2. A _____ triangle is a triangle that contains a 90° angle.
3. The sum of the measures of the interior angles in a triangle is ___ degrees.

In Problems 4 and 5, find the measure of angle B in each triangle.

4.

5.

Congruent Triangles

Figure 15

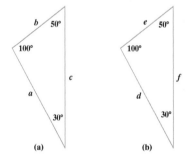

Two triangles are **congruent** if the corresponding angles have the same measure and the corresponding sides have the same length. See Figures 15(a) and 15(b). We see that the corresponding angles in triangle (a) and (b) are equal. Also, the lengths of the corresponding sides are equal: $a = d, b = e$, and $c = f$.

It is not necessary to verify that all three angles and all three sides are the same measure to determine whether two triangles are congruent.

DETERMINING CONGRUENT TRIANGLES

1. Two triangles are congruent if two of the angles are equal and the lengths of the corresponding sides between the two angles are equal. See Figure 16(a).
2. Two triangles are congruent if the lengths of the corresponding sides of the triangle are equal. See Figure 16(b).
3. Two triangles are congruent if the lengths of two corresponding sides are equal and the measures of the angles between the two sides are equal. See Figure 16(c).

Figure 16

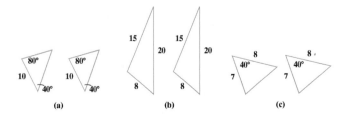

Figure 17

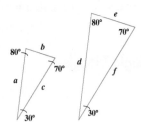

Similar Triangles

Two triangles are **similar** if the corresponding angles are equal and the lengths of the corresponding sides are proportional. That is, triangles are similar if they have the same shape. In Figure 17 the triangles are similar because the corresponding angles are equal and the corresponding sides are proportional: $\dfrac{d}{a} = \dfrac{e}{b} = \dfrac{f}{c}$. It is not necessary to verify that all three angles are congruent and all three sides are proportional to determine whether two triangles are similar.

DETERMINING SIMILAR TRIANGLES

1. Two triangles are similar if two of the corresponding angles are equal. See Figure 18(a).
2. Two triangles are similar if the lengths of all three sides of each triangle are proportional. See Figure 18(b).
3. Two triangles are similar if two corresponding sides are proportional and the angles between the corresponding sides are congruent. See Figure 18(c).

Figure 18

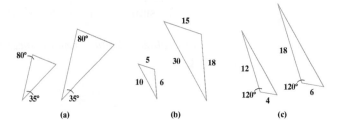

(a)   (b)   (c)

EXAMPLE 3 Finding the Missing Length in Similar Triangles

Given that the triangles in Figure 19 are similar, find the missing length.

Figure 19

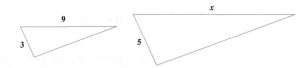

Solution

Because the triangles are similar, the corresponding sides are proportional. That is, $\dfrac{3}{5} = \dfrac{9}{x}$. We solve this equation for x.

$$\frac{3}{5} = \frac{9}{x}$$

Multiply both sides by the LCD, 5x: $5x \cdot \left(\dfrac{3}{5}\right) = 5x \cdot \left(\dfrac{9}{x}\right)$

Simplify: $3x = 45$

Divide both sides by 3: $x = 15$

The missing length is 15 units.

Quick ✔

6. Two triangles are _____ if the corresponding angles have the same measure and the corresponding sides have the same length.

7. Two triangles are _____ if corresponding angles of the triangle are equal and the lengths of the corresponding sides are proportional.

In Problem 8, given that the following triangles are similar, find the missing length.

8.

3 Identify Quadrilaterals

A **quadrilateral** is a polygon with four sides. A **parallelogram** is a quadrilateral in which both pairs of opposite sides are parallel. A **rectangle** is a parallelogram that contains a right angle. A **square** is a rectangle with all sides of equal length. A **rhombus** is a parallelogram that has all sides equal in length. A **trapezoid** is a quadrilateral with exactly one pair of opposite sides that are parallel.

Figure	Sketch
Parallelogram	
Rectangle	
Square	
Rhombus	
Trapezoid	

4 Work with Circles

Figure 20

A *circle* is also a plane figure. A **circle** is a figure made up of all points in the plane that are a fixed distance from a point called the **center.** A **radius** of the circle is a line segment drawn from the center of the circle to any point on the circle. A **diameter** of the circle is a line segment which has endpoints on the circle and passes through the center of the circle. See Figure 20. Notice that the length of the diameter d of a circle is twice the length of the radius r. That is, $d = 2r$.

EXAMPLE 4 **Finding the Length of the Diameter of a Circle**

Find the length of the diameter of a circle with radius 4 cm.

Solution

The length of the diameter is twice the length of the radius.

$$d = 2 \cdot r$$
$$d = 2 \cdot 4 \text{ cm}$$
$$d = 8 \text{ cm}$$

The diameter of the circle is 8 cm. ■

EXAMPLE 5 **Finding the Length of the Radius of a Circle**

Find the length of the radius of a circle with diameter 18 yards.

Solution

The length of the radius is one-half the length of the diameter.

$$r = \frac{1}{2} \cdot d$$
$$r = \frac{1}{2} \cdot 18 \text{ yards}$$
$$r = 9 \text{ yards}$$

The radius of the circle is 9 yards. ■

Quick ✔

9. A _____ of a circle is a line segment drawn from the center of the circle to any point on the circle.

10. *True or False:* The length of the diameter of a circle is exactly twice the length of the radius.

In Problems 11–14, find the length of the radius or diameter of each circle.

11. $d = 15$ inches, find r.   12. $d = 24$ feet, find r.

13. $r = 3.6$ yards, find d.   14. $r = 9$ cm, find d.

B.2 EXERCISES

MyMathLab *Powered by CourseCompass™ and MathXL®*

| Math XL PRACTICE | WATCH | DOWNLOAD | READ | REVIEW |

1–14. *are the* Quick ✔*s that follow each* EXAMPLE

Building Skills

In Problems 15–18, find the measure of the missing angle of the triangle. See Objective 2.

15.

16.

17.

18.

In Problems 19–22, determine the length of the missing side of the triangle. (These are similar triangles.) See Objective 2.

19.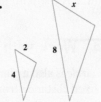

20.

21. **22.**

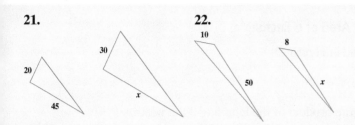

In Problems 27–30, find the length of the radius of the circle. See Objective 4.

27. $d = 14$ cm   **28.** $d = 58$ inches

29. $d = 11$ yards   **30.** $d = 27$ feet

In Problems 23–26, find the length of the diameter of the circle. See Objective 4.

23. $r = 5$ in.   **24.** $r = 16$ feet

25. $r = 2.5$ cm   **26.** $r = 5.9$ in.

B.3 Perimeter and Area of Polygons and Circles

OBJECTIVES

1 Find the Perimeter and Area of a Rectangle and a Square

2 Find the Perimeter and Area of a Parallelogram and a Trapezoid

3 Find the Perimeter and Area of a Triangle

4 Find the Circumference and Area of a Circle

Figure 21

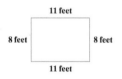

The **perimeter** of a polygon is the distance around the polygon. Put another way, the perimeter of a polygon is the sum of the lengths of the sides.

1 Find the Perimeter and Area of a Rectangle and a Square

A rectangle is a polygon, so the perimeter of a rectangle is the sum of the lengths of the sides.

EXAMPLE 1 Finding the Perimeter of a Rectangle

Find the perimeter of the rectangle in Figure 21.

Solution

The perimeter of the rectangle is the sum of the lengths of the sides, so

$$\text{perimeter} = 11 \text{ feet} + 8 \text{ feet} + 11 \text{ feet} + 8 \text{ feet}$$
$$= 38 \text{ feet}$$

Did you notice that the perimeter from Example 1 can also be written as

$$\text{perimeter} = 2 \cdot 11 \text{ feet} + 2 \cdot 8 \text{ feet?}$$

In general, the perimeter of a rectangle is written $P = 2l + 2w$.

A different measure of a polygon is its *area*. The **area** of a polygon is the amount of surface the polygon covers. Consider the rectangle shown in Figure 22. If we count the number of 1-unit by 1-unit squares within the rectangle, we see that the area of the rectangle is 6 square units. The area can also be found by multiplying the number of units of length by the number of units of width.

Figure 22

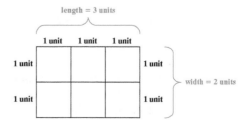

We can generalize this result to say that the area of a rectangle is the product of its length and width.

Figure 23

EXAMPLE 2 Finding the Area of a Rectangle

Find the area of the rectangle in Figure 23.

Solution

The area of the rectangle is the product of the length and the width, so

$$area = 6 \text{ feet} \cdot 10 \text{ feet}$$
$$= 60 \text{ square feet}$$

We give a summary of how to find the perimeter and area of a rectangle.

Figure	Sketch	Perimeter	Area
Rectangle		$P = 2l + 2w$	$A = lw$

Figure 24

EXAMPLE 3 Finding the Perimeter and Area of a Rectangle

Find **(a)** the perimeter and **(b)** the area of the rectangle shown in Figure 24.

Solution

(a) The perimeter of the rectangle is

$$P = 2l + 2w$$
$$P = 2 \cdot 7.5 \text{ cm} + 2 \cdot 3.5 \text{ cm}$$
$$= 15 \text{ cm} + 7 \text{ cm}$$
$$= 22 \text{ cm}$$

The perimeter of the rectangle is 22 cm.

(b) The area of the rectangle is

$$A = lw$$
$$= 7.5 \text{ cm} \cdot 3.5 \text{ cm}$$
$$= 26.25 \text{ square cm}$$

The area of the given rectangle is 26.25 square cm.

Quick ✔

1. The _____ of a polygon is the distance around the polygon.

2. The ___ of a polygon is the amount of surface the polygon covers.

In Problems 3 and 4, find the perimeter and area of each rectangle.

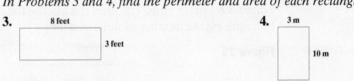

We can find the perimeter and area of a square using the same methods we use to find the perimeter and area of a rectangle. A square is a rectangle that has four congruent sides, so to find the perimeter of a square we use

$$perimeter = side + side + side + side = 4 \cdot side = 4s$$

where *s* is the length of a side.

Figure 25

3 cm

EXAMPLE 4 Finding the Perimeter of a Square

Find the perimeter of the square in Figure 25.

Solution

The perimeter of the square is

$$\text{perimeter} = 4 \cdot s$$
$$= 4 \cdot 3 \text{ cm}$$
$$= 12 \text{ cm} \qquad \blacksquare$$

We know that the area of a rectangle is found by finding the product of the length and the width. In a square, the sides are congruent, so

$$\text{area} = \text{side} \cdot \text{side} = \text{side}^2$$

Figure 26

7 inches

EXAMPLE 5 Finding the Area of a Square

Find the area of the square in Figure 26.

Solution

The area of the square is

$$\text{area} = \text{side}^2$$
$$= (7 \text{ inches})^2$$
$$= 49 \text{ square inches} \qquad \blacksquare$$

We summarize the formulas for the perimeter and area of a square in the following table.

Figure	Sketch	Perimeter	Area
Square	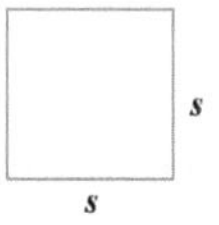	$P = 4s$	$A = s^2$

Quick ✔

5. *True or False:* The area of a square is the sum of the lengths of the sides.

In Problems 6 and 7, find the perimeter and area of each square.

6. 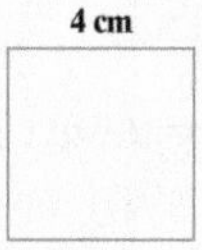   4 cm

7.    1.5 yards

EXAMPLE 6 Finding the Perimeter and Area of a Geometric Figure

Find **(a)** the perimeter and **(b)** the area of the region shown in Figure 27.

Figure 27

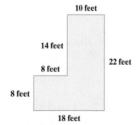

10 feet

14 feet

22 feet

8 feet

8 feet

18 feet

Solution

(a) The perimeter is the distance around the polygon. So,

$$\text{Perimeter} = 8 \text{ feet} + 8 \text{ feet} + 14 \text{ feet} + 10 \text{ feet} + 22 \text{ feet} + 18 \text{ feet}$$
$$= 80 \text{ feet}$$

(b) Notice the region can be divided into an 8-foot by 8-foot square plus a 10-foot by 22-foot rectangle. To find the area, we find the area of the square and add it to the area of the rectangle.

$$\text{Area} = \text{Area of square} + \text{Area of rectangle}$$
$$= (8 \text{ feet})^2 + (10 \text{ feet})(22 \text{ feet})$$
$$= 64 \text{ square feet} + 220 \text{ square feet}$$
$$= 284 \text{ square feet}$$

Quick ✔ *In Problem 8, find the perimeter and area of the figure.*

8.

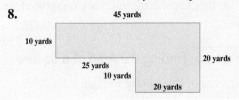

EXAMPLE 7 Painting a Room

You've decided to paint your rectangular bedroom. Two walls are 14 feet long and 7 feet high, and the other two walls are 10 feet long and 7 feet high.

(a) Ignoring the window and door openings in the bedroom, what is the area of the walls in your bedroom?

(b) You know that one gallon of paint will cover 300 square feet. How many one-gallon cans of paint must you purchase to paint your bedroom?

Solution

(a) The bedroom consists of two walls that are 14 feet long and 7 feet high. The area of these two walls is

$$\text{area} = l \cdot w \cdot 2$$
$$\text{area} = 14 \text{ feet} \cdot 7 \text{ feet} \cdot 2$$
$$= 196 \text{ square feet}$$

The area of the other two walls is

$$\text{area} = l \cdot w \cdot 2$$
$$\text{area} = 10 \text{ feet} \cdot 7 \text{ feet} \cdot 2$$
$$= 140 \text{ square feet}$$

The total area to be painted is

$$\text{area} = 196 \text{ square feet} + 140 \text{ square feet}$$
$$= 336 \text{ square feet}$$

(b) A one-gallon can of paint covers 300 square feet. You have 336 square feet, so you will need to purchase 2 gallons of paint.

2 Find the Perimeter and Area of a Parallelogram and a Trapezoid

Recall that a parallelogram is a quadrilateral in which opposite sides are parallel. A trapezoid is a quadrilateral with exactly one pair of opposite sides that are parallel. The following table gives the formulas for the perimeters and areas of parallelograms and trapezoids.

Figure	Sketch	Perimeter	Area
Parallelogram		$P = 2a + 2b$	$A = b \cdot h$
Trapezoid		$P = a + b + c + B$	$A = \dfrac{1}{2}h(b + B)$

Figure 28

EXAMPLE 8 Finding the Perimeter and Area of a Parallelogram

Find **(a)** the perimeter and **(b)** the area of parallelogram shown in Figure 28.

Solution

(a) The perimeter of the parallelogram is

$$P = 2l + 2w$$
$$= 2 \cdot 12 \text{ feet} + 2 \cdot 5 \text{ feet}$$
$$= 24 \text{ feet} + 10 \text{ feet}$$
$$= 34 \text{ feet}$$

The perimeter of the parallelogram is 34 feet.

(b) The area of the parallelogram is

$$A = b \cdot h$$
$$= 12 \text{ feet} \cdot 4 \text{ feet}$$
$$= 48 \text{ square feet}$$

The area of the parallelogram is 48 square feet.

Figure 29

EXAMPLE 9 Finding the Perimeter and Area of a Trapezoid

Find **(a)** the perimeter and **(b)** the area of the trapezoid shown in Figure 29.

Solution

(a) The perimeter of the trapezoid is

$$\text{Perimeter} = 7 \text{ inches} + 8 \text{ inches} + 10 \text{ inches} + 15 \text{ inches}$$
$$= 40 \text{ inches}$$

The perimeter of the trapezoid is 40 inches.

(b) The area of the trapezoid is

$$A = \frac{1}{2}h(b + B)$$

$$= \frac{1}{2} \cdot 6 \text{ inches} \cdot (15 \text{ inches} + 10 \text{ inches})$$

$$= \frac{1}{2} \cdot 6 \text{ inches} \cdot 25 \text{ inches}$$

$$= 75 \text{ square inches}$$

The area of the trapezoid is 75 square inches.

Quick ✔

9. To find the area of a trapezoid, we use the formula $A =$ _____ where ___ is the height of the trapezoid and the bases have lengths ___ and ___.

In Problems 10 and 11, find the perimeter and area of each figure.

10.

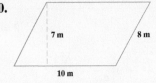

11.

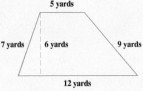

3 Find the Perimeter and Area of a Triangle

Recall that a triangle is a polygon with three sides. The following table gives the formulas for the perimeter and area of a triangle.

Figure	Sketch	Perimeter	Area
Triangle	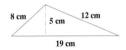	$P = a + b + c$	$A = \dfrac{1}{2}bh$

Figure 30

EXAMPLE 10 Finding the Perimeter and Area of a Triangle

Find **(a)** the perimeter and **(b)** the area of the triangle shown in Figure 30.

Solution

(a) To find the perimeter of the triangle, add the lengths of the three sides of the triangle.

$$\text{perimeter} = a + b + c$$
$$= 8\text{ cm} + 12\text{ cm} + 19\text{ cm}$$
$$= 39\text{ cm}$$

The perimeter of the triangle shown in Figure 30 is 39 cm.

(b) We use $A = \dfrac{1}{2}bh$ with base $= b = 19$ cm and height $= h = 5$ cm.

$$A = \frac{1}{2}bh = \frac{1}{2} \cdot 19\text{ cm} \cdot 5\text{ cm} = 47.5 \text{ square cm}$$

The area of the triangle in Figure 30 is 47.5 square cm. ∎

Quick ✔

12. *True or False:* The area of a triangle is given by the formula $A = \dfrac{1}{2}bh$, where b is the base and h is the height.

In Problems 13 and 14, find the perimeter and area of each triangle.

13.

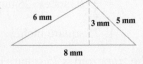

14.

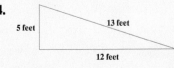

4 Find the Circumference and Area of a Circle

The **circumference** of a circle is the distance around a circle. We use the diameter or the radius of the circle to find the circumference of a circle according to the formulas given below. We also give the formula for the area of a circle.

Figure	Sketch	Perimeter	Area
Circle	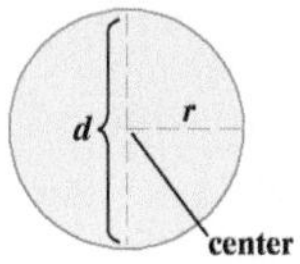	$C = \pi d$ where d is the length of diameter $C = 2\pi r$ where r is the length of radius	$A = \pi r^2$

Figure 31

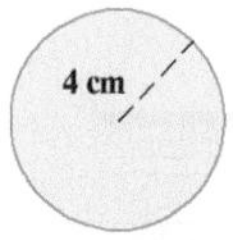

(a)

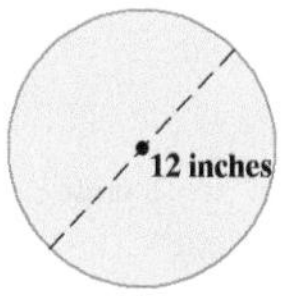

12 inches

(b)

EXAMPLE 11 Finding the Circumference of a Circle

Find the circumference of the circles in Figure 31.

Solution

(a) We know the length of the radius is 4 cm so we use the formula $C = 2\pi r$.

$$C = 2\pi r$$

$r = 4$ cm: $\qquad = 2 \cdot \pi \cdot 4 \text{ cm}$

$$= 8 \cdot \pi \text{ cm}$$

Use a calculator: $\qquad \approx 25.13 \text{ cm}$

The exact circumference of the circle is 8π cm, and 25.13 cm is the approximate circumference, to the nearest hundredth of a centimeter.

(b) The length of the diameter is given to be 12 inches, so we use $C = \pi d$.

$$C = \pi d$$

$d = 12$ inches: $\qquad = \pi \cdot 12 \text{ inches}$

$$= 12\pi \text{ inches}$$

Use a calculator: $\qquad \approx 37.70 \text{ inches}$

The exact circumference of the circle is 12π in., and 37.70 in. is the approximate circumference, to the nearest hundredth of an inch. ■

Figure 32

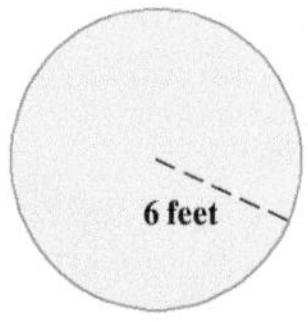

6 feet

EXAMPLE 12 Finding the Area of a Circle

Find the area of the circle in Figure 32.

Solution

The circle in Figure 32 has radius with length 6 feet, so we substitute $r = 6$ feet in the equation $A = \pi r^2$.

$$A = \pi r^2$$

$$= \pi \cdot (6 \text{ feet})^2$$

$$= \pi(36) \text{ square feet}$$

$$= 36\pi \text{ square feet}$$

Use a calculator: $\quad \approx 113.10 \text{ square feet}$

The area of the circle is exactly 36π square feet or approximately 113.10 square feet. ■

Quick ✔

15. The _____ of a circle is the distance around the circle.

16. The area of a circle is given by the formula $A = \pi d^2$.

In Problems 17 and 18, find the circumference and area of each circle.

17.

4 feet

18.

24 cm

B.3 EXERCISES

MyMathLab

PRACTICE   WATCH   DOWNLOAD   READ   REVIEW

1–18. are the Quick ✔*s that follow each* EXAMPLE

Building Skills

In Problems 19–22, find the perimeter and area of each rectangle. See Objective 1.

19.

10 feet

4 feet

20.

12 miles

8 miles

21.

5 m

15 m

22.

2 cm

20 cm

In Problems 23 and 24, find the perimeter and area of each square. See Objective 1.

23.

6 km

6 km

24.

13 yards

13 yards

In Problems 25–28, find the perimeter and area of each figure. See Objective 1.

25.

7 feet

6 feet

15 feet

14 feet

8 feet

22 feet

26.

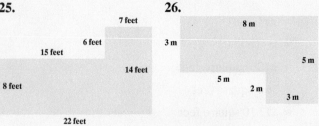

8 m

3 m

5 m

5 m

2 m

3 m

27.

13 m

2 m

8 m

2 m

8 m

2 m

28.

5 yards

20 yards

5 yards

10 yards

10 yards

In Problems 29–36, find the perimeter and area of each quadrilateral. See Objective 2.

29.

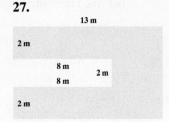

6 feet   5 feet

9 feet

30.

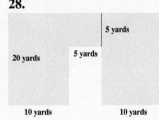

4 cm   2 cm

14 cm

31.

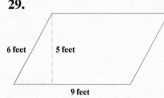

9 mm   10 mm

4 mm

32.

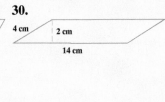

19 in.   20 in.

8 in.

33.

8 in.

8 in.   7 in.   8 in.

16 in.

34.

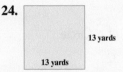 

10 m

6 m   5 m   6 m

14 m

35.

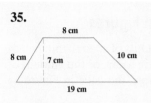

36.

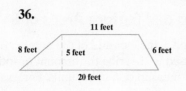

43.

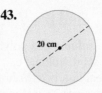

44.

In Problems 37–40, find the perimeter and area of each triangle. See Objective 3.

37.

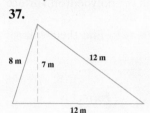

38.

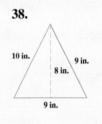

Applying the Concepts

In Problems 45 and 46, find the area of the shaded region.

45.

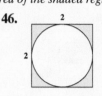

46.

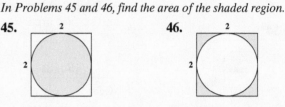

39.

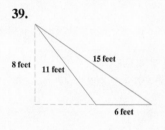

40.

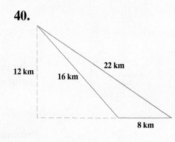

47. How many feet will a wheel with a diameter of 20 inches travel after 5 revolutions?

48. How many feet will a wheel with a diameter of 18 inches travel after 3 revolutions?

In Problems 41–44, find (a) the circumference and (b) the area of each circle. For both the circumference and area, provide exact answers and approximate answers rounded to the nearest hundredth. See Objective 4.

41.

42.

B.4 Volume and Surface Area

OBJECTIVES

1. Identify Solid Figures
2. Find the Volumes and Surface Areas of Solid Figures

In Words

Polyhedra is the plural form of the Greek word *polyhedron*.

1 Identify Solid Figures

A **geometric solid** is a three-dimensional region of space enclosed by planes and curved surfaces. Examples of geometric solids are cubes, pyramids, spheres, cylinders, and cones.

There are some geometric solids that you see and use every day. When you grab a box of cereal, you are holding a rectangular solid. When you reach for a can of soup, you are reaching for a circular cylinder.

We first discuss *polyhedra*. A **polyhedron** is a three-dimensional solid formed by connecting polygons. Figure 33 shows an example of a polyhedron called a hexagonal dipyramid. Notice that the top and bottom are formed by six connected triangles.

Each of the planes of a polyhedron is called a **face.** The line segment which is the intersection of any two faces of a polyhedron is called an **edge.** The point of intersection of three or more edges is called a **vertex.**

Figure 33
Hexagonal Dipyramid

Figure 34

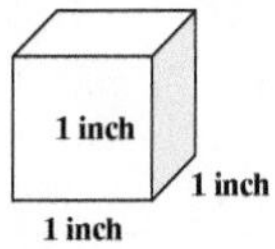

1 inch
1 inch
1 inch

Work Smart

Volume is measured in cubic units. Surface area is measured in square units.

Figure 35

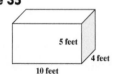

5 feet
4 feet
10 feet

2 Find the Volumes and Surface Areas of Solid Figures

The **volume** of a polyhedron is the measure of the number of units of space contained in the solid. Volume can be used to describe the amount of soda in a can, or the amount of cereal in a box. Volume is measured in cubic units. For example, the cube in Figure 34 represents 1 cubic inch.

The **surface area** of a polyhedron is the sum of the areas of the faces of the polyhedron. For example, because each face in the cube shown in Figure 34 has an area of 1 square inch, and a cube has six faces, the surface area of the cube is 6 square inches. Because surface area is the sum of the areas of each polygon in the polyhedron, surface area is measured in square units.

Table 2 shows some common geometric solids, and formulas to find their volume and surface area.

Table 2		
Solids		**Formulas**
Cube	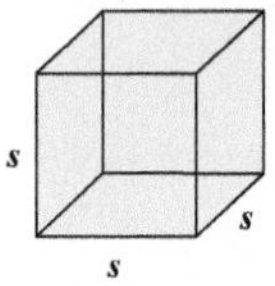	**Volume:** $V = s^3$ **Surface Area:** $S = 6s^2$
Rectangular Solid	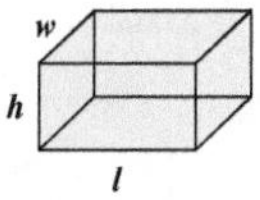	**Volume:** $V = lwh$ **Surface Area:** $S = 2lw + 2lh + 2wh$
Sphere	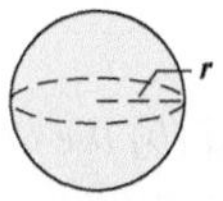	**Volume:** $V = \dfrac{4}{3}\pi r^3$ **Surface Area:** $S = 4\pi r^2$
Right Circular Cylinder	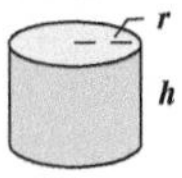	**Volume:** $V = \pi r^2 h$ **Surface Area:** $S = 2\pi r^2 + 2\pi rh$
Cone	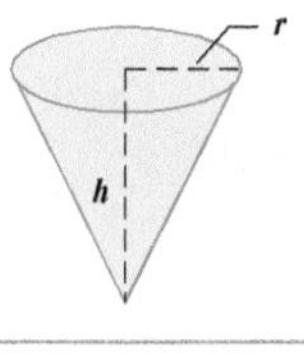	**Volume:** $V = \dfrac{1}{3}\pi r^2 h$
Square Pyramid	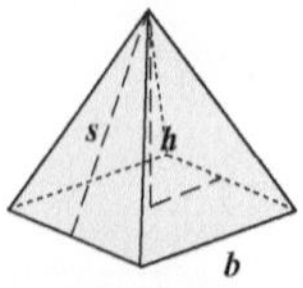	**Volume:** $V = \dfrac{1}{3}b^2 h$ **Surface Area:** $S = b^2 + 2bs$

EXAMPLE 1 Finding the Volume and Surface Area of a Rectangular Solid

Find the volume and surface area of the rectangular solid shown in Figure 35.

Solution

We have that $l = 10$ feet, $h = 5$ feet, and $w = 4$ feet. The volume of the rectangular solid is

$$V = lwh$$
$$= (10 \text{ feet})(4 \text{ feet})(5 \text{ feet})$$
$$= 200 \text{ cubic feet}$$

The volume of the rectangular solid is 200 cubic feet.

The surface area of the rectangular solid is

$$S = 2lw + 2lh + 2wh$$
$$= 2(10 \text{ feet})(4 \text{ feet}) + 2(10 \text{ feet})(5 \text{ feet}) + 2(4 \text{ feet})(5 \text{ feet})$$
$$= 220 \text{ square feet}$$

The surface area of the rectangular solid is 220 square feet. ■

Figure 36

EXAMPLE 2 Finding the Volume of a Right Circular Cylinder

Find the volume and surface area of the right circular cylinder shown in Figure 36.

Solution

We have that $h = 10$ inches and $r = 3$ inches. The volume of the right circular cylinder is

$$V = \pi r^2 h$$
$$= \pi(3 \text{ in.})^2(10 \text{ in.})$$
$$= 90\pi \text{ in.}^3$$
$$\approx 282.74 \text{ in.}^3$$

The volume of the right circular cylinder is exactly 90π cubic inches and approximately 282.74 cubic inches.

The surface area of the right circular cylinder is

$$V = 2\pi r^2 + 2\pi rh$$
$$= 2\pi(3 \text{ in.})^2 + 2\pi(3 \text{ in.})(10 \text{ in.})$$
$$= 18\pi \text{ in.}^2 + 60\pi \text{ in.}^2$$
$$= 78\pi \text{ in.}^2$$
$$\approx 245.04 \text{ in.}^2$$

The surface area of the right circular cylinder is exactly 78π square inches and approximately 245.04 square inches. ■

Quick ✔

1. A _____ is a three-dimensional solid formed by connecting polygons.
2. The _____ of a polyhedron is the sum of the areas of the faces of the polyhedron.
3. *True or False:* The volume of a right circular cylinder is measured in square units.
4. *True or False:* The volume of a rectangular solid is the product of the length, width, and height.

In Problems 5 and 6, find the volume and surface area of the following solids.

5.

6.

B.4 EXERCISES

PRACTICE   WATCH   DOWNLOAD   READ   REVIEW

1–6. *are the* Quick ✔s *that follow each* EXAMPLE

Building Skills

See Objective 2.

7. Find the volume *V* and surface area *S* of a rectangular box with length 10 feet, width 5 feet, and height 12 feet.

8. Find the volume *V* and surface area *S* of a rectangular box with length 2 meters, width 6 meters, and height 9 meters.

9. Find the volume *V* and surface area *S* of a sphere with radius 6 centimeters.

10. Find the volume *V* and surface area *S* of a sphere with radius 10 inches.

11. Find the volume *V* and surface area *S* of a right circular cylinder with radius 2 inches and height 8 inches.

12. Find the volume *V* and surface area *S* of a right circular cylinder with radius 3 inches and height 6 inches.

13. Find the volume *V* of a cone with radius 10 mm and height 8 mm.

14. Find the volume *V* of a cone with radius 20 feet and height 30 feet.

15. Find the volume *V* and surface area *S* of a square pyramid with height 10 feet, slant height 12 feet, and base 8 feet.

16. Find the volume *V* and surface area *S* of a square pyramid with height 5 m, slant 8 m, and base 10 m.

Applying the Concepts

17. Rain Gutter A rain gutter is in the shape of a rectangular solid. How much water, in cubic inches, can the gutter hold if it is 4 inches in height, 3 inches wide, and 12 feet long?

18. Water for the Horses A trough for horses in the shape of a rectangular solid is 10 feet long, 2 feet wide, and 3 feet deep. How much water can the trough hold?

19. A Can of Peaches A can of peaches is in the shape of a right circular cylinder. The can has a 4-inch diameter and is 6 inches tall. What is the volume of the can? What is the surface area of the can? Express your answers as decimals rounded to the nearest hundredth.

20. Coffee Can A coffee can is in the shape of a right circular cylinder. The can has an 8-inch diameter and is 10 inches tall. What is the volume of the can? What is the surface area of the can? Express your answers as decimals rounded to the nearest hundredth.

21. Ice Cream Cone A waffle cone for ice cream has a diameter of 8 cm and a height of 16 cm. How much ice cream can the cone hold if the ice cream is flush with the top of the cone? Express your answer as a decimal rounded to the nearest hundredth.

22. Water Cooler The cups at the water cooler are cone-shaped. How much water can a cup hold if it has a 5-inch diameter and is 8 inches in height? Express your answer as a decimal rounded to the nearest hundredth.

Answers to Selected Exercises

Chapter 1 Operations on Real Numbers and Algebraic Expressions

Section 1.1 Success in Mathematics   Answers will vary.

Section 1.2 Fractions, Decimals, and Percents   1. factors; product   2. $2 \cdot 2 \cdot 3$ 3. $2 \cdot 3 \cdot 3$ 4. $3 \cdot 5 \cdot 5$ 5. $2 \cdot 2 \cdot 2 \cdot 3 \cdot 5$ 6. prime
7. $3 \cdot 3 \cdot 3 \cdot 17$ 8. 24   9. 10   10. 360   11. 21   12. 180   13. equivalent fractions   14. $\frac{5}{10}$ 15. $\frac{30}{48}$ 16. $\frac{1}{4} = \frac{3}{12}; \frac{5}{6} = \frac{10}{12}$
17. $\frac{5}{12} = \frac{25}{60}; \frac{4}{15} = \frac{16}{60}$ 18. $\frac{9}{20} = \frac{36}{80}; \frac{11}{16} = \frac{55}{80}$ 19. $\frac{9}{16}$ 20. in lowest terms   21. $\frac{2}{5}$ 22. $\frac{2}{7}$ 23. hundredths   24. tenths
25. thousands   26. thousandths   27. ones   28. ten-thousands   29. 0.2   30. 0.93   31. 1.40   32. 14.398   33. 690.00   34. 60.0
35. 0.4   36. $0.\overline{428571}$ 37. 1.375   38. 0.833... or $0.8\overline{3}$ 39. $0.\overline{5}$ or 0.555...   40. $\frac{13}{20}$ 41. $\frac{1}{5}$ 42. $\frac{5}{8}$ 43. hundred; 35; 35   44. 0.23
45. 0.01   46. 0.724   47. 1.27   48. 0.8926   49. 100%   50. 15%   51. 80%   52. 130%   53. 39.8%   54. 0.4%   55. $5 \cdot 5$
57. $2 \cdot 2 \cdot 7$ 59. $3 \cdot 7$ 61. $2 \cdot 2 \cdot 3 \cdot 3$ 63. $2 \cdot 2 \cdot 5$ 65. $2 \cdot 3 \cdot 5$ 67. $2 \cdot 5 \cdot 5$ 69. 53 is prime.   71. $2 \cdot 2 \cdot 3 \cdot 3 \cdot 7$ 73. 42   75. 60
77. 210   79. 90   81. 60   83. 72   85. $\frac{8}{12}$ 87. $\frac{18}{24}$ 89. $\frac{21}{3}$ 91. $\frac{4}{8}$ and $\frac{3}{8}$ 93. $\frac{9}{15}$ and $\frac{10}{15}$ 95. $\frac{20}{24}$ and $\frac{15}{24}$ 97. $\frac{44}{60}$ and $\frac{21}{60}$
99. $\frac{20}{90}$ and $\frac{35}{90}$ and $\frac{21}{90}$ 101. $\frac{2}{3}$ 103. $\frac{19}{9}$ 105. $\frac{1}{2}$ 107. $\frac{4}{5}$ 109. hundredths place   111. tens place   113. thousandths place
115. 578.2   117. 350   119. 3682.010   121. 30   123. 0.625   125. $0.\overline{285714}$ 127. 0.3125   129. $0.\overline{230769}$ 131. 1.16   133. 2.2
135. 2.67   137. 0.519   139. $\frac{3}{4}$ 141. $\frac{9}{10}$ 143. $\frac{491}{500}$ 145. $\frac{101}{400}$ 147. 0.37   149. 0.0602   151. 0.001   153. 20%   155. 27.5%
157. 200%   159. 84 months   161. 20 days   163. $\frac{13}{20}$ 165. 70%   167. 77.27%   169. (a) 33.33%   (b) 16.67%   (c) 25%   171. 21.43%
173. 2, 3, 5, 7, 11, 13, 17, 19, 23, 29, 31, 37, 41, 43, 47, 53, 59, 61, 67, 71, 73, 79, 83, 89, 97

Section 1.3 The Number Systems and the Real Number Line   1. $\{1, 3, 5, 7\}$ 2. {Alabama, Alaska, Arkansas, Arizona}   3. $\varnothing$ or { }
4. True   5. rational   6. 12   7. 12, 0   8. $-5, 12, 0$ 9. $\frac{11}{5}, -5, 12, 2.\overline{76}, 0, \frac{18}{4}$ 10. π 11. All numbers listed
12.   13. inequality   14. $<$ 15. $<$ 16. $>$ 17. $>$ 18. $=$ 19. $<$
20. absolute value   21. 15   22. $\frac{3}{4}$ 23. $A = \{0, 1, 2, 3, 4\}$ 25. $D = \{1, 2, 3, 4\}$ 27. $E = \{6, 8, 10, 12, 14\}$ 29. 3   31. $-4, 3, 0$
33. 2.303003000...   35. All numbers listed   37. π 39. $\frac{5}{5} = 1$ 41.   43. True   45. True
47. True   49. False   51. $<$ 53. $>$ 55. $>$ 57. $=$ 59. 12   61. 4   63. $\frac{3}{8}$ 65. 2.1
67. (a)   (b) $-4.5, -1, -\frac{1}{2}, \frac{3}{5}, 1, 3.5, |-7| = 7$ (c) (i) $-1, 1, |-7| = 7$ (ii) All numbers listed
69. -100, Integers, Rational, Real   71. -10.5 Rational, Real   73. $\frac{75}{25}$, Natural, Whole, Integers, Rational, Real   75. 7.56556555..., Irrational, Real
77. True   79. False   81. True   83. True   85. True   87. Irrational numbers   89. Real numbers   91. 0   93. True   95. True
97. $\{7, 8, 9, 10, 11, 12, 13, 14, 15\}$ 99. $\{10, 11, 12, 13, 14, 15\}$ 101. $\{11, 12\}$ 103. $\{2, 4, 6, 8, 10\}$ 105. (a) $\{1\}, \{2\}, \{3\}, \{4\}, \{1, 2\}, \{1, 3\}, \{1, 4\},$
$\{2, 3\}, \{2, 4\}, \{3, 4\}, \{1, 2, 3\}, \{1, 2, 4\}, \{1, 3, 4\}, \{2, 3, 4\}, \{1, 2, 3, 4\}, \varnothing$ (b) 16   107. A rational number is any number that can be written as the
quotient of two integers, denominator not equal to zero. Natural numbers, whole numbers and integers are rational numbers. Terminating and repeating
decimals are also rational numbers.

Section 1.4 Adding, Subtracting, Multiplying, and Dividing Integers   1. sum   2. 27   3. -8 4. 14   5. -7 6. -17 7. 3
8. -1 9. 2   10. -4 11. 14   12. -6 13. 10   14. negative   15. -4 16. -3 17. -24 18. -56 19. -7 20. $-\frac{3}{7}$
21. 21   22. $\frac{8}{5}$ 23. 5.75   24. difference   25. (-10) 26. 80   27. -178 28. -18 29. -2572 30. -21 31. -58 32. 12
33. 550   34. positive   35. -21 36. -52 37. 80   38. 108   39. 325   40. True   41. 108   42. 360   43. $\frac{1}{6}$ 44. $-\frac{1}{2}$
45. True   46. -5 47. -7 48. 9   49. 15   51. 4   53. 4   55. -19 57. 21   59. -328 61. -11 63. 43   65. 325
67. -125 69. 11   71. -8 73. -28 75. 54   77. 0   79. -41 81. -31 83. 172   85. 40   87. -56 89. 0   91. 144
93. -126 95. -90 97. 210   99. 120   101. $\frac{1}{8}$ 103. $-\frac{1}{4}$ 105. 1   107. 5   109. 7   111. -15 113. $\frac{7}{2}$ 115. $-\frac{10}{7}$ 117. $\frac{35}{4}$
119. -72 121. 60   123. 171   125. -15 127. -42 129. $\frac{15}{4}$ 131. 40   133. -238 135. $28 + (-21) = 7$ 137. $-21 - 47 = -68$
139. $-12 \cdot 18 = -216$ 141. $-36 \div (-108)$ or $\frac{-36}{-108} = \frac{1}{3}$ 143. -3.25 dollars   145. -6 yards   147. $-\$48$ 149. 14 miles   151. \$655

153. No; -125 cases   **155.** 25,725 feet   **157.** $-3, -5$ **159.** $-12, 2$ **161. (a)** $1, 2, 1.5, 1.\overline{6}, 1.6, 1.625, 1.615, 1.619, 1.618,...$ **(b)** 1.618
(c) Answers may vary   **163.** The problem $42 \div 4$ may be written equivalently as $42 \cdot \frac{1}{4}$.

Section 1.5 Adding, Subtracting, Multiplying, and Dividing Rational Numbers Expressed as Fractions and Decimals   **1.** $-\frac{2}{7}$ **2.** $-\frac{3}{5}$

3. -6 **4.** $\frac{27}{32}$ **5.** $-\frac{8}{3}$ **6.** $-\frac{6}{25}$ **7.** $\frac{3}{4}$ **8.** $-\frac{3}{22}$ **9.** 1 **10.** $\frac{1}{12}$ **11.** $\frac{5}{7}$ **12.** -4 **13.** $-\frac{20}{31}$ **14.** $\frac{50}{49}$ **15.** $-\frac{3}{8}$ **16.** $-\frac{16}{7}$
17. $\frac{5}{27}$ **18.** 7 **19.** $-\frac{6}{5}$ **20.** $\frac{10}{11}$ **21.** $-\frac{3}{7}$ **22.** $\frac{1}{7}$ **23.** $\frac{5}{36}$ **24.** $\frac{29}{42}$ **25.** $-\frac{13}{4}$ **26.** $\frac{13}{55}$ **27.** $-\frac{25}{16}$ **28.** $\frac{15}{4}$ **29.** 21.014
30. 64.57 **31.** 22.368 **32.** 337.5788 **33.** -71.412 **34.** -89.112 **35.** 4.78 **36.** 65.884 **37.** -0.1035 **38.** -899.5 **39.** 0.0135
40. 0.0198 **41.** 0.25 **42.** 8.36 **43.** -0.094 **44.** -0.03 **45.** $\frac{2}{3}$ **47.** $-\frac{19}{9}$ **49.** $-\frac{1}{2}$ **51.** $\frac{4}{5}$ **53.** $\frac{12}{25}$ **55.** -25 **57.** $-\frac{2}{3}$
59. 8 **61.** $\frac{31}{3}$ **63.** $\frac{6}{11}$ **65.** $\frac{5}{3}$ **67.** $-\frac{1}{5}$ **69.** $\frac{5}{6}$ **71.** $-\frac{1}{9}$ **73.** $-\frac{2}{3}$ **75.** $\frac{9}{11}$ **77.** -12 **79.** 32 **81.** $\frac{3}{2}$ **83.** $\frac{1}{2}$ **85.** 2
87. $\frac{1}{3}$ **89.** $\frac{5}{2}$ **91.** $-\frac{13}{12}$ **93.** $\frac{1}{4}$ **95.** $\frac{9}{5}$ **97.** $-\frac{1}{6}$ **99.** $\frac{33}{40}$ **101.** $\frac{139}{36}$ **103.** $-\frac{7}{18}$ **105.** -6.5 **107.** 8.4 **109.** 55.92
111. 1.49 **113.** 42.55 **115.** 24.94 **117.** 9 **119.** 24.3 **121.** 490 **123.** 0.95 **125.** $-\frac{11}{30}$ **127.** $-\frac{4}{3}$ **129.** $-\frac{2}{3}$ **131.** $-\frac{1}{4}$
133. $-\frac{129}{35}$ **135.** 1.6 **137.** $-\frac{2}{21}$ **139.** -50.526 **141.** -16 **143.** -15 **145.** -6.58 **147.** -7.9 **149.** $-\frac{25}{14}$ **151.** 58.39
153. 30.96 **155.** $\frac{1}{8}$ **157.** 21 hours   **159.** 18 students   **161.** $-\$68.79$ **163.** $\$2.40$ **165.** 13.2 **167.** $\frac{86}{15}$

Putting the Concepts Together (Sections 1.2–1.5)   **1.** $\frac{7}{8} = \frac{35}{40}, \frac{9}{20} = \frac{18}{40}$ **2.** $\frac{1}{3}$ **3.** $0.\overline{285714}$ **4.** $\frac{3}{8}$ **5.** 0.123 **6.** 6.25%

7. (a) $-12, -\frac{14}{7} = -2, 0, 3$ **(b)** $-12, -\frac{14}{7} = -2, -1.25, 0, 3, 11.2$ **(c)** $\sqrt{2}$ **(d)** All the numbers in the set are real numbers.   **8.** $<$

9. -11 **10.** -65 **11.** -27 **12.** 27 **13.** -5.5 **14.** -10 **15.** -100 **16.** 72 **17.** -5 **18.** 16 **19.** -9 **20.** -3 **21.** $\frac{31}{5}$
22. $\frac{31}{36}$ **23.** $-\frac{17}{36}$ **24.** $\frac{9}{5}$ **25.** $-\frac{1}{28}$ **26.** 0 **27.** 10.76 **28.** 7.646 **29.** 1.46 **30.** 22.232

Section 1.6 Properties of Real Numbers   **1.** 1 **2.** 8 feet   **3.** 8 hours, 20 minutes   **4.** 5 pounds, 8 ounces   **5.** $b; a$ **6.** 0 **7.** 22
8. $\frac{3}{20}$ **9.** 11.98 **10.** -78 **11.** $-\frac{36}{331}$ **12.** 349 **13.** 14 **14.** 14 **15.** -24.2 **16.** $\frac{50}{13}$ **17.** 0 **18.** undefined   **19.** 0

20. undefined   **21.** 156 inches   **23.** 45 meters   **25.** 10 gallons, 2 quarts   **27.** 11 pounds, 4 ounces   **29.** $4\frac{1}{2}$ hours = 4 hours 30 min
31. Additive Inverse Property   **33.** Multiplicative Identity Property   **35.** Multiplicative Inverse Property   **37.** Additive Inverse Property
39. $\frac{0}{a} = 0$ **41.** Commutative Property of Multiplication   **43.** Commutative Property of Addition   **45.** $\frac{a}{0}$ is undefined   **47.** 29 **49.** 18
51. -65 **53.** 347 **55.** -90 **57.** undefined   **59.** -34 **61.** 0 **63.** 0 **65.** $-\frac{20}{3}$ **67.** $\$203.16$ **69.** $-3 - (4 - 10)$
71. $-15 + 10 - (4 - 8)$ **73.** 44 feet per second   **75.** There is no real number that equals 1 when multiplied by 0.   **77.** The quotient $\frac{0}{4} = 0$
because $4 \cdot 0 = 0$. The quotient $\frac{4}{0}$ is undefined because we should be able to determine a real number $\square$ such that $0 \cdot \square = 4$. But because the product of 0
and every real number is 0, there is no replacement value for $\square$.   **79.** The product of a non-zero real number and its multiplicative inverse
(reciprocal) equals 1, the multiplicative identity.

Section 1.7 Exponents and the Order of Operations   **1.** 11^5 **2.** $(-7)^4$ **3.** $(-2)^3$ **4.** 16 **5.** 49 **6.** $-\frac{1}{216}$ **7.** 0.81 **8.** -16
9. 16 **10.** 15 **11.** -31 **12.** 12 **13.** 31 **14.** -3 **15.** 40 **16.** -63 **17.** 4 **18.** $-\frac{8}{7}$ **19.** $\frac{4}{7}$ **20.** $\frac{5}{3}$ **21.** 20 **22.** 40
23. -9 **24.** 48 **25.** $-\frac{5}{11}$ **26.** 41 **27.** 12 **28.** -108 **29.** 10 **30.** 4 **31.** 5^2 **33.** $\left(\frac{3}{5}\right)^3$ **35.** 64 **37.** 64 **39.** 1000
41. $\frac{27}{64}$ **43.** 2.25 **45.** -9 **47.** -1 **49.** 0 **51.** $\frac{1}{64}$ **53.** $-\frac{1}{27}$ **55.** 14 **57.** -3 **59.** 2500 **61.** 160 **63.** 20 **65.** 4
67. $\frac{3}{5}$ **69.** -1 **71.** 42 **73.** 5 **75.** -4 **77.** 115 **79.** -5 **81.** $\frac{169}{4}$ **83.** -24 **85.** $-\frac{13}{12}$ **87.** 0.5 **89.** 12 **91.** $-\frac{1}{2}$
93. 36 **95.** 1 **97.** 24 **99.** $\frac{133}{8}$ **101.** $\frac{2}{5}$ **103.** 3 **105.** $\frac{3}{2}$ **107.** $\frac{64}{27}$ **109.** $-\frac{1}{6}$ **111.** $2^3 \cdot 3^2$ **113.** $2^4 \cdot 3$ **115.** $(4 \cdot 3 + 6) \cdot 2$
117. $(4 + 3) \cdot (4 + 2)$ **119.** $(6 - 4) + (3 - 1)$ **121.** $\$514.93$ **123.** 603.19 in.^{2} **125.** $\$1060.90$ **127.** $115.75°$
129. The expression -3^2 means "take the opposite of three squared": $-(3 \cdot 3) = -9$. The base is the number 3. The expression $(-3)^2$ means use -3 as a
base twice: $-3 \cdot -3 = 9$.

Section 1.8 Simplifying Algebraic Expressions   **1.** To substitute the numerical value for each variable into the expression and simplify.

2. -7 **3.** 9 **4.** 2 **5.** $\$220$ **6.** $5x^2; 3xy$ **7.** $9ab; -3bc; 5ac; -ac^2$ **8.** $\frac{2mn}{5}; -\frac{3n}{7}$ **9.** $\frac{m^2}{3}; -8$ **10.** 2 **11.** 1 **12.** -1
13. 5 **14.** $-\frac{2}{3}$ **15.** $\frac{1}{6}$ **16.** like   **17.** like   **18.** unlike   **19.** unlike   **20.** $6x + 12$ **21.** $-5x - 10$ **22.** $-2k + 14$ **23.** $6x + 9$

24. $-5x$ **25.** $-4x^2$ **26.** $-8x + 3$ **27.** $-8x + 14$ **28.** $-2a + 9b - 4$ **29.** $12ac - 5a + b$ **30.** $8ab^2 - a^2b$ **31.** $2rs - \dfrac{3}{2}r^2 - 5$

32. remove all parentheses and combine like terms. **33.** $-2x - 1$ **34.** $-2m - n - 7$ **35.** $a - 11b$ **36.** $6x - 2$ **37.** 13 **39.** 17

41. -21 **43.** 104 **45.** $\dfrac{17}{5}$ **47.** 225 **49.** 153 **51.** $2x^3, 3x^2; -x, 6; 2, 3, -1, 6$ **53.** $z^2, \dfrac{2y}{3}, 1, \dfrac{2}{3}$ **55.** unlike **57.** like **59.** like

61. unlike **63.** $3m + 6$ **65.** $18n^2 + 12n - 6$ **67.** $-x + y$ **69.** $-4x + 3y$ **71.** $3x$ **73.** $6z$ **75.** $10m + 10n$ **77.** $2.2x^7$

79. $10y^6$ **81.** $-6w - 12y + 13z$ **83.** $-3k + 15$ **85.** $4n - 8$ **87.** $-3x + 3$ **89.** $4n - 2$ **91.** $-4n + 20$ **93.** $\dfrac{5}{6}x$ **95.** $-\dfrac{11}{2}$

97. $-3.5x - 6$ **99.** $6x - 0.06$ **101.** 32 **103.** 27 **105.** 0 **107.** -13 **109.** -7 **111.** -12 **113.** 44 **115.** $-\dfrac{3}{2}$ **117.** 36

119. $78.70 **121.** $4819 **123.** (a) $8w - 8$ (b) 32 yards **125.** $228.88 **127.** $-3x^2 + 7x - 3$ **129.** The sum $2x^2 + 4x^2$ is not equal to $6x^4$ because when we combine like terms, we add the coefficients of the like terms and keep the variables and exponents the same. Put another way, $2x^2 + 4x^2 = (2 + 4)x^2 = 6x^2$.

Chapter 1 Review **1.** $2 \cdot 2 \cdot 2 \cdot 3$ **2.** $3 \cdot 29$ **3.** $3 \cdot 3 \cdot 3 \cdot 3$ **4.** $2 \cdot 2 \cdot 31$ **5.** prime **6.** 72 **7.** 72 **8.** $\dfrac{14}{30}$ **9.** $\dfrac{12}{4}$

10. $\dfrac{1}{6} = \dfrac{4}{24}, \dfrac{3}{8} = \dfrac{9}{24}$ **11.** $\dfrac{9}{16} = \dfrac{27}{48}, \dfrac{7}{24} = \dfrac{14}{48}$ **12.** $\dfrac{5}{12}$ **13.** $\dfrac{1}{2}$ **14.** $\dfrac{4}{5}$ **15.** 21.76 **16.** 15 **17.** $0.88\ldots = 0.\overline{8}$ **18.** 0.28125 **19.** 1.83

20. 2.4 **21.** $\dfrac{3}{5}$ **22.** $\dfrac{3}{8}$ **23.** $\dfrac{108}{125}$ **24.** 0.41 **25.** 7.60 **26.** 0.0903 **27.** 0.0035 **28.** 23% **29.** 117% **30.** 4.5% **31.** 300%

32. (a) $\dfrac{3}{5}$ (b) 60% **33.** $A = \{0, 1, 2, 3, 4, 5, 6\}$ **34.** $B = \{1, 2, 3\}$ **35.** $C = \{-2, -1, 0, 1, 2, 3, 4, 5\}$ **36.** $D = \{-2, -1, 0, 1, 2, 3\}$

37. $\dfrac{9}{3} = 3, 11$ **38.** $0, \dfrac{9}{3} = 3, 11$ **39.** $-6, 0, \dfrac{9}{3} = 3, 11$ **40.** $-6, -3.25, 0, \dfrac{9}{3} = 3, 11, \dfrac{5}{7}$ **41.** 5.030030003... **42.** All numbers listed

43. $-\dfrac{4}{3}, 3.5$ **44.** $-\dfrac{5}{2}, 5.5$ **45.** False **46.** True **47.** True **48.** True **49.** $-\dfrac{1}{2}$

50. 7 **51.** -6 **52.** -8.2 **53.** $=$ **54.** $<$ **55.** $>$ **56.** $>$ **57.** $>$ **58.** $<$ **59.** Rational numbers are numbers that are the quotient of two integers provided the denominator does not equal 0. Rational numbers also have decimals that either terminate or do not terminate, but repeat a block of decimals. Irrational numbers have decimals that neither terminate nor repeat. **60.** natural numbers **61.** 7 **62.** -4
63. -34 **64.** -95 **65.** -4 **66.** 47 **67.** -53 **68.** -115 **69.** -22 **70.** -7 **71.** 21 **72.** 67 **73.** 26 **74.** -36
75. 12 **76.** -40 **77.** -1118 **78.** -8037 **79.** -715 **80.** $-11,130$ **81.** 5 **82.** -12 **83.** 5 **84.** -25 **85.** -8
86. $-\dfrac{16}{5}$ **87.** $-\dfrac{10}{3}$ **88.** $-\dfrac{30}{7}$ **89.** -13 **90.** 45 **91.** $-43 + 101 = 58$ **92.** $45 + (-28) = 17$ **93.** $-10 - (-116) = 106$
94. $74 - 56 = 18$ **95.** $13 + (-8) = 5$ **96.** $-60 - (-10) = -50$ **97.** $-21 \cdot (-3) = 63$ **98.** $54 \cdot (-18) = -972$
99. $-34 \div (-2)$ or $\dfrac{-34}{-2} = 17$ **100.** $-49 \div 14$ or $\dfrac{-49}{14} = -\dfrac{7}{2}$ **101.** 26 yards **102.** $-3°F$ **103.** $24°F$ **104.** 87 points

105. $\dfrac{1}{2}$ **106.** $-\dfrac{1}{3}$ **107.** $-\dfrac{2}{3}$ **108.** $-\dfrac{7}{5}$ **109.** $\dfrac{5}{4}$ **110.** $-\dfrac{5}{28}$ **111.** $-\dfrac{1}{20}$ **112.** $-\dfrac{3}{2}$ **113.** $\dfrac{4}{17}$ **114.** $-\dfrac{2}{3}$ **115.** $-\dfrac{3}{10}$

116. -32 **117.** $\dfrac{1}{3}$ **118.** $-\dfrac{2}{5}$ **119.** $\dfrac{3}{7}$ **120.** 3 **121.** $\dfrac{7}{20}$ **122.** $\dfrac{31}{36}$ **123.** $-\dfrac{59}{245}$ **124.** $\dfrac{13}{12}$ **125.** $-\dfrac{19}{12}$ **126.** $-\dfrac{11}{4}$ **127.** 0

128. $-\dfrac{23}{24}$ **129.** 48.5 **130.** -24.66 **131.** 82.98 **132.** -53.74 **133.** 0.0804 **134.** -260.154 **135.** 18.4 **136.** -25.79

137. 2.3 **138.** -22.9 **139.** -5.418 **140.** -0.732 **141.** -98.93; yes **142.** 24 friends **143.** $\dfrac{23}{2}$ or $11\dfrac{1}{2}$ inches **144.** $186.81

145. Associative Property of Multiplication **146.** Multiplicative Inverse Property **147.** Multiplicative Inverse Property **148.** Commutative Property of Multiplication **149.** Commutative Property of Multiplication **150.** Additive Inverse Property **151.** Identity Property of Addition **152.** Identity Property of Addition **153.** Commutative Property of Addition **154.** Multiplicative Identity Property **155.** Multiplication Property of Zero **156.** Associative Property of Addition **157.** 29 **158.** 99 **159.** 18 **160.** 121 **161.** 3.4 **162.** 5.3 **163.** -33

164. 6 **165.** undefined **166.** 0 **167.** -334 **168.** 2 **169.** 0 **170.** 1 **171.** 0 **172.** 130 **173.** $-\dfrac{5}{3}$ **174.** $-\dfrac{150}{13}$ **175.** 3^4

176. $\left(\dfrac{2}{3}\right)^3$ **177.** $(-4)^2$ **178.** $(-3)^3$ **179.** 125 **180.** 32 **181.** 81 **182.** -64 **183.** -81 **184.** $\dfrac{1}{64}$ **185.** -4 **186.** -76

187. 206 **188.** 32 **189.** 2 **190.** $\dfrac{1}{2}$ **191.** $\dfrac{6}{5}$ **192.** $\dfrac{7}{5}$ **193.** 21 **194.** -18 **195.** -729 **196.** -3 **197.** $3x^2, -x, 6; 3, -1, 6$

198. $2x^2y^3, -\dfrac{y}{5}, 2, -\dfrac{1}{5}$ **199.** like **200.** unlike **201.** unlike **202.** like **203.** $-3x$ **204.** $-4x - 15$ **205.** $-4.1x^4 + 0.3x^3$
206. $-3x^4 + 6x^2 + 12$ **207.** $18 - x$ **208.** $4x - 18$ **209.** $9x - 4$ **210.** -1 **211.** $98.70

Chapter 1 Test **1.** 42 **2.** $\dfrac{7}{22}$ **3.** 1.44 **4.** $\dfrac{17}{40}$ **5.** 0.006 **6.** 18.3% **7.** $\dfrac{1}{3}$ **8.** $\dfrac{9}{4}$ **9.** $-\dfrac{320}{3}$ **10.** -102 **11.** -12.16

12. -20 **13.** undefined **14.** -14 **15.** 55 **16.** (a) 6 (b) 0, 6 (c) $-2, 0, 6$ (d) $-2, -\dfrac{1}{2}, 0, 2.5, 6$ (e) none (f) All those listed.

17. $<$ **18.** $=$ **19.** -7 **20.** 15 **21.** -102 **22.** -343 **23.** $-16x - 28$ **24.** $-4x^2 + 5x + 4$ **25.** $531.85 **26.** $4x + 10$

Chapter 2 Equations and Inequalities in One Variable

Section 2.1 Linear Equations: The Addition and Multiplication Properties of Equality **1.** solutions **2.** yes **3.** no **4.** yes **5.** no

6. {32} **7.** {14} **8.** {12} **9.** {−15} **10.** $\left\{\dfrac{7}{3}\right\}$ **11.** {−1} **12.** $\left\{\dfrac{5}{8}\right\}$ **13.** $\left\{-\dfrac{13}{12}\right\}$ **14.** \$12,455 **15.** $\dfrac{1}{3}$ **16.** {2} **17.** {−2}

18. $\left\{\dfrac{5}{2}\right\}$ **19.** $\left\{-\dfrac{7}{3}\right\}$ **20.** False **21.** {9} **22.** {−9} **23.** {−30} **24.** {6} **25.** $\left\{\dfrac{8}{3}\right\}$ **26.** $\left\{-\dfrac{5}{14}\right\}$ **27.** Yes **29.** No **31.** Yes

33. Yes **35.** {20} **37.** {−12} **39.** {19} **41.** {−13} **43.** {2} **45.** $\left\{\dfrac{1}{4}\right\}$ **47.** $\left\{\dfrac{19}{24}\right\}$ **49.** {−6.1} **51.** {5} **53.** {−4}

55. $\left\{\dfrac{7}{2}\right\}$ **57.** $\left\{-\dfrac{5}{2}\right\}$ **59.** {21} **61.** {121} **63.** {40} **65.** $\left\{\dfrac{3}{5}\right\}$ **67.** $\left\{-\dfrac{1}{3}\right\}$ **69.** {9} **71.** $\left\{-\dfrac{4}{9}\right\}$ **73.** $\left\{-\dfrac{5}{3}\right\}$ **75.** {2}

77. {−3} **79.** $\left\{\dfrac{2}{3}\right\}$ **81.** {−6} **83.** {19} **85.** {283} **87.** {−50} **89.** {41.1} **91.** $\left\{\dfrac{20}{3}\right\}$ **93.** {−4} **95.** {−12} **97.** $\left\{\dfrac{1}{2}\right\}$

99. $\left\{\dfrac{3}{16}\right\}$ **101.** $\left\{-\dfrac{5}{4}\right\}$ **103.** \$18,499.80 **105.** \$68 **107.** 12 **109.** $r = 0.18$ or 18% **111.** $x = 48 - \lambda$ **113.** $x = \dfrac{14}{\theta}$ **115.** $\lambda = \dfrac{50}{9}$

117. $\theta = -\dfrac{6}{7}$ **119.** To find the solution of an equation means to find all values of the variable that satisfy the equation. **121.** An algebraic expression differs from an equation in that the expression does not contain an equal sign, and an equation does. An equation using the expression $x - 10$ is $x - 10 = 22$. Solving for x, $x = 32$.

Section 2.2 Linear Equations: Using the Properties Together **1.** add 11 to each side of the equation **2.** {3} **3.** {2} **4.** {18} **5.** $\left\{\dfrac{3}{2}\right\}$

6. {2} **7.** {−18} **8.** $\left\{\dfrac{5}{2}\right\}$ **9.** {−8} **10.** {2} **11.** $\left\{\dfrac{4}{3}\right\}$ **12.** {13} **13.** {6} **14.** {2} **15.** {6} **16.** $\left\{-\dfrac{7}{2}\right\}$ **17.** False

18. {1} **19.** $\left\{-\dfrac{5}{3}\right\}$ **20.** 52 hours **21.** {1} **23.** {−2} **25.** {−3} **27.** $\left\{\dfrac{3}{2}\right\}$ **29.** {−3} **31.** {12} **33.** {4} **35.** {−2}

37. {−5} **39.** {−8} **41.** {−5} **43.** {−21} **45.** {−6} **47.** {−8} **49.** {3} **51.** $\left\{-\dfrac{7}{2}\right\}$ **53.** {7} **55.** {−18} **57.** $\left\{\dfrac{1}{3}\right\}$

59. $\left\{-\dfrac{27}{16}\right\}$ **61.** {2} **63.** $\left\{-\dfrac{3}{4}\right\}$ **65.** $\left\{\dfrac{1}{3}\right\}$ **67.** {0} **69.** $\left\{\dfrac{15}{2}\right\}$ **71.** $\left\{\dfrac{1}{2}\right\}$ **73.** {−7} **75.** $\left\{\dfrac{7}{2}\right\}$ **77.** McDonald's: 16 grams;

Burger King: 22 grams **79.** width: $\dfrac{13}{3}$ feet or 4 feet 4 inches; length: $\dfrac{32}{3}$ feet or 10 feet 8 inches **81.** \$8 **83.** Yes **85.** $\left\{\dfrac{51}{7}\right\}$ **87.** {2.47}

89. {−5, 6} **91.** $\dfrac{20}{3}$ **93.** $-\dfrac{5}{4}$ **95.** The first is an expression because it does not have an equal sign. The second is an equation because it does have an equal sign. In general, an expression contains the sum, difference, product, and/or quotient of terms. An equation may be thought of as the equality of two algebraic expressions. **97.** Adding $2x$ to both sides will lead to the correct solution, but it may be easier to combine like terms on the left side of the equation before adding $2x$ to each side. A series of steps leading to the solution would be (1) combining like terms on the left side of the equation; (2) isolating x on the right side by subtracting $5x$ from both sides; (3) isolating the constants by adding 5 to each side; (4) dividing both sides by 4 to obtain $x = 2$.

Section 2.3 Solving Linear Equations Involving Fractions and Decimals; Classifying Equations **1.** least common denominator **2.** {10}

3. $\left\{-\dfrac{5}{18}\right\}$ **4.** 70 **5.** {−14} **6.** $\left\{\dfrac{35}{3}\right\}$ **7.** 100 **8.** {100} **9.** {50} **10.** 1 **11.** {50} **12.** {160} **13.** {4} **14.** {3000}

15. True **16.** ∅ **17.** all real numbers **18.** all real numbers **19.** ∅ or { } **20.** all real numbers **21.** the empty set, { } or ∅ **22.** all real numbers; identity **23.** {4}; conditional **24.** ∅ or { }; contradiction **25.** ∅ or { }; contradiction **26.** \$500 **27.** $\left\{\dfrac{9}{2}\right\}$ **29.** {−2} **31.** {−6}

33. $\left\{\dfrac{2}{3}\right\}$ **35.** {6} **37.** $\left\{\dfrac{25}{8}\right\}$ **39.** {−20} **41.** {1} **43.** {30} **45.** {−4} **47.** {50} **49.** {4.8} **51.** {150} **53.** {−12}

55. {60} **57.** {5} **59.** {2} **61.** {75} **63.** ∅ or { }; contradiction **65.** all real numbers; identity **67.** $\left\{-\dfrac{1}{2}\right\}$; conditional equation

69. ∅ or { }; contradiction **71.** ∅ or { }; contradiction **73.** all real numbers; identity **75.** $\left\{-\dfrac{3}{4}\right\}$ **77.** all real numbers

79. $\left\{-\dfrac{1}{3}\right\}$ **81.** {−20} **83.** $\left\{\dfrac{7}{2}\right\}$ **85.** ∅ or { } **87.** {−2} **89.** {3} **91.** ∅ or { } **93.** {−4} **95.** {39}

97. {0} **99.** $\left\{\dfrac{2}{3}\right\}$ **101.** {−1.70} **103.** {−13.2} **105.** \$50 **107.** \$18,000 **109.** \$8.50 **111.** \$80 **113.** 15 quarters **115.** 6 units

117. \$12,050 **119.** Answers will vary. A linear equation with one solution is $2x + 5 = 11$. A linear equation with no solution is $2x + 5 = 6 + 2x - 9$. A linear equation that is an identity is $2(x + 5) - 3 = 4x - (2x - 7)$. To form an identity or a contradiction, the variable expressions must be eliminated, leaving either a true (identity) or a false (contradiction) statement. **121.** The student didn't multiply each term of the equation by 6. Solving using that (incorrect) method gives the second step $4x - 5 = 3x$, and solving for x gives $x = 5$. The correct method to solve the equation is to multiply ALL terms by 6. The correct second step is $4x - 30 = 3x$, producing the correct solution $x = 30$.

Section 2.4 Evaluating Formulas and Solving Formulas for a Variable **1.** formula   **2.** 59°F   **3.** size 40   **4.** $312.50   **5.** 5936 persons
6. principal; Interest   **7.** $50 interest; $2550 total   **8.** 36 square inches   **9.** $A = \pi r^2$ **10. (a)** 187 ft^2 **(b)** $46.75   **11.** 28.27 ft^2
12. The extra large pizza is the better buy.   **13.** $C = \dfrac{5F - 160}{9}$ **14.** $h = \dfrac{A - 2\pi r^2}{2\pi r}$ **15.** False   **16.** $y = \dfrac{7 - x}{2}$ or $y = -\dfrac{1}{2}x + \dfrac{7}{2}$
17. $y = \dfrac{15 - 5x}{-3}$ or $y = \dfrac{5}{3}x - 5$ **18.** $b = \dfrac{28 - 3a}{8}$ or $b = -\dfrac{3}{8}a + \dfrac{7}{2}$ **19.** $t = 24 - 6rs$ **20. (a)** $\dfrac{d}{r} = t$ **(b)** $t = 9\dfrac{1}{6}$ hours or 9 hours 10 min
21. (a) $\dfrac{I}{Pr} = t$ **(b)** $t = 0.5$ year   **22. (a)** $p = \dfrac{R}{q}$ **(b)** $40   **23.** Rogan 1099.14 feet; Nurek 984.3 feet   **25.** $104   **27.** $650   **29.** 20°C
31. $3   **33. (a)** 50 units **(b)** 144 square units   **35. (a)** 36.2 meters **(b)** 70 square meters   **37. (a)** 36 units **(b)** 81 square units
39. (a) 31.4 cm **(b)** 78.5 cm^2 **41.** $\dfrac{616}{9}$ in.^{2} **43.** $r = \dfrac{d}{t}$ **45.** $d = \dfrac{C}{\pi}$ **47.** $t = \dfrac{I}{Pr}$ **49.** $b = \dfrac{2A}{h}$ **51.** $a = P - b - c$
53. $r = \dfrac{A - P}{Pt}$ **55.** $b = \dfrac{2A}{h} - B$ **57.** $y = -3x + 12$ **59.** $y = 2x - 5$ **61.** $y = \dfrac{-4x + 13}{3}$ or $y = -\dfrac{4}{3}x + \dfrac{13}{3}$
63. $y = 3x - 12$ **65. (a)** $C = R - P$ **(b)** $450   **67. (a)** $r = \dfrac{I}{Pt}$ **(b)** 3%   **69. (a)** $x = 2\sigma + \mu$ **(b)** 130   **71. (a)** $m = \dfrac{y - 5}{x}$
(b) -2 **73. (a)** $r = \dfrac{A - P}{Pt}$ **(b)** 0.04 or 4%   **75. (a)** $h = \dfrac{V}{\pi r^2}$ **(b)** 5 mm   **77. (a)** $b = \dfrac{2A}{h}$ **(b)** 18 ft   **79.** 1834.05
81. (a) $h = \dfrac{V}{\pi r^2}$ **(b)** 10 inches   **83.** medium (12")   **85. (a)** 12 hours **(b)** $336   **87.** 50.5 square inches   **89.** 96π cm$^3 \approx 301.59$ cm^3
91. (a) $I = \dfrac{D - P}{0.02} + 234{,}600$ **(b)** $250,650   **93. (a)** 62 tiles **(b)** $372 **(c)** Yes   **95. (a)** 4948 ft^2 **(b)** $1237   **97. (a)** 1080 in.^{2}
(b) 7.5 ft^2 **99.** Multiply by $\dfrac{1\,\text{ft}^2}{144\,\text{in}^2}$ **101.** Both answers are correct. When solving for y, the first student left the entire numerator over 2.
The second student simplified the expression to $y = \dfrac{-x + 6}{2} = \dfrac{-x}{2} + \dfrac{6}{2} = -\dfrac{1}{2}x + 3$.

Putting the Concepts Together (Sections 2.1–2.4) **1. (a)** Yes **(b)** No   **2. (a)** No **(b)** Yes   **3.** $\left\{-\dfrac{2}{3}\right\}$ **4.** $\{-40\}$ **5.** $\{-6\}$
6. $\{3\}$ **7.** $\{-6\}$ **8.** $\left\{-\dfrac{7}{3}\right\}$ **9.** $\left\{-\dfrac{57}{2}\right\}$ **10.** $\{25\}$ **11.** $\{6\}$ **12.** $\left\{\dfrac{74}{5}\right\}$ or $\{14.8\}$ **13.** contradiction; $\varnothing$ or $\{\ \}$ **14.** identity; all real
numbers   **15.** $5000   **16. (a)** $b = \dfrac{2A}{h} - B$ **(b)** 6 in.   **17. (a)** $h = \dfrac{V}{\pi r^2}$ **(b)** 13 in.   **18.** $y = -\dfrac{3}{2}x + 7$

Section 2.5 Introduction to Problem Solving: Direct Translation Problems **1.** $5 + 17$ **2.** $-2 \cdot 6$ **3.** $\dfrac{25}{3}$ **4.** $7 - 4$ **5.** $2a - 2$
6. $3 + \dfrac{z}{4}$ **7.** $z + 50$ **8.** $x - 15$ **9.** $75 - d$ **10.** $3l - 2$ **11.** $2q + 3$ **12.** $3b - 5$ **13.** equations   **14.** $3y = 21$ **15.** $3 + x = 5x$
16. $x - 10 = \dfrac{x}{2}$ **17.** $y - 3 = 5y$ **18.** mathematical modeling   **19.** $s + \dfrac{2}{3}s = 15$, where s represents the amount Sean pays; Sean pays $9 and
Connor pays $6   **20.** False   **21.** $n + (n + 2) + (n + 4) = 270$; 88, 90, 92   **22.** $n + (n + 2) + (n + 4) + (n + 6) = 72$; 15, 17, 19, 21
23. $76 = x + (x + 24) + \dfrac{1}{2}(x + 24)$, where $x =$ length of smallest piece of ribbon; 16 inches, 40 inches, 20 inches   **24.** $x + 2x = 18{,}000$, where
$x =$ amount invested in stocks; $6000 in stocks; $12,000 in bonds   **25.** 150 miles   **26.** 100 minutes   **27.** $-5 + x$
29. $x\left(\dfrac{2}{3}\right)$ or $\dfrac{2}{3}x$ **31.** $\dfrac{1}{2}x$ **33.** $x - (-25)$ **35.** $\dfrac{x}{3}$ **37.** $x + \dfrac{1}{2}$ **39.** $6x + 9$ **41.** $2(13.7 + x)$ **43.** $2x + 31$ **45.** Braves: r;
Clippers: $r + 5$ **47.** Bill's amount: b; Jan's amount: $b + 0.55$ **49.** Janet's share: j; Kathy's share: $200 - j$ **51.** number adults: a; number
children: $1433 - a$ **53.** $x + 15 = -34$ **55.** $35 = 3x - 7$ **57.** $\dfrac{x}{-4} + 5 = 36$ **59.** $2(x + 6) = x + 3$ **61.** 83   **63.** -14
65. 54, 55, 56   **67.** Verrazano-Narrows Bridge; 4260 ft; Golden Gate Bridge: 4200 ft   **69.** $11,215   **71.** CD: $8500; bonds: $11,500
73. Stocks: $20,000; bonds: $12,000   **75.** Smart Start: 2 g; Go Lean: 8 g   **77.** $29,140   **79.** 150 miles   **81.** 2000 pages   **83.** Jensen: $36,221;
Maureen: $35,972   **85.** 5, 6, 7, and 8   **87.** Answers may vary.   **89.** Answers may vary.   **91.** 20°, 40°, 120°   **93.** The process of taking a verbal
description of a problem and developing a mathematical equation that can be used to solve the problem is mathematical modeling. We often make
assumptions to make the mathematics more manageable in the mathematical models.   **95.** Both students are correct; however, the value for n will
not be the same for both students. Answers may vary.

Section 2.6 Problem Solving: Direct Translation Problems Involving Percent **1.** 100   **2.** multiplication; times   **3.** 801   **4.** 2.52
5. 36   **6.** 3.5   **7.** 40%   **8.** 37.5%   **9.** 20.5%   **10.** 110%   **11.** 50   **12.** 150   **13.** 80   **14.** 75   **15.** 33,150,000   **16.** $39,975
17. $7300   **18.** $2.50 per gallon.   **19.** $659   **20.** $151,020   **21.** 80   **23.** 14   **25.** 4.8   **27.** 210   **29.** 72   **31.** 20   **33.** 40%
35. 7.5%   **37.** 200%   **39.** $54   **41.** $102,000   **43.** $25,000   **45.** $68   **47.** $570   **49.** $400   **51.** winner: 530; loser: 318
53. $285,700   **55.** 1057 votes   **57.** 30.74 million   **59.** 7.1%   **61.** 17.2%   **63.** $24   **65.** 28.6%   **67. (a)** $31,314.38 **(b)** 43.7%
69. 12.9%   **71.** The equation should be $x + 0.5x = 12.81$. Jack's new hourly wage is a percentage of his current hourly wage, so multiplying 5% by
his original wage gives his hourly raise. His current hourly wage is $12.20.

Section 2.7 Problem Solving: Geometry and Uniform Motion   **1.** 90   **2.** 39° and 51°   **3.** 70° and 110°   **4.** 180   **5.** 35°, 40°, and 105°   **6.** True   **7.** False   **8.** width is 1.5 feet; length is 3 feet   **9.** 5 feet   **10.** False   **11.** José's speed is 13 mph and Luis' speed is 8 mph.   **12.** It takes $\frac{1}{2}$ hour to catch up to Tanya. Each of you has traveled 20 miles.   **13.** $x = 47.5$; 47.5°, 132.5°   **15.** $x = 44$; 44°, 46°   **17.** 42°, 44°, 94°   **19.** 58°, 60°, 62°   **21.** length = 32 feet; width = 12 feet   **23.** 42 ft by 84 ft   **25.** 26.5 in.   **27. (a)** $62t$ **(b)** $68t$ **(c)** $62t + 68t$ **(d)** $62t + 68t = 585$ **29.** $528(t + 10) = 880t$ **31.** length = 14 in.; width = 4 in.   **33.** 40 ft   **35.** 40 ft; 32 ft   **37. (a)** length = 11 yards; width = 19 yards **(b)** 209 yd^2 **39.** 13 hours   **41.** fast car: 60 mph; slow car: 48 mph   **43.** freeway: 4.5 hours; 2-lane: 1.5 hours   **45.** 6 mph   **47.** 49°, 49°, 82°   **49.** $x = 3$ **51.** $x = 15$ **53.** $x = 12$ **55.** Complementary angles are those whose measures sum to 90° and supplementary angles have measures that sum to 180°.   **57.** Answers may vary. The equation $65t + 40t = 115$ is describing the sum of distances whereas the equation $65t - 40t = 115$ represents the difference of distances.

Section 2.8 Solving Linear Inequalities in One Variable

1. True   **2.**   **3.**

4.   **5.**   **6.** True   **7.** False   **8.** $[-3, \infty)$

9. $(-\infty, 12)$ **10.** $(-\infty, 2.5]$ **11.** $(125, \infty)$ **12.** solve   **13.** Addition Property of Inequality

14. $\{n | n > 3\}$; $(3, \infty)$ **15.** $\{x | x < 4\}$; $(-\infty, 4)$

16. $\{n | n \leq -4\}$; $(-\infty, -4]$ **17.** $\{x | x > -1\}$; $(-1, -\infty)$

18. negative   **19.** False   **20.** $\{k | k < -6\}$; $(-\infty, -6)$

21. $\left\{n | n \geq -\frac{5}{2}\right\}$; $\left[-\frac{5}{2}, \infty\right)$ **22.** $\{k | k < -8\}$; $(-\infty, -8)$

23. $\left\{p | p \geq \frac{3}{5}\right\}$; $\left[\frac{3}{5}, \infty\right)$ **24.** $\{x | x > 7\}$; $(7, \infty)$

25. $\{n | n > -3\}$; $(-3, \infty)$ **26.** $\{x | x > -4\}$; $(-4, \infty)$

27. $\{x | x \leq -6\}$; $(-\infty, -6]$ **28.** $\{x | x > 8\}$; $(8, \infty)$

29. $\left\{x | x \leq \frac{19}{8}\right\}$; $\left(-\infty, \frac{19}{8}\right]$ **30.** all real numbers or $(-\infty, \infty)$ **31.** the empty set or $\varnothing$

32. $\{x | x \geq -67\}$; $[-67, \infty)$ **33.** $\varnothing$ or $\{\ \}$

34. $\{x | x > 4\}$; $(4, \infty)$ **35.** $\{x | x$ is any real number$\}$; $(-\infty, \infty)$

36. at most 20 boxes   **37.** $(2, \infty)$ **39.** $(-\infty, -1]$ **41.** $[-3, \infty)$

43. $(-\infty, 4)$ **45.** $(-\infty, 2)$ **47.** $\varnothing$ or $\{\ \}$ **49.** $(-\infty, \infty)$ **51.** <; Addition Property of Inequality

53. >; Multiplication Property of Inequality   **55.** ≤; Addition Property of Inequality   **57.** ≤; Multiplication Property of Inequality

59. $\{x | x < 4\}$; $(-\infty, 4)$ **61.** $\{x | x \geq 2\}$; $[2, \infty)$ **63.** $\{x | x \leq 5\}$; $(-\infty, 5]$

65. $\{x | x > -7\}$; $(-7, \infty)$ **67.** $\{x | x > 3\}$; $(3, \infty)$ **69.** $\{x | x \geq 2\}$; $[2, \infty)$

71. $\{x | x \geq -1\}$; $[-1, \infty)$ **73.** $\{x | x > -7\}$; $(-7, \infty)$

75. $\left\{x | x \leq \frac{2}{3}\right\}$; $\left(-\infty, \frac{2}{3}\right]$ **77.** $\{x | x < -20\}$; $(-\infty, -20)$

79. $\varnothing$ or $\{\ \}$ **81.** $\{n | n$ is any real number$\}$; $(-\infty, \infty)$

83. $\{n | n > 5\}$; $(5, \infty)$ **85.** $\{w | w$ is any real number$\}$; $(-\infty, \infty)$

87. $\left\{y \middle| y < -\frac{3}{2}\right\}; \left(-\infty, -\frac{3}{2}\right)$ **89.** $x \geq 16{,}000$ **91.** $x \leq 20{,}000$ **93.** $x > 12{,}000$ **95.** $x > 0$ **97.** $x \leq 0$

99. $\{x | x > 4\}; (4, \infty)$ **101.** $\left\{x \middle| x < \frac{3}{4}\right\}; \left(-\infty, \frac{3}{4}\right)$

103. $\{x | x \text{ is any real number}\}; (-\infty, \infty)$ **105.** $\{a | a < -1\}; (-\infty, -1)$

107. $\{n | n \text{ is any real number}\}; (-\infty, \infty)$ **109.** $\left\{x \middle| x \geq \frac{4}{3}\right\}; \left[\frac{4}{3}, \infty\right)$

111. $\{x | x < 25\}; (-\infty, 25)$ **113.** $\varnothing$ or $\{\ \}$

115. $\{x | x > 5.9375\}; (5.9375, \infty)$ **117.** at most 1250 miles   **119.** at least 32   **121.** more than 400 minutes

123. greater than $50,361.11   **125.** at least 74   **127.** $\{x | -33 < x < -14\}$ **129.** $\{x | -4 \leq x \leq 6\}$ **131.** $\{x | -2 \leq x < 9\}$
133. $\{x | -8 \leq x < 4\}$ **135.** A left parenthesis is used to indicate that the solution is greater than a number. A left bracket is used to show that the solution is greater than or equal to a given number.   **137.** When solving an inequality and the variables are eliminated and a true statement results, the solution is all real numbers. When solving an inequality and the variables are eliminated and a false statement results, the solution is the empty set.

Chapter 2 Review   **1.** No   **2.** No   **3.** No   **4.** Yes   **5.** $\{16\}$ **6.** $\{20\}$ **7.** $\{-16\}$ **8.** $\{-7\}$ **9.** $\{-95\}$ **10.** $\{50\}$ **11.** $\{24\}$

12. $\{80\}$ **13.** $\{-6\}$ **14.** $\{5\}$ **15.** $\left\{-\frac{1}{3}\right\}$ **16.** $\left\{\frac{3}{8}\right\}$ **17.** $\{4\}$ **18.** $\{5\}$ **19.** $20,100   **20.** $2.55   **21.** $\{-4\}$ **22.** $\{4\}$

23. $\{9\}$ **24.** $\{-21\}$ **25.** $\{-4\}$ **26.** $\{-6\}$ **27.** $\{4\}$ **28.** $\{-5\}$ **29.** $\{6\}$ **30.** $\{-6\}$ **31.** $\left\{\frac{4}{3}\right\}$ **32.** $\{5\}$ **33.** $\{2\}$

34. $\{7\}$ **35.** 14   **36.** width = 19 yards; length = 29 yards   **37.** $\left\{-\frac{35}{12}\right\}$ **38.** $\left\{-\frac{62}{3}\right\}$ **39.** $\{-2\}$ **40.** $\left\{\frac{6}{5}\right\}$ **41.** $\left\{\frac{3}{2}\right\}$

42. $\{3\}$ **43.** $\{4\}$ **44.** $\{-1\}$ **45.** $\left\{-\frac{7}{2}\right\}$ **46.** $\{-3\}$ **47.** $\{58\}$ **48.** $\{-10.5\}$ **49.** $\varnothing$ or $\{\ \}$; contradiction   **50.** $\varnothing$ or $\{\ \}$; contradiction

51. $\{0\}$; conditional equation   **52.** $\{0\}$; conditional equation   **53.** all real numbers; identity   **54.** all real numbers; identity   **55.** $15.75

56. 3 dimes   **57.** 48 in.^{2} **58.** 64 cm   **59.** $\frac{3}{2}$ yards   **60.** 15 mm   **61.** $H = \frac{V}{LW}$ **62.** $P = \frac{I}{rt}$ **63.** $W = \frac{S - 2LH}{2L + 2H}$

64. $M = \frac{p - mv}{V}$ **65.** $y = \frac{-2x + 10}{3}$ or $y = -\frac{2}{3}x + \frac{10}{3}$ **66.** $x = \frac{14 + 7y}{6}$ **67.** (a) $P = \frac{A}{(1 + r)^t}$ (b) $2238.65

68. (a) $h = \frac{A - 2\pi r^2}{2\pi r}$ (b) 5 cm   **69.** $11.25   **70.** $\frac{9}{4}\pi$ ft$^2 \approx 7.1$ ft^2 **71.** $x - 6$ **72.** $x - 8$ **73.** $-8x$ **74.** $\frac{x}{10}$ **75.** $2(6 + x)$

76. $4(5 - x)$ **77.** $6 + x = 2x + 5$ **78.** $6x - 10 = 2x + 1$ **79.** $x - 8 = \frac{1}{2}x$ **80.** $\frac{6}{x} = 10 + x$ **81.** $4(2x + 8) = 16$

82. $5(2x - 8) = -24$ **83.** Sarah's age: s; Jacob's age: $s + 7$ **84.** Consuelo's speed: c; Jose's speed: $2c$
85. Max's amount: m; Irene's amount: $m - 6$ **86.** Victor's amount: v; Larry's amount: $350 - v$ **87.** 153 pounds   **88.** 12, 13, 14
89. Juan: $11,000; Roberto: $9000   **90.** 100 miles   **91.** 5.2   **92.** 60   **93.** 13%   **94.** 50   **95.** $18.50   **96.** $30   **97.** $40   **98.** $200
99. $125,000   **100.** winner: 500 votes; loser: 400 votes   **101.** 80°, 10°   **102.** 100°, 80°   **103.** 30°, 60°, 90°   **104.** 50°, 45°, 85°
105. length = 31 in.; width = 8 in.   **106.** length = 28 cm; width = 7 cm   **107.** (a) length = 20 ft; width = 40 ft   (b) 800 ft^2

108. 50 ft; 40 ft   **109.** 5 hours   **110.** 65 mph   **111.**   **112.**

113.   **114.**   **115.**

116.   **117.** $(-\infty, -4)$ **118.** $[7, \infty)$ **119.** $[2, \infty)$ **120.** $(-\infty, 3)$

121. $\left\{x \middle| x < -\frac{13}{2}\right\}; \left(-\infty, -\frac{13}{2}\right)$ **122.** $\left\{x \middle| x \geq -\frac{7}{3}\right\}; \left[-\frac{7}{3}, \infty\right)$

123. $\left\{x \middle| x \geq -\frac{4}{5}\right\}; \left[-\frac{4}{5}, \infty\right)$ **124.** $\{x | x > -12\}; (-12, \infty)$

125. $\varnothing$ or $\{\ \}$ **126.** $\{x | x \text{ is any real number}\}; (-\infty, \infty)$

127. $\{x|x > 3\}; (3, \infty)$ **128.** $\left\{x|x < -\dfrac{38}{5}\right\}; \left(-\infty, -\dfrac{38}{5}\right)$ **129.** at most 65 miles

130. more than 150

Chapter 2 Test

1. $\{-17\}$ **2.** $\left\{-\dfrac{4}{9}\right\}$ **3.** $\{4\}$ **4.** $\left\{\dfrac{10}{13}\right\}$ **5.** $\left\{\dfrac{5}{8}\right\}$ **6.** $\{5\}$ **7.** $\varnothing$ or $\{\ \}$ **8.** all real numbers

9. (a) $l = \dfrac{V}{wh}$ **(b)** 9 in. **10. (a)** $y = -\dfrac{2}{3}x + 4$ **(b)** $y = -\dfrac{4}{3}$ **11.** $6(x-8) = 2x - 5$ **12.** 60 **13.** $15, 16, 17$

14. 10 in., 24 in., 26 in. **15.** 3.5 hours **16.** shorter piece is 5 feet; longer is 16 feet **17.** \$36

18. $\{x|x \le 6\}; (-\infty, 6]$ 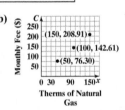 **19.** $\left\{x|x > \dfrac{5}{4}\right\}; \left(\dfrac{5}{4}, \infty\right)$ **20.** at most 200 minutes

Chapter 3 Introduction to Graphing and Equations of Lines

Section 3.1 The Rectangular Coordinate System and Equations in Two Variables

1. *x*-axis; *y*-axis; origin **2.** *x*-coordinate; *y*-coordinate

3. False **4.** False

5. $\left(-\dfrac{3}{2}, \dfrac{5}{2}\right)$ [graph] **(a)** I **(b)** III **(c)** IV **(d)** *x*-axis **(e)** *y*-axis **(f)** II

6. [graph] **(a)** II **(b)** I **(c)** III **(d)** *x*-axis **(e)** *y*-axis **(f)** IV

7. (a) $(2, 3)$ **(b)** $(1, -3)$ **(c)** $(-3, 0)$ **(d)** $(-2, -1)$ **(e)** $(0, 2)$ **8.** True **9. (a)** Yes **(b)** No **(c)** No

10. (a) No **(b)** Yes **(c)** Yes **11.** $(3, 4)$ **12.** $(-3, 1)$ **13.** $\left(\dfrac{1}{2}, -\dfrac{2}{3}\right)$

14.

x	y	(x, y)
−2	−12	(−2, −12)
0	−2	(0, −2)
1	3	(1, 3)

15.

x	y	(x, y)
−1	7	(−1, 7)
2	−2	(2, −2)
5	−11	(5, −11)

16.

x	y	(x, y)
−5	2	(−5, 2)
−2	−4	(−2, −4)
2	−12	(2, −12)

17.

x	y	(x, y)
−6	−6	(−6, −6)
−1	−4	(−1, −4)
2	$-\dfrac{14}{5}$	$\left(2, -\dfrac{14}{5}\right)$

18. (a)

x therms	50 therms	100 therms	150 therms
C($)	$76.30	$142.61	$208.91

$(50, 76.30); (100, 142.61); (150, 208.91)$

(b) [graph] $(150, 208.91)$; $(100, 142.61)$; $(50, 76.30)$; Monthly Fee (\$); Therms of Natural Gas

19. [graph]
Quadrant I: B
Quadrant II: A, E
Quadrant III: C
Quadrant IV: D, F

21. [graph]
Quadrant I: C, E
Quadrant III: F
Quadrant IV: B
x-axis: A, G; *y*-axis: D, G

23. [graph]
Positive *x*-axis: A
Negative *x*-axis: D
Positive *y*-axis: C
Negative *y*-axis: B

25. $A(4, 0)$: *x*-axis; $B(-3, 2)$: quadrant II; $C(1, -4)$: quadrant IV; $D(-2, -4)$: quadrant III; $E(3, 5)$: quadrant I; $F(0, -3)$: *y*-axis

27. A No **29.** A Yes **31.** A Yes
B Yes B No B No
C Yes C Yes C Yes

33. $(4, 1)$ **35.** $(5, -1)$ **37.** $(-3, 3)$

39.

x	y	(x, y)
−3	3	(−3, 3)
0	0	(0, 0)
1	−1	(1, −1)

41.

x	y	(x, y)
−2	7	(−2, 7)
−1	4	(−1, 4)
4	−11	(4, −11)

43.

x	y	(x, y)
−1	8	(−1, 8)
2	2	(2, 2)
3	0	(3, 0)

45.

x	y	(x, y)
−4	6	(−4, 6)
1	6	(1, 6)
12	6	(12, 6)

47.

x	y	(x, y)
1	$\dfrac{7}{2}$	$\left(1, \dfrac{7}{2}\right)$
−4	1	(−4, 1)
−2	2	(−2, 2)

49.

x	y	(x, y)
4	7	(4, 7)
−4	3	(−4, 3)
−6	2	(−6, 2)

51.

x	y	(x, y)
0	−3	(0, −3)
−2	0	(−2, 0)
2	−6	(2, −6)

53. $A\,(2, -16)$
$B(-3, -1)$
$C\left(-\dfrac{1}{3}, -9\right)$

55. $A(2, -6)$
$B(0, 0)$
$C\left(\dfrac{1}{6}, -\dfrac{1}{2}\right)$

57. $A(4, -8)$
$B(4, -19)$
$C(4, 5)$

59. $A(3, 4)$
$B(-6, -2)$
$C\left(\dfrac{1}{2}, \dfrac{7}{3}\right)$

61. $A\left(-4, -\dfrac{4}{3}\right)$
$B(-2, -1)$
$C\left(-\dfrac{2}{3}, -\dfrac{7}{9}\right)$

63. $A(20, 23)$
$B(-4, -17)$
$C(2.6, -6)$

65. (a) $24.85 (b) $54.70 (c) 6 CDs (d) It costs
$34.80 to order 3 CDs.

67. (a) 21.14% (b) 25.58% (c) 34.46% (d) 2055 (e) Answers may vary. The result is not reasonable since it is unlikely the trend will be linear over this time frame.

69.

a	b	(a, b)
2	-8	(2, -8)
0	-4	(0, -4)
-5	6	(-5, 6)

71.

p	q	(p, q)
0	$\dfrac{10}{3}$	$\left(0, \dfrac{10}{3}\right)$
$\dfrac{5}{2}$	0	$\left(\dfrac{5}{2}, 0\right)$
-10	$\dfrac{50}{3}$	$\left(-10, \dfrac{50}{3}\right)$

73. $k = 4$ **75.** $k = 2$

77. $k = \dfrac{1}{2}$

79. Points may vary; line

81.

x	y	(x, y)
-2	0	(-2, 0)
-1	-3	(-1, -3)
0	-4	(0, -4)
1	-3	(1, -3)
2	0	(2, 0)

83.

x	y	(x, y)
-2	10	(-2, 10)
-1	3	(-1, 3)
0	2	(0, 2)
1	1	(1, 1)
2	-6	(2, -6)

85. The first quadrant is the upper right hand corner of the rectangular coordinate system. The quadrants are then II, III, and IV going in a counterclockwise direction. Points in quadrant I have both the x- and y-coordinates positive; points in quadrant II have a negative x-coordinate and a positive y-coordinate; points in quadrant III have both the x- and y-coordinates negative; points in quadrant IV have a positive x-coordinate and a negative y-coordinate. A point on the x-axis has y-coordinate equal to zero. A point on the y-axis has x-coordinate that is equal to zero.

87.

89.

91.

93.

Section 3.2 Graphing Equations in Two Variables

1.

2.

3. linear; standard form **4.** Linear **5.** Not linear **6.** Linear

7.

8.

9. (a) $(0, 3000)$, $(10,000, 3800)$, $(25,000, 5000)$ (b)

10. Intercepts

11. Intercepts: $(0, 3)$, $(4, 0)$; x-intercept: 4; y-intercept: 3 **12.** Intercept: $(0, -2)$; y-intercept: -2; no x-intercept **13.** False

14.

15.

16.

17.

18.

19.

20.

21. Linear **23.** Not linear **25.** Not linear **27.** Linear **29.** $y = 2x$ **31.** $y = 4x - 2$

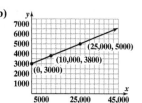 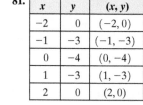

33. $y = -2x + 5$ **35.** $x + y = 5$ **37.** $-2x + y = 6$ **39.** $4x - 2y = -8$ **41.** $x = -4y$ **43.** $y + 7 = 0$

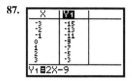 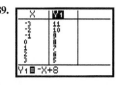 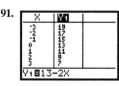 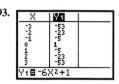

45. $y - 2 = 3(x + 1)$ **47.** $(0, -5), (5, 0)$ **49.** $(0, 4), (2, 0)$ **51.** $(0, -3)$ **53.** $(-5, 0)$ **55.** $(0, -4), (-6, 0)$

57. $(0, 0)$ **59.** $(0, -5), (5, 0)$ **61.** $(0, 8), (6, 0)$ **63.** $(4, 0)$ **65.** $(0, -2)$

67. $3x + 6y = 18$ **69.** $-x + 5y = 15$ **71.** $\frac{1}{2}x = y + 3$ **73.** $9x - 2y = 0$ **75.** $y = -\frac{1}{2}x + 3$ **77.** $\frac{1}{3}y + 2 = 2x$

79. $\frac{x}{2} + \frac{y}{3} = 1$ **81.** $4y - 2x + 1 = 0$ **83.** $x = 5$ **85.** $y = -6$ **87.** $y - 12 = 0$ **89.** $3x - 5 = 0$

91. $y = 2x - 5$ **93.** $y = -5$ **95.** $2x + 5y = -20$ **97.** $2x = -6y + 4$ **99.** $x - 3 = 0$ **101.** $3y - 12 = 0$

103. $y = 2$ **105.** $x = 7$ **107.** $y = 5$ **109.** $x = -2$ **111.** $y = 4$ **119. (a)** $(0, 500), (4, 900), (10, 1500)$

       113. $x = -9$ **(b)**

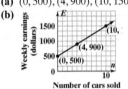

115. $x = 2y$

117. $y = x + 2$

(c) If she sells 0 cars, her weekly earnings are $500.

121. The "steepness" of the lines is the same.

123. The lines get more steep as the coefficient of x gets larger.

125. $(0, -6), (-2, 0), (3, 0)$ **127.** $(0, 14), (-3, 0), (2, 0), (5, 0)$

129. The graph of an equation is the set of all ordered pairs (x, y) that make the equation a true statement.

131. Two points are needed to graph a line. A third point is used to verify your results.

133. $y = 2x - 9$

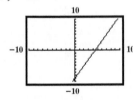

135. $y + 2x = 13$ or $y = -2x + 13$

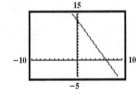

137. $y = -6x^2 + 1$

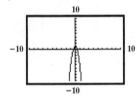

Section 3.3 Slope

1. $\frac{3}{5}$ **2.** False   **3.** True   **4.** positive   **5.**

$m = 2$; y increases by 2 when x increases by 1

6.

$m = -\frac{9}{5}$; y decreases by 9 when x increases by 5, or y increases by 9 when x decreases by 5.

7. 0; undefined

8. Slope undefined; when y increases by 1, there is no change in x.

9. $m = 0$; there is no change in y when x increases by 1 unit.

10. **(a)**  **(b)** **(c)**

11. 8%

12. $m = 0.12$; between 10,000 and 14,000 miles driven, the average annual cost of operating on a Chevy Cobalt is $0.12 per mile.

13. $-\dfrac{3}{2}$ **15.** $\dfrac{1}{2}$ **17.** $-\dfrac{2}{3}$

19. **(a), (b)** **(c)** $m = \dfrac{1}{2}$; for every 2-unit increase in x, there is a 1-unit increase in y.

21. **(a), (b)** **(c)** $m = -2$; the value of y decreases by 2 when x increases by 1.

23. $m = -2$; y decreases by 2 when x increases by 1.   **25.** $m = -1$; y decreases by 1 when x increases by 1.   **27.** $m = -\dfrac{5}{3}$; y decreases by 5 when x increases by 3.   **29.** $m = \dfrac{3}{2}$; y increases by 3 when x increases by 2.   **31.** $m = \dfrac{2}{3}$; y increases by 2 when x increases by 3.   **33.** $m = \dfrac{1}{3}$; y increases by 1 when x increases by 3.   **35.** $m = 2$; y increases by 2 when x increases by 1.   **37.** m is undefined.   **39.** $m = 0$ **41.** $m = 0$; the line is horizontal, so there is no change in y when x increases by 1.   **43.** slope is undefined; the line is vertical.

45.   **47.**   **49.**   **51.**   **53.**   **55.**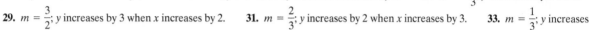

57.   **59.**   **61.**   **63.** $m = -\dfrac{1}{2}$ $m = 2$ **65.**   **67.** $\dfrac{1}{3}$ **69.** 12 in. or 1 ft

71. 16%   **73.** $m = 2.26$ million; the population was increasing at an average rate of about 2.26 million people per year.

75. Points may vary. $(-2, 1), (0, -5)$ $m = -3$

77. Points may vary. $(-2, -2), (0, 4)$ $m = 3$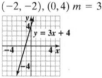

79. $m = -2$ **81.** $m = \dfrac{q}{p}$ **83.** $m = \dfrac{6}{a - 6}$ **85.** $MR = 2$; For every hot dog sold, revenue increases by $2.   **87.** The line is a vertical line. Answers will vary, but the points should be of the form (a, y_1) and (a, y_2) where a is a specific value and y_1, y_2 are any two different values. Because the line is a vertical line, the slope is undefined.

Section 3.4 Slope-Intercept Form of a Line

1. slope: 4, y-intercept: -3 **2.** slope: -3, y-intercept: 7   **3.** slope: $-\dfrac{2}{5}$, y-intercept: 3   **4.** slope: 0; y-intercept: 8

5. slope: undefined; y-intercept: none

6.   **7.**   **8.**   **9.**   **10.**   **11.**   **12.**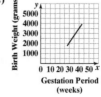

13. point-plotting, using intercepts, using slope and a point

14. $y = 3x - 2$ **15.** $y = -\dfrac{1}{4}x + 3$ **16.** $y = -1$

17. **(a)** 2075 grams   **(b)** 2933 grams   **(c)** slope = 143. Birth weight increases by 143 grams for each additional week of pregnancy.   **(d)** A gestation period of 0 weeks does not make sense.   **(e)**

 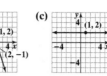

Birth Weight (grams)

Gestation Period (weeks)

18. (a) $y = 0.38x + 50$ **(b)** \$78.50 **(c)** 90 miles **(d)**

19. $m = 5$; y-intercept $= 2$ **21.** $m = 1$; y-intercept $= -9$

23. $m = -10$; y-intercept $= 7$ **25.** $m = -1$; y-intercept $= -9$

27. $m = -2$; y-intercept $= 4$ **29.** $m = -\dfrac{2}{3}$; y-intercept $= 8$

31. $m = \dfrac{5}{3}$; y-intercept $= -3$ **33.** $m = \dfrac{1}{2}$; y-intercept $= -\dfrac{5}{2}$ **35.** $m = 0$; y-intercept $= -5$ **37.** m is undefined; no y-intercept

39. **41.** **43.** **45.** **47.** **49.** **51.**

53. **55.** $y = -x + 8$ **57.** $y = \dfrac{6}{7}x - 6$ **59.** $y = -\dfrac{1}{3}x + \dfrac{2}{3}$ **61.** $x = -5$ **63.** $y = 3$ **65.** $y = 5x$

67. **69.** **71.** **73.** **75.** **77.**

79. **81.** **83.** **85.** **87.** **89.**

91. (a) $y = 0.08x + 400$ **(b)** \$496 **(c)**

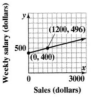

93. (a) 41.7 cents **(b)** 2005 **(c)** Each year, the cost per minute declines 3.583 cents. **(d)** No because the cost per minute would eventually become negative using this model. **(e)**

95. $B = -4$ **97.** $A = -4$

99. $B = -3$ **101. (a)** $y = 40x + 4000$

(b) \$24,000 **(c)** 375 calculators

(d)

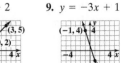

103. The line has a positive slope with a negative y-intercept. Possible equations are (a) and (e).

Section 3.5 Point-Slope Form of a Line

1. $y - y_1 = m(x - x_1)$ **2.** True

3. $y = 3x - 5$ **4.** $y = \dfrac{1}{3}x - 5$ **5.** $y = -4x - 3$ **6.** $y = -\dfrac{5}{2}x - 5$ **7.** $y = 3$ **8.** $y = x + 2$ **9.** $y = -3x + 1$

10. $x = 3$

11. Horizontal line, $y = b$; Vertical line, $x = a$; Point-slope, $y - y_1 = m(x - x_1)$; Slope-intercept, $y = mx + b$; Standard form, $Ax + By = C$ **12. (a)** $y = -100x + 790$ **(b)** 390 gallons **(c)** The number of gallons of gasoline sold will decrease by 100 if the price per gallon increases by \$1.

13. $y = 3x - 1$

15. $y = -2x$

17. $y = \frac{1}{4}x - 3$

19. $y = -6x + 13$

21. $y = -7$

23. $x = -4$

25. $y = \frac{2}{3}x + 2$

27. $y = -\frac{3}{4}x$

29. $x = -3$ **31.** $y = -5$ **33.** $y = -4.3$ **35.** $x = \frac{1}{2}$ **37.** $y = 2x + 4$ **39.** $y = -4x + 6$

41. $y = -\frac{3}{2}x - \frac{5}{2}$ **43.** $y = 2x - 5$ **45.** $y = -3$ **47.** $x = 2$ **49.** $y = 0.25x + 0.575$

51. $y = x - \frac{11}{4}$

53. $y = 5x - 22$

55. $y = 5$

57. $y = x + 2$

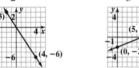

59. $y = \frac{1}{2}x + 4$

61. $x = 5$

63. $y = -7x + 2$

65. $y = -\frac{2}{3}x + 7$

67. $y = -\frac{3}{2}x$

69. $y = \frac{2}{5}x - 2$

71. **(a)** When 60 packages are shipped, the expenses are $1635.

(b)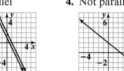

(c) $y = \frac{9}{4}x + 1500$

(d) $1950

(e) Expenses increase by $2.25 for each additional package.

73. **(a)** $(0, 820); (25, 985)$ **(b)**

(c) $y = 6.6x + 820$ **(d)** 952 fatalities   **(e)** Each year, the number of fatalities increases by 6.6.

75. $y = 3x + 14$ **77.** $y = -2x - 2$ **79.** $y = 6x - \frac{7}{2}$ **81.** $y = -x - 7$

83. $y = \frac{1}{5}x - 2$ **85.** $y = -\frac{3}{2}x + 2$

87. Yes. Although the point-slope form of the line will look different, the slope-intercept form of the line will be the same.

Section 3.6 Parallel and Perpendicular Lines   **1.** slopes; y-intercepts; x-intercepts

2. Not parallel

3. Parallel

4. Not parallel

5. $y = 2x - 1$

6. $y = -\frac{3}{2}x$

7. $x = 3$

8. $y = 5$

9. perpendicular   **10.** False   **11.** $\frac{1}{4}$ **12.** $-\frac{4}{5}$ **13.** 5

14. Perpendicular

15. Not perpendicular

16. Perpendicular

17. $y = -\frac{1}{2}x$

18. $y = \frac{3}{2}x + 2$

19. $y = -5$

20. $x = 3$

	Slope of the Given Line	Slope of a Line Parallel to the Given Line	Slope of a Line Perpendicular to the Given Line
21.	$m = -3$	$m_1 = -3$	$m_2 = \dfrac{1}{3}$
23.	$m = \dfrac{1}{2}$	$m_1 = \dfrac{1}{2}$	$m_2 = -2$
25.	$m = -\dfrac{4}{9}$	$m_1 = -\dfrac{4}{9}$	$m_2 = \dfrac{9}{4}$
27.	$m = 0$	$m_1 = 0$	$m_2 = $ undefined

29. perpendicular   **31.** parallel   **33.** perpendicular   **35.** perpendicular   **37.** perpendicular   **39.** parallel   **41.** parallel

43. $y = 3x - 14$ **45.** $y = -4x - 4$ **47.** $y = -7$ **49.** $x = -1$ **51.** $y = \dfrac{3}{2}x - 13$ **53.** $y = -\dfrac{1}{2}x - \dfrac{21}{2}$ **55.** $y = -2x + 11$

57. $y = \dfrac{1}{4}x$ **59.** $x = -2$ **61.** $y = 5$ **63.** $y = \dfrac{5}{2}x$ **65.** $y = -\dfrac{3}{5}x - 9$

67. $y = 7x - 26$ **69.** $y = \dfrac{1}{5}x + \dfrac{43}{5}$ **71.** $y = -7x + 41$ **73.** $y = -2x - 10$ **75.** $y = 3x - 2$ **77.** $x = 5$

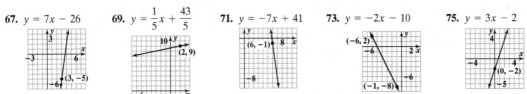

79. $y = -\dfrac{4}{3}x + 2$ **81.** $y = -2x - 5$ **83. (a)** $m_1 = 3$, $m_2 = -3$ **(b)** neither   **85. (a)** $m_1 = 2$, $m_2 = 2$ **(b)** parallel

87. (a) $m_1 = \dfrac{1}{2}$, $m_2 = \dfrac{1}{2}$ **(b)** parallel   **89. (a)** $m_1 = \dfrac{5}{3}$, $m_2 = -\dfrac{3}{5}$ **(b)** perpendicular

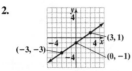

91.

parallelogram

93.

rectangle

95.

right triangle

97.
right triangle

99. $B = 2$ **101.** $A = 4$ **103.**

not an altitude

105. L_1 could be parallel to L_2. L_1 could be perpendicular to L_2. L_1 and L_2 could intersect, but not at right angles. L_1 could be the same as, or coincident with, L_2.

Putting the Concepts Together (Sections 3.1–3.6)

1. yes. $(1, -2)$ is a solution   **2.**   **3.**   **4. (a)** x-intercept is $-\dfrac{3}{4}$ **(b)** y-intercept is 3

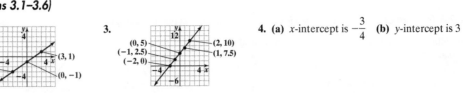

5. x-intercept is $\dfrac{3}{2}$; y-intercept is 2   **6. (a)** slope $= -\dfrac{2}{3}$ **(b)** y-intercept $= -\dfrac{4}{3}$ **7.** slope $= -\dfrac{1}{3}$

8. (a) $m = \dfrac{2}{5}$ **(b)** $m = -\dfrac{5}{2}$ **9.** The lines are parallel. Answers may vary.   **10.** $y = 3x + 1$ **11.** $y = -6x - 2$ **12.** $y = -2x + 7$

13. $y = -\dfrac{5}{2}x - 20$ **14.** $y = \dfrac{1}{4}x + 5$ **15.** $y = -8$ **16.** $x = 2$ **17.** $m = 11$. Every package increases expenses by \$11.

18. (a) $y = 8350x - 2302$, where x is the weight, in carats, and y is the price in dollars.   **(b)** For every 1-carat increase in weight, the cost increases by \$8350.   **(c)** \$4044

Section 3.7 Linear Inequalities in Two Variables

1. (a) No **(b)** Yes **(c)** Yes   **2. (a)** Yes **(b)** Yes **(c)** No   **3.** solid; dashed   **4.** half-plane

5.   **6.**   **7.**   **8.**   **9.**   **10.**   **11.**

12.   **13.**   **14. (a)** $0.2s + 0.25t \le 2$ **(b)** Yes **(c)** No   **15.** A is a solution.   **17.** C is a solution.
19. A and C are solutions.   **21.** B is a solution.   **23.** B is a solution.   **25.** A is a solution.

27.   **29.**   **31.**   **33.**   **35.**   **37.**

39.   **41.**   **43.**   **45.**   **47.**   **49.**

51.   **53.**   **55.**   **57.** $x + y \ge 26$ 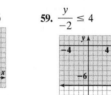 **59.** $\dfrac{y}{-2} \le 4$ **61.** $x \le y - 3$

63. $x + 3y < 0$ **65.** $2x - \dfrac{1}{2}y \ge 5$ **67.** $-2x > -1$ **69. (a)** $3s + 5a \le 120$ **(b)** No **(c)** Yes
71. (a) $3.1s + 5.7b \le 22$ **(b)** No **(c)** Yes

73.   **75.**   **77.**

79. If (a, b) satisfies the inequality, then (a, b) is a solution to the linear inequality. If (a, b) satisfies $Ax + By = C$, then (a, b) lies on the boundary line.

81. 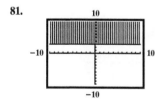 **83.** 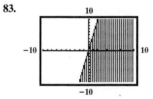 **85.**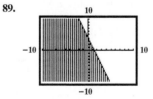

87. 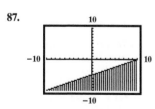 **89.** 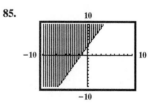 **91.**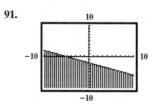

Chapter 3 Review

1–4.

$A(3, -2)$ quadrant IV;
$B(-1, -3)$ quadrant III;
$C(-4, 0)$ x-axis; $D(0, 2)$
y-axis

5. $A(1, 4)$; quadrant I; $B(-3, 0)$; x-axis   **6.** $A(0, 1)$; y-axis; $B(-2, 2)$; quadrant II   **7.** A: Yes; B: No

8. A: Yes; B: No   **9. (a)** $\left(4, -\dfrac{4}{3}\right)$ **(b)** $(-6, 2)$ **10. (a)** $(4, 4)$ **(b)** $(-2, -2)$

11.

x	y	(x, y)
-2	-8	$(-2, -8)$
0	-5	$(0, -5)$
4	1	$(4, 1)$

12.

x	y	(x, y)
-3	5	$(-3, 5)$
2	0	$(2, 0)$
4	-2	$(4, -2)$

13.

x	y	(x, y)
-18	2	$(-18, 2)$
-6	-2	$(-6, -2)$
24	-12	$(24, -12)$

14.

x	y	(x, y)
-3	-8	$(-3, -8)$
3	1	$(3, 1)$
5	4	$(5, 4)$

15.

x	C	(x, C)
1	7	$(1, 7)$
2	9	$(2, 9)$
3	11	$(3, 11)$

Shipping cost (dollars)
Number of items purchased

16.

x	E	(x, E)
500	1050	$(500, 1050)$
1000	1100	$(1000, 1100)$
2000	1200	$(2000, 1200)$

17.   **18.**   **19.**

20.   **21.**

p	C	(p, C)
20	80	$(20, 80)$
50	140	$(50, 140)$
80	200	$(80, 200)$

22.

p	F	(p, F)
100	800	$(100, 800)$
200	1100	$(200, 1100)$
500	2000	$(500, 2000)$

23. $(-2, 0), (0, -4)$ **24.** $(0, 1)$ **25.** $(0, 9), (-3, 0)$ **26.** $(0, -6), (3, 0)$ **27.** $(3, 0)$ **28.** $\left(0, -\dfrac{2}{5}\right), (1, 0)$

29.   **30.**   **31.**   **32.**   **33.**   **34.**

35.   **36.**   **37.** $\dfrac{4}{3}$ **38.** -2 **39.** -8 **40.** 2 **41.** $\dfrac{1}{4}$ **42.** $-\dfrac{1}{6}$ **43.** undefined   **44.** 0 **45.** 0

46. undefined   **47.**   **48.**   **49.**   **50.**

51. $m = 45$; the cost to produce 1 additional bicycle is \$45.   **52.** 5% **53.** $m = -1; b = \dfrac{1}{2}$ **54.** $m = 1; b = -\dfrac{3}{2}$

55. $m = \dfrac{3}{4}; b = 1$ **56.** $m = -\dfrac{2}{5}; b = \dfrac{8}{5}$

57.   **58.** 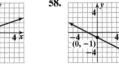   **59.** 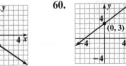   **60.** 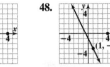   **61.**   **62.**

63. 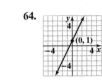   **64.**   **65.** $y = -\dfrac{3}{4}x + \dfrac{2}{3}$ **66.** $y = \dfrac{1}{5}x + 10$ **67.** $x = -12$ **68.** $y = -4$ **69.** $y = x - 20$

70. $y = -x - 8$ **71. (a)** \$360   **(b)** 7 days   **(c)**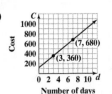

Cost
$(7, 680)$
$(3, 360)$
Number of days

72. (a) $(22, 418), (35, 665)$, $m = 19$
(b) It costs \$19 more for each additional day.
(c) $C = 19d$
(d) \$152

73. $y = 6x - 3$ **74.** $y = -2x + 8$ **75.** $y = -\dfrac{1}{2}x + \dfrac{1}{2}$ **76.** $y = \dfrac{2}{3}x - \dfrac{7}{3}$ **77.** $y = -\dfrac{1}{2}$ **78.** $x = -\dfrac{4}{7}$ **79.** $x = -5$ **80.** $y = 0$

81. $y = \dfrac{8}{7}x + 8$ **82.** $y = \dfrac{3}{2}x - 6$ **83.** $y = 3x - 4$ **84.** $y = -\dfrac{2}{5}x - 5$ **85.** $A = -4d + 24$ **86.** $F = -\dfrac{1}{3}m + 15$ **87.** not parallel

88. parallel   **89.** $y = -x + 2$ **90.** $y = 2x + 8$ **91.** $y = -3x + 7$ **92.** $y = -3x + 7$ **93.** $x = 5$ **94.** $y = -12$ **95.** $-\dfrac{2}{3}$

96. $-\dfrac{9}{4}$ **97.** perpendicular   **98.** not perpendicular   **99.** $y = \dfrac{1}{3}x + 5$ **100.** $y = -\dfrac{1}{2}x + 1$ **101.** $y = -\dfrac{3}{2}x - \dfrac{3}{2}$ **102.** $y = x + 1$

103. A, B are solutions.   **104.** C is a solution.

105.   **106.**   **107.**   **108.**   **109.**   **110.**

111.   **112.**   **113.** $0.25x + 0.1y \geq 12$ **114.** $2x - \dfrac{1}{2}y \leq 10$

Chapter 3 Test   **1.** No   **2. (a)** 4   **(b)** $-\dfrac{4}{3}$ **3. (a)** $m = \dfrac{4}{3}$ **(b)** $b = 8$

4.   **5.**   **6.** $-\dfrac{1}{6}$ **7. (a)** $-\dfrac{3}{2}$ **(b)** $\dfrac{2}{3}$ **8.** neither; Answers may vary.   **9.** $y = -4x - 15$ **10.** $y = 2x + 14$

11. $y = -3x - 11$ **12.** $y = \dfrac{1}{2}x - 2$ **13.** $y = -\dfrac{3}{2}x + 8$ **14.** $y = 5$ **15.** $x = -2$

16. $8 per package

17.   **18.**   **19.**

Cumulative Reviews Chapters 1–3

1. -16 **2.** $\dfrac{1}{4}$ **3.** -4 **4.** 8   **5.** $4m^2 + 5m - 9$ **6.** $\{-7\}$ **7.** $\left\{-\dfrac{25}{12}\right\}$ **8.** $B = \dfrac{2A - hb}{h}$ or $B = \dfrac{2A}{h} - b$

9. $\{x \mid x > -4\}$ or $(-4, \infty)$ 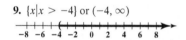   **10.** $\{x \mid x \leq 5\}$ or $(-\infty, 5]$ 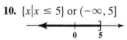   **11.**   **12.**   **13.**

14. $y = -\dfrac{4}{3}x + 2$ **15.** $y = -3x - 8$ **16.**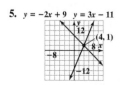

17. Shawn needs to score at least 91 on the final exam to earn an A.   **18.** A person 62 inches tall would be considered obese if they weighed 160 pounds or more.   **19.** The angles measure 55° and 125°.   **20.** The cylinder should be about 5.96 inches tall.   **21.** The three consecutive even integers are 24, 26, and 28.

Chapter 4 Systems of Linear Equations and Inequalities

Section 4.1 Solving Systems of Linear Equations by Graphing   **1.** System of linear equations   **2.** solution   **3. (a)** No   **(b)** Yes   **(c)** No
4. (a) Yes   **(b)** Yes   **(c)** Yes

5. $y = -2x + 9$ $y = 3x - 11$ **6.** $3x - y = -11$ 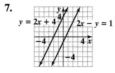   **7.** 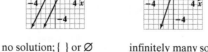   **8.**   **9.** consistent   **10.** independent
11. inconsistent   **12.** True
13. One solution; consistent; independent
14. Infinitely many solutions; consistent; dependent
15. No solution; inconsistent

no solution; { } or Ø   infinitely many solutions

16. After 100 miles; the cost is $60. **17. (a)** No **(b)** Yes **(c)** No **19. (a)** No **(b)** Yes **(c)** Yes **21. (a)** No **(b)** No **(c)** No

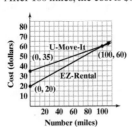

23. **25.** **27.** **29.**

31. **33.** **35.** **37.**

no solution; { } or ∅

infinitely many solutions

39. one solution; consistent; independent; $(3, 2)$
41. no solution; inconsistent   **43.** infinitely many solutions; consistent; dependent   **45.** one solution; consistent; independent; $(-1, -2)$ **47.** one solution; consistent; independent   **49.** no solution; inconsistent
51. infinitely many solutions; consistent; dependent
53. one solution; consistent; independent

55. no solution; inconsistent   **57.** infinitely many solutions; consistent; dependent

59. **61.** **63.** **65.** **67.**

$(-3, 3)$; consistent; independent

no solution; inconsistent

$(2, 4)$; consistent; independent

infinitely many solutions; consistent; dependent

infinitely many solutions; consistent; dependent

69.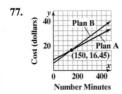

$(-4, 0)$; consistent; independent

71.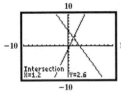

The break-even point is $(100, 2500)$. San Diego T-shirt Company must sell 100 T-shirts to break even at a cost/revenue of $2500.

73.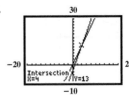

The break-even point is $(5, 7.5)$. The company needs to sell 5 boxes of skates to break even at a cost/revenue of $7500.

75.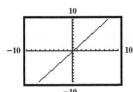

$\begin{cases} y = 62 + 0.12x \\ y = 50 + 0.2x \end{cases}$

The cost for driving 150 miles is the same for both companies ($80). Choose Acme to drive 200 miles.

77.

$\begin{cases} y = 8.95 + 0.08x \\ y = 5.95 + 0.07x \end{cases}$

The cost is the same ($16.45) when 150 minutes are used. Choose Plan B for 100 long-distance minutes.

79. $c = 3$ **81.** $c = 1$
83.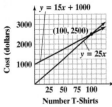

85.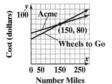

87.

infinitely many solutions

89. The three possibilities for a solution of a system of two linear equations containing two variables are (1) lines intersecting at a single point (one solution); (2) the lines are coincident (a single line in the plane) so an infinite number of solutions; (3) parallel lines (no solution).

Section 4.2 Solving Systems of Linear Equations Using Substitution **1.** $1; -1$ **2.** $(2, 4)$ **3.** $(-3, 5)$ **4.** $\left(\dfrac{3}{2}, 7\right)$ **5.** $\left(-\dfrac{4}{3}, \dfrac{1}{2}\right)$
6. ∅ or { }   **7.** infinitely many solutions   **8.** False   **9.** Infinitely many solutions   **10.** No solution; { } or ∅   **11.** No solution; { } or ∅
12. During the year 2060   **13.** $(4, -1)$ **15.** $(-1, 1)$ **17.** $(-3, -4)$ **19.** $(-4, -7)$ **21.** $\left(-\dfrac{2}{3}, 2\right)$ **23.** $\left(2, -\dfrac{1}{3}\right)$ **25.** $\left(\dfrac{1}{4}, \dfrac{1}{6}\right)$
27. no solution; inconsistent   **29.** infinitely many solutions; dependent   **31.** no solution; inconsistent   **33.** infinitely many solutions; dependent
35. $\left(2, -\dfrac{1}{3}\right)$ **37.** no solution; { } or ∅   **39.** infinitely many solutions   **41.** $\left(\dfrac{5}{3}, -\dfrac{1}{2}\right)$ **43.** no solution; { } or ∅   **45.** infinitely many solutions
47. $\left(\dfrac{5}{4}, -\dfrac{7}{4}\right)$ **49.** infinitely many solutions   **51.** $\left(-\dfrac{5}{2}, 4\right)$ **53.** length 10 ft; width 7 ft   **55.** $8000 in money market; $4000 in international fund   **57.** $1,000,000   **59.** 5 and 12   **61.** $A = \dfrac{7}{6}$; $B = -\dfrac{1}{2}$ **63.** Answers may vary.   **65.** Answers may vary.

67. A reasonable first step is to multiply the first equation by 6 to clear fractions, and multiply the second equation by 4 to clear fractions. Then the system would be $\begin{cases} 2x - y = 4 \\ 6x + 2y = -5 \end{cases}$. To solve for y, multiply the first equation by 2. Answers may vary.

Section 4.3 Solving Systems of Linear Equations Using Elimination
1. additive inverses **2.** $(-4, -2)$ **3.** $(8, 3)$ **4.** $(6, -5)$ **5.** $(5, 0)$
6. dependent; infinitely **7.** No solution; $\{ \}$ or $\varnothing$ **8.** Infinitely many solutions **9.** Infinitely many solutions **10.** Cheeseburger: $1.75; shake: $2.25
11. $(2, -1)$ **13.** $(6, 4)$ **15.** $\left(-\dfrac{11}{4}, \dfrac{1}{2} \right)$ **17.** $(-1, -3)$ **19.** no solution; $\{ \}$ or $\varnothing$; inconsistent **21.** infinitely many solutions; dependent

23. infinitely many solutions; dependent **25.** no solution; $\{ \}$ or $\varnothing$; inconsistent **27.** $(-5, 8)$ **29.** $\left(\dfrac{3}{2}, -\dfrac{3}{4} \right)$ **31.** no solution; $\{ \}$ or $\varnothing$

33. $(12, -9)$ **35.** infinitely many solutions **37.** $\left(\dfrac{6}{29}, -\dfrac{8}{29} \right)$ **39.** $\left(\dfrac{1}{2}, 4 \right)$ **41.** $(-1, 2.1)$ **43.** $(-2, -6)$ **45.** $(50, 30)$ **47.** $(1, 5)$

49. $(5, 2)$ **51.** $\left(-\dfrac{9}{17}, \dfrac{31}{17} \right)$ **53.** $\left(\dfrac{8}{3}, -\dfrac{4}{7} \right)$ **55.** infinitely many solutions **57.** $(1, -3)$ **59.** $(-4, 0)$ **61.** $\left(-\dfrac{8}{5}, \dfrac{27}{10} \right)$ **63.** $(-4, -5)$

65. no solution; $\{ \}$ or $\varnothing$ **67.** $\left(\dfrac{106}{37}, \dfrac{16}{37} \right)$ **69.** hamburger 280 cal; Coke 210 cal **71.** tomatoes: 10 hr; zucchini: 15 hr; no

73. 60 lb Arabica; 40 lb Robusta **75.** $70°$ and $20°$ **77.** $\left(-\dfrac{3}{a}, 1 \right)$ **79.** $\left(-3a - b, \dfrac{3}{2}a - \dfrac{3}{2}b \right)$ **81.** It is easier to eliminate y because the signs on y are opposites. Multiply the second equation by 3, to form $6x + 3y = 15$. Then add the equations, obtaining $7x = 21$. So $x = 3$. Substitute $x = 3$ into either the first equation or the second equation and solve for y, $y = -1$. **83.** Both of you will obtain the correct solution. Other strategies are: multiply equation (1) by one-third and adding; solving equation (2) for y and substituting this expression into equation (1); and graphing the equations and finding the point of intersection.

Putting the Concepts Together (Sections 4.1–4.3)
1. (a) No **(b)** Yes **(c)** No **2. (a)** infinitely many **(b)** consistent **(c)** dependent
3. (a) one **(b)** consistent **(c)** independent **4.** $(1, 1)$ **5.** $(5, -1)$ **6.** $(1, -5)$ **7.** $(-1, 0)$ **8.** $(-4, 5)$ **9.** $(-3, -1)$
10. $\left(-\dfrac{1}{3}, 3 \right)$ **11.** infinitely many solutions **12.** $(2.5, 3)$ **13.** no solution; $\{ \}$ or $\varnothing$

Section 4.4 Solving Direct Translation, Geometry, and Uniform Motion Problems Using Systems of Linear Equations
1. 43 and 61
2. Width: 50 yards; length: 150 yards **3.** True **4.** $180°$ **5.** $36°$ and $54°$ **6.** $49°$ and $131°$ **7.** True **8.** Airspeed: 350 mph; wind resistance: 50 mph **9.** $2x$; $12 + \dfrac{1}{2}y$ **11.** $2l + 2w$ **13.** $8(r - c)$; 16 **15.** 33, 49 **17.** 14, 37 **19.** Thursday 35,000; Friday 42,000
21. $12,000 in stocks; $9000 in bonds **23.** length 12 ft; width 9 ft **25.** length 25 m; width 10 m **27.** $40°$, $50°$ **29.** $22.5°$, $157.5°$
31. current 0.4 mph; still water 3.9 mph **33.** bike 11 mph; wind 1 mph **35.** northbound 60 mph; southbound 72 mph **37.** 4 hr
39. wind 25 mph; Piper 175 mph **41.** 24

Section 4.5 Solving Mixture Problems Using Systems of Linear Equations
1. number of units; rate; amount

2.

	Number	$\cdot$ Cost per Person	= Amount
Adults	a	42.95	$42.95a$
Children	c	15.95	$15.95c$
Total	9		332.55

3. 45 dimes **4.** principal; rate; time **5.** True **6.** $40,000 in Aa-rated bonds: $50,000 in B-rated bond **7.** 5 pounds of Brazilian coffee and 15 pounds of Colombian coffee **8.** Mix 120 gallons of the ice cream with 5% butterfat and 80 gallons of the ice cream with 15% butterfat.

9.

	Number	$\cdot$ Cost	= Total
Adult	a	4	$4a$
Student	s	1.5	$1.5s$
Total	215		580

$\begin{cases} a + s = 215 \\ 4a + 1.5s = 580 \end{cases}$

11.

	P	$\cdot$ r	= I
Savings	s	0.05	$0.05s$
Money Market	m	0.03	$0.03m$
Total	1600		50

$\begin{cases} s + m = 1600 \\ 0.005s + 0.03m = 50 \end{cases}$

13.

	lb	$\cdot$ Price	= Total
Mild	m	7.5	$7.5m$
Robust	r	10	$10r$
Total	12	8.75	$8.75(12)$

$\begin{cases} m + r = 12 \\ 7.5m + 10r = 8.75(12) \end{cases}$

15. $32a$; $24c$ **17.** $0.1A$; $0.07B$ **19.** $5.85r$; $4.20y$; 128.85 **21.** 315 **23.** 400 **25.** 60 nickels, 90 dimes **27.** first-class $0.42; postcard $0.27
29. $7500 in 5% account; $2500 in 8% account **31.** $3200 in risky plan; $1800 in safer plan **33.** 2 lb arbequina; 3 lb green **35.** 48.9 lb of the $2.75 per pound coffee; 51.1 lb of the $5 per pound coffee **37.** 80 lb rye; 100 lb bluegrass **39.** 20 ml 30% saline solution **41.** 70 liters
43. 1.2 gal **45.** $6200 at 5%; $3800 at 7.5% loss **47.** The percentage ethanol in the final solution is greater than the percentage of ethanol in either of the two original solutions.

Section 4.6 Systems of Linear Inequalities
1. solution **2. (a)** Solution **(b)** Not a solution **3.** dashed; solid

4. **5.** **6.** **7.**

8. (a)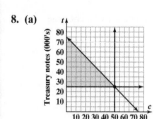

(b) Yes **(c)** No

9. (a) Yes **(b)** Yes **(c)** Yes **11. (a)** Yes **(b)** No **(c)** No

13. **15.** **17.** **19.** **21.**

23. **25.** **27.** 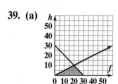 **29.** **31.** 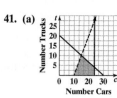 **33.**

35. **37.** **39. (a)** **(b)** No **(c)** Yes **41. (a)** **(b)** No **(c)** No

43. **45.**

no solution; { } or ∅

47. $\begin{cases} y \geq 0 \\ y \geq x \\ y \leq \frac{1}{2}(x+6) \end{cases}$

49. Answers may vary. Graph each equation in the system. The overlapping shaded region represents the solution of the system.

51. (a) $\begin{cases} y \geq x \\ y \geq -2x \end{cases}$ **(b)** $\begin{cases} y \leq x \\ y \geq -2x \end{cases}$ **(c)** $\begin{cases} y \geq x \\ y \leq -2x \end{cases}$

(d) $\begin{cases} y \leq x \\ y \leq -2x \end{cases}$ Answers may vary.

Chapter 4 Review **1. (a)** No **(b)** Yes **(c)** No **2. (a)** No **(b)** No **(c)** Yes **3. (a)** Yes **(b)** Yes **(c)** Yes **4. (a)** No **(b)** No **(c)** No

5. **6.** **7.** **8.** **9.** **10.** **11.**

$(6, 1)$ $(0, 3)$ $(-4, 4)$ $(-4, -1)$ $(2, -3)$ $(0, 0)$ no solution

12.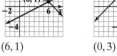

infinitely many solutions

13. None; inconsistent **14.** None; inconsistent **15.** Infinitely many; consistent; dependent
16. Infinitely many; consistent; dependent **17.** One; consistent; independent **18.** One; consistent; independent

19. (a) $\begin{cases} y = 70 + 0.1x \\ y = 100 + 0.04x \end{cases}$ **20. (a)** $\begin{cases} y = 50 + 40x \\ y = 350 + 10x \end{cases}$ **21.** $(2, 1)$ **22.** $(1, -1)$ **23.** $(7, -2)$ **24.** $(4, -2)$
(b) 500 fliers **(b)** 10 sq yd **25.** $(18, 11)$ **26.** $(-6, 8)$ **27.** $(2, -2)$ **28.** $(3, -1)$

29. Infinitely many solutions **30.** Infinitely many solutions
31. No solution; { } or ∅ **32.** Infinitely many solutions

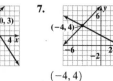

33. $\left(\frac{3}{2}, 1\right)$ **34.** $\left(\frac{1}{3}, -1\right)$ **35.** width 125 m; length 200 m

36. -3 **37.** $(0, -12)$ **38.** $(-3, 7)$ **39.** $(-3, 4)$
40. $(-3, 0)$ **41.** no solution; { } or ∅
42. infinite number of solutions **43.** $(-2, 2)$

(c) Printer A **(c)** tile

44. $(3, -2.5)$ **45.** $\left(\frac{1}{2}, -2\right)$ **46.** $\left(-\frac{3}{2}, 1\right)$ **47.** Infinitely many solutions **48.** $\left(\frac{6}{7}, \frac{5}{2}\right)$ **49.** $(-20, -13)$ **50.** $\left(\frac{1}{3}, \frac{2}{3}\right)$

51. No solution **52.** $\left(-\frac{1}{7}, 0\right)$ **53.** 2.4 lb cookies; 1.6 lb chocolates **54.** 400 individual tickets; 325 block tickets **55.** $\frac{3}{8}, \frac{1}{3}$ **56.** 26, 32
57. $32,000 in stocks, $18,000 in bonds **58.** 14 notebooks, 10 calculators **59.** 77.5°, 102.5° **60.** 40°, 50° **61.** 15 m by 22 m **62.** 110°, 40°
63. plane 450 mph, wind 50 mph **64.** current 2 mph, paddling 6 mph **65.** cyclist 10 mph, wind 2 mph **66.** faster 8 mph; slower 6 mph

67.

	Number	· Value	= Total Value
Dimes	d	0.10	0.10d
Nickels	n	0.05	0.05n
Total	35		2.25

68.

	P	· r	= I
Savings	s	0.065	0.065s
Mutual Fund	m	0.08	0.08m
Total	15,000		1050

69. 676
70. 7 dimes; 4 quarters
71. $7000 at 5%, $12,000 at 9%
72. $10,000 bonds, $15,000 stocks
73. 3 quarts 30% sugar solution

74. 60 pints   **75.** 3 lb peanuts; 2 lb almonds   **76.** 4 liters 35% acid; 16 liters 60% acid   **77. (a)** Yes **(b)** Yes **(c)** No
78. (a) No **(b)** Yes **(c)** Yes   **79. (a)** Yes **(b)** No **(c)** No   **80. (a)** No **(b)** Yes **(c)** Yes   **81. (a)** No **(b)** Yes **(c)** No
82. (a) No **(b)** Yes **(c)** No

83.   **84.**   **85.**   **86.**   **87.**

88.   **89.**   **90.**   **91.**   **92.**

93.   **94.**   **95.**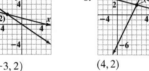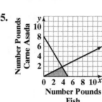

Chapter 4 Test   **1. (a)** No **(b)** No **(c)** Yes   **2. (a)** Yes **(b)** No **(c)** No   **3. (a)** one **(b)** consistent **(c)** independent
4. (a) none **(b)** inconsistent **(c)** not applicable   **5.**   **6.**   **7.** $(0, -3)$ **8.** $(-12, -1)$ **9.** $(-3, 3)$
$(-3, 2)$ $(4, 2)$ **10.** $(-2, -4)$ **11.** $\left(3, -\frac{1}{2}\right)$ **12.** $(2.5, 3)$
13. infinitely many solutions
14. airplane 200 mph; wind 25 mph
15. 7 containers vanilla; 4 containers peach
16. $52.5°, 127.5°$
17. 15 basketballs, 25 volleyballs

18.   **19.**   **20.**

Chapter 5 Exponents and Polynomials

Section 5.1 Adding and Subtracting Polynomials   **1.** Monomial   **2.** 1   **3.** Yes; Coefficient 12; Degree 6   **4.** No
5. Yes; Coefficient 10; Degree 0   **6.** No   **7.** $m + n$ **8.** Yes; Coefficient 3; Degree 7   **9.** No   **10.** Yes; Coefficient -1; Degree 3
11. True   **12.** standard form   **13.** Yes; degree 3   **14.** No   **15.** No   **16.** Yes; degree 4   **17.** False   **18.** $12x^2 + 3x + 3$
19. $2z^4 + 4z^3 - z^2 + z - 1$ **20.** $5x^2y + 6x^2y^2 - xy^2$ **21.** $5x^3 - 15x^2 + 3x + 7$ **22.** $8y^3 - 3y^2 - 3y - 6$ **23.** $11x^2y + 2x^2y^2 - 9xy^2$
24. $a^2b + a^2b^3 + 2ab^2 - 5ab$ **25.** $7a^2 - 4ab - 12b^2$ **26. (a)** 1 **(b)** -214 **(c)** 101   **27. (a)** 40 **(b)** -20 **28.** $1875
29. Yes; coefficient $\frac{1}{2}$; degree 3   **31.** Yes; coefficient $\frac{1}{7}$; degree 2   **33.** No   **35.** Yes; coefficient 12; degree 5   **37.** No
39. Yes; coefficient 4; degree 0   **41.** Yes; $6x^2 - 10$; degree 2; binomial   **43.** No   **45.** No   **47.** Yes; $\frac{1}{8}$; degree 0; monomial
49. Yes; $-\frac{1}{2}t^4 + 3t^2 + 6t$; degree 4; trinomial   **51.** No   **53.** Yes; $5z^3 - 10z^2 + z + 12$; degree 3; polynomial
55. Yes; $2xy^4 + 3x^2y^2 + 4$; degree 5; trinomial   **57.** $7x - 10$ **59.** $-2m^2 + 5$ **61.** $-2p^2 + p + 8$ **63.** $-3y^2 - 2y - 4$
65. $\frac{5}{4}p^2 + \frac{1}{6}p - 3$ **67.** $6m^2 - 4mn - n^2$ **69.** $4n^2 - 8n + 5$ **71.** $-x - 16$ **73.** $14x^2 - 3x - 5$ **75.** $4y^3 - 3y - 4$
77. $2y^3 - y^2 - 4y$ **79.** $\frac{14}{9}q^2 - \frac{23}{8}q + 2$ **81.** $-8m^2n^2 - 4mn - 7$ **83.** $-4x - 5$ **85.** $-x^2 - x + 15$ **87.** $2p^2 + 10p + 16$
89. $y^3 - 2y^2 + 11y - 14$ **91. (a)** 3 **(b)** 48 **(c)** 13   **93. (a)** -2 **(b)** $\frac{3}{4}$ **(c)** 4.75   **95.** 45   **97.** -328 **99.** $3t - 3$ **101.** $3x^2 - 3x - 3$
103. $9xy^2 + 1$ **105.** $-y^2 + 15y + 1$ **107.** $\frac{7}{3}q^2 + \frac{5}{3}$ **109.** $13d^2 + d + 10$ **111.** $6a^2 + 5a - 3$ **113.** $-2x^2 - 2xy + y^2$ **115.** $-5x + 12$
117. $3x^2 + 4x - 3$ **119.** $-14x^2 + 4x - 13$ **121.** $-3x + 5$ **123.** 26 ft   **125. (a)** $438 million **(b)** $2119.6 million **(c)** $4156 million
127. (a) $-2.125x^2 + 105x$ **(b)** $1250   **129. (a)** $10x$ **(b)** $500 **(c)** $15,000   **131.** $16x - 12$ **133.** $7x + 18$ **135.** $2x - 5$
137. Answers may vary.   **139.** To find the degree of a polynomial in one variable, use the largest exponent on any term in the polynomial. To find the degree of a polynomial in more than one variable, find the degree of each term in the polynomial. The degree of the term ax^my^n is the sum of the exponents, $m + n$. The highest degree of all of the terms is the degree of the polynomial.

Section 5.2 Multiplying Monomials: The Product and Power Rules
1. exponential **2.** $m + n$ **3.** False **4.** 27 **5.** -3125 **6.** c^8
7. y^9 **8.** a^9b^6 **9.** 2^8 **10.** $(-3)^6$ **11.** b^{10} **12.** False **13.** $8n^3$ **14.** $-125x^{12}$ **15.** $49a^6b^2$ **16.** $8a^{11}$ **17.** $-18m^3n^9$
18. $-16x^4y^4$ **19.** 1024 **21.** -128 **23.** m^9 **25.** b^{20} **27.** x^8 **29.** p^9 **31.** $(-n)^7$ **33.** 64 **35.** 64 **37.** $(-m)^{18}$
39. m^{14} **41.** $(-b)^{20}$ **43.** $27x^6$ **45.** $25z^4$ **47.** $\frac{1}{4}a^2$ **49.** $81p^{28}q^8$ **51.** $-8m^6n^3$ **53.** $25x^2y^4z^6$ **55.** $12x^5$ **57.** $-40a^{10}$
59. $-7m^4$ **61.** $6x^7$ **63.** $6x^6y^4$ **65.** $-5m^2n^4$ **67.** $-40x^5y^6$ **69.** $4x^3$ **71.** $-5x^3$ **73.** b^6 **75.** $81b^4$ **77.** $9p^5$ **79.** $27x^6y^2$
81. $-30cd^2$ **83.** $25x^8$ **85.** $-2x^7y^6$ **87.** $72x^{14}$ **89.** $4q^6$ **91.** $16x^{14}$ **93.** $-\frac{24}{5}m^{17}n^9$ **95.** x^6 **97.** $48x^2$ **99.** The product rule for
exponential expressions is a "shortcut" for writing out each exponential expression in expanded form. For example, $x^2 \cdot x^3 = (x \cdot x) \cdot (x \cdot x \cdot x) = x^5$.
101. The product to a power rule generalizes the result of using a product as a factor several times. That is, $(a \cdot b)^n = (a \cdot b) \cdot (a \cdot b) \cdot (a \cdot b) \ldots =$
$a \cdot a \cdot a \cdot \ldots \cdot b \cdot b \cdot b \cdot \ldots = a^n \cdot b^n$. **103.** The expression $4x^2 + 3x^2$ is a sum of terms: because the bases are the same, add the coefficient and retain the
common base. The expression $(4x^2)(3x^2)$ is a product: multiply the constant terms and, since the bases are the same, add the exponents on the variable bases.

Section 5.3 Multiplying Polynomials
1. $3x^3 - 6x^2 + 12x$ **2.** $-2a^4b^3 + 4a^3b^3 - 3a^3b^2$ **3.** $3n^5 - \frac{9}{8}n^4 - \frac{6}{7}n^3$ **4.** $x^2 + 9x + 14$
5. $2n^2 - 5n - 3$ **6.** $6p^2 - 7p + 2$ **7.** $x^2 + 7x + 12$ **8.** $y^2 + 2y - 15$ **9.** $a^2 - 6a + 5$ **10.** $2x^2 + 11x + 12$ **11.** $6y^2 + y - 15$
12. $6a^2 - 11a + 4$ **13.** $15x^2 - 14xy - 8y^2$ **14.** $A^2 - B^2$ **15.** $a^2 - 16$ **16.** $9w^2 - 49$ **17.** $x^2 - 4y^6$ **18.** False
19. perfect square trinomial **20.** False **21.** $z^2 - 18z + 81$ **22.** $p^2 + 2p + 1$ **23.** $16 - 8a + a^2$ **24.** $9z^2 - 24z + 16$
25. $25p^2 + 10p + 1$ **26.** $4w^2 + 28wy + 49y^2$ **27.** False **28.** $x^3 - 8$ **29.** $3y^3 + 4y^2 + 8y - 8$ **30.** $x^3 - 8$ **31.** $3y^3 + 5y^2 - 17y + 5$
32. $-24a^3 - 34a^2 + 10a$ **33.** $15x^2 + 54x - 24$ **34.** $x^3 + 4x^2 + x - 6$ **35.** $6x^2 - 10x$ **37.** $2n^2 - 3n$ **39.** $12n^4 + 6n^3 - 15n^2$
41. $4x^4y^2 - 3x^3y^3$ **43.** $x^2 + 12x + 35$ **45.** $y^2 + 2y - 35$ **47.** $6m^2 + 11my - 10y^2$ **49.** $x^2 + 5x + 6$ **51.** $q^2 - 13q + 42$
53. $6x^2 + 7x - 3$ **55.** $x^4 + 4x^2 + 3$ **57.** $42 - 13x + x^2$ **59.** $10u^2 + 17uv + 6v^2$ **61.** $10a^2 - ab - 2b^2$ **63.** $x^2 - 9$ **65.** $4z^2 - 25$
67. $16x^4 - 1$ **69.** $4x^2 - 9y^2$ **71.** $x^2 - \frac{1}{9}$ **73.** $x^2 - 4x + 4$ **75.** $25k^2 - 30k + 9$ **77.** $x^2 + 4xy + 4y^2$ **79.** $4a^2 - 12ab + 9b^2$
81. $x^2 + x + \frac{1}{4}$ **83.** $x^3 + x^2 - 5x - 2$ **85.** $2y^3 - 12y^2 + 19y - 3$ **87.** $2x^3 - 7x^2 + 4x + 3$ **89.** $2b^3 + 2b^2 - 24b$ **91.** $-x^3 + 9x$
93. $10y^5 + 3y^4 + 4y^3 + 3y^2 + 2y + 2$ **95.** $b^3 + 2b^2 - 5b - 6$ **97.** $12n - 8n^2 - 4n^3$ **99.** $8a^2 - 10ab - 3b^2$ **101.** $\frac{1}{4}x^2 - 9$
103. $0.25b^2 + 3b + 9$ **105.** $x^6 + x^4 - 3x^2 - 3$ **107.** $2x^3 + x^2 - 7x - 2$ **109.** $-5x^7 + 4x^6 - 6x^5$ **111.** $5x^3 + 21x^2 + 2x$
113. $-3w^3 + 3w^2 + 36w$ **115.** $3a^3 + 24a^2 + 48a$ **117.** $2n^2 + 6n$ **119.** $24ab$ **121.** $-x^2 + 3x + 2$ **123.** $4x^2 + 4x + 1$
125. $x^3 - 3x^2 + 3x - 1$ **127.** $2x^2 - 9$ **129.** $2x^2 + 7x - 15$ **131.** $2x^2 + x - 1$ **133.** $4x^3 + x^2 - 3x$ **135.** $x^2 + 12x + 20$
137. $x^2 + 3x + 2$ **139.** $(x^2 - x)$ square inches **141.** $(\pi x^2 + 4\pi x + 4\pi)$ square feet **143.** (a) a^2, ab, ab, b^2 (b) $a^2 + 2ab + b^2$ (c) length: $a + b$,
width: $a + b$, area: $(a + b)^2 = a^2 + 2ab + b^2$ **145.** $x^3 + 2x^2 - 4x - 8$ **147.** $9 - x^2 - 2xy - y^2$ **149.** $x^3 + 6x^2 + 12x + 8$
151. $z^4 + 12z^3 + 54z^2 + 108z + 81$ **153.** To square the binomial $(3a - 5)^2$, use the pattern $A^2 - 2AB + B^2$. This means, square the first term, take
the product of -2 times the first term times the second term, and square the second term. So $(3a - 5)^2 = (3a)^2 - 2(3a)(5) + 5^2 = 9a^2 - 30a + 25$.
155. The FOIL method can be used to multiply only binomials.

Section 5.4 Dividing Monomials: The Quotient Rule and Integer Exponents
1. a^{m-n} **2.** False **3.** $3^2 = 9$ **4.** $\frac{7c}{5}$ **5.** $-\frac{3wz^7}{2}$
6. $\frac{a^n}{b^n}; b \neq 0$ **7.** $\frac{p^4}{16}$ **8.** $-\frac{8a^6}{b^{12}}$ **9.** (a) 1; (b) -1; (c) 1 **10.** (a) 1; (b) 2; (c) 1 **11.** (a) $\frac{1}{16}$ (b) $\frac{1}{16}$ (c) $-\frac{1}{16}$ **12.** $\frac{1}{8}$
13. (a) $\frac{1}{y^8}$ (b) $\frac{1}{y^8}$ (c) $-\frac{1}{y^8}$ **14.** (a) $\frac{2}{m^5}$ (b) $\frac{1}{32m^5}$ (c) $-\frac{1}{32m^5}$ **15.** 9 **16.** -100 **17.** $\frac{5z^2}{2}$ **18.** $\frac{8}{7}$ **19.** $\frac{25}{9a^2}$ **20.** $-\frac{27n^{12}}{8}$
21. $-\frac{20}{a^2}$ **22.** $\frac{2}{mn}$ **23.** $-\frac{4a^3b^3}{3}$ **24.** $\frac{9x^2}{7y^3}$ **25.** $\frac{z^6}{9y^4}$ **26.** $\frac{4w^4}{49z^6}$ **27.** $-\frac{2}{p^{11}}$ **28.** $-\frac{4}{k}$ **29.** 16 **31.** x^9 **33.** $4y^3$ **35.** $-\frac{2m^7}{3}$
37. $2m^8n^2$ **39.** $\frac{27}{8}$ **41.** $\frac{x^{15}}{27}$ **43.** $\frac{x^{20}}{y^{28}}$ **45.** $\frac{49a^4b^2}{c^6}$ **47.** 1 **49.** -1 **51.** 18 **53.** 1 **55.** 1 **57.** $24a$ **59.** $\frac{1}{1000}$ **61.** $\frac{1}{m^2}$
63. $-\frac{1}{a^2}$ **65.** $-\frac{4}{y^3}$ **67.** $\frac{11}{18}$ **69.** $\frac{25}{4}$ **71.** $\frac{z^2}{3}$ **73.** $-\frac{m^6}{8n^3}$ **75.** 16 **77.** $6x^4$ **79.** $\frac{5m^3}{2}$ **81.** $40m^3$ **83.** $\frac{5z^5}{6y^4}$ **85.** $\frac{-7m^{10}n^6}{3}$
87. $\frac{7y^4}{z^2}$ **89.** $\frac{y^4}{16x^4}$ **91.** $\frac{48}{b^3}$ **93.** 4 **95.** $\frac{1}{8}$ **97.** 81 **99.** $\frac{1}{x^9}$ **101.** x^{13} **103.** $\frac{4}{x^3}$ **105.** $\frac{3z^3}{2x^3}$ **107.** $\frac{1}{4x^3y^9}$ **109.** $-\frac{1}{a^{12}}$
111. $\frac{27}{m^6}$ **113.** $\frac{x^4y^6}{9}$ **115.** $\frac{2}{p^7}$ **117.** 12 **119.** $\frac{2x^8}{3}$ **121.** $\frac{16y}{27x^{18}}$ **123.** $\frac{9y}{2z^3}$ **125.** $216x^3y^6$ **127.** $\frac{5ab^7}{3}$ **129.** $\frac{2x^6}{5}$
131. $3x^3$ cubic meters **133.** $V = \frac{\pi d^2 h}{4}$ **135.** $9\pi x^3$ square units **137.** $\frac{1}{x^n}$ **139.** $x^{6n-2}y^2$ **141.** $\frac{x^{6a^2}y^{3ab}}{z^{3ac}}$ **143.** $\frac{9}{8a^{10n}}$ **145.** The quotient

$\frac{11^6}{11^4} \neq 1^2$ because $\frac{11^6}{11^4} = \frac{11 \cdot 11 \cdot 11 \cdot 11 \cdot 11 \cdot 11}{11 \cdot 11 \cdot 11 \cdot 11} = \frac{\cancel{11} \cdot \cancel{11} \cdot \cancel{11} \cdot \cancel{11} \cdot 11 \cdot 11}{\cancel{11} \cdot \cancel{11} \cdot \cancel{11} \cdot \cancel{11}} = 11^2$. **147.** When simplifying the expression $-12x^0$, the exponent 0 only
applies to the base x, so $-12x^0 = -12 \cdot 1 = -12$. However, $(-12x)^0 = 1$ because the entire expression is raised to the 0 power. **149.** His answer is
incorrect. To raise a factor to a power, multiply exponents. Your friend added exponents.

Putting the Concepts Together (Sections 5.1–5.4)
1. Yes; degree 6; trinomial **2.** (a) 0 (b) -4 (c) 2 **3.** $8x^4 - 4x^2 + 14$
4. $5x^2y + 3xy + 2y^2$ **5.** $-6m^3n^2 + 2m^2n^4$ **6.** $5x^2 - 17x - 12$ **7.** $8x^2 - 26xy + 21y^2$ **8.** $25x^2 - 64$ **9.** $4x^2 + 12xy + 9y^2$
10. $6a^3 + 22a^2 - 40a$ **11.** $16m^4 + 4m^3 + 10m^2 - 20m - 24$ **12.** $-8x^8z^9$ **13.** $-\frac{15}{mn}$ **14.** $-3a^3b^2$ **15.** $\frac{1}{2x^2y^2}$ **16.** $\frac{7b^2}{2a}$ **17.** $\frac{r^5}{q^7t^2}$
18. $\frac{8}{27r^6}$ **19.** $\frac{y^4}{16x^6}$ **20.** $\frac{64y^8}{81x^{24}}$

Section 5.5 Dividing Polynomials 1. $\dfrac{4x^4}{2x} + \dfrac{8x^2}{2x}$ 2. $2n^2 - 4n + 1$ 3. $6k^2 - 9 + \dfrac{5}{2k^2}$ 4. $\dfrac{xy^3}{4} + \dfrac{2y}{x} - \dfrac{1}{x^2}$ 5. standard

6. quotient; remainder; dividend 7. $x - 8$ 8. $x - 4$ 9. $4x + 5 + \dfrac{6}{x + 3}$ 10. $4x^2 - 11x + 23 - \dfrac{45}{x + 2}$ 11. $x^2 + 4x + 10 + \dfrac{60}{2x - 5}$

12. $4x - 3 + \dfrac{-7x + 7}{x^2 + 2}$ 13. $2x - 1$ 15. $3a + 9 - \dfrac{1}{a^2}$ 17. $\dfrac{n^4}{5} - \dfrac{2n^2}{5} - 1$ 19. $\dfrac{5r^2}{3} - 3$ 21. $-x^2 + 3x - \dfrac{9}{x^2}$ 23. $\dfrac{3}{8} + \dfrac{z^2}{2} - \dfrac{z}{4}$

25. $-7x + 5y$ 27. $-\dfrac{6y}{x} + 15$ 29. $-\dfrac{5}{a} - \dfrac{2c^2}{a^2b}$ 31. $x - 7$ 33. $x - 5$ 35. $x^2 + 6x - 3$ 37. $x^3 - 3x^2 + 6x - 2$

39. $x^2 - 2x + 3 + \dfrac{5}{x + 1}$ 41. $2x + 3$ 43. $x^2 + 6x + 7 + \dfrac{16}{x - 2}$ 45. $2x^3 + 5x^2 + 9x - 4 - \dfrac{17}{x - 4}$ 47. $x^2 + 4x - 3 + \dfrac{2}{2x - 1}$

49. $x - 4 - \dfrac{4}{5 + x}$ 51. $2x - 1 + \dfrac{6}{1 + 2x}$ 53. $x + 2 + \dfrac{2x - 4}{x^2 - 2}$ 55. $a^2 + a - 30$ 57. $-x^2 - x - 6$ 59. $-2ab + 2b^2$

61. $\dfrac{2}{x^2} + \dfrac{7}{2} - \dfrac{3x^2}{2} + 3x$ 63. $\dfrac{2x^7y^8z^{12}}{3}$ 65. $2x - 6$ 67. $n^2 - 6n + 9$ 69. $-10x^5 - 10x^3 + 40x^6$ 71. $6pq - 2q^2 - p^2$

73. $x^3 + 6x^2 + 4x - 5$ 75. $15rs^2 - 4r^2s$ 77. $-3x^5 + 6x^3 - 3x^2$ 79. $4x$ 81. $-x + \dfrac{2}{x^2} - \dfrac{4}{x}$ 83. $-\dfrac{1}{2x} - \dfrac{2}{x^2} + \dfrac{1}{x^3}$ 85. x ft

87. $(z + 3)$ in. 89. $(4x + 4)$ ft 91. (a) $0.004x^2 - 0.8x + 180 + \dfrac{5000}{x}$ (b) $182.11 per computer 93. 6 95. When the divisor is a mono-mial, divide each term in the numerator by the denominator. When dividing by a binomial, use long division. Answers may vary.

Section 5.6 Applying Exponent Rules: Scientific Notation 1. scientific notation 2. positive 3. False 4. 4.32×10^2 5. 1.0302×10^4
6. 5.432×10^6 7. 9.3×10^{-2} 8. 4.59×10^{-5} 9. 8×10^{-8} 10. left 11. True 12. 310 13. 0.901 14. 170,000 15. 7
16. 0.00089 17. 6×10^7 18. 8×10^{-3} 19. 1.5×10^4 20. 2.8×10^{-5} 21. 4×10^5 22. 2×10^{-4} 23. 5×10^3 24. 6.25×10^{-5}
25. $2.7032 \times 10^8 = 270,320,000$ barrels 26. $3.72 \times 10^8 = 372,000,000$ barrels 27. 3×10^5 29. 6.4×10^7 31. 5.1×10^{-4} 33. 1×10^{-9}
35. 8.007×10^9 37. 3.09×10^{-5} 39. 6.2×10^2 41. 4×10^0 43. 6.656×10^9 45. 7.051×10^{10} 47. 1.702×10^8 km
49. 3×10^{-5} mm 51. 2.5×10^{-7} m 53. 3.11×10^{-3} kg 55. 420,000 57. 100,000,000 59. 0.0039 61. 0.4 63. 3760
65. 0.0082 67. 0.00006 69. 7,050,000 71. 0.000000000000001 73. 0.00225 75. 500,000 77. 3×10^9 79. 8.4×10^{-3}
81. 3×10^8 83. 2.5×10^1 85. 8×10^8 87. 9×10^{15} 89. 1.116×10^7 miles 91. $\approx 1.68 \times 10^3$ pounds 93. (a) 1.55×10^9
(b) 3.0×10^8 (c) 5.2 gal 95. (a) 1.791×10^8 (b) 4.48×10^7 (c) 25% 97. 2.5×10^{-4} m 99. 8×10^{-10} m 101. 7.15×10^{-8} m
103. $1.2348\pi \times 10^{-14}$ m^3 105. $2.88\pi \times 10^{-25}$ m^3 107. To convert a number written in decimal notation to scientific notation, count the number of decimal places, N, that the decimal point must be moved to arrive at a number x such that $1 \le x < 10$. If the original number is greater than or equal to 1, move the decimal point to the left that many places and write the number in the form $x \times 10^N$. If the original number is between 0 and 1, move the decimal point to the right that many places and write the number in the form $x \times 10^{-N}$. 109. The number 34.5×10^4 is incorrect because the number 34.5 is not a number between 1 (inclusive) and 10. The correct answer is 3.45×10^5.

Chapter 5 Review 1. Yes; coefficient 4; degree 3 2. No 3. No 4. Yes; coefficient 1; degree 3 5. No 6. No
7. Yes; degree 0; monomial 8. Yes; degree 5; binomial 9. Yes; degree 6; trinomial 10. Yes; degree 10; trinomial 11. $9x^2 + 8x - 2$
12. $m^3 + mn - 5m$ 13. $-x^2y + 12x$ 14. $-7y^2 - 6yz + 9z^2$ 15. $-2x^2 - 2$ 16. $-20y^2 - 8y + 5$ 17. (a) 0 (b) 8 (c) 2
18. (a) 3 (b) 2 (c) $\dfrac{11}{4}$ 19. 0 20. 29 21. 279,936 22. $-\dfrac{1}{243}$ 23. 16,777,216 24. 1 25. x^{13} 26. m^6 27. r^{12} 28. m^{24}
29. $1024x^5$ 30. $64n^6$ 31. $81x^8y^4$ 32. $4x^6y^8$ 33. $15x^6$ 34. $-36a^4$ 35. $16y^5$ 36. $-12p^6$ 37. $12w^4$ 38. $-\dfrac{3}{4}z^3$ 39. $108x^8$
40. $80a^6$ 41. $-8x^5 + 6x^4 - 2x^3$ 42. $2x^7 + 4x^6 - x^4$ 43. $6x^2 - 7x - 5$ 44. $4x^2 - 5x - 6$ 45. $x^2 - 3x - 40$ 46. $w^2 + 9w - 10$
47. $24m^3 - 22m^2 + 7m - 3$ 48. $8y^5 + 12y^4 + 4y^3 + 6y^2 - 6y - 9$ 49. $x^2 + 8x + 15$ 50. $2x^2 - 17x + 8$ 51. $6m^2 + 17m - 14$
52. $48m^2 - 26m - 4$ 53. $21x^2 + 5xy - 6y^2$ 54. $20x^2 + 7xy - 3y^2$ 55. $x^2 - 16$ 56. $4x^2 - 25$ 57. $4x^2 + 12x + 9$
58. $49x^2 - 28x + 4$ 59. $9x^2 - 16y^2$ 60. $64m^2 - 36n^2$ 61. $25x^2 - 20xy + 4y^2$ 62. $4a^2 + 12ab + 9b^2$ 63. $x^2 - 0.25$
64. $r^2 - 0.0625$ 65. $y^2 + \dfrac{4}{3}y + \dfrac{4}{9}$ 66. $y^2 - y + \dfrac{1}{4}$ 67. 36 68. $\dfrac{1}{343}$ 69. x^4 70. $\dfrac{1}{x^8}$ 71. 1 72. -1 73. 1 74. -1
75. $\dfrac{5x^2}{2y^3}$ 76. $\dfrac{x^2}{3y^8}$ 77. $\dfrac{x^{15}}{y^{10}}$ 78. $\dfrac{343}{x^6}$ 79. $\dfrac{8m^6n^3}{p^{12}}$ 80. $\dfrac{81m^4n^8}{p^{20}}$ 81. $-\dfrac{1}{25}$ 82. 64 83. $\dfrac{81}{16}$ 84. 27 85. $\dfrac{7}{12}$ 86. $\dfrac{1}{8}$
87. $\dfrac{2x^3y^5}{3}$ 88. $\dfrac{3}{7xy^{10}}$ 89. $\dfrac{9m^4}{16}$ 90. $\dfrac{64}{9m^6n^6}$ 91. $\dfrac{8r^4s^6}{9}$ 92. $\dfrac{32}{3r^{10}s^{15}}$ 93. $6x^5 - 4x^4 + 5$ 94. $3x^4 + 5x^2 - 6x$ 95. $4n^3 + 1 - \dfrac{5}{2n^4}$
96. $6n - 4 - \dfrac{16}{5n^2}$ 97. $-\dfrac{p^3}{8} - \dfrac{1}{4} + \dfrac{1}{2p^2}$ 98. $-\dfrac{p^2}{2} + 1 - \dfrac{3}{2p^2}$ 99. $4x - 7$ 100. $x + 6$ 101. $x^2 + 7x + 5 + \dfrac{6}{x - 1}$
102. $2x^2 - 3x - 12 - \dfrac{16}{x - 2}$ 103. $x^2 - 2x + 4$ 104. $3x^2 + 15x + 77 + \dfrac{378}{x - 5}$ 105. 2.7×10^7 106. 1.23×10^9 107. 6×10^{-5}
108. 3.05×10^{-6} 109. 3×10^0 110. 8×10^0 111. 0.0006 112. 0.00125 113. 613,000 114. 80,000 115. 0.37
116. 54,000,000 117. 6×10^3 118. 4.2×10^{-8} 119. 2×10^2 120. 2×10^8 121. 4×10^{15} 122. 2×10^2

Chapter 5 Test 1. Yes; degree 5; binomial 2. (a) 5 (b) 21 (c) 26 3. $7x^2y^2 - 6x - 3y$ 4. $10m^3 + m^2 - 6$ 5. $-6x^5 + 18x^4 - 15x^3$
6. $2x^2 - 3x - 35$ 7. $4x^2 - 28x + 49$ 8. $16x^2 - 9y^2$ 9. $6x^3 + x^2 - 25x + 8$ 10. $2x - \dfrac{8}{3} + \dfrac{3}{x^3}$ 11. $3x^2 - 11x + 33 + \dfrac{-94}{x + 3}$
12. $-12x^4y^6$ 13. $\dfrac{2m^3}{3n^5}$ 14. $\dfrac{n^{24}}{m^{30}}$ 15. $\dfrac{x^{22}}{y^{14}}$ 16. $\dfrac{8m^7}{n^7}$ 17. 1.2×10^{-5} 18. 210,100 19. 3.57×10^4 20. 2×10^{-7}

Cumulative Review Chapters 1–5

1. (a) $\{\sqrt{25}\}$ **(b)** $\{0, \sqrt{25}\}$ **(c)** $\left\{-6, -\frac{4}{2}, 0, \sqrt{25}\right\}$ **(d)** $\left\{-6, -\frac{4}{2}, 0, 1.4, \sqrt{25}\right\}$ **(e)** $\{\sqrt{7}\}$ **(f)** $\left\{-6, -\frac{4}{2}, 0, 1.4, \sqrt{7}, \sqrt{25}\right\}$ **2.** $-\frac{4}{9}$

3. -19 **4.** $6x^3 + 5x^2 - 3x$ **5.** $-18x + 8$ **6.** $\{1\}$ **7.** $4(x - 5) = 2x + 10$ **8.** \$640 **9.** 45 mi/h

10. $\{x | x < -3\}$ or $(-\infty, -3);$ ←———|——|——→ **11.** $-\frac{1}{2}$ **12.** $-\frac{3}{2}$ **13.** **14.**
$\qquad\qquad\qquad\qquad\qquad\qquad\qquad$ -3 $\quad$ 0

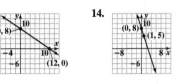

15. $(3, -7)$ **16.** No solution **17.** $6x^3 - 3x^2 + 7x$ **18.** $28m^2 - 13m - 6$
19. $9m^2 - 4n^2$ **20.** $49x^2 + 14xy + y^2$ **21.** $4m^3 - 19m + 15$
22. $\frac{2}{x} + \frac{1}{y}$ **23.** $x^2 - 3x + 9$ **24.** $-24n^4$ **25.** $-\frac{5n^8}{2m^2}$

26. $\frac{1}{64x^6y^{24}z^{12}}$ **27.** $\frac{1}{2x^{12}y^3}$ **28.** 6.05×10^{-5} **29.** 2,175,000 **30.** 7.14×10^5

Chapter 6 Factoring Polynomials

Section 6.1 Greatest Common Factor and Factoring by Grouping
1. greatest common factor **2.** factors **3.** 8 **4.** 3 **5.** 7
6. $7y^2$ **7.** $2z$ **8.** $4xy^3$ **9.** $2x + 3$ **10.** $3(k + 8)$ **11.** factor **12.** Distributive **13.** $5z(z + 6)$ **14.** $12p(p - 1)$
15. $4y(4y^2 - 3y + 1)$ **16.** $2m^2n^2(3m^2 + 9mn^2 - 11n^3)$ **17.** $-4y(y - 2)$ **18.** $-3a(2a^2 - 4a + 1)$ **19.** False **20.** $(a - 5)(2a + 3)$
21. $(z + 5)(7z - 4)$ **22.** $(x + y)(4 + b)$ **23.** $(3z - 1)(2a - 3b)$ **24.** $(2b + 1)(4 - 5a)$ **25.** $3(z + 4)(z^2 + 2)$ **26.** $2n(n + 1)(n^2 - 2)$
27. 2 **29.** 1 **31.** 4 **33.** x^2 **35.** $7x$ **37.** $15ab^2$ **39.** $2abc^2$ **41.** 3 **43.** $2(x - 4)^2$ **45.** $6(x - 3)^2$ **47.** $6(2x - 3)$
49. $-3x(x - 4)$ **51.** $5x^2y(1 - 3xy)$ **53.** $3x(x^2 + 2x - 1)$ **55.** $-5x(x^2 - 2x + 3)$ **57.** $3(3m^5 - 6m^3 - 4m^2 + 27)$
59. $-4z(3z^2 - 4z + 2)$ **61.** $-5(3b^3 + b - 2)$ **63.** $15ab^2(ab^2 - 4b + 3a^2)$ **65.** $(x - 3)(x - 5)$ **67.** $(x - 1)(x^2 + y^2)$
69. $(4x + 1)(x^2 + 2x + 5)$ **71.** $(x + 3)(y + 4)$ **73.** $(y + 1)(z - 1)$ **75.** $(x - 1)(x^2 + 2)$ **77.** $(2t - 1)(t^2 - 2)$ **79.** $(2t - 1)(t^3 - 3)$
81. $4(y - 5)$ **83.** $7m(4m^2 + m + 9)$ **85.** $6m^2n(2mnp - 3)$ **87.** $3(p + 3)(3p + 1)$ **89.** $3(2x - y)(3a - 2b)$ **91.** $(x - 2)(x - 2)$ or
$(x - 2)^2$ **93.** $3x(5x - 2)(x^2 + 2)$ **95.** $-3x(x^2 - 2x + 3)$ **97.** $4b(4b - 3)$ **99.** $(4y + 3)(3x - 2)$ **101.** $\frac{1}{3}x^2\left(x - \frac{2}{3}\right)$

103. $-2t(8t - 75)$ **105.** $150(140 - p)$ **107.** $4x^3(2x^2 - 7)$ **109.** $2\pi r(r + 4)$ **111.** $x - 2$ **113.** $4x^{2n} + 5$ **115.** $3x^3 - 4x^2 + 2$

117. $x^4 - 3x + 2$ **119.** $\frac{3}{5}x^3 - \frac{1}{2}x + 1$ **121.** To find the greatest common factor, (1) determine the GCF of the coefficients of the variable
factors (the largest number that divides evenly into a set of numbers). (2) For each variable factor common to all the terms, determine the
smallest exponent that the variable factor is raised to. (3) Find the product of these common factors. This is the GCF.
$\quad$ To factor the GCF from a polynomial, (1) identify the GCF of the terms that make up the polynomial. (2) Rewrite each term as the product of the
GCF and the remaining factor. (3) Use the Distributive Property "in reverse" to factor out the GCF. (4) Check using the Distributive Property.
123. $3a(x + y) - 4b(x + y) \neq (3a - 4b)(x + y)^2$ because when checking, the product $(3a - 4b)(x + y)^2$ is equal to
$(3a - 4b)(x + y)^2 = (3a - 4b)(x^2 + 2xy + y^2)$, not $3a(x + y) - 4b(x + y) = 3ax + 3ay - 4bx - 4by$.

Section 6.2 Factoring Trinomials of the Form $x^2 + bx + c$
1. quadratic trinomial **2.** negative **3.** False **4.** $(y + 5)(y + 4)$
5. $(z - 7)(z - 2)$ **6.** True **7.** $(y - 5)(y + 3)$ **8.** $(w - 3)(w + 4)$ **9.** Prime **10.** $(q + 9)(q - 5)$ **11.** $(x + 4y)(x + 5y)$
12. $(m + 7n)(m - 6n)$ **13. (a)** $x^2 - x - 12$ **(b)** $n^2 + 9n - 10$ **14.** $(n + 8)(n - 7)$ **15.** $(y - 7)(y - 5)$ **16.** False
17. $4(m + 3)(m - 7)$ **18.** $3z(z - 1)(z + 5)$ **19.** $-1(w + 5)(w - 2)$ **20.** $-2(a + 6)(a - 2)$ **21.** $(x + 2)(x + 3)$
23. $(m + 3)(m + 6)$ **25.** $(x - 3)(x - 12)$ **27.** $(p - 2)(p - 6)$ **29.** $(x - 4)(x + 3)$ **31.** $(x - 4)(x + 5)$ **33.** $(z - 3)(z + 15)$
35. $(x - 2y)(x - 3y)$ **37.** $(r - 2s)(r + 3s)$ **39.** $(x - 4y)(x + y)$ **41.** prime **43.** $3(x + 2)(x - 1)$ **45.** $3n(n - 3)(n - 5)$
47. $5z(x - 8)(x + 4)$ **49.** $x(x - 6)(x + 3)$ **51.** $-2(y - 2)^2$ **53.** $x^2(x + 8)(x - 4)$ **55.** $x(x + 5)(x - 3)$ **57.** $(x + 4y)(x - 7y)$
59. prime **61.** $(k - 5)(k + 4)$ **63.** $(x - 5y)(x + 6y)$ **65.** $(st - 3)(st - 5)$ **67.** $-3p(p - 2)(p + 1)$ **69.** $-(x + 3)(x - 2)$
71. prime **73.** $n^2(n - 6)(n + 5)$ **75.** $(m + 5n)(m - 3n)$ **77.** $(s + 5)(s + 7)$ **79.** prime **81.** $(mn - 6)(mn - 2)$
83. $-x(x - 14)(x + 2)$ **85.** $(y - 6)^2$ **87.** $-2x(x^2 - 10x + 18)$ **89.** $-7xy(3x^2 + 2y)$ **91.** $-16(t + 1)(t - 5)$ **93.** $(x + 6)$ meters
and $(x + 3)$ meters **95.** $(x + 5)$ inches and $(x - 3)$ inches **97.** $-7, -5, 5, 7$ **99.** $-20, -4, 4, 20$ **101.** 1 **103.** 6, 10, 12

Section 6.3 Factoring Trinomials of the Form $ax^2 + bx + c, a \neq 1$
1. True **2.** $(3x + 2)(x + 1)$ **3.** $(7y + 1)(y + 3)$
4. $(3x - 4)(x - 3)$ **5.** $(5p - 1)(p - 4)$ **6.** $(2n + 1)(n - 9)$ **7.** $(4w + 3)(w - 2)$ **8.** close **9.** $(3x + 2)(4x + 3)$
10. $(6y - 5)(2y + 7)$ **11.** Look for a common factor **12.** $4(2x + 3)(x - 5)$ **13.** $3(6x - y)(5x + 2y)$ **14.** False **15.** $-(6y + 1)(y - 4)$
16. $-3(2x - 5)(x + 3)$ **17.** $-6; 1$ **18.** False **19.** $(3x + 4)(x - 2)$ **20.** $(5z + 3)(2z + 3)$ **21.** $3(4x + 3)(2x - 1)$
22. $-(5n - 1)(2n - 3)$ **23.** $(2x + 3)(x + 1)$ **25.** $(5n + 2)(n + 1)$ **27.** $(5y - 3)(y + 1)$ **29.** $-(4p + 1)(p - 3)$
31. $(5w - 2)(w + 3)$ **33.** $(7t + 2)(t + 5)$ **35.** $(6n - 5)(n - 2)$ **37.** $(x - 2)(5x - 1)$ **39.** $(2x + y)(x + y)$ **41.** $(2m + n)(m - 2n)$
43. $2(3x - 2y)(x + y)$ **45.** $-(2x - 3)(x + 5)$ **47.** $(2x + 3)(x + 5)$ **49.** $(5w - 2)(w + 3)$ **51.** $(2w + 1)(2w - 5)$
53. $(9z - 2)(3z + 1)$ **55.** $(3y + 2)(2y - 3)$ **57.** $(2m - 1)(2m + 5)$ **59.** $(3n + 1)(4n + 5)$ **61.** $(6x - 5)(3x + 1)$
63. $2(3x + 2y)(2x - y)$ **65.** $4(2x + 1)(x + 3)$ **67.** $(3x + 5)(2x - 1)$ **69.** $-(4p + 3)(2p - 3)$ **71.** $(3x - 4)(5x - 1)$
73. $-(y + 4)(4y - 3)$ **75.** $2(x - 2y)(5x + 6y)$ **77.** $(3x - 4)(3x - 2)$ **79.** $-3(8x^2 + 4x - 3)$ **81.** $4x^2y^2(x - 2y - 1)$
83. $(m + 3n)(4m + n)$ **85.** prime **87.** $6(2x + 5y)(2x - y)$ **89.** $3(3m + 8n)(2m - n)$ **91.** $-2x^2(2x + 5)(x - 1)$

93. $-2x(4x + 3)(3x - 5)$ **95.** $(x^2 + 1)(2x - 7)(3x - 2)$ **97.** $(2x + 7)$ meters and $(3x - 4)$ meters   **99.** $2x - 5$ **101.** $(9z^2 + 8)(3z^2 + 2)$
103. $(3x^n + 1)(x^n + 6)$ **105.** ± 2 or ± 14 **107.** Trial and error may be used when the value of a and/or the value of c are prime numbers, or numbers with few factors. Grouping can be used when the product of a and c is not a very large number. Examples may vary.

Section 6.4 Factoring Special Products   **1.** perfect square trinomial   **2.** $(A - B)^2$ **3.** $(x - 6)^2$ **4.** $(4x + 5)^2$ **5.** $(3a - 10b)^2$
6. $(z - 4)^2$ **7.** $(2n + 3)^2$ **8.** prime   **9.** greatest common factor   **10.** $4(z + 3)^2$ **11.** $2a(5a + 4)^2$ **12.** difference; two squares
13. $(P - Q)(P + Q)$ **14.** $(z - 5)(z + 5)$ **15.** $(9m - 4n)(9m + 4n)$ **16.** $\left(4a - \frac{2}{3}b\right)\left(4a + \frac{2}{3}b\right)$ **17.** True   **18.** $(10k^2 - 9w)(10k^2 + 9w)$
19. $(x - 2)(x + 2)(x^2 + 4)$ **20.** False   **21.** $3(7x - 4)(7x + 4)$ **22.** $-3ab(3a - 5b)(3a + 5b)$ **23.** sum; two cubes
24. False   **25.** $(z + 5)(z^2 - 5z + 25)$ **26.** $(2p - 3q^2)(4p^2 - 6pq^2 + 9q^4)$ **27.** $2a(3 - 2a)(9 + 6a + 4a^2)$ **28.** $-3(5b - 1)(25b^2 + 5b + 1)$
29. $(x + 5)^2$ **31.** $(2p - 1)^2$ **33.** $(4x + 3)^2$ **35.** $(x - 2y)^2$ **37.** $(2z - 3)^2$ **39.** $(4x - 7y)(4x + 7y)$ **41.** $(2x - 5)(2x + 5)$
43. $(10n^4 - 9p^2)(10n^4 + 9p^2)$ **45.** $(k - 2)(k + 2)(k^2 + 4)(k^4 + 16)$ **47.** $(5p^2 - 7q)(5p^2 + 7q)$ **49.** $(3 + x)(9 - 3x + x^2)$
51. $(2x - 3y)(4x^2 + 6xy + 9y^2)$ **53.** $(x^2 - 2y)(x^4 + 2x^2y + 4y^2)$ **55.** $(3c + 4d^3)(9c^2 - 12cd^3 + 16d^6)$ **57.** $2(2x + 5y)(4x^2 - 10xy + 25y^2)$
59. $(4m + 5n)^2$ **61.** $2(x - 3)^2$ **63.** $3a(4a + 3)^2$ **65.** $2x(x^2 + 5x + 8)$ **67.** $x^2y^2(x - y)(x + y)$ **69.** $(x^4 - 5y^5)(x^4 + 5y^5)$
71. $2t(t - 3)(t^2 + 3t + 9)$ **73.** $3s(s^2 + 2)(s^4 - 2s^2 + 4)$ **75.** $2x(x - 3)(x + 3)(x^2 + 9)$ **77.** $xy(x - y)(x + y)$
79. $(xy + 1)(x^2y^2 - xy + 1)$ **81.** prime   **83.** $2(x - 2)^2$ **85.** prime   **87.** $xy^3(x + 6)(x^2 - 6x + 36)$ **89.** $3n^2(4n - 1)^2$
91. $(x - 2)(x + 2)(2x + 5)$ **93.** $(2y + 5)(y - 4)(y + 4)$ **95.** $(2x + 5)$ meters   **97.** $-3(2x - 1)$ **99.** $x(x^2 - 3xy + 3y^2)$
101. $(x - 2)(x + 4)$ **103.** $(x + 1)(2a - 5)(a - 6)$ **105.** $x(5x + 13)$ **107.** First identify the problem as a sum or a difference of cubes. Identify A and B and rewrite the problem as $A^3 + B^3$ or $A^3 - B^3$. The sum of cubes can be factored into the product of a binomial and a trinomial where the binomial factor is $A + B$ and the trinomial factor is A^2 minus the product AB plus B^2. The difference of cubes also can be factored into the product of a binomial and a trinomial, but here the binomial factor is $A - B$ and the trinomial factor is the sum of A^2, the product AB, and B^2.   **109.** The correct factorization of $x^3 + y^3$ is $(x + y)(x^2 - xy + y^2)$. The trinomial factor $(x^2 - xy + y^2)$ is not a perfect square trinomial. A perfect square trinomial is $(x - y)^2 = (x^2 - 2xy + y^2)$.

Section 6.5 Summary of Factoring Techniques   **1.** greatest common factor   **2.** $2(p - 5)(p + 9)$ **3.** $-3(3x + y)(5x - 2y)$
4. $(10x - 9y)(10x + 9y)$ **5.** $2a(b - 11)(b + 11)$ **6.** $(p - 6q)^2$ **7.** $3(5x + 3)^2$ **8.** $(5y - 4)(25y^2 + 20y + 16)$
9. $-3(2a - b)(4a^2 + 2ab + b^2)$ **10.** False   **11.** $(x - 1)(x + 1)(x^2 + 1)$ **12.** $-4y(3x - 2)(3x + 2)$ **13.** grouping
14. True   **15.** $(2x + 3)(x^2 + 2)$ **16.** $3(2x + 3)(x - 1)(x + 1)$ **17.** $-3(z^2 - 3z + 7)$ **18.** $3x(2y^2 + 5x^2)$ **19.** $(x - 10)(x + 10)$
21. $(t + 3)(t - 2)$ **23.** $(x + y)(1 + 2a)$ **25.** $(a - 2)(a^2 + 2a + 4)$ **27.** $(a - 3b)(a + 2b)$ **29.** $(2x - 7)(x + 1)$ **31.** $2(x - 5y)(x + 2y)$
33. $(3 - a)(3 + a)$ **35.** $(u - 11)(u - 3)$ **37.** $(x - a)(y - b)$ **39.** $(w + 2)(w + 4)$ **41.** $(6a - 7b^2)(6a + 7b^2)$ **43.** $(x + 4m)(x - 2m)$
45. $(3xy - 2)(2xy - 3)$ **47.** $(x + 1)(x^2 + 1)$ **49.** $6(2z^2 + 2z + 3)$ **51.** $(7c - 1)(2c + 3)$ **53.** $(3m + 4n^2)(9m^2 - 12mn^2 + 16n^4)$
55. $2j^2(j - 1)(j + 1)(j^2 + 1)$ **57.** $(4a - b)(2a + 5b)$ **59.** $2a(a^2 + 3)$ **61.** $3(2z - 1)(2z + 1)$ **63.** prime   **65.** $2a(2a + b)(4a^2 - 2ab + b^2)$
67. $(pq + 7)(pq - 1)$ **69.** $(s + 2)^2(s - 2)$ **71.** $-2x(3x + 1)(2x - 1)$ **73.** $(5v + 2)(2v - 1)$ **75.** $-n^2(n - 4)(n + 1)$
77. $-2ab(2a^2 - a + 1)$ **79.** $-p(p - 4)(p + 3)$ **81.** $-8x(2x - 3y)(2x + 3y)$ **83.** $2(n - 5)(n^2 - 3)$ **85.** $4(4x - 3)(x + 1)$
87. $(3x^2 + 2)(x^2 + 4)$ **89.** $-xy(2x - 3y)(x + y)$ **91.** $x(x - 5)(x - 3)$ **93.** $2x$ ft., $(2x + 1)$ ft., $(x - 3)$ ft.   **95.** $(2m - n + p)(2m - n - p)$
97. $(x + y - z)(x - y + z)$ **99.** $(x - y - 4)(x - y - 2)$ **101.** $(x + y - a + b)(x + y + a - b)$ **103.** The student initially wrote the sum of terms as a product of terms by enclosing the binomial $-3x - 12$ in parentheses. Then in the second step, the student writes the factor $-3(x - 4)$ and concludes that the factorization of $x^2 + 4x - 3x - 12$ is $(x - 3)(x + 4)$, even though both terms do not have the common factor of $(x + 4)$. The student obtained the correct answer, but the first two steps are incorrect; the correct factorization is $x^2 + 4x - 3x - 12 = x(x + 4) - 3(x + 4) = (x + 4)(x - 3)$.

Putting the Concepts Together (Sections 6.1–6.5)   **1.** $5x^2y$ **2.** $(x - 4)(x + 1)$ **3.** $(x^2 - 3)(x^4 + 3x^2 + 9)$ **4.** $(2x + 1)(6x + 5z)$
5. $(x + 6y)(x - y)$ **6.** $(x + 4)(x^2 - 4x + 16)$ **7.** prime   **8.** $3(x + 6y)(x - 2y)$ **9.** $4z^2(3z^3 - 11z - 6)$ **10.** prime
11. $m^2(m + 2)(4m - 3)$ **12.** $(5p - 2)(p - 3)$ **13.** $(2m + 5)(5m - 3)$ **14.** $6(3m - 1)(2m + 1)$ **15.** $(2m - 5)^2$ **16.** $(5x + 4y)(x - y)$
17. $S = 2\pi r(h + r)$ **18.** $h = 16t(3 - t)$

Section 6.6 Solving Polynomial Equations by Factoring   **1.** $a = 0; b = 0$ **2.** $\{-3, 0\}$ **3.** $\left\{-\frac{5}{4}, 2\right\}$ **4.** quadratic   **5.** second
6. False   **7.** $\{2, 4\}$ **8.** $\left\{-\frac{1}{2}, 3\right\}$ **9.** $\left\{-\frac{5}{2}, 1\right\}$ **10.** $\{-5, -4\}$ **11.** $\left\{-2, \frac{2}{5}\right\}$ **12.** $\left\{-4, \frac{1}{3}\right\}$ **13.** False   **14.** $\{-6, 4\}$
15. $\left\{-\frac{3}{5}, 1\right\}$ **16.** $\left\{\frac{4}{3}\right\}$ **17.** $\{-6, 3\}$ **18.** $\{-2, 3\}$ **19.** After 1 second or 4 seconds   **20.** True   **21.** $\left\{-3, 3, \frac{5}{4}\right\}$ **22.** $\{-2, -1, 0\}$
23. $\{-4, 0\}$ **25.** $\{-3, 9\}$ **27.** $\left\{-\frac{1}{3}, 5\right\}$ **29.** $\left\{-\frac{3}{5}, \frac{2}{7}\right\}$ **31.** linear   **33.** quadratic   **35.** $\{-1, 4\}$ **37.** $\{-7, -2\}$ **39.** $\left\{-\frac{1}{2}, 0\right\}$
41. $\left\{-\frac{1}{2}, 2\right\}$ **43.** $\{3\}$ **45.** $\{0, 6\}$ **47.** $\{-2, 3\}$ **49.** $\{2, 9\}$ **51.** $\left\{\frac{1}{4}, 1\right\}$ **53.** $\{-4, 6\}$ **55.** $\{-5, 10\}$ **57.** $\{-5, 1\}$
59. $\{-3, 0, 2\}$ **61.** $\{-3, -2, 2\}$ **63.** $\left\{-\frac{3}{2}, 2, -2\right\}$ **65.** $\left\{-\frac{3}{5}, 4\right\}$ **67.** $\{-4, 5\}$ **69.** $\{-5\}$ **71.** $\left\{-\frac{3}{4}, 7\right\}$ **73.** $\{-4, 2\}$
75. $\left\{-4, -\frac{1}{2}, 4\right\}$ **77.** $\{20\}$ **79.** $\{-10, 10\}$ **81.** $\left\{-3, -\frac{2}{3}, 5\right\}$ **83.** $\left\{-\frac{1}{2}, \frac{3}{2}, 5\right\}$ **85.** $\{0, 8\}$ **87.** $\left\{-4, \frac{3}{2}\right\}$ **89.** $\left\{-6, \frac{1}{2}\right\}$
91. 1 sec, 3 sec   **93.** 1 sec   **95.** -4 and -3 or 3 and 4   **97.** $-12, -10,$ and $-8,$ or 8, 10, and 12   **99.** 15 by 17
101. 8 teams   **103.** $(x - 3)(x + 5) = 0$; at least 2nd degree   **105.** $(z - 6)^2 = 0$; at least 2nd degree
107. $(x + 3)(x - 1)(x - 5) = 0$; at least 3rd degree   **109.** $\{a, -b\}$ **111.** $\{0, 2a\}$

113. The student divided by the variable x instead of writing the quadratic equation in standard form, factoring, and using the Zero-Product Property. The correct solution is

$$15x^2 = 5x$$
$$15x^2 - 5x = 0$$
$$5x(3x - 1) = 0$$
$$5x = 0 \quad \text{or} \quad 3x - 1 = 0$$
$$x = 0 \quad \text{or} \quad 3x = 1$$
$$x = \frac{1}{3}$$

115. We write a quadratic equation in standard form, $ax^2 + bx + c = 0$, so that when the quadratic polynomial on the left side of the equation is factored, we can apply the Zero-Product Property, which says that if $a \cdot b = 0$, then $a = 0$ or $b = 0$.

Section 6.7 Modeling and Solving Problems with Quadratic Equations
1. **(a)** After 4 seconds and after 6 seconds **(b)** After 10 seconds
2. 8 km by 13 km **3.** height = 8 yards, base = 12 yards **4.** $x = 12, x - 3 = 9$ **5.** 7 inches and 24 inches **6.** 6 inches high, 8 inches wide
7. 4, 14 **9.** 2, 9 **11.** base = 26; height = 8 **13.** base = 18; height = 16 **15.** base = 13; height = 11 **17.** $B = 53; b = 43$
19. 9, 12 **21.** 12, 5 **23.** 256, 252, 240, 220, 192, 156, 112, 60, 0 feet **25.** 6 sec **27.** width = 4 m; length = 12 m **29.** base = 6 ft; height = 18 ft
31. 30 inches **33.** width = 12 mm; length = 25 mm **35.** width = 4 cm; height = 25 cm **37. (a)** width = 25 in.; height = 42 in.
(b) 28 in. by 45 in. **39.** 6 ft **41.** width = 7 ft; length = 14 feet **43.** If you have two positive numbers that satisfy the projectile motion word problem, one answer is the height of the object on its upward path, and the other represents the height of the object on its downward path. There is only one positive number that satisfies the equation if the object is dropped from a height above the ground.

Chapter 6 Review
1. 12 **2.** 27 **3.** 10 **4.** 4 **5.** x^2 **6.** m **7.** $15ab^2$ **8.** $6x^3y^2z$ **9.** $2(2a + 1)^2$ **10.** $9(x - y)$
11. $-6a^2(3a + 4)$ **12.** $-3x(3x - 4)$ **13.** $5y^2z(3 + y^5 + 4y)$ **14.** $7xy(x^2 - 3xy + 2y^2)$ **15.** $(5 - y)(x + 2)$ **16.** $(a + b)(z + y)$
17. $(5m + 2n)(m + 3n)$ **18.** $(2x + y)(y + x)$ **19.** $(x + 2)(8 - y)$ **20.** $(y^2 + 1)(x - 3)$ **21.** $(x + 3)(x + 2)$ **22.** $(x + 2)(x + 4)$
23. $(x - 7)(x + 3)$ **24.** $(x + 5)(x - 2)$ **25.** prime **26.** prime **27.** $(x - 3y)(x - 5y)$ **28.** $(m + 5n)(m - n)$ **29.** $-(p + 6)(p + 5)$
30. $-(y - 5)(y + 3)$ **31.** $3x(x^2 + 11x + 12)$ **32.** $4(x + 1)(x + 8)$ **33.** $2(x - 7y)(x + 6y)$ **34.** $4y(y + 5)(y - 2)$
35. $(5y - 6)(y + 4)$ **36.** $(y - 7)(6y + 1)$ **37.** $(2x - 3)(x - 1)$ **38.** $(2x + 7)(3x + 1)$ **39.** prime **40.** $(4m + 3)(2m + 3)$
41. $3m(m + n)(3m + 7n)$ **42.** $2(7m + n)(m + n)$ **43.** $x(5x + 2)(3x - 1)$ **44.** $p^2(3p - 1)(2p + 1)$ **45.** $(2x - 3)^2$ **46.** $(x - 5)^2$
47. $(x + 3y)^2$ **48.** prime **49.** $2(2m + 1)^2$ **50.** $2(m - 6)^2$ **51.** $(2x - 5y)(2x + 5y)$ **52.** $(7x - 6y)(7x + 6y)$ **53.** prime
54. prime **55.** $(x - 3)(x + 3)(x^2 + 9)$ **56.** $(x - 5)(x + 5)(x^2 + 25)$ **57.** $(m + 3)(m^2 - 3m + 9)$ **58.** $(m + 5)(m^2 - 5m + 25)$
59. $(3p - 2)(9p^2 + 6p + 4)$ **60.** $(4p - 1)(16p^2 + 4p + 1)$ **61.** $(y^3 + 4z^2)(y^6 - 4y^3z^2 + 16z^4)$ **62.** $(2y + 3z^2)(4y^2 - 6yz^2 + 9z^4)$
63. $(5a - 2b)(3a^2 - 5b^2)$ **64.** $(4a - 3b)(3a + b)$ **65.** prime **66.** $(x - 12y)(x + 2y)$ **67.** $x(x - 7)(x + 6)$ **68.** $3x^4(x - 7)(x - 3)$
69. $(3x + 1)(2x + 3)$ **70.** $(2z + 3)(5z - 3)$ **71.** $(3x + 2)(9x^2 - 6x + 4)$ **72.** $(2z - 1)(4z^2 + 2z + 1)$ **73.** $2(2y - 1)(y + 5)$
74. $xy^2(5x - 3)(x - 1)$ **75.** $(5k - 9m)(5k + 9m)$ **76.** $(x^2 - 3)(x^2 + 3)$ **77.** prime **78.** prime **79.** $\left\{\frac{3}{2}, 4\right\}$ **80.** $\left\{-7, -\frac{1}{2}\right\}$
81. $\{-3, 15\}$ **82.** $\{2, 5\}$ **83.** $\{0, -2\}$ **84.** $\left\{-\frac{9}{2}, 0\right\}$ **85.** $\{-1, 3\}$ **86.** $\{-3, -1\}$ **87.** $\{-4, -2\}$ **88.** $\left\{-\frac{1}{2}, \frac{3}{2}\right\}$
89. $\{-14, 0, 3\}$ **90.** $\{-3, 0, 6\}$ **91.** $\left\{-3, \frac{4}{3}, 3\right\}$ **92.** $\left\{-\frac{5}{2}, -2\right\}$ **93.** 5 sec **94.** 2 sec or 3 sec **95.** 9 ft by 6 ft **96.** 3 yd by 5 yd
97. 8 ft, 6 ft **98.** 24 ft, 10 ft

Chapter 6 Test
1. $4x^4y^2$ **2.** $(x - 4)(x + 4)(x^2 + 16)$ **3.** $9x(2x - 3)(x + 1)$ **4.** $(x - 7)(y - 4)$ **5.** $(3x + 5)(9x^2 - 15x + 25)$
6. $(y - 12)(y + 4)$ **7.** $(6m + 5)(m - 1)$ **8.** prime **9.** $(x - 5)(4 + y)$ **10.** $3y(x - 7)(x + 2)$ **11.** prime
12. $2(x^2 - 3y)(x^4 + 3x^2y + 9y^2)$ **13.** $3x(3x + 1)(x + 4)$ **14.** $(3m + 2)(2m + 1)$ **15.** $2(2m^2 - 3mn + 2)$
16. $(5x + 7y)^2$ **17.** $\left\{-\frac{1}{5}, -3\right\}$ **18.** $\{0, 2\}$ **19.** length = 7 in.; width = 5 in. **20.** legs: 12 in., 5 in., hypotenuse: 13 in.

Chapter 7 Rational Expressions and Equations

Section 7.1 Simplifying Rational Expressions
1. rational expression **2. (a)** $-\frac{1}{8}$ **(b)** $\frac{3}{16}$ **3. (a)** -1 **(b)** 9 **4.** $\frac{11}{2}$ **5.** 4
6. undefined **7.** $x = -7$ **8.** $n = -\frac{5}{3}$ **9.** $x = -3$ or $x = 1$ **10.** simplify **11.** False **12.** $\frac{n + 4}{2}$ **13.** $\frac{z + 1}{2}$ **14.** $\frac{a + 7}{2a + 7}$
15. $\frac{z^2 - 3}{z - 2}$ **16.** $\frac{2k + 1}{2k - 1}$ **17.** False **18.** -7 **19.** $\frac{-4}{4x - 1}$ **20.** $-\frac{5z + 1}{3}$ **21. (a)** 2 **(b)** $\frac{1}{2}$ **(c)** 0 **23. (a)** 1 **(b)** 3 **(c)** $\frac{5}{3}$
25. (a) -3 **(b)** 0 **(c)** $-\frac{15}{7}$ **27. (a)** 0 **(b)** $-\frac{7}{2}$ **(c)** $-\frac{3}{4}$ **29.** 0 **31.** 5 **33.** $\frac{3}{2}$ **35.** $-6, 6$ **37.** 2, 5 **39.** $-2, 0, 3$
41. $\frac{x - 2}{3}$ **43.** $z + 1$ **45.** $\frac{1}{p + 2}$ **47.** -1 **49.** $-2k$ **51.** $\frac{x - 1}{x + 4}$ **53.** $\frac{6}{x - 5}$ **55.** -3 **57.** $\frac{b - 5}{4}$ **59.** $\frac{x + 3}{x - 3}$
61. $\frac{x - 3}{x - 5}$ **63.** $-(x + y)$ **65.** $\frac{x^2 + 1}{x + 1}$ **67.** $-\frac{4 + c}{c - 4}$ **69.** $\frac{2(x - 2)}{3(x - 5)}$ **71.** $\frac{-(x - 3)}{x - 2}$ **73.** $\frac{2}{t^2 + 9}$ **75.** $\frac{-3}{w - 1}$ **77. (a)** 5 mg/mL

(b) 4 mg/mL   **79.** Yes; BMI = 27.5   **81.** \$15,600   **83.** $\dfrac{c^4 + 1}{c^6 + 1}$ **85.** $\dfrac{(x-2)(x^2-3)}{x^3-9}$ **87.** $\dfrac{(t^2+4)(t+2)}{t^2-2t+4}$ **89. (a)** The x^2s cannot be

divided out because they are not factors.   **(b)** When the factors $x - 2$ are divided out, the result is $\dfrac{1}{3}$, not 3.   **91.** A rational expression is

undefined if the denominator is equal to zero. Division by zero is not allowed in the real number system. The expression $\dfrac{x^2-9}{3x-6}$ is undefined

for $x = 2$ because when 2 is substituted for x, we get $\dfrac{2^2-9}{3(2)-6} = \dfrac{4-9}{6-6} = \dfrac{-5}{0}$, which is undefined.   **93.** $\dfrac{x-7}{7-x} = -1$ because $x - 7$ and $7 - x$ are

opposites: $\dfrac{x-7}{7-x} = \dfrac{x-7}{-1(-7+x)} = \dfrac{x-7}{-1(x-7)} = \dfrac{\cancel{x-7}}{-1\cancel{(x-7)}} = \dfrac{1}{-1} = -1.$ The expression $\dfrac{x-7}{x+7}$ is in simplest form because $x - 7$ and $x + 7$ are not

opposites and they have no common factor.

Section 7.2 Multiplying and Dividing Rational Expressions   **1.** factor; common factors   **2.** False   **3.** $\dfrac{5p(p+3)}{2}$ **4.** $\dfrac{7}{3(x+5)}$

5. False   **6.** $-\dfrac{3a}{7}$ **7.** $\dfrac{1}{3}$ **8.** $\dfrac{3}{2};\dfrac{4}{3}$ **9.** $\dfrac{6(x+1)}{x(2x-1)}$ **10.** $\dfrac{(x-3)^2}{(x-4)^2}$ **11.** $\dfrac{q+1}{(q-5)(q+5)}$ **12.** $\dfrac{x-1}{4}$ **13.** $\dfrac{7x}{4(x-2)}$ **14.** $\dfrac{6m}{m+2n}$

15. $\dfrac{2x}{x-5}$ **17.** $\dfrac{x}{(x+1)^2}$ **19.** $p - 1$ **21.** 1   **23.** $\dfrac{1}{3x}$ **25.** $\dfrac{2(m-4)}{(m+4)}$ **27.** x **29.** 1   **31.** $\dfrac{10}{3}$ **33.** 1   **35.** $-\dfrac{4}{11}$ **37.** $\dfrac{4}{3y(y-3)}$

39. $\dfrac{a}{3}$ **41.** $\dfrac{3x}{x-4}$ **43.** $\dfrac{4-w}{(w+2)(w+4)}$ **45.** $-\dfrac{(x-y)^2}{x}$ **47.** $-\dfrac{1}{2}$ **49.** $\dfrac{3(2n+3)(n-3)}{2(n+4)}$ **51.** $\dfrac{x}{4y^2(x-2y)}$ **53.** $\dfrac{2a-b}{2a(a+b)}$

55. $\dfrac{(t+3)(t-2)}{3}$ **57.** -1 **59.** $\dfrac{x(x+3)}{(x+1)^2}$ **61.** $\dfrac{a+b}{2}$ **63.** $\dfrac{1}{3}$ **65.** $\dfrac{(x-a)^2}{2(x+a)}$ **67.** $\dfrac{1}{3(x-y)}$ **69.** $\dfrac{9}{8}$ **71.** $\dfrac{x-y}{(x+y)^3}$

73. $\dfrac{4x}{(x-2)(x-3)}$ **75.** $\dfrac{1}{x}\,\text{ft}^2$ **77.** $\dfrac{2(x+2)}{x-3}\,\text{in.}^2$ **79.** $\dfrac{1-x}{4}$ **81.** $\dfrac{2a^2}{3}$ **83.** $\dfrac{(x+y)^2}{(x^2-xy+y^2)(x+2)}$

85. $3p^5q^2(p^2+3pq+9q^2)(p-q)$ **87.** $6x + 12$ **89.** To multiply two rational expressions, (1) factor the polynomials in the numerator and

denominator; (2) multiply the numerators and denominators using $\dfrac{a}{b}\cdot\dfrac{c}{d} = \dfrac{a\cdot c}{b\cdot d}$; (3) divide out common factors in the numerators and denominators.

Leave the result in factored form.   **91.** The error is in incorrectly dividing out the factors $(n - 6)$ and $(6 - n)$. The correct method is

$\dfrac{n^2-2n-24}{6n-n^2} = \dfrac{-1\cancel{(n-6)}(n+4)}{n\cancel{(6-n)}} = \dfrac{-(n+4)}{n}.$

Section 7.3 Adding and Subtracting Rational Expressions with a Common Denominator   **1.** $\dfrac{a+b}{c}$ **2.** False   **3.** $\dfrac{4}{x-2}$

4. $x + 1$ **5.** $\dfrac{11x-3}{6x-5}$ **6.** $\dfrac{1}{x-5}$ **7.** $\dfrac{2(4y-3)}{2y-5}$ **8.** $\dfrac{z+1}{2z}$ **9.** $x + 3$ **10.** $\dfrac{x+8}{3}$ **11.** $\dfrac{x+2}{x-7}$ **12.** True   **13.** $\dfrac{3x-1}{x-5}$

14. 2   **15.** $\dfrac{2}{n-3}$ **16.** $\dfrac{2k+3}{2(k-1)}$ **17.** $\dfrac{7p}{4}$ **19.** $2n$ **21.** $\dfrac{2a-1}{a}$ **23.** $\dfrac{2(5c-2)}{c-1}$ **25.** 2   **27.** $7x$ **29.** 2   **31.** $\dfrac{1}{a-5}$

33. $\dfrac{x}{x+3}$ **35.** $-\dfrac{x}{2}$ **37.** $-\dfrac{c+3}{c}$ **39.** 3   **41.** -1 **43.** $x - 1$ **45.** 1   **47.** $\dfrac{2(2p+3q)}{p-q}$ **49.** $\dfrac{2p^2+2p+1}{p-1}$ **51.** $\dfrac{4b}{a-b}$

53. -1 **55.** $\dfrac{2}{x-y}$ **57.** $-\dfrac{1}{x}$ **59.** -1 **61.** 0   **63.** $n - 1$ **65.** $\dfrac{3}{v+3}$ **67.** $\dfrac{x+1}{x-1}$ **69.** $\dfrac{x^2+3}{x(x-3)}$ **71.** $2(x-1)$

73. $\dfrac{3x+3y-2}{x-y}$ **75.** $\dfrac{p+2q}{p^2-6q^2}$ **77.** $12a$ **79.** $\dfrac{n-3}{n+1}$ **81.** $\dfrac{4}{n}$ **83.** $\dfrac{x}{x+3}$ **85.** $\dfrac{4x-2}{x+2}$ **87.** $\dfrac{2(6x-1)}{x}\,\text{cm}$ **89.** $\dfrac{6x+7y}{x^2-y^2}$

91. $\dfrac{-x(x-1)}{(3x-1)(x+2)}$ **93.** $\dfrac{-5x+12}{x-2}$ **95.** $-4n-6$ **97.** The expression is incorrect because the subtraction symbol was not applied to both

terms of the second numerator. The correct method is $\dfrac{x-2}{x} - \dfrac{x+4}{x} = \dfrac{x-2-x-4}{x} = \dfrac{-6}{x}.$ **99.** The correct answer is (c). The answer (a) $\dfrac{7}{2x}$ is

incorrect because the denominators were added; and the answer (b) $\dfrac{7}{x^2}$ is incorrect because the denominators were multiplied.

Section 7.4 Finding the Least Common Denominator and Forming Equivalent Rational Expressions   **1.** least common denominator

2. False   **3.** $24x^2y^3$ **4.** $42a^3b^3$ **5.** True   **6.** $15z(z+1)$ **7.** $(x-1)(x+5)^2$ **8.** $-3(x-7)(x+7)$ **9.** $x + 3$ **10.** $\dfrac{12p^2}{16p^3(p-2)}$

11. LCD $= 60a^2b^3$; $\dfrac{3}{6a^2b} = \dfrac{30b^2}{60a^2b^3}, \dfrac{-5}{20ab^3} = \dfrac{-15a}{60a^2b^3}$ **12.** LCD $= (x-5)(x-2)(x+1)$; $\dfrac{5}{x^2-4x-5} = \dfrac{5x-10}{(x-5)(x-2)(x+1)}$;

$\dfrac{-3}{x^2-7x+10} = \dfrac{-3x-3}{(x-5)(x-2)(x+1)}$ **13.** $5x^2$ **15.** $60x^3y^2$ **17.** $x(x+1)$ **19.** $2x+1$ **21.** $4(b-3)$ **23.** $p(p+1)(p-2)$

25. $(r+2)^2(r+1)(r-2)$ **27.** $-(x-4)$ **29.** $-2(x+3)(x-3)$ **31.** $-(x-1)(x+2)$ **33.** $\dfrac{12x^2}{3x^3}$ **35.** $\dfrac{3c+c^2}{a^2b^2c^2}$ **37.** $\dfrac{(x-4)^2}{(x-4)(x+4)}$

39. $\dfrac{9n^2 - 9n}{6(n-1)(n+1)}$ **41.** $\dfrac{4t^2 - 4t}{t-1}$ **43.** $\dfrac{6xy}{9y^2}, \dfrac{4}{9y^2}$ **45.** $\dfrac{6a+2}{4a^3}, \dfrac{4a^3 - a^2}{4a^3}$ **47.** $\dfrac{2m+2}{m(m+1)}, \dfrac{3m}{m(m+1)}$ **49.** $\dfrac{2y^2 - 5y + 2}{4y(2y-1)}, \dfrac{y^2}{4y(2y-1)}$

51. $\dfrac{-1}{-(x-1)}, \dfrac{2x}{-(x-1)}$ **53.** $\dfrac{-3x}{-(x-7)}, \dfrac{-5}{-(x-7)}$ **55.** $\dfrac{4x}{(x+2)(x-2)}, \dfrac{2x-4}{(x+2)(x-2)}$ **57.** $\dfrac{x^2+2x+1}{(x+3)(x-3)(x+1)}, \dfrac{x^2+5x+6}{(x+3)(x-3)(x+1)}$

59. $\dfrac{6x-3}{(x+4)(2x-1)}, \dfrac{2x-1}{(x+4)(2x-1)}$ **61.** $3x; \dfrac{3}{3x}, \dfrac{1}{3x}$ **63.** $(r-4)(r+4); \dfrac{12r+48}{(r-4)(r+4)}, \dfrac{12r-48}{(r-4)(r+4)}$

65. $(x+2)(x-2)(x^2-2x+4)(x^2+2x+4)$ **67.** $p^2(p-1)(p-3)$ **69.** $4a^2b^2(a+b)(a-b)(a^2+ab+b^2)$ **71.** To write an equivalent rational expression with a given denominator, (1) write each denominator in factored form; (2) determine the "missing factor(s)" (Answer the question "What factor(s) does the new denominator have that is missing from the original denominator?") (3) Multiply the original expression by $1 = \dfrac{\text{missing factor}}{\text{missing factor}}$; (3) find the product and leave the denominator in factored form.

Section 7.5 Adding and Subtracting Rational Expressions with Unlike Denominators **1.** 72 **2.** $\dfrac{25}{36}$ **3.** $\dfrac{7}{30}$

4. least common denominator **5.** True **6.** $\dfrac{3b + 10a^2}{24a^3b^2}$ **7.** $\dfrac{6x^2 + 35y}{90x^3y^2}$ **8.** $\dfrac{2(4x-1)}{(x-4)(x+2)}$ **9.** $\dfrac{3n-13}{(n-3)(n+1)}$ **10.** $\dfrac{1}{z+2}$

11. $\dfrac{2}{(x+5)(x-5)}$ **12.** $\dfrac{-16ab - 15}{20a^2b^3}$ **13.** $\dfrac{2(x-10)}{x(x-4)}$ **14.** $\dfrac{x-11}{(x-5)(x+4)(x-1)}$ **15.** $\dfrac{(x+8)(x-1)}{4x(x-3)}$ **16.** True **17.** $\dfrac{14-5p}{6p(p-1)}$

18. $\dfrac{2x-5}{x-1}$ **19.** $\dfrac{4x}{(x+1)(x-1)}$ **20.** $\dfrac{2}{x-2}$ **21.** $-\dfrac{5}{6}$ **23.** $\dfrac{5}{3x}$ **25.** $\dfrac{2a^2 + 7a - 3}{(2a-1)(2a+1)}$ **27.** $-\dfrac{2}{x-4}$ **29.** $\dfrac{2a^2 - 3a - 12}{4a(a-5)}$

31. $\dfrac{5}{x}$ **33.** $\dfrac{8}{75}$ **35.** $\dfrac{(m-4)(m+4)}{m}$ **37.** $\dfrac{2(4x-3)}{(x-3)(x+3)}$ **39.** $\dfrac{6(x+1)}{(x+3)^2}$ **41.** $\dfrac{-4(a-1)}{a+3}$ **43.** $\dfrac{x}{x-2}$ **45.** $\dfrac{20-9y}{12y^2}$ **47.** $\dfrac{6}{5x}$

49. $-\dfrac{3}{2x+3}$ **51.** $\dfrac{2(n^2-2)}{n(n-2)}$ **53.** $\dfrac{2x^2 - 5x + 15}{x(x-3)}$ **55.** $-\dfrac{1}{a(a-1)}$ **57.** $\dfrac{2n+5}{2n+1}$ **59.** $\dfrac{4x-5}{x-2}$ **61.** $\dfrac{3x-28}{x-9}$ **63.** $\dfrac{4n^2 - 7n + 9}{n^2(n-3)(n-1)}$

65. $-\dfrac{13}{2a(a-2)}$ **67.** $-\dfrac{n^2 - n - 3}{(n+2)(n-2)(n+3)}$ **69.** $\dfrac{2x^2 + x + 1}{(x+1)(x-1)^2}$ **71.** $\dfrac{-3n+5}{(n+3)(n-2)}$ **73.** $\dfrac{x}{x-2}$ **75.** $\dfrac{x-4}{x}$ **77.** $\dfrac{6}{m(m-2)}$

79. $\dfrac{x^2+4}{(x+2)(x+3)}$ **81.** $\dfrac{x+3}{(x+1)(x-1)}$ **83.** $\dfrac{2x^2 - x + 10}{(x+3)(x-2)(x+2)}$ **85.** $\dfrac{2x^2 - 5x + 3}{(x+6)(x-7)}$ **87.** $\dfrac{7x-5}{4}$ units **89.** $\dfrac{a+2}{a(a-1)^2}$

91. $\dfrac{x^3 - 2x^2 + 4x + 3}{x^2(x+1)(x-1)}$ **93.** $\dfrac{1}{a+b}$ **95.** $\dfrac{x^2 + 2x + 5}{(x-4)(x+1)}$ **97.** $\dfrac{-x^3 + 6x^2 - 11x + 10}{x-2}$ **99.** The steps to add or subtract rational expressions with unlike denominators are (1) find the least common denominator; (2) rewrite each rational expression with the common denominator; (3) add or subtract the rational expressions from step 2; (4) simplify the result. **101.** To complete the subtraction problem $\dfrac{3x+1}{(2x+5)(x-1)} - \dfrac{x-4}{(2x+5)(x-1)}$, distribute the subtraction sign to both the x and the -4 in the numerator of the second term to form $\dfrac{3x+1-x+4}{(2x+5)(x-1)} = \dfrac{2x+5}{(2x+5)(x-1)}$. Then divide out the common factor $(2x+5)$ to arrive at the result $\dfrac{1}{x-1}$.

Section 7.6 Complex Rational Expressions **1.** complex rational expression **2.** simplify **3.** $\dfrac{k+1}{2}$ **4.** $\dfrac{1}{4n}$ **5.** False **6.** $\dfrac{3}{2}$

7. $\dfrac{1}{3+y}$ **8.** $\dfrac{3}{x+5}$ **9.** 13 **10.** $\dfrac{y+2x}{2y-x}$ **11.** $\dfrac{2}{17}$ **13.** $\dfrac{3(x-2)}{2}$ **15.** $\dfrac{9}{x-3}$ **17.** $\dfrac{n(m+2n)}{2m}$ **19.** $\dfrac{5b^2 + 4a}{a(5b+4)}$ **21.** $-\dfrac{2}{y+4}$

23. $\dfrac{3(y-24)}{2(5-6y^2)}$ **25.** $\dfrac{15}{16}$ **27.** $\dfrac{1}{2}$ **29.** $\dfrac{b-7}{b}$ **31.** $\dfrac{x+4}{x}$ **33.** $-\dfrac{x+y}{x^2y^2}$ **35.** $\dfrac{ab+1}{ab+2}$ **37.** $\dfrac{18n}{5}$ **39.** $\dfrac{x^2 + 2xy - y^2}{xy}$

41. $-\dfrac{1}{2x+7}$ **43.** $-b$ **45.** $\dfrac{x+1}{x+3}$ **47.** $\dfrac{2b-a}{2b}$ **49.** $2y$ **51.** $\dfrac{n+1}{5n-9}$ **53.** $\dfrac{11(2n+3)}{72}$ **55.** $-\dfrac{x^3}{x+3}$ **57. (a)** $R = \dfrac{R_1 R_2}{R_2 + R_1}$

(b) $\dfrac{15}{4}$ ohms **59.** $\dfrac{x}{1+3x}$ **61.** $\dfrac{x}{2-5x}$ **63.** $\dfrac{2x+1}{x+1}$ **65.** $\dfrac{5-2x}{2-x}$ **67.** The expression $\dfrac{2}{x+1}{\dfrac{1}{x-5}}$ is not in simplified form. Simplified form is the form $\dfrac{p}{q}$ where p and q are polynomials that have no common factors. **69.** Answers may vary.

Putting the Concepts Together (Sections 7.1–7.6) **1.** -35 **2. (a)** The expression is undefined for $a = 6$. **(b)** The expression is undefined for $y = 0$ or $y = -4$. **3. (a)** $\dfrac{a-4b}{2}$ **(b)** $-\dfrac{x+2}{x+1}$ **4.** The LCD is $8(a+2b)(a-4b)$. **5.** $\dfrac{7}{3x^2 - x} = \dfrac{35x}{5x^2(3x-1)}$ **6.** $\dfrac{-2y^2}{y+1}$ **7.** $\dfrac{2(m-1)^2}{m^2}$

8. $\dfrac{2(y-1)}{5(y-3)}$ **9.** $4x+1$ **10.** $\dfrac{1}{x+1}$ **11.** $\dfrac{1}{2x-1}$ **12.** $\dfrac{15m+17}{(m+3)(3m+2)}$ **13.** $\dfrac{m}{(m+5)(m+4)}$ **14.** $-\dfrac{1}{m-1}$ **15.** $\dfrac{a(a+24)}{3(a^2+6)}$

Section 7.7 Rational Equations **1.** rational equation **2.** $\left\{\dfrac{2}{3}\right\}$ **3.** $\{-18\}$ **4.** $\{-6\}$ **5.** $\{4\}$ **6.** $\{-5,6\}$ **7.** extraneous solutions

8. $\{5\}$ **9.** True **10.** $\{ \ \}$ or $\varnothing$ **11.** After $2\dfrac{1}{2}$ hours and after 10 hours **12.** $x = \dfrac{4g}{R}$ **13.** $r = 1 - \dfrac{a}{S}$ or $r = \dfrac{S-a}{S}$ **14.** $p = \dfrac{fq}{q-f}$

15. $\{2\}$ **17.** $\left\{-\dfrac{3}{4}\right\}$ **19.** $\{-7\}$ **21.** $\left\{\dfrac{1}{2}\right\}$ **23.** $\{7\}$

25. $\{\ \}$ or $\varnothing$ **27.** $\{-3\}$ **29.** $\left\{\dfrac{3}{4}\right\}$ **31.** $\left\{-\dfrac{5}{6}\right\}$ **33.** $\{-4\}$

35. $\{-3, -2\}$ **37.** $\{-1\}$ **39.** $\left\{-\dfrac{2}{3}, \dfrac{1}{2}\right\}$ **41.** $\{\ \}$ or $\varnothing$

43. $\{-5, 5\}$ **45.** $\left\{-\dfrac{1}{2}\right\}$ **47.** $y = \dfrac{2}{x}$ **49.** $R = \dfrac{E}{I}$

51. $b = \dfrac{2A}{h} - B$ or $b = \dfrac{2A - Bh}{h}$ **53.** $y = \dfrac{x}{z} - 3$ or $y = \dfrac{x - 3z}{z}$

55. $S = \dfrac{RT}{T - R}$ **57.** $y = \dfrac{an - p}{am}$ **59.** $x = \dfrac{Ay}{y - A}$

61. $y = \dfrac{xz}{2z - 6x}$ **63.** $x = \dfrac{cy}{y - 1}$ **65.** $\dfrac{4x + 5}{x(x + 5)}$

67. $\{-2, 3\}$ **69.** $\dfrac{x + 7}{2}$ **71.** $\left\{-\dfrac{1}{6}, 1\right\}$ **73.** $\{-1, 5\}$

75. $\dfrac{x^3 - x^2 + 4}{x(x + 2)(x - 2)}$ **77.** $\dfrac{(x - 3)(x - 1)}{3x}$ **79.** $\dfrac{5}{a}$ **81.** $\{\ \}$ or $\varnothing$

83. 2   **85.** 1 hour and 9 hours   **87.** 80%

89. $k = 33$ **91.** The error occurred when the student incorrectly multiplied $-2[(x - 1)(x + 1)]$ on the right side of the equation. The correct solution is

$$\dfrac{2}{x - 1} - \dfrac{4}{x^2 - 1} = -2$$

$$\dfrac{2}{x - 1} - \dfrac{4}{(x - 1)(x + 1)} = -2$$

$$[(x - 1)(x + 1)]\left(\dfrac{2}{x - 1} - \dfrac{4}{(x - 1)(x + 1)}\right) = -2[(x - 1)(x + 1)]$$

$$2(x + 1) - 4 = -2(x - 1)(x + 1)$$

$$2x + 2 - 4 = -2(x^2 - 1)$$

$$2x - 2 = -2x^2 + 2$$

$$2x^2 + 2x - 4 = 0$$

$$x^2 + x - 2 = 0$$

$$(x + 2)(x - 1) = 0$$

$$x + 2 = 0 \quad \text{or} \quad x - 1 = 0$$

$$x = -2 \qquad\qquad x = 1$$

93. To *simplify* a rational expression means to add, subtract, multiply, or divide the rational expressions and express the result in a form in which there are no common factors in the numerator or denominator. To *solve* an equation means to find the value(s) of the variable that satisfy the equation. Answers will vary.

Section 7.8 Models Involving Rational Equations
1. proportion   **2.** $\left\{-\dfrac{2}{3}\right\}$ **3.** $\{3\}$ **4.** \$233.38   **5.** 210 miles   **6.** similar

7. $XY = 8$ **8.** 60 feet   **9.** 2 hours   **10.** $3\dfrac{1}{3}$ hours or 3 hours, 20 minutes   **11.** 20 mph   **12.** 6 mph   **13.** $\{12\}$ **15.** $\left\{\dfrac{18}{7}\right\}$

17. $\{16\}$ **19.** $\left\{\dfrac{24}{5}\right\}$ **21.** $\left\{-\dfrac{4}{5}\right\}$ **23.** $\{-2\}$ **25.** $\left\{\dfrac{5}{7}\right\}$ **27.** $\{-3, 2\}$ **29.** $\{2, 5\}$ **31.** $\{-2, 9\}$ **33.** $XZ = 12$ **35.** $n = 3; ZY = 5$

37. $x = 30; AB = 28$ **39.** $2x$ **41.** $t - 3$ **43.** $\dfrac{1}{5} + \dfrac{1}{3} = \dfrac{1}{t}$ **45.** $\dfrac{1}{b + 4} + \dfrac{1}{b} = \dfrac{1}{7}$ **47.** $r - 2$ **49.** $r - 48$ **51.** $\dfrac{4}{14 - c} = \dfrac{7}{14 + c}$

53. $\dfrac{12}{r + 3} = \dfrac{8}{r - 3}$ **55.** 145 miles   **57.** $8\dfrac{1}{3}$ lb   **59.** 37,245 rubles   **61.** 24 ft   **63.** 1.875 hr   **65.** $\dfrac{24}{7} \approx 3.4$ minutes   **67.** $\dfrac{36}{7} \approx 5.1$ hr

69. 15 hr   **71.** 24 hr   **73.** 4 km per hour   **75.** 1 hour, 40 minutes   **77.** 40 mph   **79.** 35 mph   **81.** $x = 6$ **83.** $x = \dfrac{98}{5}$ **85.** $x = \dfrac{72}{5}$

87. The time component is not correctly placed. The times in the table should be $\dfrac{10}{r + 1}$ and $\dfrac{10}{r - 1}$. The equation will incorporate the 5 hours: time traveled downstream + time traveled upstream = 5 hours.   **89.** One equation to solve the problem is $\dfrac{1}{8} + \dfrac{1}{6} = \dfrac{1}{t}$ where t is the number of hours required to complete the job together. Answers may vary.

Section 7.9 Variation
1. $t = ks$ **2.** constant of proportionality

3. $y = 3x$
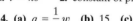

4. (a) $q = \dfrac{1}{4}w$ (b) 15 (c)
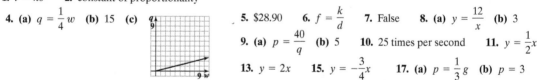

5. \$28.90   **6.** $f = \dfrac{k}{d}$ **7.** False   **8.** (a) $y = \dfrac{12}{x}$ (b) 3

9. (a) $p = \dfrac{40}{q}$ (b) 5   **10.** 25 times per second   **11.** $y = \dfrac{1}{2}x$

13. $y = 2x$ **15.** $y = -\dfrac{3}{4}x$ **17.** (a) $p = \dfrac{1}{3}g$ (b) $p = 3$

19. (a) $y = -\dfrac{3}{4}x$ (b) $x = -\dfrac{5}{3}$ **21.** $y = \dfrac{6}{x}$ **23.** $y = \dfrac{12}{x}$ **25.** $y = \dfrac{2}{7x}$ **27.** (a) $e = \dfrac{8}{n}$ (b) $e = \dfrac{1}{2}$ **29.** (a) $b = \dfrac{3}{4a}$ (b) $a = \dfrac{5}{6}$

31. direct variation; $\dfrac{2}{3}$ **33.** neither   **35.** inverse variation; 9   **37.** direct variation; 2   **39.** $\dfrac{9}{2}$ **41.** $P = 75$ **43.** $t = 42$ **45.** $b = 18$

47. 10 representatives   **49.** 120 board feet   **51.** 6.25 atmospheres   **53.** 150 bags   **55.** $m = 90$ **57.** $q = 24$ **59.** (a) $e = \dfrac{1.989 \times 10^{-25}}{\lambda}$
(b) 3.978×10^{-19} joules   **61.** Answers will vary.

Chapter 7 Review
1. (a) $\dfrac{1}{2}$ (b) -4 (c) 1   **2.** (a) 0 (b) -1 (c) 1   **3.** (a) 0 (b) 9 (c) 49   **4.** (a) -1 (b) $-\dfrac{2}{3}$ (c) 42

5. $\dfrac{7}{3}$ **6.** $\dfrac{1}{2}$ **7.** none   **8.** none   **9.** -10 or -2 **10.** -1 or 4   **11.** $\dfrac{y + 2}{5}$ **12.** $\dfrac{x(x - 4)}{5}$ **13.** $\dfrac{3}{k + 2}$ **14.** $-\dfrac{2}{x - 3}$

15. $\dfrac{x + 5}{2x - 1}$ **16.** $\dfrac{3x - 1}{2(x^2 - 2x + 4)}$ **17.** $\dfrac{2m^2}{n^2}$ **18.** $\dfrac{y^3}{6x}$ **19.** $\dfrac{14}{9n^2}$ **20.** $\dfrac{1}{ab^7}$ **21.** $-\dfrac{5(x - 2)}{x + 3}$ **22.** $-\dfrac{4(x - 3)(x + 3)}{(x - 9)^2}$

23. $\dfrac{x - 2}{4(x - 3)}$ **24.** $15x^3$ **25.** $\dfrac{x + 5}{x + 6}$ **26.** $\dfrac{y + 1}{y - 3}$ **27.** $\dfrac{x^3}{(x + 1)(x + 9)}$ **28.** $\dfrac{y - 2}{3y + 1}$ **29.** $\dfrac{9}{x - 3}$ **30.** $\dfrac{10}{x + 4}$ **31.** m

32. $\dfrac{1}{m}$ **33.** $\dfrac{1}{m-2}$ **34.** $2m+3$ **35.** $\dfrac{1}{3m}$ **36.** $\dfrac{2}{b}$ **37.** $y+7$ **38.** $\dfrac{1}{m-6}$ **39.** $-\dfrac{7}{x-y}$ **40.** $\dfrac{4}{a-b}$ **41.** $\dfrac{3x-5}{x^2-25}$

42. $\dfrac{x+4}{x-3}$ **43.** $12x^4y^7$ **44.** $60a^3b^4c^7$ **45.** $8a(a+2)$ **46.** $5a(a+6)$ **47.** $4(x-3)(x+1)$ **48.** $x(x-7)(x+7)$ **49.** $\dfrac{6xy^6}{x^4y^7}$

50. $\dfrac{11a^4b^3}{a^7b^5}$ **51.** $\dfrac{(x-1)(x+2)}{(x-2)(x+2)}$ **52.** $\dfrac{(m+2)(m-2)}{(m+7)(m-2)}$ **53.** $\dfrac{20x^2y}{24x^5},\dfrac{21}{24x^5}$ **54.** $\dfrac{12}{10a^3},\dfrac{11a^2b}{10a^3}$ **55.** $\dfrac{-4x}{-(x-2)},\dfrac{6}{-(x-2)}$

56. $\dfrac{-3}{-(m-5)},\dfrac{-2m}{-(m-5)}$ **57.** $\dfrac{2m+4}{(m+7)(m-2)(m+2)},\dfrac{m^2-m-2}{(m+7)(m-2)(m+2)}$ **58.** $\dfrac{n^2+3n-10}{n(n-5)(n+5)},\dfrac{n^2}{n(n-5)(n+5)}$

59. $\dfrac{4xz+8y^4}{x^2y^3z}$ **60.** $\dfrac{5y+x}{10x^2y^2}$ **61.** $\dfrac{x^2-5x+14}{(x+7)(x-7)}$ **62.** $\dfrac{2x^2+13x-9}{(2x+3)(2x-3)}$ **63.** $\dfrac{-2(2x+5)}{x(x-2)}$ **64.** $\dfrac{2x^2-6x-5}{x(x+5)}$ **65.** $\dfrac{3x-1}{4x+1}$

66. $\dfrac{3x-4}{(x-1)(x-2)}$ **67.** $\dfrac{-(4m-9)(m-4)}{(m+3)(m-3)}$ **68.** $\dfrac{2m^2+5m-2}{(m-5)(m+2)}$ **69.** $\dfrac{4}{m-2}$ **70.** $\dfrac{m+n}{m-n}$ **71.** $\dfrac{5x+12}{x+3}$ **72.** $\dfrac{7x+13}{x+2}$

73. $-\dfrac{3}{23}$ **74.** $\dfrac{18}{11}$ **75.** $\dfrac{2m^2-10m}{m^2+10}$ **76.** $\dfrac{6+4m^2}{6m-5m^2}$ **77.** $\dfrac{1}{6}$ **78.** $\dfrac{56}{9}$ **79.** $-\dfrac{y+8}{y-2}$ **80.** $-\dfrac{5y+50}{5y+22}$ **81.** $x=-5$ or $x=0$

82. $x=-6$ or $x=6$ **83.** $\{-4\}$ **84.** $\left\{\dfrac{2}{3}\right\}$ **85.** $\{5\}$ **86.** $\left\{\dfrac{14}{3}\right\}$ **87.** $\{38\}$ **88.** $\left\{\dfrac{9}{7}\right\}$ **89.** $\{\ \}$ or $\varnothing$ **90.** $\{\ \}$ or $\varnothing$ **91.** $\left\{-\dfrac{5}{2}\right\}$

92. $\{24\}$ **93.** $k=\dfrac{4}{y}$ **94.** $y=\dfrac{x}{6}$ **95.** $y=\dfrac{xz}{x-z}$ **96.** $z=\dfrac{xy}{x+y}$ **97.** $\{4\}$ **98.** $\{5\}$ **99.** $\{1\}$ **100.** $\{3\}$ **101.** $x=15$

102. $x=3.5$ **103.** 8 tanks **104.** \$26.25 **105.** 1.2 hours **106.** $\dfrac{15}{8}\approx1.9$ hours **107.** 15 min **108.** $\dfrac{28}{3}\approx9.3$ hours **109.** 9 mph

110. 55 mph **111.** 70 mph **112.** 45 mph **113.** $y=\dfrac{1}{4}x$ **114.** $y=6x$ **115.** $f=16$ **116.** $p=110$ **117.** \$507.50 **118.** 160 mi

119. $y=\dfrac{48}{x}$ **120.** $y=\dfrac{54}{x}$ **121.** $r=9$ **122.** $s=\dfrac{1}{4}$ **123.** 78 mph **124.** 25 liters

Chapter 7 Test

1. 2 **2.** $x=5$ or $x=-2$ **3.** $-\dfrac{x+3}{2}$ **4.** $\dfrac{14}{5x^2}$ **5.** $\dfrac{25}{9}$ **6.** $\dfrac{x-y}{2x-3y}$ **7.** y **8.** $\dfrac{x-5}{x+3}$ **9.** $-\dfrac{1}{y-z}$ or $\dfrac{1}{z-y}$

10. $\dfrac{2(x+3)(x-1)}{(x-2)(2x+1)}$ **11.** $\dfrac{x^2-5x-2}{(x+2)(x+3)(x-1)}$ **12.** $\dfrac{y-3}{3y}$ **13.** $\{-20,5\}$ **14.** $\{2\}$ **15.** $y=\dfrac{xz}{x-z}$ **16.** $\{5\}$ **17.** $x=\dfrac{24}{5}$

18. \$33 **19.** 36 min **20.** 4 mph **21.** $m=30$

Cumulative Review Chapters 1–7

1. -144 **2.** $9x-11$ **3.** $\left\{\dfrac{19}{6}\right\}$ **4.** all real numbers **5.** $\{4\}$ **6.** 7 feet **7.** $44,46,48$

8. $x\ge1$ ⟶ **9.** $9x^2-12xy+4y^2$ **10.** $\dfrac{16}{a^{16}b^{12}}$ **11.** $\dfrac{27z^9}{y^{12}}$ **12.** $2b(4a-7)(a+6)$ **13.** $\left\{0,\dfrac{1}{6},5\right\}$ **14.** 10 cm

15. 0 **16.** $-\dfrac{3(x+1)}{5x(2x-3)}$ **17.** $\dfrac{(x-2)(x+1)}{4(x+2)}$ **18.** $\dfrac{1}{x-6}$ **19.** $\dfrac{17x+30}{2(x-2)(x+2)}$ **20.** $\dfrac{4(10-3x)}{85x}$ **21.** $\{\ \}$ or $\varnothing$ **22.** $\{-16\}$

23. 10 inches **24.** 9 hr **25.** 7 mph **26.** $\dfrac{4}{3}$ **27.** $y=-\dfrac{3}{2}x+5$ or $3x+2y=10$ **28.**

29. $-\dfrac{3}{5},\dfrac{5}{3}$ **30.** $(-4,3)$

Chapter 8 Roots and Radicals

Section 8.1 Introduction to Square Roots

1. $b^2;a$ **2.** -8 and 8 **3.** $-\dfrac{5}{7}$ and $\dfrac{5}{7}$ **4.** -0.6 and 0.6 **5.** principal square root **6.** radicand

7. 10 **8.** -3 **9.** $\dfrac{5}{7}$ **10.** 0.6 **11.** 12 **12.** 13 **13.** 17 **14.** 7 **15.** ≈5.92 **16.** ≈-2.45 **17.** True **18.** rational; 7

19. irrational; ≈8.43 **20.** not a real number **21.** rational; -4 **22.** $|a|$ **23.** $|b|$ **24.** $4|p|$ **25.** $|w+3|$ **26.** $5b$ **27.** $z-6$

28. $2h-5$ **29.** $-1,1$ **31.** $-\dfrac{1}{3},\dfrac{1}{3}$ **33.** $-6,6$ **35.** $-0.5,0.5$ **37.** 12 **39.** -3 **41.** 15 **43.** $\dfrac{1}{11}$ **45.** 0.2 **47.** -18 **49.** $\dfrac{4}{9}$

51. 35 **53.** 10 **55.** 14 **57.** 8 **59.** 13 **61.** 2.828 **63.** 5.48 **65.** 7.5 **67.** not a real number **69.** rational; 20 **71.** rational; $\dfrac{1}{2}$

73. irrational; 7.35 **75.** irrational; 7.07 **77.** d **79.** $|x-9|$ **81.** $2m-n$ **83.** 1.73 **85.** 0.63 **87.** not a real number

89. 6 **91.** -8 **93.** not a real number **95.** 5 **97.** 6.71 **99.** 25 ft **101.** 16 km **103.** 7 m **105.** 14 in. **107.** 398 m

109. 2 **111.** 5 **113.** The number $-\sqrt{9}$ is a real number because it denotes the opposite, or negative, of the principal square root of 9, namely 3. The number $\sqrt{-9}$ is not a real number because there is no real number whose square is -9.

Section 8.2 Simplifying Square Roots

1. $\sqrt{a}\cdot\sqrt{b}$ **2.** 25 **3.** $2\sqrt{5}$ **4.** $2\sqrt{6}$ **5.** $6\sqrt{2}$ **6.** $2+\sqrt{5}$

7. $\dfrac{-1+2\sqrt{2}}{2}$ or $-\dfrac{1}{2}+\sqrt{2}$ **8.** False **9.** $6y^4$ **10.** $3x^6\sqrt{5}$ **11.** $2ab^5\sqrt{7}$ **12.** $5y^5\sqrt{y}$ **13.** $11a^2\sqrt{a}$ **14.** $4b^4\sqrt{2ab}$

15. $2x^3y^6\sqrt{3xy}$ **16.** $\dfrac{\sqrt{a}}{\sqrt{b}}$ **17.** $\dfrac{7a\sqrt{a}}{10}$ **18.** $\dfrac{\sqrt{11}}{4m}$ **19.** 5 **20.** $3b^2\sqrt{b}$ **21.** $2\sqrt{2}$ **23.** $2\sqrt{10}$ **25.** $3\sqrt{2}$ **27.** $\sqrt{33}$

29. $3\sqrt{5}$ **31.** $5\sqrt{5}$ **33.** $\sqrt{42}$ **35.** $7\sqrt{2}$ **37.** $3\sqrt{30}$ **39.** 5 **41.** $3+\sqrt{2}$ **43.** x^5 **45.** n^{72} **47.** $3y^2$ **49.** $2z^7\sqrt{6}$

51. $7x^3\sqrt{x}$ **53.** $4b^2\sqrt{3b}$ **55.** $3mn^2\sqrt{2m}$ **57.** $5c^2d\sqrt{3}$ **59.** $\dfrac{5}{6}$ **61.** $\dfrac{\sqrt{11}}{3}$ **63.** $\dfrac{y^8}{11}$ **65.** $\dfrac{\sqrt{3}}{a^2}$ **67.** $\dfrac{x^2\sqrt{x}}{y^4}$ **69.** $\dfrac{2xy^2\sqrt{5y}}{z^2}$

71. $\dfrac{\sqrt{15}}{x^2}$ **73.** $\dfrac{5a}{2}$ **75.** $\dfrac{8n^2\sqrt{n}}{3}$ **77.** $3\sqrt{7}$ **79.** $\dfrac{2\sqrt{3}}{5}$ **81.** $12a^3$ **83.** $\dfrac{x^2\sqrt{x}}{3}$ **85.** $2a^2bc^3\sqrt{3}$ **87.** $q^2r^2\sqrt{15pq}$ **89.** $\dfrac{2x^3\sqrt{x}}{y^6}$

91. $3a^{12}\sqrt{3a}$ **93.** $\dfrac{-4-9\sqrt{2}}{6}$ **95.** $\dfrac{1-\sqrt{2}}{2}$ **97.** $x=90\sqrt{2}$ **99.** $x=7\sqrt{5}$ **101.** $x=2\sqrt{34}$ **103.** $x=2\sqrt{73}$ **105. (a)** $\dfrac{\sqrt{6}}{\pi}\,$hz

(b) 0.78 **107.** x^{24} **109.** $16s^{18n}$ **111.** When simplifying $\sqrt{\dfrac{x^4}{y}}$, it must be stated that $y>0$ because if $y=0$, the denominator would be 0; division by zero is undefined in the set of real numbers. If $y<0$, the radicand is negative, but the square root of a negative number is not a real number.

113. The expression $\sqrt{\dfrac{315}{5}}=\dfrac{3\sqrt{35}}{\sqrt{5}}$ is not completely simplified because $\dfrac{3\sqrt{35}}{\sqrt{5}}=3\sqrt{\dfrac{35}{5}}=3\sqrt{7}$. Another strategy to simplify $\sqrt{\dfrac{315}{5}}$ is $\sqrt{\dfrac{315}{5}}=\sqrt{63}=\sqrt{9\cdot7}=3\sqrt{7}$.

Section 8.3 Adding and Subtracting Square Roots   **1.** radicand   **2.** $14\sqrt{3}$ **3.** $-\sqrt{11}+2\sqrt{10}$ **4.** $-8\sqrt{13}+\sqrt{6}$
5. $12\sqrt{5x}$ **6.** False   **7.** False   **8.** $9\sqrt{2}$ **9.** $-2\sqrt{3}$ **10.** $5\sqrt{5}-3\sqrt{2}$ **11.** $8\sqrt{3z}$ **12.** $-8a\sqrt{3a}$ **13.** $6\sqrt{3}$ **15.** $2a\sqrt{2a}$
17. $\sqrt{15}+\sqrt{7}$ **19.** 0 **21.** $-\sqrt{2}$ **23.** $-3\sqrt{6}-6\sqrt{11}$ **25.** $2\sqrt{22}$ **27.** $-\sqrt{3}$ **29.** $7\sqrt{3}$ **31.** $16\sqrt{5xy}$ **33.** $-3\sqrt{3}$
35. $21\sqrt{15}$ **37.** $11\sqrt{5}-4\sqrt{6}$ **39.** $-\sqrt{6x}$ **41.** $-8a\sqrt{3a}$ **43.** $-\dfrac{16}{5}\sqrt{5}$ **45.** $7\sqrt{14}$ **47.** 0 **49.** $-5\sqrt{y}$ **51.** $\sqrt{6}+9\sqrt{5}$
53. $9\sqrt{2x}-5\sqrt{2}$ **55.** $-2n\sqrt{5n}$ **57.** $3\sqrt{5}$ **59.** $18\sqrt{3}$ **61.** $18\sqrt{2}-36\sqrt{3}$ **63.** 0 **65.** $5x\sqrt{5y}-5x\sqrt{5}$ **67.** $a^4\sqrt{10a}+6a\sqrt{3a}$
69. $7+13\sqrt{2}$ **71.** $-1+5\sqrt{3}$ **73.** $\dfrac{7}{6}\sqrt{3}$ **75.** $\dfrac{9}{20}\sqrt{3}$ **77.** $\dfrac{5}{6}\sqrt{15}$ **79.** $\dfrac{11}{3}\sqrt{6}$ **81.** $24\sqrt{3}$ cm   **83.** $\left(18\sqrt{2}+32\sqrt{3}\right)$ inches
85. 23.3 ft   **87.** $13+8\sqrt{3}$ **89.** In the expression $6-2\sqrt{x}-10+5\sqrt{x}$, the terms 6 and -10 are like terms, and $-2\sqrt{x}$ and $5\sqrt{x}$ are like terms. The expression $6-2\sqrt{x}-10+5\sqrt{x}$ has not been correctly simplified. The correct simplification $6-2\sqrt{x}-10+5\sqrt{x}=$ $6-10-2\sqrt{x}+5\sqrt{x}=-4+3\sqrt{x}$.   **91.** When multiplying square roots, we multiply the radicands: $\sqrt{a\cdot b}=\sqrt{a}\cdot\sqrt{b}$ is the Product Rule for square roots. However, when adding square roots, the square root symbol acts as a grouping symbol. The operation under the radical sign must be done first, and then the radicand may be simplified, if possible. So $\sqrt{a+b}\ne\sqrt{a}+\sqrt{b}$.

Section 8.4 Multiplying Expressions with Square Roots   **1.** True   **2.** $\sqrt{15}$ **3.** $\sqrt{14z}$ **4.** $5b\sqrt{3}$ **5.** $6k^2\sqrt{2}$ **6.** $2z^3\sqrt{5z}$
7. $a;a$ **8.** 11 **9.** 31 **10.** 21 **11.** $-30\sqrt{2}$ **12.** 44 **13.** $-15+3\sqrt{7}$ **14.** $3\sqrt{5}-5$ **15.** $-4\sqrt{2}+2\sqrt{5}$ **16.** $-4+4\sqrt{3}$
17. $19+7\sqrt{7}$ **18.** $42+\sqrt{5n}-5n$ **19.** $-18+14\sqrt{3}$ **20.** $-32-11\sqrt{7}$ **21.** False   **22.** $67+16\sqrt{3}$ **23.** $4-4\sqrt{7z}+7z$
24. $49-12\sqrt{5}$ **25.** conjugates   **26.** 33 **27.** -47 **28.** $1-80n$ **29.** 3 **31.** $7x$ **33.** $\sqrt{39}$ **35.** $\sqrt{14a}$ **37.** $-2\sqrt{15}$
39. $24\sqrt{3}$ **41.** $-9x^2$ **43.** $72\sqrt{6}$ **45.** $270\sqrt{6}$ **47.** $-45\sqrt{6}$ **49.** $32x^2\sqrt{3x}$ **51.** 37 **53.** $7x$ **55.** $24+8\sqrt{5}$ **57.** $12-3\sqrt{6}$
59. $21\sqrt{5}+4\sqrt{3}$ **61.** $a\sqrt{2}+2\sqrt{a}$ **63.** $33+11\sqrt{3}$ **65.** $1+\sqrt{5}$ **67.** $23-9\sqrt{3}$ **69.** $3-14\sqrt{x}+8x$
71. $20-15\sqrt{2}+8\sqrt{3}-6\sqrt{6}$ **73.** $8x\sqrt{3}-7x$ **75.** $19+8\sqrt{3}$ **77.** $9x-12\sqrt{x}+4$ **79.** 1 **81.** $33+20\sqrt{2}$ **83.** -389
85. 34 **87.** $3m^3\sqrt{5}$ **89.** $-5\sqrt{2}$ **91.** $12\sqrt{2n}$ **93.** 32 **95.** $a+\sqrt{ab}+b$ **97.** $27+2\sqrt{30}$ **99.** $m\sqrt{2}-m$
101. $9s+4$ **103.** -120 **105.** $10a^2\sqrt{a}$ **107.** $-\dfrac{9}{2}\sqrt{3}$ **109.** 4 **111.** 9 **113.** $126\sqrt{3}$ square units   **115.** $112\sqrt{7}$ square units
117. $\left(12+18\sqrt{3}\right)$ square units   **119.** 147π m^2 **121.** 126π in.^{2} **123.** $12\sqrt{30}$ square units   **125.** $50\sqrt{14}$ square units
127. No. $\left(\sqrt{5}+\sqrt{7}\right)^2\ne\left(\sqrt{5}\right)^2+\left(\sqrt{7}\right)^2$. When squaring a binomial, we use the pattern $A^2+2AB+B^2$. So $\left(\sqrt{5}+\sqrt{7}\right)^2=$ $\left(\sqrt{5}\right)^2+2\left(\sqrt{5}\right)\left(\sqrt{7}\right)+\left(\sqrt{7}\right)^2=5+2\sqrt{35}+7=12+2\sqrt{35}$.   **129.** Answers will vary. The answer is correct, but it is not in simplest form. The correct answer is $\sqrt{12x^2}\cdot\sqrt{2x^3}=\sqrt{24x^5}=\sqrt{4x^4\cdot6x}=2x^2\sqrt{6x}$.

Section 8.5 Dividing Expressions with Square Roots   **1.** $\sqrt{\dfrac{a}{b}}$ **2.** 3 **3.** $\sqrt{7}$ **4.** $\dfrac{4}{5}$ **5.** $\sqrt{6}-\sqrt{15}$

6. rationalize the denominator   **7.** True   **8.** $\dfrac{\sqrt{2}}{2}$ **9.** $-\dfrac{\sqrt{6}}{15}$ **10.** $\dfrac{\sqrt{5}}{2}$ **11.** False   **12.** $4-2\sqrt{3}$ **13.** $9+3\sqrt{5}$

14. $\dfrac{4\sqrt{3}-\sqrt{21}}{9}$ **15.** $\dfrac{3\sqrt{3}+\sqrt{3x}}{9-x}$ **16.** $2-\sqrt{6}$ **17.** 4 **19.** $-\dfrac{1}{5}$ **21.** $3\sqrt{2}$ **23.** $2\sqrt{7}$ **25.** $-5\sqrt{y}$ **27.** 8

29. $\dfrac{3\sqrt{5}}{5}$ **31.** $\dfrac{10\sqrt{6}}{3}$ **33.** $-\dfrac{8\sqrt{2}}{3}$ **35.** $\dfrac{2\sqrt{x}}{x}$ **37.** $\dfrac{9\sqrt{2y}}{2}$ **39.** $\dfrac{\sqrt{3}}{2}$ **41.** $\dfrac{3\sqrt{2n}}{2n}$ **43.** $\dfrac{4\sqrt{3}}{9}$ **45.** $\dfrac{\sqrt{6ab}}{21b}$ **47.** $-\dfrac{7\sqrt{10}}{12}$

49. $2-\sqrt{3}$; 1 **51.** $\sqrt{6}+1$; 5 **53.** $-1+3\sqrt{14}$; -125 **55.** $\sqrt{p}-3\sqrt{q}$; $p-9q$ **57.** $\dfrac{3-\sqrt{5}}{4}$ **59.** $\dfrac{27+3\sqrt{3}}{26}$ **61.** $\dfrac{24-4\sqrt{7}}{29}$

63. $\dfrac{3\sqrt{y}+18}{y-36}$ **65.** $32\sqrt{2}+48$ **67.** $\dfrac{6\sqrt{2}+\sqrt{42}}{15}$ **69.** $\dfrac{n\sqrt{n}-n}{n-1}$ **71.** $\dfrac{2\sqrt{x}-3x}{4-9x}$ **73.** $\dfrac{\sqrt{55}+\sqrt{30}}{5}$ **75.** $\dfrac{\sqrt{3}+1}{2}$

77. $\sqrt{3}-\sqrt{6}$ **79.** $\dfrac{\sqrt{2}}{2}$ **81.** $\dfrac{3\sqrt{5}}{10}-\dfrac{\sqrt{2}}{2}$ **83.** $7\sqrt{2}$ **85.** $-\dfrac{\sqrt{6}}{3}$ **87.** $\dfrac{5\sqrt{7}}{98}$ **89.** $2\sqrt{2x}$ **91.** $\dfrac{2\sqrt{3}}{3}$ **93.** $-8\sqrt{2}+6\sqrt{5}$

95. $\dfrac{\sqrt{30}}{10}$ **97.** $4-2\sqrt{3}$ **99.** $\dfrac{\sqrt{2}}{10}$ **101.** $\dfrac{\sqrt{7xy}}{7x^2y}$ **103.** $11-6\sqrt{2}$ **105. (a)** 0.2679 **(b)** $2-\sqrt{3}$ **(c)** 0.2679

(d) They are the same.   **107. (a)** 2.0291 **(b)** $\dfrac{10\sqrt{3}+5}{11}$ **(c)** 2.0291 **(d)** They are the same.   **109. (a)** -1.7836 **(b)** $-\dfrac{4+6\sqrt{2}}{7}$

(c) -1.7836 **(d)** They are the same.   **111. (a)** 0.2101 **(b)** $\dfrac{5\sqrt{2}-\sqrt{6}}{22}$ **(c)** 0.2101 **(d)** They are the same.   **113.** $-2-\sqrt{3}$

115. $-2\sqrt{3}-3\sqrt{2}+\sqrt{6}+3$ **117.** $\dfrac{2x-7\sqrt{xy}-4y}{x-16y}$ **119.** x cannot be canceled in the expression $\dfrac{3\sqrt{xy}}{x}$ because the x in the numerator is

part of the radicand and the x in the denominator is not. The quotient rule says $\dfrac{\sqrt{a}}{\sqrt{b}}=\sqrt{\dfrac{a}{b}}$.   **121.** Neither student is correct. The correct approach is

$$\dfrac{3}{\sqrt{2}+\sqrt{3}}\cdot\dfrac{\sqrt{2}-\sqrt{3}}{\sqrt{2}-\sqrt{3}}=\dfrac{3\left(\sqrt{2}-\sqrt{3}\right)}{\left(\sqrt{2}\right)^2-\left(\sqrt{3}\right)^2}=\dfrac{3\left(\sqrt{2}-\sqrt{3}\right)}{2-3}=\dfrac{3\left(\sqrt{2}-\sqrt{3}\right)}{-1}=-3\sqrt{2}+3\sqrt{3}.$$

Putting the Concepts Together (Sections 8.1–8.5)   1. (a) irrational; $\sqrt{98}\approx9.90$ **(b)** rational; $\sqrt{361}=19$ **2.** $-6\sqrt{2}$ **3.** $4xy^3\sqrt{2x}$

4. $\dfrac{5}{2x}$ **5.** 7 **6.** $3m^3$ **7.** $3\sqrt{3}$ **8.** $3\sqrt{2}$ **9.** $6\sqrt{6}$ **10.** -42 **11.** $60\sqrt{2}+18\sqrt{5}$ **12.** $24-26\sqrt{3}$ **13.** -11

14. $11-4\sqrt{7}$ **15.** $-2+\sqrt{7}$ **16.** $\dfrac{3\sqrt{2}}{x^2}$ **17.** $\dfrac{2\sqrt{6}}{3}$ **18.** $-2\sqrt{3}+6$

Section 8.6 Solving Equations Containing Square Roots   1. radical equation   **2.** yes   **3.** no   **4.** yes   **5.** True   **6.** $\{14\}$
7. $\{-8\}$ **8.** $\{36\}$ **9.** $\{12\}$ **10.** extraneous solutions   **11.** $\{3\}$ **12.** $\{4\}$ **13.** False   **14.** $\{-4\}$ **15.** $\{4\}$ **16.** $\{\ \}$ or $\varnothing$
17. $\{6\}$ **18.** $\{-1,10\}$ **19.** $\{4\}$ **20.** False   **21.** $\{16\}$ **22.** 49 **23.** Yes   **25.** No   **27.** Yes   **29.** Yes   **31.** $\{16\}$ **33.** $\{-4\}$
35. $\{7\}$ **37.** $\{4\}$ **39.** $\{9\}$ **41.** $\{\ \}$ or $\varnothing$ **43.** $\{-1\}$ **45.** $\{3,6\}$ **47.** $\{1\}$ **49.** $\{\ \}$ or $\varnothing$ **51.** $\{9\}$ **53.** $\{6,9\}$ **55.** $\{9\}$

57. $\{6\}$ **59.** $\{1\}$ **61.** $\{0\}$ **63.** $\{-5\}$ **65.** $\{5\}$ **67.** $\{\ \}$ or $\varnothing$ **69.** $\{-1\}$ **71.** $\left\{\dfrac{13}{4}\right\}$ **73.** $\{23\}$ **75.** $\{20\}$ **77.** $\{-1\}$

79. $\{16\}$ **81.** $\{2\}$ **83.** $\left\{\dfrac{1}{4}\right\}$ **85.** $\{-3,8\}$ **87.** $\{-4,7\}$ **89.** $\{4\}$ **91.** $\{-1,2\}$ **93.** $\{\ \}$ or $\varnothing$ **95.** $\{3\}$ **97.** $\{\ \}$ or $\varnothing$

99. (a) 8 seconds   **(b)** $\dfrac{5\sqrt{3}}{2}$ seconds   **101.** about 28 ft   **103. (a)** about 42 ft   **(b)** Yes   **105.** 11 **107.** 3 **109.** $A=\pi r^2$

111. $h=\dfrac{3V}{S^2}$ **113.** $a=\dfrac{b^2-b}{2}$ **115.** $n=\dfrac{1}{2}m$ **117.** The student's work is incorrect. The student did not square the first step correctly
to obtain the second step. Using the property $\left(\sqrt{a}\right)^2=a$ for $a>0$ is correct, but the student incorrectly squared the right side of the equation.
The student should have used the pattern $A^2-2AB+B^2$ to simplify the right side of the equation, and then proceed to solve for x.

Section 8.7 Higher Roots and Rational Exponents   1. radicand; index   **2.** -5 **3.** True   **4.** 2 **5.** -3 **6.** not a real number
7. 2 **8.** 7 **9.** w **10.** $12p$ **11.** $\sqrt[n]{a}\cdot\sqrt[n]{b}$ **12.** False   **13.** $-2\sqrt[3]{4}$ **14.** $5n\sqrt[3]{2}$ **15.** $3b^3$ **16.** 3 **17.** $4m^3\sqrt[3]{2}$ **18.** $\sqrt[n]{a}$
19. (a) $\sqrt{49}=7$ **(b)** $\sqrt[3]{-64}=-4$ **(c)** $-\sqrt{100}=-10$ **(d)** $\sqrt{-100}$ not a real number   **20. (a)** $\sqrt[5]{p}$ **(b)** $\sqrt[3]{4n}$ **(c)** $4\sqrt[3]{n}$
21. (a) $b^{\frac{1}{2}}$ **(b)** $5p^{\frac{1}{3}}$ **(c)** $(10p)^{\frac{1}{4}}$ **22.** False   **23.** $\sqrt[n]{a^m};\left(\sqrt[n]{a}\right)^m$ **24. (a)** $\left(\sqrt{25}\right)^3=125$ **(b)** $\left(\sqrt[3]{64}\right)^2=16$ **(c)** $\left(-\sqrt[4]{16}\right)^3=-8$
(d) $\left(\sqrt[3]{-8}\right)^4=16$ **(e)** $\left(\sqrt{-49}\right)^5$ not a real number   **25. (a)** $d^{\frac{3}{4}}$ **(b)** $y^{\frac{8}{5}}$ **(c)** $\left(11a^2b\right)^{\frac{3}{4}}$ **26. (a)** $\sqrt[5]{z^4}=\left(\sqrt[5]{z}\right)^4$ **(b)** $2\sqrt[3]{n^2}=2\left(\sqrt[3]{n}\right)^2$
(c) $\sqrt[3]{(2n)^2}=\left(\sqrt[3]{2n}\right)^2$ **27. (a)** $\dfrac{1}{36^{\frac{1}{2}}}=\dfrac{1}{6}$ **(b)** $\dfrac{1}{8^{\frac{4}{3}}}=\dfrac{1}{16}$ **(c)** $-\dfrac{1}{25^{\frac{3}{2}}}=-\dfrac{1}{125}$ **28. (a)** $7^{\frac{1}{6}}$ **(b)** $11^{\frac{3}{5}}$ **(c)** 4 **(d)** $a^{\frac{11}{2}}$ **29.** $\sqrt[3]{8}$ or 2

31. $\sqrt[4]{16}$ or 2 **33.** $\sqrt[3]{81}$ or 3 **35.** $\sqrt[5]{-32}$ or -2 **37.** 3 **39.** not a real number   **41.** -5 **43.** 5 **45.** 0 **47.** 3 **49.** 5
51. n **53.** r **55.** $3a$ **57.** $2\sqrt[3]{2}$ **59.** not a real number   **61.** $-2\sqrt[3]{5}$ **63.** 3 **65.** $-2n^2\sqrt[4]{2}$ **67.** $4\sqrt[3]{2}$ **69.** $3x\sqrt[3]{3}$
71. $2b$ **73.** $-3z^2\sqrt[3]{2}$ **75.** -2 **77.** -2 **79.** -6 **81.** not a real number   **83.** $\sqrt{2a}$ **85.** $7\sqrt[4]{z}$ **87.** $-3\sqrt[3]{r}$ **89.** $c^{\frac{1}{2}}$

91. $(2y)^{\frac{1}{2}}$ **93.** $7a^{\frac{1}{2}}$ **95.** $\left(\sqrt{64}\right)^3=512$ **97.** $\dfrac{1}{\sqrt{81}}=\dfrac{1}{9}$ **99.** $\left(\sqrt[3]{64}\right)^2=16$ **101.** $-\dfrac{1}{\left(\sqrt{9}\right)^3}=-\dfrac{1}{27}$ **103.** $\left(\sqrt[4]{-81}\right)^3$ not a real number

105. $\dfrac{1}{\left(\sqrt{49}\right)^3}=\dfrac{1}{343}$ **107.** $\sqrt[3]{u^2}=\left(\sqrt[3]{u}\right)^2$ **109.** $4\sqrt[3]{x^2}=4\left(\sqrt[3]{x}\right)^2$ **111.** $\sqrt[3]{(5n)^2}=\left(\sqrt[3]{5n}\right)^2$ **113.** $p^{\frac{5}{4}}$ **115.** $5t^{\frac{3}{4}}$ **117.** $(5a)^{\frac{2}{3}}$ **119.** 16

121. $\dfrac{1}{36}$ **123.** x^6 **125.** $4n^{\frac{1}{3}}$ or $4\sqrt[3]{n}$ **127.** $x^{\frac{1}{4}}$ or $\sqrt[4]{x}$ **129.** $\dfrac{1}{2x}$ **131.** -125 **133.** $\dfrac{1}{6}$ **135.** $-\dfrac{1}{25}$ **137.** 127 **139.** 5 **141.** $\dfrac{125}{8}$

143. $\dfrac{1}{y^2}$ **145.** $\dfrac{1}{4}$ **147.** 6 **149.** $\dfrac{1}{\sqrt[4]{x}}$ **151.** $-2\sqrt{a}$ **153.** $81x\sqrt[6]{x^5}$ **155.** The expression $a^{\frac{1}{n}}$ is undefined when a is negative and n is even
because an even root of a negative number is not defined. For example, $\sqrt{-16}$ is undefined because the principal square root of a negative real number
is not a real number.

Chapter 8 Review   1. $-2,2$ **2.** $-9,9$ **3.** -1 **4.** -5 **5.** 0.4 **6.** 0.2 **7.** $\dfrac{5}{4}$ **8.** 6 **9.** 4 **10.** 12 **11.** 21 **12.** 11

13. rational; -3 **14.** irrational; -3.46 **15.** irrational; 3.74 **16.** not a real number   **17.** $|4x-9|$ **18.** $|16m-25|$ **19.** $2\sqrt{7}$

20. $3\sqrt{5}$ **21.** $10\sqrt{2}$ **22.** $5\sqrt{6}$ **23.** $-1+\sqrt{2}$ **24.** $\dfrac{-1+\sqrt{3}}{2}$ **25.** a^{18} **26.** x^8 **27.** $4x^5$ **28.** $7a^6$ **29.** $3n^4\sqrt{2n}$

30. $2y^{12}\sqrt{2y}$ **31.** $\dfrac{3}{x^4}$ **32.** $\dfrac{2}{x^2}$ **33.** $\dfrac{9y^2}{5}$ **34.** $\dfrac{6}{11n^4}$ **35.** $-2\sqrt{7}$ **36.** $3\sqrt{11}$ **37.** $\sqrt{x}$ **38.** $-\sqrt{n}$ **39.** $25a\sqrt{ab}$

40. $3x\sqrt{3xy}$ **41.** $5\sqrt{3}$ **42.** $8\sqrt{2}$ **43.** $4+\sqrt{5}$ **44.** $6-2\sqrt{3}$ **45.** $19n^2\sqrt{2n}$ **46.** $9a^2\sqrt{14a}$ **47.** $2\sqrt{2}+2\sqrt{3}$

48. $\dfrac{9}{2}\sqrt{6}+\dfrac{2}{3}\sqrt{3}$ **49.** $\dfrac{11}{20}\sqrt{3}$ **50.** $-\dfrac{8}{5}\sqrt{2}$ **51.** $4\sqrt{6}$ **52.** $4\sqrt{15}$ **53.** $7x^2\sqrt{6x}$ **54.** $6y^2\sqrt{5y}$ **55.** $-128\sqrt{10}$ **56.** -200

57. $8a$ **58.** $45n$ **59.** -24 **60.** -154 **61.** $3\sqrt{a}+3\sqrt{5a}$ **62.** $2x+2x\sqrt{2}$ **63.** $6+12\sqrt{3}+4\sqrt{6}+24\sqrt{2}$

64. $15+10\sqrt{6}-9\sqrt{3}-18\sqrt{2}$ **65.** $4\sqrt{y}+12-2y\sqrt{2}-6\sqrt{2y}$ **66.** $\sqrt{x}+9+3x\sqrt{3}+27\sqrt{3x}$ **67.** $11-6\sqrt{2}$ **68.** $21-8\sqrt{5}$

69. $11x+6x\sqrt{2}$ **70.** $13n+4n\sqrt{3}$ **71.** $9-25x$ **72.** $4x-16$ **73.** $3\sqrt{6}$ **74.** $3\sqrt{5}$ **75.** $\dfrac{\sqrt{6}}{2x}$ **76.** $\dfrac{x\sqrt{15}}{6}$ **77.** $\sqrt{5}+\sqrt{6}$

78. $\sqrt{6}-\sqrt{3}$ **79.** $2\sqrt{7}$ **80.** $5\sqrt{5}$ **81.** $\dfrac{\sqrt{6}}{4}$ **82.** $\dfrac{\sqrt{10}}{25}$ **83.** $-2-3\sqrt{5};-41$ **84.** $-3+2\sqrt{7};-19$ **85.** $4+2\sqrt{2}$

86. $\dfrac{6-\sqrt{3}}{11}$ **87.** $-2+2\sqrt{2}$ **88.** $\sqrt{3}+1$ **89.** Yes **90.** Yes **91.** $\{-13\}$ **92.** $\{13\}$ **93.** $\{2\}$ **94.** $\{9\}$ **95.** $\{3,5\}$

96. $\{6\}$ **97.** $\left\{\dfrac{1}{4}\right\}$ **98.** $\{-3\}$ **99.** $\{3\}$ **100.** $\{2\}$ **101.** $\{\ \}$ or $\varnothing$ **102.** $\{10\}$ **103.** 18π square cm **104.** 6 in. **105.** -2

106. not a real number **107.** $2x\sqrt[4]{3}$ **108.** $5x\sqrt[4]{5}$ **109.** $2n\sqrt[3]{3n}$ **110.** $3z\sqrt[4]{2z^2}$ **111.** -2 **112.** not a real number **113.** $x^{\frac{3}{4}}$

114. $z^{\frac{1}{3}}$ **115.** $2\sqrt{x^3}=2x\sqrt{x}$ **116.** $\sqrt[3]{3v}$ **117.** 9 **118.** 32 **119.** $-\dfrac{1}{64}$ **120.** $\dfrac{1}{8}$ **121.** 4 **122.** 36 **123.** $\dfrac{1}{x^{\frac{3}{4}}}$ **124.** $\dfrac{a^{\frac{1}{3}}}{9}$

Chapter 8 Test **1.** $-6\sqrt{3}$ **2.** $5xy\sqrt{2y}$ **3.** $\dfrac{4x}{3}$ **4.** 7 **5.** $\sqrt{2}$ **6.** $17\sqrt{3}$ **7.** $15\sqrt{3}$ **8.** $12\sqrt{3}-4\sqrt{2}$ **9.** $19-8\sqrt{3}$

10. $2x\sqrt{3x}$ **11.** $2-10\sqrt{2}$ **12.** $\dfrac{-1+3\sqrt{2}}{2}$ **13.** $\dfrac{6\sqrt{5}}{5}$ **14.** $-3\sqrt{2}+6$ **15.** $\{5\}$ **16.** $\{5\}$ **17.** $\{7,-3\}$ **18.** $3x\sqrt[3]{4x^2}$

19. $\dfrac{1}{9}$ **20.** $3\sqrt{5}\approx6.7$ feet

Chapter 9 Quadratic Equations

Section 9.1 Solving Quadratic Equations Using the Square Root Property
1. $\sqrt{p};-\sqrt{p}$ **2.** False **3.** $\{-6,6\}$ **4.** $\{-2\sqrt{5},2\sqrt{5}\}$

5. $\{-5,5\}$ **6.** $\{-3\sqrt{2},3\sqrt{2}\}$ **7.** $\left\{-\dfrac{\sqrt{2}}{2},\dfrac{\sqrt{2}}{2}\right\}$ **8.** $\left\{-\dfrac{4\sqrt{5}}{5},\dfrac{4\sqrt{5}}{5}\right\}$ **9.** two **10.** $\{-8,14\}$ **11.** $\left\{\dfrac{-1-2\sqrt{7}}{5},\dfrac{-1+2\sqrt{7}}{5}\right\}$

12. $\{-7,-1\}$ **13.** $\{-2-2\sqrt{2},-2+2\sqrt{2}\}$ **14.** no real solution **15.** no real solution **16.** False **17.** 13 **18.** $5\sqrt{10},15.8$

19. $6\sqrt{2},8.5$ **20.** Yes. The ladder reaches 28.9 feet up on the wall. **21.** $\{-12,12\}$ **23.** $\{0\}$ **25.** $\{-2\sqrt{3},2\sqrt{3}\}$ **27.** $\left\{-\dfrac{2}{3},\dfrac{2}{3}\right\}$

29. $\left\{-\dfrac{2\sqrt{3}}{3},\dfrac{2\sqrt{3}}{3}\right\}$ **31.** $\{-4\sqrt{2},4\sqrt{2}\}$ **33.** $\{-13,13\}$ **35.** $\{-5\sqrt{2},5\sqrt{2}\}$ **37.** no real solution **39.** $\left\{-\dfrac{1}{3},\dfrac{1}{3}\right\}$ **41.** $\{-8,8\}$

43. $\{-6,6\}$ **45.** $\left\{-\dfrac{5\sqrt{3}}{3},\dfrac{5\sqrt{3}}{3}\right\}$ **47.** no real solution **49.** $\{-4\sqrt{2},4\sqrt{2}\}$ **51.** $\{-6,-2\}$ **53.** $\left\{\dfrac{2}{3},\dfrac{4}{3}\right\}$

55. $\{-5-\sqrt{6},-5+\sqrt{6}\}$ **57.** $\{6-2\sqrt{2},6+2\sqrt{2}\}$ **59.** $\left\{-\dfrac{5}{3},1\right\}$ **61.** $\left\{\dfrac{5-\sqrt{15}}{2},\dfrac{5+\sqrt{15}}{2}\right\}$ **63.** $\{-3,5\}$ **65.** $\left\{-\dfrac{1}{2},-\dfrac{1}{4}\right\}$

67. $\left\{\dfrac{-2-3\sqrt{6}}{9},\dfrac{-2+3\sqrt{6}}{9}\right\}$ **69.** no real solution **71.** $\{-9,1\}$ **73.** $\{-3,4\}$ **75.** $c=10$ **77.** $c=3\sqrt{2}\approx4.24$

79. $a=8\sqrt{2}\approx11.31$ **81.** $\{4,9\}$ **83.** $\left\{-1,\dfrac{1}{2}\right\}$ **85.** $\{-2\sqrt{2},2\sqrt{2}\}$ **87.** $\{-\sqrt{15},\sqrt{15}\}$ **89.** $\left\{-\dfrac{\sqrt{15}}{5},\dfrac{\sqrt{15}}{5}\right\}$ **91.** no real solution

93. $\{-4,3\}$ **95.** $\{-3\sqrt{3},3\sqrt{3}\}$ **97.** $\{5\}$ **99.** $\left\{\dfrac{-4-\sqrt{10}}{2},\dfrac{-4+\sqrt{10}}{2}\right\}$

125. The error is in the third step where only the positive square root was taken. The correct solution is
$$(x-5)^2-4=0$$
$$(x-5)^2=4$$
$$x-5=\pm2$$
$$x-5=2\quad\text{or}\quad x-5=-2$$
$$x=7\qquad\qquad x=3$$
The solution set is $\{3,7\}$

101. $\left\{-\dfrac{\sqrt{6}}{3},\dfrac{\sqrt{6}}{3}\right\}$ **103.** $\left\{-\dfrac{3}{2},4\right\}$ **105.** $\{-2\sqrt{10},2\sqrt{10}\}$

107. no real solution **109.** $2\sqrt{10}$ **111. (a)** $2\sqrt{30}$ ft
(b) 11.0 ft **113.** $20\sqrt{26}\approx102$ yd **115. (a)** 13.8 ft **(b)** 13 ft 9.6 in.
117. (a) -2.08 or 0.08 **(b)** 8% **119.** $x^2-16=0$
121. $x^2-6=0$ **123.** $x^2-45=0$

Section 9.2 Solving Quadratic Equations by Completing the Square
1. $100;(x-10)^2$ **2.** $x-\dfrac{b}{2}$ **3.** $9;(p+3)^2$ **4.** $81;(b-9)^2$

5. $\dfrac{9}{4};\left(w+\dfrac{3}{2}\right)^2$ **6.** False **7.** $\{-7,-1\}$ **8.** $\{-8,4\}$ **9.** $\{-4-\sqrt{7},-4+\sqrt{7}\}$ **10.** $\{5-\sqrt{6},5+\sqrt{6}\}$ **11.** False **12.** $\{-9,1\}$

13. $\left\{\dfrac{-5-\sqrt{65}}{2},\dfrac{-5+\sqrt{65}}{2}\right\}$ **14.** 2 **15.** $\left\{-2,\dfrac{5}{2}\right\}$ **16.** $\left\{\dfrac{2-\sqrt{10}}{3},\dfrac{2+\sqrt{10}}{3}\right\}$ **17.** no real solution **18.** $\{3-\sqrt{2},3+\sqrt{2}\}$

19. $64; (x + 8)^2$ **21.** $36; (z - 6)^2$ **23.** $\frac{4}{9}; \left(k + \frac{2}{3}\right)^2$ **25.** $\frac{81}{4}; \left(y - \frac{9}{2}\right)^2$ **27.** $\frac{1}{4}; \left(t + \frac{1}{2}\right)^2$ **29.** $\frac{1}{16}; \left(s - \frac{1}{4}\right)^2$ **31.** $\{-3, 7\}$

33. $\left\{-2 - \sqrt{11}, -2 + \sqrt{11}\right\}$ **35.** $\{-3, 6\}$ **37.** $\{3, 5\}$ **39.** no real solution   **41.** $\{-1, 4\}$ **43.** $\left\{4 - 2\sqrt{7}, 4 + 2\sqrt{7}\right\}$ **45.** $\{-5, -2\}$

47. $\left\{\frac{-7 - \sqrt{249}}{2}, \frac{-7 + \sqrt{249}}{2}\right\}$ **49.** $\{-8, -2\}$ **51.** $\{-3, 1\}$ **53.** $\left\{-\frac{1}{2}, \frac{3}{2}\right\}$ **55.** $\left\{\frac{-2 - \sqrt{10}}{3}, \frac{-2 + \sqrt{10}}{3}\right\}$

57. $\left\{\frac{-1 - \sqrt{6}}{2}, \frac{-1 + \sqrt{6}}{2}\right\}$ **59.** no real solution   **61.** $\left\{\frac{3 - \sqrt{2}}{2}, \frac{3 + \sqrt{2}}{2}\right\}$ **63.** $\left\{\frac{6 - \sqrt{37}}{2}, \frac{6 + \sqrt{37}}{2}\right\}$ **65.** $\{-4, 6\}$ **67.** $\left\{\frac{1}{2}\right\}$

69. $\left\{-3 - 2\sqrt{3}, -3 + 2\sqrt{3}\right\}$ **71.** $\left\{-2\sqrt{5}, 2\sqrt{5}\right\}$ **73.** $\left\{\frac{-3 - \sqrt{15}}{3}, \frac{-3 + \sqrt{15}}{3}\right\}$ **75.** $\left\{\frac{-5 - \sqrt{97}}{2}, \frac{-5 + \sqrt{97}}{2}\right\}$ **77.** $\{-3, 3\}$

79. $\{-6, 2\}$ **81.** $\{-12, 2\}$ **83.** $\left\{-3\sqrt{2}, 3\sqrt{2}\right\}$ **85.** $\left\{-2\sqrt{3}, 2\sqrt{3}\right\}$ **87.** $\left\{\frac{-6 - 3\sqrt{10}}{2}, \frac{-6 + 3\sqrt{10}}{2}\right\}$ **89.** $\left\{\frac{2}{3}, 3\right\}$

91. $\left\{-1 - \sqrt{34}, -1 + \sqrt{34}\right\}$ **93.** $15\sqrt{2}$ **95.** 3 and 6   **97.** -4 or 6   **99.** $6 - 3\sqrt{3}$ or $6 + 3\sqrt{3}$ **101.** (a) 9 (b) $\{3, 6\}$ (c) $3 + 6 = 9$

103. (a) 2 (b) $\left\{1 - \frac{\sqrt{6}}{2}, 1 + \frac{\sqrt{6}}{2}\right\}$ (c) $1 - \frac{\sqrt{6}}{2} + 1 + \frac{\sqrt{6}}{2} = 2$ **105.** (a) $-\frac{3}{4}$; (b) $\left\{-\frac{3}{2}, \frac{1}{2}\right\}$; (c) $\left(-\frac{3}{2}\right)\left(\frac{1}{2}\right) = -\frac{3}{4}$

107. (a) -7; (b) $\left\{1 - 2\sqrt{2}, 1 + 2\sqrt{2}\right\}$; (c) $\left(1 - 2\sqrt{2}\right)\left(1 + 2\sqrt{2}\right) = -7$ **109.** center $= (5, -3)$, radius $= 2$

111. center $= (10, 8)$, radius $= \sqrt{142}$ **113.** To find the number that must be added to $x^2 - 9x$ to make a perfect square trinomial, take half of the coefficient of x, which is -9, and square that value: $\left(\frac{1}{2} \cdot -9\right)^2 = \left(-\frac{9}{2}\right)^2 = \frac{81}{4}$. So $x^2 - 9x + \frac{81}{4} = \left(x - \frac{9}{2}\right)^2$.

Section 9.3 Solving Quadratic Equations Using the Quadratic Formula **1.** $\frac{-b \pm \sqrt{b^2 - 4ac}}{2a}$ **2.** (a) $a = 1; b = 5; c = -3$

(b) $a = 4; b = -3; c = 1$ **3.** $\left\{-\frac{4}{3}, -1\right\}$ **4.** $\left\{-6, -\frac{1}{2}\right\}$ **5.** $\left\{-\frac{2}{3}, -\frac{3}{2}\right\}$ **6.** $\left\{-\frac{5}{4}, \frac{1}{2}\right\}$ **7.** False   **8.** $\left\{-2 - \sqrt{6}, -2 + \sqrt{6}\right\}$

9. $\left\{\frac{3 - \sqrt{2}}{4}, \frac{3 + \sqrt{2}}{4}\right\}$ **10.** True   **11.** $\left\{\frac{4 - \sqrt{10}}{2}, \frac{4 + \sqrt{10}}{2}\right\}$ **12.** $\left\{\frac{5}{4}\right\}$ **13.** no real solution   **14.** 1000   **15.** $b^2 - 4ac$

16. factoring   **17.** factoring   **18.** the quadratic formula   **19.** 0; factoring; $\left\{\frac{1}{3}\right\}$ **20.** 1; factoring; $\left\{\frac{2}{3}, 1\right\}$

21. 20; quadratic formula; $\left\{\frac{1 - \sqrt{5}}{4}, \frac{1 + \sqrt{5}}{4}\right\}$ **22.** $\left\{-\sqrt{6}, \sqrt{6}\right\}$ **23.** $\left\{-\frac{7}{2}, 5\right\}$ **24.** $\left\{\frac{-2 - \sqrt{7}}{3}, \frac{-2 + \sqrt{7}}{3}\right\}$

25. $-2x^2 + x + 4 = 0; a = -2, b = 1, c = 4$ **27.** $x^2 + 0x + 4 = 0; a = 1, b = 0, c = 4$ **29.** $\frac{3}{2}x^2 - \frac{6}{5}x - 2 = 0; a = \frac{3}{2}, b = -\frac{6}{5}, c = -2$

31. $0.5x^2 - x + 3 = 0; a = 0.5, b = -1, c = 3$ **33.** $\{-8, 3\}$ **35.** $\left\{-4, -\frac{3}{2}\right\}$ **37.** $\left\{\frac{1 - \sqrt{21}}{2}, \frac{1 + \sqrt{21}}{2}\right\}$ **39.** $\left\{\frac{-2 - \sqrt{7}}{3}, \frac{-2 + \sqrt{7}}{3}\right\}$

41. $\left\{\frac{1}{2}, \frac{3}{2}\right\}$ **43.** $\left\{\frac{-7 - 3\sqrt{5}}{2}, \frac{-7 + 3\sqrt{5}}{2}\right\}$ **45.** $\left\{\frac{5 - \sqrt{17}}{4}, \frac{5 + \sqrt{17}}{4}\right\}$ **47.** $\{3, 4\}$ **49.** $\left\{-\frac{2}{3}, 2\right\}$ **51.** $\left\{-3 - \sqrt{5}, -3 + \sqrt{5}\right\}$

53. $\left\{\frac{2 - \sqrt{2}}{2}, \frac{2 + \sqrt{2}}{2}\right\}$ **55.** $\left\{\frac{-5 - \sqrt{33}}{4}, \frac{-5 + \sqrt{33}}{4}\right\}$ **57.** $\left\{\frac{1}{5}, \frac{1}{3}\right\}$ **59.** $\left\{-\frac{3}{2}\right\}$ **61.** $\{-6, 3\}$ **63.** $\left\{\frac{4 - \sqrt{10}}{3}, \frac{4 + \sqrt{10}}{3}\right\}$ **65.** $\{3\}$

67. $\left\{\frac{-1 - \sqrt{61}}{2}, \frac{-1 + \sqrt{61}}{2}\right\}$ **69.** no real solution   **71.** $\left\{-2\sqrt{3}, 2\sqrt{3}\right\}$ **73.** $\left\{-\frac{3}{2}, 6\right\}$ **75.** $\{0, 5\}$ **77.** -39; no real solution

79. 25; factoring   **81.** 0; factoring   **83.** 40; quadratic formula   **85.** 0; factoring   **87.** -56; no real solution   **89.** $\left\{\frac{3 - \sqrt{3}}{3}, \frac{3 + \sqrt{3}}{3}\right\}$

91. $\left\{-\frac{5}{3}, 1\right\}$ **93.** no real solution   **95.** $\left\{-\frac{1}{2}\right\}$ **97.** $\left\{-5 - 2\sqrt{5}, -5 + 2\sqrt{5}\right\}$ **99.** $\{0, 3\}$ **101.** $\{-5, -2\}$ **103.** $\left\{-4, \frac{1}{2}\right\}$

105. no real solution   **107.** (a) $\$1515$ (b) 996 or 2004   **109.** (a) 43 (b) 37 (c) 33 (d) 2029   **111.** $-3 - 3\sqrt{2}$ and $-3 + 3\sqrt{2}$

113. -1 and 5   **115.** $\left\{-4\sqrt{2}, \sqrt{2}\right\}$ **117.** $\left\{\frac{2\sqrt{3}}{3}, \sqrt{3}\right\}$ **119.** If the discriminant is a perfect square, or if the discriminant is equal to zero the quadratic equation is factorable.

Putting the Concepts Together (Sections 9.1–9.3) **1.** (a) $\left\{-\frac{\sqrt{5}}{2}, \frac{\sqrt{5}}{2}\right\}$ (b) $\left\{2 - 2\sqrt{3}, 2 + 2\sqrt{3}\right\}$ (c) $\left\{\frac{-3 - \sqrt{3}}{2}, \frac{-3 + \sqrt{3}}{2}\right\}$

2. (a) add 81; $z^2 - 18z + 81 = (z - 9)^2$ (b) add $\frac{81}{4}$; $y^2 + 9y + \frac{81}{4} = \left(y + \frac{9}{2}\right)^2$ (c) add $\frac{4}{25}$; $m^2 + \frac{4}{5}m + \frac{4}{25} = \left(m + \frac{2}{5}\right)^2$

3. (a) $\{-7, -5\}$ (b) no real solution (c) $\left\{4 - 3\sqrt{2}, 4 + 3\sqrt{2}\right\}$ **4.** (a) $\left\{-4 - 2\sqrt{5}, -4 + 2\sqrt{5}\right\}$ (b) $\left\{-\frac{3}{2}, 4\right\}$ (c) $\left\{-\frac{9}{2}\right\}$ **5.** $\{-2, 3\}$

6. $\left\{\frac{-1 - \sqrt{11}}{2}, \frac{-1 + \sqrt{11}}{2}\right\}$ **7.** $\left\{\frac{-2 - \sqrt{3}}{2}, \frac{-2 + \sqrt{3}}{2}\right\}$ **8.** (a) 64 (b) factoring (c) Answers may vary.

9. (a) $5\sqrt{15}$ feet (b) 19.4 feet   **10.** (a) $\$12,000$ (b) 60 or 160 texts.

Section 9.4 Problem Solving Using Quadratic Equations **1.** False **2.** base = 8 inches; height = 10 inches **3.** $a^2 + b^2 = c^2$
4. 7.7 m by 11.7 m **5.** False **6.** length = 4.1 feet; width = 31 feet **7.** ages 30 and 63 years **8.** The cannonball will be 50 feet above the ground after 0.51 s and after 5.74 s. **9.** width = 6 m, length = 15 m **11.** width = 3 in.; length = 12 in. **13.** height = 5 cm; base = 8 cm
15. height = 11 ft; base = 12 ft **17.** Longer leg: $\dfrac{3 + 3\sqrt{3}}{2} \approx 4.1$ inches; shorter leg: $\dfrac{-3 + 3\sqrt{3}}{2} \approx 1.1$ inches.
19. leg = $3\sqrt{3} \approx 5.2$ m; hypotenuse = $6\sqrt{3} \approx 10.4$ m **21.** $-17, -16$ and $16, 17$ **23.** $14, 15$ **25.** $-1 - 2\sqrt{6}$ or $-1 + 2\sqrt{6}$
27. $5 - 2\sqrt{3}$ or $5 + 2\sqrt{3}$ **29. (a)** 41 ft **(b)** 116 ft **(c)** 1.52 s and 4.10 s **(d)** 5.625 s **31. (a)** 43 fruit flies **(b)** 75 fruit flies **(c)** 2.18 hours
33. (a) 9 **(b)** 20 **(c)** 15 **35. (a)** $(180 - x)°$ **(b)** 30° or 125° **37. (a)** \$146.40 **(b)** \$992.40 **(c)** approximately 3 months
(d) approximately 13 months **39.** leg = 1, hypotenuse = $\sqrt{2}$ **41.** leg = $\sqrt{6}$, hypotenuse = $2\sqrt{3}$ **43.** leg = 2, leg = 2
45. long leg = $5\sqrt{3}$; hypotenuse = 10 **47.** short leg = $3\sqrt{3}$; hypotenuse = $6\sqrt{3}$

Section 9.5 The Complex Number System **1.** -1 **2.** $\sqrt{N}i$ **3.** real; imaginary **4.** True **5.** $4i$ **6.** $\sqrt{2}i$ **7.** $2\sqrt{6}i$ **8.** $9 + 12i$
9. $-7 - 2\sqrt{5}i$ **10.** $2 - \sqrt{2}i$ **11.** $2 + 2i$ **12.** $-8 + 11i$ **13.** $5 + 5\sqrt{3}i$ **14.** $24 + 12i$ **15.** $-2 + 14i$ **16.** -10
17. $-6 - 8i$ **18.** $-1 - 5i$ **19.** 53 **20.** 97 **21.** $-4 - 6i$ **22.** $-\dfrac{48}{17} - \dfrac{12}{17}i$ **23.** $1 - \dfrac{8}{3}i$ **24.** $\dfrac{5}{2} - \dfrac{1}{2}i$ **25.** $\left\{-\dfrac{\sqrt{10}i}{2}, \dfrac{\sqrt{10}i}{2}\right\}$
26. $\left\{-3 - 2\sqrt{2}i, -3 + 2\sqrt{2}i\right\}$ **27.** $25i$ **29.** $-2\sqrt{13}i$ **31.** $5 + 2i$ **33.** $12 - 3\sqrt{3}i$ **35.** $-\dfrac{3}{2} + \dfrac{\sqrt{2}}{2}i$ **37.** $-\dfrac{1}{2} + \sqrt{3}i$
39. $1 + 3i$ **41.** -10 **43.** $-3 + 21i$ **45.** $13 - 10i$ **47.** $-8 - i$ **49.** $12 + \sqrt{2}i$ **51.** $-5\sqrt{10}i$ **53.** $15 + 12i$
55. $-10 - 10i$ **57.** $-3 - 16i$ **59.** -256 **61.** $24 - 42i$ **63.** $7 - 24i$ **65.** -20 **67.** $-6\sqrt{2}$ **69.** $1 - 31i$ **71.** $-3 - 2i; 13$
73. $6 - 3\sqrt{2}i; 54$ **75.** $4 + 8i$ **77.** $3 + 2i$ **79.** $\dfrac{3}{2} + \dfrac{3}{2}i$ **81.** $-1 + \dfrac{1}{2}i$ **83.** $-\dfrac{27}{4} + 2i$ **85.** $-\dfrac{3}{13} + \dfrac{2}{13}i$ **87.** $\left\{1 - \dfrac{\sqrt{6}}{2}i, 1 + \dfrac{\sqrt{6}}{2}i\right\}$
89. $\left\{-1 - 2\sqrt{3}i, -1 + 2\sqrt{3}i\right\}$ **91.** $\{5 - 2i, 5 + 2i\}$ **93.** $\left\{-2 - \sqrt{5}i, -2 + \sqrt{5}i\right\}$ **95.** $\left\{-\dfrac{3}{2}, 8\right\}$ **97.** $\left\{-2\sqrt{2}, 2\sqrt{2}\right\}$
99. $\left\{1 - \sqrt{2}i, 1 + \sqrt{2}i\right\}$ **101.** $\left\{\dfrac{1 - \sqrt{105}}{4}, \dfrac{1 + \sqrt{105}}{4}\right\}$ **103.** $\dfrac{1}{3} - \dfrac{\sqrt{14}}{3}i$ or $\dfrac{1}{3} + \dfrac{\sqrt{14}}{3}i$ **105.** $1 - 3i$ or $1 + 3i$ **107.** The product of two
complex conjugates is always a real number because the product of the conjugates is in the form $(a + bi)(a - bi) = (a)^2 - (abi) + (abi) - (bi)^2$. When simplified, the terms $-(abi) + (abi) = 0$, and $(bi)^2 = (b^2)(i)^2 = (b^2)(-1) = -b^2$. So, the product contains no imaginary numbers, only real numbers.
109. $\left\{5 - \sqrt{15}i, 5 + \sqrt{15}i\right\}$

Chapter 9 Review **1.** $\{-5, 5\}$ **2.** $\{-12, 12\}$ **3.** $\left\{-\dfrac{3}{2}, \dfrac{3}{2}\right\}$ **4.** $\left\{-\dfrac{2}{5}, \dfrac{2}{5}\right\}$ **5.** $\left\{-2\sqrt{3}, 2\sqrt{3}\right\}$ **6.** $\left\{-3\sqrt{2}, 3\sqrt{2}\right\}$ **7.** $\left\{-\dfrac{5}{3}, 1\right\}$
8. $\{-1, 6\}$ **9.** $\left\{-5 - \sqrt{2}, -5 + \sqrt{2}\right\}$ **10.** $\left\{2 - \sqrt{2}, 2 + \sqrt{2}\right\}$ **11.** no real solution **12.** no real solution **13.** $\left\{2 - 2\sqrt{6}, 2 + 2\sqrt{6}\right\}$
14. $\left\{-4 - 2\sqrt{7}, -4 + 2\sqrt{7}\right\}$ **15.** $c = 4\sqrt{13} \approx 14.42$ **16.** $c = 6\sqrt{5} \approx 13.42$ **17.** $a = 2\sqrt{33} \approx 11.49$ **18.** $b = 8\sqrt{2} \approx 11.31$
19. (a) $3\sqrt{2}$ ft by $3\sqrt{2}$ ft **(b)** 4.24 ft by 4.24 ft **20. (a)** $10\sqrt{2}$ ft **(b)** 14.1 ft **21.** $36; (x - 6)^2$ **22.** $25; (x + 5)^2$ **23.** $\dfrac{1}{9}; \left(y + \dfrac{1}{3}\right)^2$
24. $\dfrac{4}{25}; \left(k - \dfrac{2}{5}\right)^2$ **25.** $\dfrac{1}{16}; \left(n - \dfrac{1}{4}\right)^2$ **26.** $\dfrac{1}{36}; \left(t + \dfrac{1}{6}\right)^2$ **27.** $\{-1, 7\}$ **28.** $\{1, 11\}$ **29.** $\{-4, 1\}$ **30.** $\{-7, -2\}$
31. $\left\{2 - 2\sqrt{5}, 2 + 2\sqrt{5}\right\}$ **32.** $\left\{1 - 2\sqrt{2}, 1 + 2\sqrt{2}\right\}$ **33.** $\left\{-\dfrac{5}{2}, 2\right\}$ **34.** $\left\{-3, -\dfrac{2}{3}\right\}$ **35.** $\left\{\dfrac{3 - \sqrt{53}}{2}, \dfrac{3 + \sqrt{53}}{2}\right\}$
36. $\left\{\dfrac{-1 - \sqrt{33}}{2}, \dfrac{-1 + \sqrt{33}}{2}\right\}$ **37.** $\left\{5 - 3\sqrt{5}, 5 + 3\sqrt{5}\right\}$ **38.** $\left\{4 - 2\sqrt{6}, 4 + 2\sqrt{6}\right\}$ **39.** $-\dfrac{5}{2}$ and $-\dfrac{1}{2}$ or $\dfrac{1}{2}$ and $\dfrac{5}{2}$ **40.** -8 or 2
41. $2x^2 - x + 3 = 0; a = 2, b = -1, c = 3$ **42.** $\dfrac{1}{2}x^2 + x - \dfrac{3}{4} = 0; a = \dfrac{1}{2}, b = 1, c = -\dfrac{3}{4}$ **43.** $\left\{\dfrac{3}{2}, 5\right\}$ **44.** $\left\{-\dfrac{3}{2}, -\dfrac{1}{2}\right\}$
45. $\left\{6 - \sqrt{31}, 6 + \sqrt{31}\right\}$ **46.** $\left\{\dfrac{3 - 3\sqrt{5}}{2}, \dfrac{3 + 3\sqrt{5}}{2}\right\}$ **47.** $\left\{-\dfrac{8}{3}, 1\right\}$ **48.** $\left\{-4, \dfrac{1}{2}\right\}$ **49.** $\left\{\dfrac{-1 - \sqrt{7}}{2}, \dfrac{-1 + \sqrt{7}}{2}\right\}$
50. $\left\{-2 - \sqrt{6}, -2 + \sqrt{6}\right\}$ **51.** $\left\{\dfrac{3 - 2\sqrt{2}}{2}, \dfrac{3 + 2\sqrt{2}}{2}\right\}$ **52.** $\left\{\dfrac{4 - \sqrt{10}}{3}, \dfrac{4 + \sqrt{10}}{3}\right\}$ **53. (a)** \$8250 **(b)** 100 or 160 texts
54. (a) \$244 **(b)** 15 dogs **55.** $b^2 - 4ac = 24$; quadratic formula; $\left\{\dfrac{4 - \sqrt{6}}{5}, \dfrac{4 + \sqrt{6}}{5}\right\}$ **56.** $b^2 - 4ac = 49$; factoring; $\{-1, 6\}$
57. $b^2 - 4ac = 169$; factoring; $\left\{-\dfrac{10}{3}, 1\right\}$ **58.** $b^2 - 4ac = 17$; quadratic formula; $\left\{\dfrac{-3 - \sqrt{17}}{2}, \dfrac{-3 + \sqrt{17}}{2}\right\}$ **59.** $b^2 - 4ac = -23$; no real solution
60. $b^2 - 4ac = -11$; no real solution **61.** $-18, -16$ and $16, 18$ **62.** $\dfrac{3}{2}; \dfrac{2}{3}$ **63.** width = 8 m, length = 14 m **64.** width = 5 yd, length = 12 yd
65. 4 ft, 8 ft **66.** leg = $\dfrac{-6 + 2\sqrt{21}}{3}$ cm, hypotenuse = $\dfrac{-3 + 4\sqrt{21}}{3}$ cm **67.** base = 12 m, height = 7 m **68.** base = 3 in., height = $\dfrac{3}{2}$ in.
69. length = 10 in., width = 4 in. **70.** length = 15 ft, width = 8 ft **71.** $\dfrac{5 + \sqrt{26}}{2} \approx 5.0$ s **72.** $\dfrac{15 - \sqrt{145}}{4} \approx 0.7$ s and $\dfrac{15 + \sqrt{145}}{4} \approx 6.8$ s
73. 5 or 25 units. **74.** $(25 - 5\sqrt{11}) \approx 8$ units or $(25 + 5\sqrt{11}) \approx 42$ units **75.** $-10i$ **76.** $-7i$ **77.** $5 + 2\sqrt{5}i$ **78.** $4 - 2\sqrt{15}i$

79. $-1 - \sqrt{3}i$ **80.** $-\dfrac{1}{2} + \dfrac{\sqrt{3}}{2}i$ **81.** $1 + 8i$ **82.** $11i$ **83.** $-16 + 10i$ **84.** $-26 + 13i$ **85.** $-10 + 7i$ **86.** $14 - 4i$

87. $-10 + 12i$ **88.** $-3 - 3i$ **89.** $2 - 23i$ **90.** $27 - 34i$ **91.** $-5 - 12i$ **92.** $-16 + 30i$ **93.** $-36\sqrt{2}$ **94.** $-48\sqrt{5}$

95. $5 - 2i$; 29 **96.** $3 + 3i$; 18 **97.** $-\dfrac{1}{3} - i$ **98.** $2 + 3i$ **99.** $\dfrac{3}{5} + \dfrac{4}{5}i$ **100.** $\dfrac{6}{5} - \dfrac{3}{5}i$ **101.** $-\dfrac{5}{2} + \dfrac{5}{2}i$ **102.** $\dfrac{5}{17} + \dfrac{3}{17}i$

103. $\left\{-\dfrac{1}{2} - \dfrac{3}{2}i, -\dfrac{1}{2} + \dfrac{3}{2}i\right\}$ **104.** $\left\{\dfrac{3}{2} - \dfrac{3}{2}i, \dfrac{3}{2} + \dfrac{3}{2}i\right\}$ **105.** $\left\{2 - 2\sqrt{2}i, 2 + 2\sqrt{2}i\right\}$ **106.** $\left\{-3 - 4\sqrt{2}i, -3 + 4\sqrt{2}i\right\}$

Chapter 9 Test **1.** $\{-3, 3\}$ **2.** $\{-10, 4\}$ **3.** $\left\{-3 - 2\sqrt{2}, -3 + 2\sqrt{2}\right\}$ **4.** $\{-2, 3\}$ **5.** $\left\{\dfrac{2 - \sqrt{10}}{2}, \dfrac{2 + \sqrt{10}}{2}\right\}$

6. $\left\{\dfrac{3 - \sqrt{13}}{4}, \dfrac{3 + \sqrt{13}}{4}\right\}$ **7. (a)** 61 **(b)** quadratic formula **(c)** Answers may vary.   **8.** $-\dfrac{1}{2} - \dfrac{3}{2}i$ **9.** $-14 - 4i$ **10.** $1 + 3i$

11. -36 **12.** $-5 - 14i$ **13.** $-20 - 48i$ **14.** $4 - \dfrac{4}{3}i$ **15.** $\dfrac{15}{17} - \dfrac{9}{17}i$ **16.** $\{2 - i, 2 + i\}$ **17.** $\left\{-2 - \dfrac{\sqrt{14}}{2}i, -2 + \dfrac{\sqrt{14}}{2}i\right\}$

18. (a) width $= (-1 + \sqrt{127})$ ft, length $= (1 + \sqrt{127})$ ft **(b)** width ≈ 10.3 ft, length ≈ 12.3 ft   **19. (a)** $\dfrac{25 + \sqrt{785}}{8}$ s **(b)** 6.6 s

20. (a) width $= (25 + 25\sqrt{161})$ yards, length $= (-50 + 50\sqrt{161})$ yards   **(b)** width ≈ 342.21 yards, length ≈ 584.43 yards

Cumulative Review Chapters 1–9 **1.** undefined   **2.** 0 **3.** $-\dfrac{1}{2}$ **4.** $\dfrac{27x^{12}}{y^2}$ **5.** $\dfrac{9}{x^2 y^6}$ **6. (a)** -1 **(b)** -2

(c) 2 **(d)** trinomial   **7. (a)** $y = \dfrac{3}{2}x - 6$ **(b)** $\dfrac{3}{2}$ **(c)** -6 **8.** $\{-14\}$ **9.** $\{-3\}$ **10.** $\left\{-2, \dfrac{3}{2}\right\}$ **11.** $\{-1, 3\}$

12.   **13.** $y = -\dfrac{3}{2}x + 1$ **15.**   **16.** 96 **17.** $(2h - 5)(3h + 2)$ **18.** $3(x + 2)(x^2 - 2x + 4)$

14. $(-3, 2)$ **19.** $(y + 2)(x - 3)$ **20.** $3x^2 + x - 1 + \dfrac{4}{2x + 1}$ **21.** $\dfrac{3}{2}x + 3 - \dfrac{2}{x}$

22. -4 **23.** $\dfrac{1}{27}$ **24.** 3.4×10^{10} **25.** 0.000304 **26.** $11 - 6\sqrt{2}$

27. $\dfrac{1}{2} - \dfrac{2}{3}i$ **28.** There were 390 general seating tickets and 190 reserved seat tickets sold.   **29.** 210 bags   **30. (a)** 10 feet **(b)** $\dfrac{9 + \sqrt{129}}{4}$ s

Chapter 10 Graphs of Quadratic Equations in Two Variables and an Introduction to Functions

Section 10.1 Quadratic Equations in Two Variables   **1.** quadratic equation

2.

x	y
−3	6
−2	1
−1	−2
0	−3
1	−2
2	1
3	6

3.

x	y
−5	0
−4	−5
−3	−8
−2	−9
−1	−8
0	−5
1	0

4.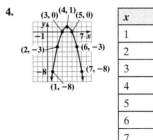

x	y
1	−8
2	−3
3	0
4	1
5	0
6	−3
7	−8

5. True   **6.** True   **7.** one   **8.** y-intercept: 6, x-intercepts: -3 and -2 **9.** y-intercept: -5, no x-intercepts

10. y-intercept: 1; x-intercept: $-\dfrac{1}{2}$ **11.** up; down   **12.** vertex; $x = -\dfrac{b}{2a}$ **13.** True   **14. (a)** Opens up **(b)** $(1, -1)$ **(c)** $x = 1$

15. (a) Opens down **(b)** $(-3, 11)$ **(c)** $x = -3$

16. 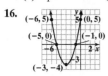   **17.**   **18.** 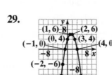   **19.** 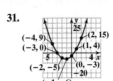   **20.** maximum value

21. True

22. Minimum; -7

23. Maximum; 33

24. (a) After 4 seconds **(b)** 271 feet

25. 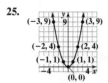   **27.** 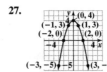   **29.**   **31.**   **33.** x-intercepts: $2, 4$; y-intercept: -8

35. x-intercepts: $-\dfrac{1}{3}, \dfrac{1}{2}$; y-intercept: -1

37. x-intercepts: $-3, 0$; y-intercept: 0

39. x-intercepts: none; y-intercept: -5

41. x-intercepts: $\dfrac{1 - \sqrt{17}}{4} \approx -0.78$, $\dfrac{1 + \sqrt{17}}{4} \approx 1.28$; y-intercept: 2 **43.** x-intercepts: $-2 - \sqrt{2} \approx -3.41$, $-2 + \sqrt{2} \approx -0.59$; y-intercept: 2

45. (a) up **(b)** $(0, 6)$ **(c)** $x = 0$ **47. (a)** down **(b)** $(4, 1)$ **(c)** $x = 4$ **49. (a)** down **(b)** $\left(\dfrac{3}{4}, \dfrac{49}{8}\right)$ **(c)** $x = \dfrac{3}{4}$

51. (a) up **(b)** $\left(\dfrac{4}{3}, -\dfrac{4}{3}\right)$ **(c)** $x = \dfrac{4}{3}$

53. opens up; vertex: $(-1, -4)$;
x-intercepts: $-3, 1$
y-intercept: -3
axis of symmetry: $x = -1$

55. opens down; vertex: $(-1, 1)$;
x-intercepts: $-2, 0$; y-intercept: 0
axis of symmetry: $x = -1$

57. opens down; vertex: $(-4, 7)$;
x-intercepts: $-4 - \sqrt{7}$,
$-4 + \sqrt{7}$
y-intercept: -9
axis of symmetry: $x = -4$

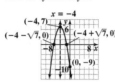

59. opens up; vertex: $(0, -9)$;
x-intercepts: $-3, 3$;
y-intercept: -9
axis of symmetry: $x = 0$

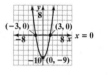

61. opens up;
vertex: $\left(\dfrac{7}{2}, -\dfrac{9}{4}\right)$;
x-intercepts: $2, 5$
y-intercept: 10
axis of symmetry: $x = \dfrac{7}{2}$

63. opens up;
vertex: $(3, 0)$;
x-intercept: 3
y-intercept: 9
axis of symmetry: $x = 3$

65. opens down; vertex: $(-1, 7)$;
x-intercepts: $\dfrac{-2 - \sqrt{14}}{2}, \dfrac{-2 + \sqrt{14}}{2}$
y-intercept: 5
axis of symmetry: $x = -1$

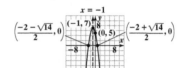

67. opens up;
vertex: $(1, -6)$;
x-intercepts: $1 - \sqrt{6}, 1 + \sqrt{6}$
y-intercept: -5
axis of symmetry: $x = 1$

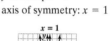

69. minimum; -4 at $x = 3$ **71.** minimum; 7 at $x = -2$ **73.** maximum; $\dfrac{15}{2}$ at $x = \dfrac{3}{2}$ **75.** maximum; $-\dfrac{19}{4}$ at $x = -\dfrac{3}{2}$

77. (a) 50 mph **(b)** 25 miles per gallon   **79. (a)** 25 yd **(b)** 625 yd^2 **81. (a)** 50 ft **(b)** 5000 ft^2

83. opens up; vertex $(-3, 1)$
axis of symmetry $x = -3$
y-intercept: 10
x-intercepts: none

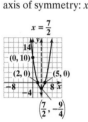

85. opens down;
vertex $\left(\dfrac{3}{2}, -\dfrac{5}{2}\right)$
axis of symmetry $x = \dfrac{3}{2}$
y-intercept: -7
x-intercepts: none

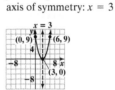

87. To find the number of x-intercepts the graph of a quadratic equation has, find the discriminant, $b^2 - 4ac$. If $b^2 - 4ac$ is positive, the parabola has two x-intercepts, which are found by letting $y = 0$ in the equation and solving for x. If $b^2 - 4ac = 0$, the vertex is the x-intercept. If $b^2 - 4ac$ is negative, there are no x-intercepts.

89. The axis of symmetry is found using the equation $x = -\dfrac{b}{2a}$. The axis of symmetry serves as a guide in graphing a parabola because every point that lies on the graph of a parabola contains a mirror-image point on the graph that lies on the opposite side of the axis of symmetry.

Section 10.2 Relations **1.** relation   **2.** corresponds; depends   **3.** {(Max, Nov. 8), (Alesia, Jan. 20), (Trent, Mar. 3), (Yolanda, Nov. 8), (Wanda, July 6), (Elvis, Jan. 8)}

4.

5. domain; range   **6.** Domain: {Max, Alesia, Trent, Yolanda, Wanda, Elvis}; Range: {Jan. 20, Mar. 3, July 6, Nov. 8, Jan. 8}
7. Domain: {1, 2, 3, 8}; Range: {5, 4, 7}   **8.** Domain: {−3, −2, −1, 2, 3}; Range: {−2, −1, 1, 2, 3, 4}   **9.** True
10. False   **11.** Domain: {x| −2 ≤ x ≤ 4}; Range: {y| −2 ≤ y ≤ 2}
12. Domain: {x|x is any real number}; Range: {y|y is any real number}

13.

Domain: {x|x is any real number}
Range: {y|y is any real number}

14.

Domain: {x|x is any real number}
Range: {y|y ≥ −3}

15. {(Physician, 120), (Teacher, 37), (Mathematician, 64), (Computer Engineer, 64), (Lawyer, 82)}; Domain: {(Physician, Teacher, Mathematician, Computer Engineer, Lawyer}; Range: {120, 37, 64, 82}
17. {(Spain, 18), (Canada, 18), (Kenya, 14), (Ireland, 3), (Serbia, 3)}; Domain: {Spain, Canada, Kenya, Ireland, Serbia}; Range: {3, 18, 14}

19.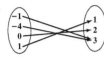
Domain: $\{-1, -4, 0, 1\}$
Range: $\{3, 2, 1\}$

21.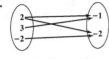
Domain: $\{2, 3, -2\}$
Range: $\{-1, -2\}$

23.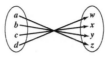
Domain: $\{a, b, c, d\}$
Range: $\{w, x, y, z\}$

25. Domain: $\{-3, 0, 2, 3\}$
Range: $\{-2, 0, 2, 4\}$
27. Domain: $\{x | x$ is any real number$\}$
Range: $\{y | y$ is any real number$\}$
29. Domain: $\{3\}$
Range: $\{y | y$ is any real number$\}$

31. Domain: $\{x | x$ is any real number$\}$
Range: $\{y | y \le 0\}$
33. Domain: $\{x | x$ is any real number$\}$
Range: $\{y | y \ge -2\}$
35. Domain: $\{x | x \ge -1\}$
Range: $\{y | y$ is any real number$\}$
37. Domain: $\{x | -1 \le x \le 5\}$
Range: $\{y | -1 \le y \le 5\}$
39. Domain: $\{x | -4 \le x \le 4\}$
Range: $\{y | -3 \le y \le 3\}$

41.
Domain: $\{x | x$ is any real number$\}$
Range: $\{y | y$ is any real number$\}$

43.
Domain: $\{x | x$ is any real number$\}$
Range: $\{y | y$ is any real number$\}$

45.
Domain: $\{x | x$ is any real number$\}$
Range: $\{y | y \le 2\}$

47.
Domain: $\{x | x$ is any real number$\}$
Range: $\left\{ y \mid y \ge -\dfrac{9}{4} \right\}$

49.
Domain: $\{x | x$ is any real number$\}$
Range: $\{y | y$ is any real number$\}$

51.
Domain: $\{x | x$ is any real number$\}$
Range: $\{y | y \ge -5\}$

53.
Domain: $\{x | x$ is any real number$\}$
Range: $\{y | y \le 6\}$

55.
Domain: $\{x | x$ is any real number$\}$
Range: $\{y | y$ is any real number$\}$

57. **(a)** Domain: $\{t | 0 \le t \le 10\}$; Range: $\{p | 0 \le p \le 900\}$ **(b)** day 5 **(c)** 5 days
59. **(a)** Domain: $\{w | 0 < w \le 5\}$; Range: $\{4.80, 5.20, 5.80, 6.45\}$ **(b)** $4.80 **(c)** $5.20
61. Answers may vary. **63. (a)** No **(b)** Answers may vary. **(c)** No; answers may vary.
65. Answers may vary. All graphs are vertical lines. **67.** A relation is a correspondence between the elements of two sets. The domain of the relation is the set of all inputs into the relation and the range is the set of all outputs of the relation.

Putting the Concepts Together (Sections 10.1 and 10.2)

1. (a) Opens up **(b)** $(1, -4)$ **(c)** $x = 1$ **(d)** $(0, -3), (-1, 0), (3, 0)$

2.
Domain: $\{x | x$ is any real number$\}$
Range: $\{y | y \ge -9\}$

3.
Domain: $\{x | x$ is any real number$\}$
Range: $\{y | y \ge -5\}$

4.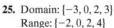
Domain $\{x | x$ is any real number$\}$
Range: $\{y | y \le 9\}$

5. (a) Minimum **(b)** -21
6. Domain: $\{a, b, c\}$; Range: $\{1, 2\}$
7. Domain: $\{1, 3\}$; Range: $\{-1, -3\}$
8. Domain: $\{x | x \ge -4\}$
Range: $\{y | y$ is any real number$\}$
9. Domain: $\{x | 1 \le x \le 7\}$
Range: $\{y | -1 \le y \le 5\}$

Section 10.3 An Introduction to Functions

1. Function **2.** False **3.** Function; Domain: $\{250, 300, 400, 500\}$; Range: $\{\$41.20, \$43.04, \$55.39, \$64.03\}$ **4.** Function; Domain: $\{12, 15, 8, 7, 4\}$; Range: $\{A, B, C, D\}$ **5.** not a function **6.** Function; Domain: $\{-3, -2, -1, 0, 1\}$; Range: $\{3, 2, 1, 0\}$
7. not a function **8.** Function; Domain: $\{3, 4, 5, 6\}$; Range: $\{8, 10, 11\}$ **9.** function **10.** not a function **11.** function **12.** not a function
13. True **14.** function **15.** not a function **16.** True **17.** 17 **18.** -7 **19.** 15 **20.** 22 **21.** not a function
23. function; Domain: $\{$Apples, Pears, Oranges, Grapes$\}$; Range: $\{\$0.99, \$1.29, \$1.99\}$ **25.** function; Domain: $\{-1, 0, 1, 2\}$; Range: $\{-1, 0, 1, 2\}$
27. not a function **29.** function; Domain: $\{a, b, c, d\}$; Range: $\{a, b\}$ **31.** function **33.** not a function **35.** function **37.** function
39. not a function **41.** not a function **43.** not a function **45.** not a function **47.** function **49.** function **51.** not a function
53. function **55.** not a function **57.** function **59. (a)** -3 **(b)** -6 **(c)** -1 **61. (a)** 4 **(b)** -2 **(c)** 8 **63. (a)** 3 **(b)** 3 **(c)** 3
65. (a) -3 **(b)** $-\dfrac{3}{2}$ **(c)** -4 **67. (a)** 3 **(b)** -12 **(c)** 13 **69. (a)** 0 **(b)** 0 **(c)** 10 **71. (a)** 1 **(b)** -32 **(c)** 3 **73.** 18 **75.** -8
77. 0 **79.** 2 **81.** $-\dfrac{1}{2}$ **83.** 7 **85.** $2\sqrt{3}$ **87.** $C = 5$ **89.** $C = 3$ **91.** $A = 5$ **93.** $G(h) = 12h$; $240
95. (a) $h(30) = 8.132$; in 1930, there were 8.132 homicides per 100,000 people. **(b)** $h(50) = 6.632$; in 1950, there were 6.632 homicides per 100,000 people. **97.** $A(r) = \pi r^2$; $A(3) = 9\pi$ in.^{2} **99.** $x = 2$ **101.** $x = 2$ **103.** $x = -4$ **105. (a)** -5 **(b)** $1 - 2h$ **(c)** $-5 - 2h$
(d) $-4 - 2h$ **(e)** $-2h$ **107.** The four ways to represent a function are: maps, ordered pairs, equations, and graphs. Answers may vary.

Chapter 10 Review

1.

2.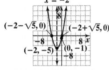

3.

4.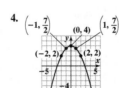

5.

6.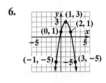

7. x-intercepts: $-3, 2$; **8.** x-intercepts: $-2, -4$; **9.** x-intercept: $\dfrac{3}{2}$; **10.** x-intercept: $-\dfrac{1}{3}$; **11.** x-intercepts: none; **12.** x-intercepts: none;
y-intercept: -6 y-intercept: 8 y-intercept: -9 y-intercept: -1 y-intercept: -5 y-intercept: -1

13. x-intercepts: $2 - \sqrt{2}, 2 + \sqrt{2}$; **14.** x-intercepts: $-2 - 3\sqrt{2}, -2 + 3\sqrt{2}$; **15. (a)** up **(b)** $(0, 5)$ **(c)** $x = 0$
y-intercept: 2 y-intercept: 14 **16. (a)** down **(b)** $(0, -4)$ **(c)** $x = 0$

17. (a) down **(b)** $(1, 1)$ **(c)** $x = 1$ **18. (a)** up **(b)** $(2, -8)$ **(c)** $x = 2$ **19. (a)** up **(b)** $\left(-3, -\dfrac{27}{2}\right)$ **(c)** $x = -3$

20. (a) down **(b)** $(-2, 6)$ **(c)** $x = -2$ **21. (a)** down **(b)** $\left(\dfrac{3}{2}, -\dfrac{7}{4}\right)$ **(c)** $x = \dfrac{3}{2}$ **22. (a)** up **(b)** $\left(-\dfrac{5}{2}, -\dfrac{5}{4}\right)$ **(c)** $x = -\dfrac{5}{2}$

23. opens up; vertex $(-1, -4)$; axis of symmetry $x = -1$; x-intercepts: $-3, 1$; y-intercept: -3

24. opens down; vertex $(3, 1)$; axis of symmetry $x = 3$; x-intercepts: $2, 4$; y-intercept: -8

25. opens down; vertex $(0, 4)$; axis of symmetry $x = 0$; x-intercepts: $-2, 2$; y-intercept: 4

26. opens up; vertex $(0, -9)$; axis of symmetry $x = 0$; x-intercepts: $-3, 3$; y-intercept: -9

27. opens down; vertex $\left(\dfrac{3}{2}, \dfrac{25}{4}\right)$; axis of symmetry $x = \dfrac{3}{2}$; x-intercepts: $-1, 4$; y-intercept: 4

28. opens up; vertex $\left(\dfrac{5}{2}, -\dfrac{9}{4}\right)$; axis of symmetry $x = \dfrac{5}{2}$; x-intercepts: $1, 4$; y-intercept: 4

29. maximum; 15 at $x = -2$ **30.** minimum; -16 at $x = -2$
31. minimum; -10 at $x = 2$ **32.** maximum; 10 at $x = -5$
33. (a) 92.9 ft **(b)** 20.1 ft **(c)** 200 ft **34. (a)** 100 m **(b)** 10,000 m^2
35. {(Alabama, 13.5), (California, 11.0), (Florida, 17.0), (Nebraska, 13.3), (New York, 13.2), (Massachusetts, 13.3), (South Dakota, 14.3)}
36. {(History, 400), (Math, 400), (Music, 200), (Psychology, 225)}
37. Domain: {Alabama, California, Florida, Nebraska, New York, Ohio, South Dakota} Range: {37, 38, 41, 45, 54, 55}
38. Domain: {History, Math, Music, Psychology} **39.** Domain: $\{-1, 0\}$ Range: {200, 225, 400} Range: $\{3, 5, -2, -4\}$
40. Domain: $\{a, b, c, d\}$ **41.** Domain: $\{a_1, a_2, a_3, a_4\}$ **42.** Domain: $\{1, 3, 5, 7\}$ Range: $\{x^2, x^3, x^4, x^5\}$ Range: $\{1, 4, 9, 16\}$ Range: $\{-3, 2, -2\}$

43. Domain: $\{-3, 0, 3\}$ **44.** Domain: $\{0, 1, 4\}$ **45.** Domain: $\{x | x$ is any real number$\}$ **46.** Domain: $\{x | x$ is any real number$\}$
Range: $\{-3, 0, 3\}$ Range: $\{-4, 0, 4\}$ Range: $\{y | y$ is any real number$\}$ Range: $\{4\}$
47. Domain: $\{5\}$ **48.** Domain: $\{x | x$ is any real number$\}$ **49.** Domain: $\{x | 0 \le x \le 6\}$ **50.** Domain: $\{x | -4 \le x \le 0\}$
Range: $\{y | y$ is any real number$\}$ Range: $\{y | y$ is any real number$\}$ Range: $\{y | 1 \le y \le 5\}$ Range: $\{y | -4 \le x \le 3\}$

51.

Domain: $\{x | x$ is any real number$\}$
Range: $\{y | y$ is any real number$\}$

52.

Domain: $\{x | x$ is any real number$\}$
Range: $\{y | y$ is any real number$\}$

53.

Domain: $\{x | x$ is any real number$\}$
Range: $\{y | y \le 4\}$

54.

Domain: $\{x | x$ is any real number$\}$
Range: $\{y | y \ge -1\}$

55. not a function **56.** function; Domain: {Alaska, Massachusetts, Minnesota, West Virginia}; Range: {16.9, 27.3, 30.7, 36.9}
57. function; Domain: $\{-4, -3, -2, -1\}$; Range: $\{0, 1\}$ **58.** not a function **59.** not a function **60.** function; Domain: $\{5, 3, 1, -1\}$; Range: $\{x, z\}$
61. function **62.** not a function **63.** not a function **64.** function **65.** not a function **66.** function **67.** function
68. not a function **69.** not a function **70.** function **71.** not a function **72.** function **73.** function **74.** not a function
75. function **76.** function **77.** not a function **78.** not a function **79.** 1 **80.** 18 **81.** -3 **82.** -10 **83.** 14 **84.** 7
85. $2\sqrt{6}$ **86.** 5 **87. (a)** $C(m) = 0.10m + 175$ **(b)** \$188

Chapter 10 Test **1. (a)** up **(b)** $(-2, -9)$ **(c)** $x = -2$ **(d)** x-intercepts: $-5, 1$; y-intercept: -5

2.

3.

4.

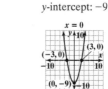

5. (a) maximum **(b)** 7 at $x = -1$ **6.** Domain: {1} Range: $\{-1, -2, -3\}$

7. Domain: $\{-2, -3\}$ **8.** Domain: $\{x | x$ is any real number$\}$
Range: $\{a, b, c\}$ Range: $\{y | y \ge -2\}$

9. Domain: $\{x | -5 \le x \le 3\}$; Range: $\{y | 0 \le y \le 4\}$
10. not a function **11.** function **12.** function **13.** function

14. not a function **15.** function **16.** -5 **17.** $-\dfrac{1}{5}$ **18.** 8 **19. (a)** 1 sec **(b)** 16 ft **20. (a)** \$3 **(b)** 9.8 years **(c)** \$35 **(d)** \$27

Appendix B Geometry Review

Section B.1 Lines and Angles
1. congruent **2.** angle **3.** right **4.** acute **5.** obtuse **6.** straight **7.** right **8.** False **9.** 75°; 165°
10. 30°; 120° **11.** Parallel **12.** False **13.** True **14.** $m\angle 1 = 140°$; $m\angle 2 = 40°$; $m\angle 3 = 140°$; $m\angle 4 = 40°$;
$m\angle 5 = 140°$; $m\angle 6 = 40°$; $m\angle 7 = 140°$ **15.** acute **17.** right **19.** straight **21.** obtuse **23.** 58° **25.** 17° **27.** 113° **29.** 172°
31. $m\angle 1 = 130°$; $m\angle 2 = 50°$; $m\angle 3 = 130°$; $m\angle 4 = 50°$; $m\angle 5 = 130°$; $m\angle 6 = 50°$; $m\angle 7 = 130°$

Section B.2 Polygons
1. isosceles **2.** right **3.** 180 **4.** 70° **5.** 42° **6.** Congruent **7.** Similar **8.** 14 units **9.** radius **10.** True
11. $\frac{15}{2}$ inches or 7.5 inches **12.** 12 feet **13.** 7.2 yards **14.** 18 cm **15.** 55° **17.** 48° **19.** 4 units **21.** 67.5 units **23.** 10 inches
25. 5 cm **27.** 7 cm **29.** $\frac{11}{2}$ yards or 5.5 yards

Section B.3 Perimeter and Areas of Polygons and Circles
1. perimeter **2.** area **3.** Perimeter: 22 feet; Area: 24 square feet **4.** Perimeter: 26 m; Area: 30 square m **5.** False
6. Perimeter: 16 cm; Area 16 square cm **7.** Perimeter: 6 yards; Area: 2.25 square yards **8.** Perimeter: 130 yards; Area: 650 square yards
9. $\frac{1}{2}h(b + B)$; h; b; B **10.** Perimeter: 36 m; Area: 70 square m **11.** Perimeter: 33 yards; Area: 51 square yards **12.** True
13. Perimeter: 19 mm; Area: 12 square mm **14.** Perimeter: 30 feet; Area: 30 square feet **15.** Circumference **16.** False
17. Circumference: 8π feet $\approx$ 25.13 feet; Area: 16π square feet $\approx$ 50.27 square feet
18. Circumference: 24π cm $\approx$ 75.40 cm; Area: 144π square cm $\approx$ 452.39 square cm **19.** Perimeter: 28 feet; Area: 40 square feet
21. Perimeter: 40 m; Area: 75 square m **23.** Perimeter: 24 km; Area: 36 square km **25.** Perimeter: 72 feet; Area: 218 square feet
27. Perimeter: 54 m; Area: 62 square m **29.** Perimeter: 30 feet; Area: 45 square feet **31.** Perimeter: 28 mm; Area: 36 square mm
33. Perimeter: 40 in; Area: 84 square in. **35.** Perimeter: 45 cm; Area: 94.5 square cm **37.** Perimeter: 32 m; Area: 42 square m
39. Perimeter: 32 feet; Area: 24 square feet **41.** Circumference: 32π in. $\approx$ 100.53 in; Area: 256π square in. $\approx$ 804.25 square in.
43. Circumference: 20π cm $\approx$ 62.83 cm; Area: 100π square cm $\approx$ 314.16 square cm **45.** π square units **47.** about 26.18 feet

Section B.4 Volume and Surface Area
1. polyhedron **2.** surface area **3.** False **4.** True **5.** Volume: 125 cubic m; Surface area: 150 square m
6. Volume: $\frac{256}{3}\pi$ cubic in. $\approx$ 268.08 cubic in.; Surface area: 64π square in. $\approx$ 201.06 square in. **7.** Volume: 600 cubic feet;
Surface Area: 460 square feet **9.** Volume: 288π cubic centimeters $\approx$ 904.78 cubic centimeters;
Surface Area: 144π square centimeters $\approx$ 452.39 square centimeters **11.** Volume: 32π cubic inches $\approx$ 100.53 cubic inches;
Surface Area: 40π square inches $\approx$ 125.66 square inches **13.** Volume: $\frac{800}{3}\pi$ cubic mm $\approx$ 837.76 cubic mm
15. Volume: $\frac{640}{3}$ cubic feet; Surface Area: 256 square feet **17.** 1728 cubic inches **19.** 75.40 cubic inches; 100.53 square inches
21. approximately 268.08 cubic cm

Applications Index

Subject Index

Photo Credits

Properties of the Real Number System (Chapter 1)

	Addition	Multiplication
Identity Properties	$a + 0 = 0 + a = a$	$1 \cdot a = a \cdot 1 = a$
Inverse Properties	$a + (-a) = (-a) + a = 0$	$a \cdot \dfrac{1}{a} = \dfrac{1}{a} \cdot a = 1 \, (a \neq 0)$
Commutative Property	$a + b = b + a$	$a \cdot b = b \cdot a$
Associative Property	$(a + b) + c = a + (b + c)$	$(ab)c = a(bc)$
Distributive Property	$a(b + c) = ab + ac$	
Division Properties	$\dfrac{0}{a} = 0, a \neq 0; \dfrac{a}{a} = 1, a \neq 0; \dfrac{a}{0}$ is undefined, $a \neq 0$	

Order of Operations (Chapter 1)

How to Evaluate Expressions

1. Perform all operations with grouping symbols first. If multiple parentheses, begin with the innermost parentheses and work outward.
2. Then evaluate the exponents.
3. Next multiplication and division, working from left to right.
4. Perform addition and subtraction, working from left to right.

Geometry Formulas (Chapter 2)

Figure	Formulas	Figure	Formulas
Square	**Area:** $A = s^2$ **Perimeter:** $P = 4s$	Cube	**Volume:** $V = s^3$ **Surface Area:** $S = 6s^2$
Rectangle	**Area:** $A = lw$ **Perimeter:** $P = 2l + 2w$	Rectangular Solid	**Volume:** $V = lwh$ **Surface Area:** $S = 2lw + 2lh + 2wh$
Circle	**Area:** $A = \pi r^2$ **Circumference:** $C = 2\pi r = \pi d$	Sphere	**Volume:** $V = \dfrac{4}{3}\pi r^3$ **Surface Area:** $S = 4\pi r^2$
Triangle	**Area:** $A = \dfrac{1}{2}bh$ **Perimeter:** $P = a + b + c$	Right Circular Cylinder	**Volume:** $V = \pi r^2 h$ **Surface Area:** $S = 2\pi r^2 + 2\pi rh$
Trapezoid	**Area:** $A = \dfrac{1}{2}h(B + b)$ **Perimeter:** $P = a + b + c + B$	Cone	**Volume:** $V = \dfrac{1}{3}\pi r^2 h$
Parallelogram	**Area:** $A = ah$ **Perimeter:** $P = 2a + 2b$		

Steps for Factoring (Chapter 6)

Step 1: Factor out the Greatest Common Factor (GCF), if any exists.

Step 2: Count the number of terms.

Step 3: (a) 2 terms

- Is it the difference of two squares? If so,
$A^2 - B^2 = (A - B)(A + B)$
- Is it the sum of two squares? If so, stop! The expression is prime.
- Is it the difference of two cubes? If so,
$A^3 - B^3 = (A - B)(A^2 + AB + B^2)$
- Is it the sum of two cubes? If so,
$A^3 + B^3 = (A + B)(A^2 - AB + B^2)$

(b) 3 terms

- Is it a perfect square trinomial? If so,
$A^2 + 2AB + B^2 = (A + B)^2$ or
$A^2 - 2AB + B^2 = (A - B)^2$
- Is the coefficient of the square term 1? If so, $x^2 + bx + c = (x + m)(x + n)$ where $mn = c$ and $m + n = b$
- Is the coefficient of the square term different from 1? If so,
  a. Use factoring by grouping
  b. Use trial and error

(c) 4 terms

- Use factoring by grouping

Step 4: Check your work by multiplying out the factored form.

Formulas for Lines and Slope (Chapter 3)

Standard form of a line	$Ax + By = C$
Equation of a vertical line	$x = a$ where a is the x-intercept
Equation of a horizontal line	$y = b$ where b is the y-intercept
Slope of a line	$m = \dfrac{y_2 - y_1}{x_2 - x_1}, x_1 \neq x_2$ Slope undefined if $x_1 = x_2$
Point-slope form of a line	$y - y_1 = m(x - x_1)$
Slope-intercept form of a line	$y = mx + b$

The Rules of Exponents (Chapter 5, Chapter 8)

If a and b are real numbers and if r and s are rational numbers, then assuming the expression is defined,

Zero Exponent Rule:	$a^0 = 1$	if $a \neq 0$
Negative Exponent Rule:	$a^{-r} = \dfrac{1}{a^r}$	if $a \neq 0$
Product Rule:	$a^r \cdot a^s = a^{r+s}$	
Quotient Rule:	$\dfrac{a^r}{a^s} = a^{r-s} = \dfrac{1}{a^{s-r}}$	if $a \neq 0$
Power Rule:	$(a^r)^s = a^{r \cdot s}$	
Product to Power Rule:	$(a \cdot b)^r = a^r \cdot b^r$	
Quotient to Power Rule:	$\left(\dfrac{a}{b}\right)^r = \dfrac{a^r}{b^r}$	if $b \neq 0$
Quotient to a Negative Power Rule:	$\left(\dfrac{a}{b}\right)^{-r} = \left(\dfrac{b}{a}\right)^r$	if $a \neq 0, b \neq 0$

Working with Rational Expressions (Chapter 7)

Multiplying Rational Expressions	$\dfrac{a}{b} \cdot \dfrac{c}{d} = \dfrac{ac}{bd} \quad b \neq 0, d \neq 0$
Adding Rational Expressions	$\dfrac{a}{c} + \dfrac{b}{c} = \dfrac{a + b}{c} \quad c \neq 0$
Subtracting Rational Expressions	$\dfrac{a}{c} - \dfrac{b}{c} = \dfrac{a - b}{c} \quad c \neq 0$
Dividing Rational Expressions	$\dfrac{a}{b} \div \dfrac{c}{d} = \dfrac{\frac{a}{b}}{\frac{c}{d}} = \dfrac{a}{b} \cdot \dfrac{d}{c} = \dfrac{ad}{bc} \quad b \neq 0, c \neq 0, d \neq 0$

Working with Square Roots (Chapter 8)

- If a is a real number, then $\sqrt{a^2} = |a|$

- **Product Property of Radicals**
  If $\sqrt{a}$ and $\sqrt{b}$ are real numbers, then $\sqrt{a} \cdot \sqrt{b} = \sqrt{ab}$

- **Quotient Property of Radicals**
  If $\sqrt{a}$ and $\sqrt{b}$ are real numbers, $b \neq 0$, then $\dfrac{\sqrt{a}}{\sqrt{b}} = \sqrt{\dfrac{a}{b}}$

- If a is a real number and $n \geq 2$ is an integer, then $a^{\frac{1}{n}} = \sqrt[n]{a}$ provided that $\sqrt[n]{a}$ exists.

- If a is a real number, $\dfrac{m}{n}$ is a rational number in lowest terms with $n \geq 2$, then
  $a^{\frac{m}{n}} = \sqrt[n]{a^m} = \left(\sqrt[n]{a}\right)^m$ provided that $\sqrt[n]{a}$ exists.

- If $\dfrac{m}{n}$ is a rational number and if a is a nonzero real number, then $a^{-\frac{m}{n}} = \dfrac{1}{a^{\frac{m}{n}}}$ or $\dfrac{1}{a^{-\frac{m}{n}}} = a^{\frac{m}{n}}$

Quadratic Equations (Chapter 9)

- **Square Root Property**
  If $x^2 = p$, then $x = \sqrt{p}$ or $x = -\sqrt{p}$

- **Pythagorean Theorem**
  In a right triangle, the square of the length of the hypotenuse is equal to the sum of the squares of the lengths of the legs. That is, $\text{leg}^2 + \text{leg}^2 = \text{hypotenuse}^2$.

- **The Quadratic Formula**
  The solutions to the equation $ax^2 + bx + c = 0$, $a \neq 0$, are given by $x = \dfrac{-b \pm \sqrt{b^2 - 4ac}}{2a}$

- **Discriminant**
  For the quadratic equation $ax^2 + bx + c = 0$, $a \neq 0$:
  - If $b^2 - 4ac > 0$, the equation has two unequal real solutions.
    - If $b^2 - 4ac$ is a perfect square, the equation has two rational solutions.
    - If $b^2 - 4ac$ is not a perfect square, the equation has two irrational solutions.
  - If $b^2 - 4ac = 0$, the equation has a repeated real solution.
  - If $b^2 - 4ac < 0$, the equation has two complex solutions that are not real.